NATIONAL CUR

STP MATHEMA

L. BOSTOCK, B.Sc.

S. CHANDLER, B.Sc.

A. SHEPHERD, B.Sc.

E. SMITH, M.Sc.

STANLEY THORNES (PUBLISHERS) LTD

First published in 1997 by
Stanley Thornes (Publishers) Ltd,
Delta Place,
27 Bath Road,
CHELTENHAM GL53 7TH

00 01 / 10 9 8 7 6

A catalogue record of this book is available from the British Library.

ISBN 0-7487-2443-5

Artwork by Mike Ing, Linda Jeffrey

Front cover image produced using material kindly supplied by I LOVE LOVE CO,
makers of The Happy Cube © Laureyssens/Creative City Ltd 1986/91.
Distributed in UK by: RIGHTRAC, 119 Sandycombe Road, Richmond Surrey TW9 2ER
Tel. 0181 940 3322

The publishers are grateful to the following for granting permission to
reproduce photographs or other copyright material:
Cordon Art, Baarn, Holland – © 1997 M.C. Escher/Cordon Art.
All rights reserved: p. 144

Typeset by Tech-Set, Gateshead, Tyne & Wear.
Printed and bound by Dan Hua Printing Co. Ltd., China

CONTENTS

INTRODUCTION

To the pupil

This book continues to help you to learn, enjoy and progress through Mathematics in the National Curriculum. As well as a clear and concise text the book offers a wide range of practical and investigational work that is relevant to the mathematics you are learning.

Everyone needs success and satisfaction in getting things right. With this in mind we have divided many of the exercises into three types of question.

The first type, identified by plain numbers, e.g. **15**, helps you to see if you understand the work. These questions are considered necessary in every chapter.

The second type, identified by an underline, e.g. **15**, are extra, but not harder, questions for quicker workers, for extra practice or for later revision.

The third type, identified by a coloured square, e.g. **15** , are for those of you who like a greater challenge.

Most chapters have a 'mixed exercise' after the main work of the chapter has been completed. This will help you to revise what you have done, either when you have finished the chapter or at a later date. All chapters end with some mathematical puzzles, practical and/or investigational work. For this work you are encouraged to share your ideas with others, to use any mathematics you are familiar with, and to try different approaches, appreciating the advantages and disadvantages of each method.

The book starts with a summary of the main results from Books 7B and 8B. After every five chapters you will find further summaries. These list the most important points that have been studied in the previous chapters and conclude with revision exercises that test the work you have studied up to that point.

At this stage you will find that you use a calculator frequently but it is unwise to rely on a calculator for work that should be done easily without one. Remember, whether you use a calculator or do the working yourself, always estimate your answer and always ask yourself the question, 'Is my answer a sensible one?'

Mathematics is an exciting and enjoyable subject when you understand what is going on. Remember, if you don't understand something, ask someone who can explain it to you. If you still don't understand, ask again. Good luck with your studies.

To the teacher

This is the third book of the STP National Curriculum Mathematics series. It is based on the ST(P) Mathematics series but has been extensively rewritten and is now firmly based on the programmes of study for Key Stages 3 and 4. Some topics are included that are not required at Level 6 for Key Stage 3. They are introduced to prepare the ground for further study in Books 10B and 11B. These topics include such things as volumes of prisms, simultaneous equations and Pythagoras' Theorem.

The majority of scientific calculators now on sale use direct keying sequences for entering functions such as $\sqrt{2}$; this is the order used in this book.

The B series of books aims to prepare pupils for about Level 6 at Key Stage 3 and for the intermediate tier at GCSE.

SUMMARY 1

MAIN RESULTS FROM BOOKS 7B AND 8B

WHOLE NUMBERS

Even numbers divide exactly by 2, e.g. 6, 10, . . .

Odd numbers do not divide exactly by 2, e.g. 3, 7, . . .

A *prime number* has only two different factors, 1 and itself,
e.g. $7 = 7 \times 1$.
(The smallest prime number is 2; 1 is not a prime number because it does not have a factor other than 1.)

Square numbers can be drawn as a square grid of dots, e.g. 9:
The smallest square number is 1.

Rectangular numbers can be drawn as a rectangular grid of dots, e.g. 6:

Triangular numbers can be drawn as a triangular grid of dots, e.g. 6:

Negative numbers are used to describe where a quantity is when it goes below a zero level.
For example, 2 °C below freezing point (0 °C) is written −2 °C and is called 'minus' 2 °C or 'negative' 2 °C.

Index numbers

The small 2 in 3^2 is called an index and it tells you how many 3s are multiplied together,

e.g. 3^2 means 3×3 and 3^5 means $3 \times 3 \times 3 \times 3 \times 3$

Common factors

A factor of a number will divide into the number exactly.
When two or more numbers have the same factor, it is called a common factor, e.g. 8 and 6 have a common factor of 2.

Common multiples

A multiple of a number has that number as a factor,

e.g. 12 is a multiple of 3, because 3 is a factor of 12.

A common multiple of two or more numbers can be divided exactly by each of those numbers,

e.g. 12 is a common multiple of 2, 3, 4, 6 and 12.

CALCULATING WITH WHOLE NUMBERS

Mixed addition and subtraction

The sign in front of a number refers to that number only.
The order in which you add or subtract does not matter,

so $1 - 5 + 8$ can be calculated in the order $1 + 8 - 5$,

i.e. $9 - 5 = 4$

Mixed operations of ×, ÷, +, − and brackets

When a calculation involves a mixture of operations, start by calculating anything inside brackets, then follow the rule 'do the multiplication and division first',

e.g. $2 + 3 \times 2 = 2 + 6$
$= 8$

and $(2 + 3) \times 2 = 5 \times 2$
$= 10$

Multiplication by 10, 100, 1000

To multiply a number by 10, or 100 or 1000, move the figures one, two or three places to the left and fill in the gaps with zeros,

e.g. $25 \times 100 = 2500$

Division

Division is the opposite of multiplication,

e.g. $6 \div 3 = 2$ because $6 = 3 \times 2$

Division by 10, 100, 1000

To divide a number by 10, or 100 or 1000, move the figures one, two or three places to the right,

e.g. $25\,000 \div 10 = 2500$

FRACTIONS

A fraction describes the size of part of a quantity.
A fraction is written in the form $\frac{2}{3}$.
The *denominator* (the bottom number) tells us the number of equal-sized parts that the quantity is divided into.
The *numerator* (the top number) tells us the number of those equal-sized parts that are being considered.

For example, $\frac{2}{3}$ of this square is shaded.

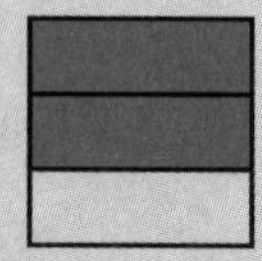

Equivalent fractions

Two fractions that describe the same sized part of a quantity are called equivalent fractions.

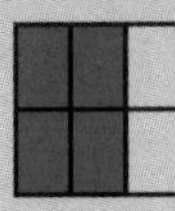

The shaded part of this square can be described as $\frac{4}{6}$ of the square or as $\frac{2}{3}$ of the square.

We can find a fraction equivalent to a given fraction by multiplying the top and bottom by the same number,

e.g. $\frac{2}{3} = \frac{2\times 2}{3\times 2} = \frac{4}{6}$ and $\frac{2}{3} = \frac{2\times 5}{3\times 5} = \frac{10}{15}$

Simplifying fractions

A fraction can be simplified to an equivalent fraction with a smaller numerator and denominator by dividing the top and bottom by the same number,

e.g. $\frac{12}{18} = \frac{12\div 6}{18\div 6} = \frac{2}{3}$ This is sometimes called *cancelling*.

Addition and subtraction of fractions

Fractions can be added or subtracted when they have the same denominator. For example, to add $\frac{1}{2}$ to $\frac{1}{3}$ we must first change them into equivalent fractions with the same denominators,

i.e. $\frac{1}{2} + \frac{1}{3} = \frac{1\times 3}{2\times 3} + \frac{1\times 2}{3\times 2} = \frac{3}{6} + \frac{2}{6} = \frac{5}{6}$

Mixed numbers and improper fractions

$1\frac{3}{4}$ is called a mixed number; $1\frac{3}{4} = 1 + \frac{3}{4}$

$= \frac{4}{4} + \frac{3}{4} = \frac{7}{4}$

$\frac{7}{4}$ is called an improper fraction.

To add mixed numbers first add the whole numbers and then add the fractions,

e.g. $1\frac{3}{5} + 2\frac{4}{5} = 3 + \frac{3}{5} + \frac{4}{5}$

$= 3 + \frac{7}{5} = 3 + 1 + \frac{2}{5} = 4\frac{2}{5}$

Similarly, when subtraction involves mixed numbers deal with the whole numbers first.

Multiplying fractions

To multiply one fraction by another fraction, we multiply their numerators together and we multiply their denominators together,

e.g. $\frac{1}{2} \times \frac{5}{3} = \frac{1\times 5}{2\times 3} = \frac{5}{6}$

Mixed numbers must be changed into improper fractions before they can be multiplied,

e.g. $1\frac{1}{2} \times \frac{3}{5} = \frac{3}{2} \times \frac{3}{5} = \frac{3\times 3}{2\times 5} = \frac{9}{10}$

To multiply by a whole number, treat it as a fraction by writing it over 1,

e.g. $4 \times \frac{3}{8} = \frac{\not{4}^{1}}{1} \times \frac{3}{\not{8}_{2}} = \frac{3}{2} = 1\frac{1}{2}$

Fractions of a quantity

To find a fraction of a quantity, multiply the fraction by the quantity,

e.g. $\frac{3}{8}$ of £20 $= £\left(\frac{3}{8} \times 20\right) = £\left(\frac{3}{8} \times \frac{20}{1}\right)$

One quantity as a fraction of another

To express one quantity as a fraction of another, first express both quantities in the same unit and then place the first quantity over the second,

e.g. 25 p as a fraction of £3 is equal to $\frac{25}{300} = \frac{1}{12}$,

or, to put it another way, 25 p is $\frac{1}{12}$ of £3.

DECIMALS

In decimal notation, numbers to the right of the decimal point represent tenths, hundredths, . . . ,

e.g. $0.53 = \frac{5}{10} + \frac{3}{100}$

Addition and subtraction of decimals

Decimals can be added or subtracted in the same way as whole numbers. We must remember to place the decimal points in line and, when necessary, to fill in any blank spaces with zeros,

e.g. to add 12.5 and 7.95, we can write them as

$$\begin{array}{r} 12.50 \\ +\ \ 7.95 \\ \hline 20.45 \end{array}$$

Multiplying and dividing decimals by 10, 100, 1000, . . .

To multiply a decimal by 10, 100, 1000, . . . , we move the point 1, 2, 3, . . . places to the right, filling in any blank spaces with zeros.

e.g. $2.56 \times 10 = 25.6$, and $2.56 \times 1000 = 2560$

To divide a decimal by 10, 100, 1000, . . . , we move the point 1, 2, 3, . . . places to the left, filling in any blank spaces with zeros.

e.g. $2.56 \div 10 = 0.256$, and $2.56 \div 1000 = 0.002\,56$

(Moving the point to the right is equivalent to moving the figures to the left, and vice-versa.)

Multiplying decimals

To multiply decimals without using a calculator, first ignore the decimal point and multiply the numbers. Then add together the decimal places in each of the decimals being multiplied; this gives the number of decimal places in the answer,

e.g. $2.5 \times 0.4 = 1.00 = 1$ $(25 \times 4 = 100)$

$[(1) + (1) = (2)]$

Dividing by a decimal

To divide by a decimal, we move the point in *both* numbers to the right until the number we are dividing by is a whole number,

e.g. $2.56 \div 0.4 = 25.6 \div 4$

Now we can use ordinary division, keeping the decimal point in the same place,

e.g. $25.6 \div 4 = 6.4$ $4\overline{)25.6}$ giving 6.4

Correcting decimals

To round (that is, to correct) a number to a specified number of decimal places, look at the figure in the next decimal place: if it is 5 or more, add 1 to the specified figure, otherwise leave the specified figure as it is,

e.g. to write 52.564 correct to 2 decimal places, we have

52.56|4 = 52.56 correct to 2 decimal places,

and to write 52.564 correct to 1 decimal place, we have

52.5|64 = 52.6 correct to 1 decimal place.

Similarly, to give 52.564 correct to the nearest whole number, we write

52|.564 = 53 correct to the nearest whole number.

When calculating with decimals we need to work to one more decimal place than is needed for the answer

e.g. $4.3 \div 7 = 0.614\ldots$

$= 0.61$ correct to 2 decimal places

PERCENTAGES

A percentage of a quantity means the number of one hundredths of the quantity,

e.g. 20% of an apple means 20 out of 100 equal-sized parts of the apple,

i.e. $20\% = \frac{20}{100}$.

INTERCHANGING PERCENTAGES, FRACTIONS AND DECIMALS

Changing a fraction to a decimal

Fractions can be changed to decimal notation by dividing the bottom number into the top number,

e.g. $\frac{3}{8} = 3 \div 8 = 0.375$

Changing a decimal to a fraction

A decimal can be expressed as a fraction by placing the numbers after the decimal point over 1, and a number of zeros equal to the number of decimal places,

e.g. $0.15 = \frac{15}{100}$, $0.7 = \frac{7}{10}$, $0.137 = \frac{137}{1000}$, $1.25 = 1\frac{25}{100}$

Changing between percentages and fractions

A percentage can be expressed as a fraction by placing the percentage over 100,

e.g. $33\% = \frac{33}{100}$ and $32\frac{1}{2}\% = 32.5\% = \frac{32.5}{100} = \frac{325}{1000} = \frac{13}{40}$

Reversing the process, a fraction can be expressed as a percentage by multiplying the fraction by 100,

e.g. $\frac{2}{5} = \frac{2}{5} \times 100\% = \frac{2}{5} \times \frac{100}{1}\% = 40\%$

Changing between percentages and decimals

A percentage can be expressed as a decimal by dividing the percentage by 100, i.e. by moving the decimal point two places to the left,

e.g. $33\% = 0.33$ and $2\frac{1}{2}\% = 2.5\% = 0.025$

and a decimal can be expressed as a percentage by multiplying the decimal by 100, i.e. by moving the decimal point two places to the right.

For example, $0.325 = 32.5\%$

To find a percentage of a quantity, first change the percentage to a decimal and then multiply the decimal by the quantity.

e.g. 15% of £80 $= 0.15 \times$ £80

DIRECTED NUMBERS

Positive and negative numbers are collectively known as directed numbers. They can be represented on a number line.

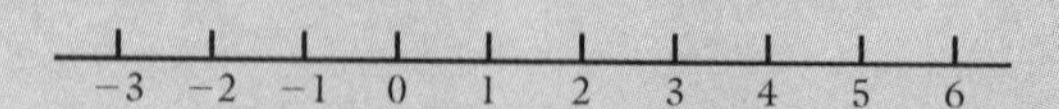

The rules for adding and subtracting directed numbers are

$$+(+2) = 2 \qquad +(-2) = -2$$
$$-(+2) = -2 \qquad -(-2) = 2$$

When two numbers of the same sign are multiplied together, the result is positive.
When two numbers of different signs are multiplied together, the result is negative.
For example, $(+2)\times(+3) = +6$ and $(-2)\times(-3) = +6$

$(+2)\times(-3) = -6$ and $(-2)\times(+3) = -6$

The same rules apply to division, for example,

$$(+8)\div(+2) = +4 \quad \text{and} \quad (-8)\div(-2) = +4$$
$$(+8)\div(-2) = -4 \quad \text{and} \quad (-8)\div(+2) = -4$$

UNITS

The *metric units of length* in common use are the kilometre (km), the metre (m), the centimetre (cm) and the millimetre (mm), where

$$1\,\text{km} = 1000\,\text{m}, \quad 1\,\text{m} = 100\,\text{cm}, \quad 1\,\text{cm} = 10\,\text{mm}$$

The *metric units of mass* (these are the units we use for weighing) are the tonne (t), the kilogram (kg), the gram (g) and the milligram (mg), where

$$1\text{ tonne} = 1000\,\text{kg}, \quad 1\,\text{kg} = 1000\,\text{g}, \quad 1\,\text{g} = 1000\,\text{mg}$$

Imperial units of length in common use are the mile, yard (yd), foot (ft) and inch (in), where

$$1\text{ mile} = 1760\text{ yards}, \quad 1\text{ yard} = 3\text{ feet}, \quad 1\text{ foot} = 12\text{ inches}$$

Imperial units of mass still in common use are the ton, hundredweight (cwt), stone, pound (lb) and ounce (oz), where

$$1\text{ ton} = 2240\,\text{lb}, \quad 1\,\text{cwt} = 112\,\text{lb},$$
$$1\text{ stone} = 14\,\text{lb}, \quad 1\,\text{lb} = 16\text{ ounces}$$

For a *rough conversion between metric and Imperial units*, use

$$1\,\text{km} \approx \tfrac{1}{2}\text{ mile}, \quad 1\text{ yard} \approx 1\,\text{m}, \quad 1\text{ inch} \approx 2.5\,\text{cm},$$
$$1\,\text{kg} \approx 2\,\text{lb}, \quad 1\text{ tonne} \approx 1\text{ ton}$$

When we need a more accurate conversion between miles and kilometres or pounds and kilograms, we can use $5\text{ miles} \approx 8\,\text{km}$, $1\,\text{kg} \approx 2.2\,\text{lb}$

CHANGING UNITS

To change to a smaller unit we multiply,

e.g. to express 2 metres in centimetres, we multiply 2 by 100,

i.e. $2\,\text{m} = 2 \times 100\,\text{cm} = 200\,\text{cm}$

To change to a larger unit we divide,

e.g. to express 20 m in km, we divide 20 by 1000,

i.e. $20\,\text{m} = 20 \div 1000\,\text{km} = 0.02\,\text{km}$

AREA

Area is measured by standard-sized squares.

$$1\,\text{cm}^2 = 10 \times 10\,\text{mm}^2 = 100\,\text{mm}^2$$
$$1\,\text{m}^2 = 100 \times 100\,\text{cm}^2 = 10\,000\,\text{cm}^2$$
$$1\,\text{km}^2 = 1000 \times 1000\,\text{m}^2 = 1\,000\,000\,\text{m}^2$$

The *area of a square* = (length of a side)^2

The *area of a rectangle* = length × breadth

VOLUME AND CAPACITY

Volume is measured by standard-sized cubes.

$$1\,\text{cm}^3 = 10 \times 10 \times 10\,\text{mm}^3 = 1000\,\text{mm}^3$$
$$1\,\text{m}^3 = 100 \times 100 \times 100\,\text{cm}^3 = 1\,000\,000\,\text{cm}^3$$

The *volume of a cuboid* = length × breadth × height

The capacity of a container is the volume of liquid it could hold.

The main metric units of capacity are the litre (l) and the millilitre (ml), where

1 litre = 1000 ml and 1 litre = 1000 cm^3

The main Imperial units of capacity are the gallon and the pint, where

1 gallon = 8 pints

Rough conversions between metric and Imperial units of capacity are given by

1 litre ≈ 1.75 pints and 1 gallon ≈ 4.5 litres

COORDINATES

Coordinates give the position of a point on a grid. They are written as a pair of numbers, e.g. (2, 4).

The first number is called the x-coordinate.
The second number is called the y-coordinate.

The x-coordinate and/or the y-coordinate of a point can be negative.

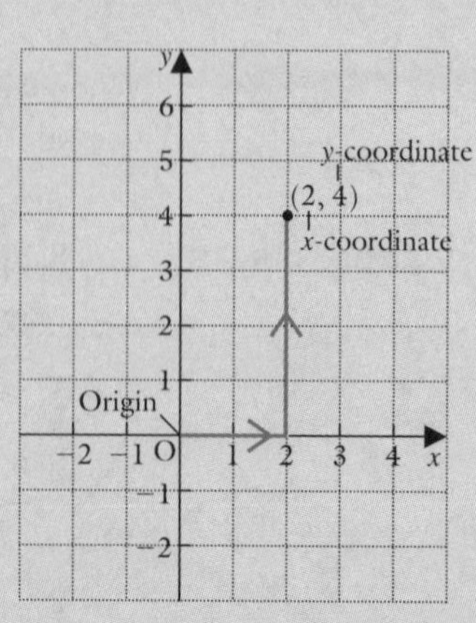

The *equation of a straight line* can be thought of as a formula that gives the y-coordinate of a point on the line in terms of its x-coordinate.
For example, for the line in the diagram, the y-coordinate of any point on the line is twice its x-coordinate plus 1.
The equation of this line is $y = 2x + 1$

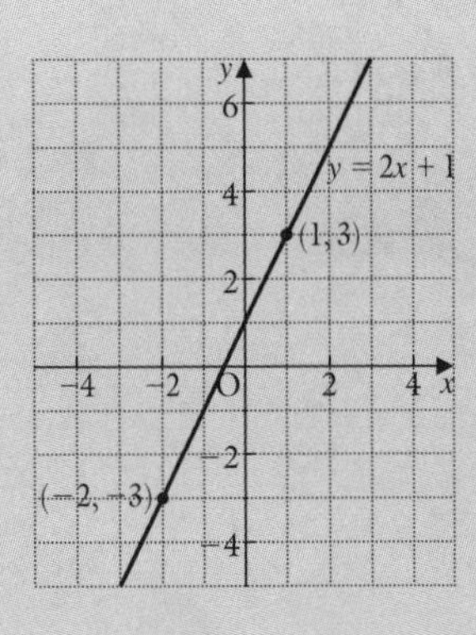

FORMULAS

A formula is a general rule for finding one quantity in terms of other quantities, for example, the formula for finding the area of a rectangle is given by

$$\text{Area} = \text{length} \times \text{breadth}$$

When letters are used for unknown numbers, the formula can be written more concisely, that is the area, $A\,\text{cm}^2$, of a rectangle measuring l cm by b cm, is given by the formula

$$A = l \times b$$

Multiplication signs between letters, or between a number and a letter can be left out,

e.g. $2p$ means $2 \times p$ and $l \times b$ can be written lb.

Divisions are usually written as fractions,

e.g. $2 \div s$ is written as $\dfrac{2}{s}$

$5n$ means $5 \times n$ or $n + n + n + n + n$

$2x + 5x$ can be simplified to $7x$.

SOLVING EQUATIONS

An equation is a relationship between an unknown number, represented by a letter, and other numbers, e.g. $2x - 3 = 5$

Solving the equation means finding the unknown number.

Provided that we do the same thing to both sides of an equation, we keep the equality; this can be used to solve the equation,

e.g. to solve $2x - 3 = 5$

first add 3 to each side: $2x - 3 + 3 = 5 + 3$

This gives $2x = 8$

Now divide both sides by 2 $x = 4$

SHAPES

The *perimeter* of a shape is the total distance all round its edge.

ANGLES

One complete revolution = 4 right angles = 360°.

1 *right angle* = 90°.

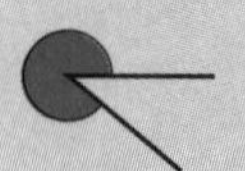

An *acute angle* is less than 90°.

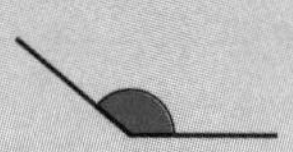

An *obtuse angle* is larger than 90° but less than 180°.

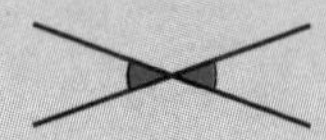

A *reflex angle* is larger than 180°.

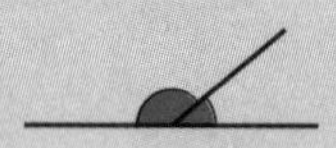

Vertically opposite angles are equal.

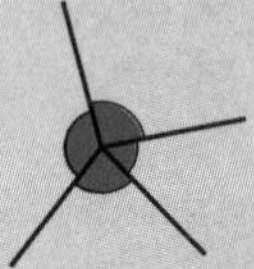

Angles on a straight line add up to 180°.

Two angles that add up to 180° are called *supplementary angles*.

Angles at a point add up to 360°.

TRIANGLES

The three angles in a triangle add up to 180°.

An *equilateral triangle* has all three sides equal and each angle is 60°.

An *isosceles triangle* has two sides equal and the angles at the base of these sides are equal.

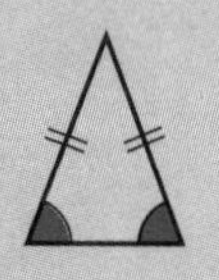

QUADRILATERALS

A quadrilateral has four sides.
The four angles in a quadrilateral add up to 360°.

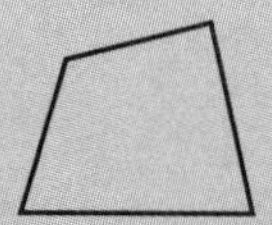

SPECIAL QUADRILATERALS

In a square
- all four sides are the same length
- both pairs of opposite sides are parallel
- all four angles are right angles.

In a rectangle
- both pairs of opposite sides are the same length
- both pairs of opposite sides are parallel
- all four angles are right angles.

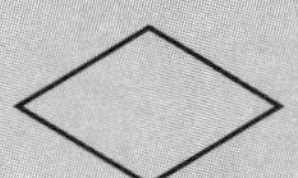

In a rhombus
- all four sides are the same length
- both pairs of opposite sides are parallel
- the opposite angles are equal.

In a parallelogram
- the opposite sides are the same length
- the opposite sides are parallel
- the opposite angles are equal.

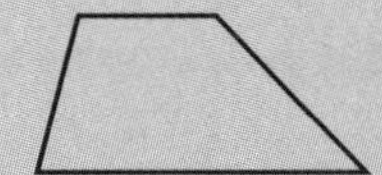

In a trapezium
- just one pair of opposite sides are parallel.

CUBES AND CUBOIDS

A cube is a solid and all of its faces are squares.
A cuboid is a rectangular block.

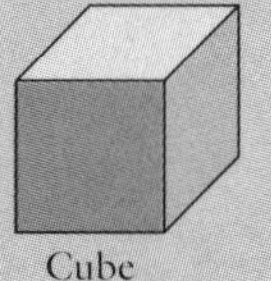

Cube

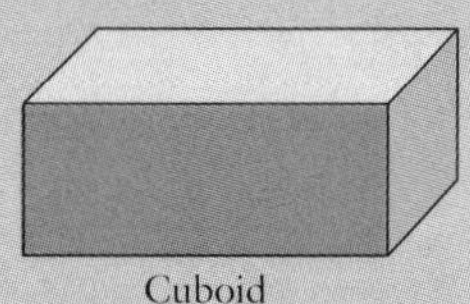

Cuboid

LINE SYMMETRY

A shape has a line of symmetry if, when it is folded along that line, one half of the shape fits exactly over the other half,

e.g. this shape has one line of symmetry.

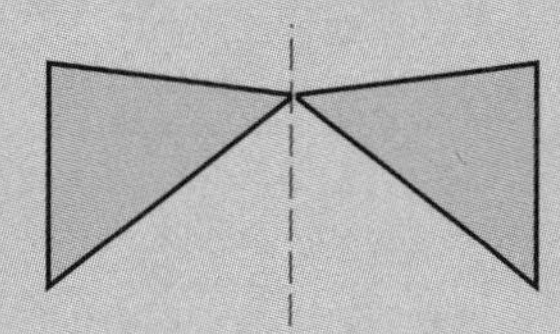

ROTATIONAL SYMMETRY

A shape has rotational symmetry if, when it is turned about a centre point to a new position, it looks the same.

e.g. this shape has rotational symmetry.

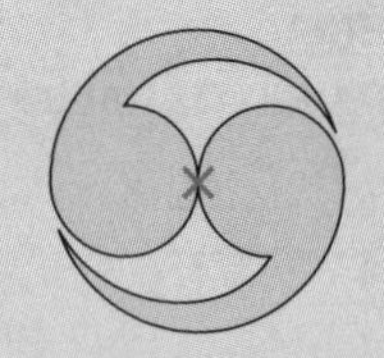

CONGRUENCE

When two figures are congruent they are exactly the same shape and size. (They can be turned over compared with one another.)

These two triangles are congruent.

TRANSFORMATIONS

Reflection in a mirror line
When an object is reflected in a mirror line, the object and its image form a symmetrical shape with the mirror line as the axis of symmetry.

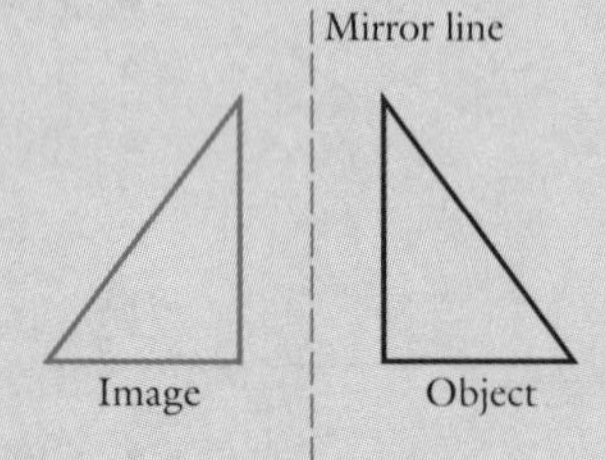

Translation
When an object is translated it moves without being turned or reflected to form an image.

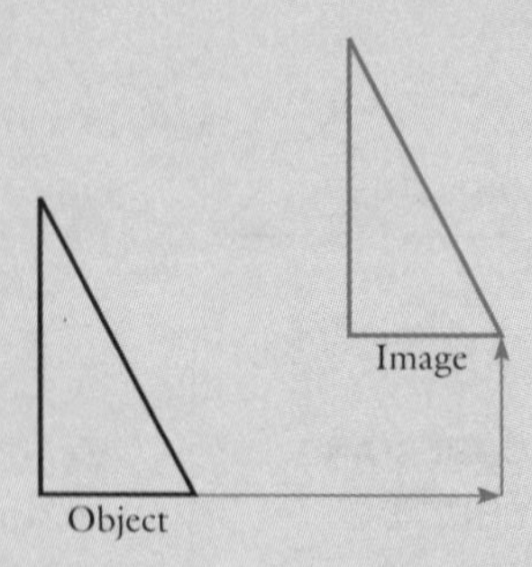

Rotation
When an object is rotated about a point to form an image, the point about which it is rotated is called the *centre of rotation* and the angle it is turned through is called the *angle of rotation*.

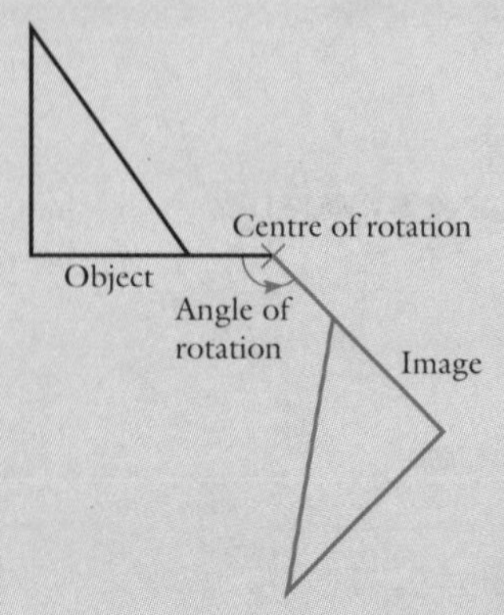

SUMMARISING DATA

For a list of values,

- the *range* is the difference between the largest value and the smallest value
- the *mean* is the sum of all the values divided by the number of values
- the *median* is the middle value when they have been arranged in order of size, (when the middle of the list is halfway between two values, the median is the average of these two values)
- the *mode* is the value that occurs most frequently. Sometimes there is no mode, sometimes there is more than one mode.

For example, for this list of lengths

$$9\text{ cm}, 10\text{ cm}, 10\text{ cm}, 12\text{ cm}, 12\text{ cm}, 12\text{ cm},$$

the range is $(12 - 9)\text{ cm} = 3\text{ cm}$,

the mode is 12 cm,

the mean is $(9 + 10 + 10 + 12 + 12 + 12) \div 6\text{ cm}$

$= 10.8\text{ cm}$ correct to 1 d.p.,

the median is $(10 + 12) \div 2\text{ cm}$, i.e. 11 cm

The mean, median and mode are together known as measures of central tendency.

PROBABILITY

Probability measures the chance that an event in the future may happen.

The probability that an event A happens is given by

$$\frac{\text{the number of ways in which } A \text{ can occur}}{\text{the total number of equally likely outcomes}}$$

Probability ranges from impossibility (0), through degrees of likelihood to certainty (1).

When we try to find a probability, we need to know all the possibilities that could happen. This is called the list of all *possible outcomes*.

When we perform experiments to find out how often an event occurs, the *relative frequency* of the event is given by

$$\frac{\text{the number of times the event occurs}}{\text{the number of times the experiment is performed}}$$

Relative frequency is used to give an approximate value for probability.

The exercises that follow are *not* intended to be worked through before starting the main part of this book. They are here for you to use when you need practice on the basic techniques.

REVISION EXERCISE 1.1 (Whole numbers)

1 Write down

a the value of the 4 in the number **i** 1407 **ii** 40 567

b the number 3592 in words

c the number two thousand seven hundred and eight in figures.

2 a Put the numbers 709, 970, 917, 794 and 799 in order with the smallest number first.

b Write 1584 **i** correct to the nearest number of tens
ii correct to the nearest number of hundreds.

3 Without using a calculator, find

a $293 + 827$ **d** $834 - 392$ **g** $263 + 713 + 429$

b $421 + 943$ **e** $747 - 559$ **h** $612 - 385$

c $513 + 748$ **f** $638 - 145$ **i** $5210 - 3763 + 2140$

4 Without using a calculator, find

a 72×8 **g** 64×50 **m** 54×300

b 49×6 **h** 38×70 **n** 382×7

c 55×10 **i** 58×90 **p** 561×9

d 38×5 **j** 73×10 **q** 423×8

e 38×100 **k** 42×600 **r** 762×6

f 29×7 **l** 292×800 **s** 359×8

5 Without using a calculator, find

a $125 \div 5$ **g** $520 \div 20$ **m** $304 \div 4$

b $276 \div 6$ **h** $420 \div 70$ **n** $435 \div 5$

c $416 \div 8$ **i** $320 \div 40$ **p** $432 \div 6$

d $413 \div 7$ **j** $1250 \div 50$ **q** $392 \div 8$

e $324 \div 9$ **k** $2560 \div 80$ **r** $371 \div 7$

f $534 \div 6$ **l** $2550 \div 30$ **s** $702 \div 9$

6 Without using a calculator, find

a $8 \times 243 - 1492$ **d** $(18 + 15) \times 3 - 38$

b $4298 - 367 \times 7$ **e** $246 \div 23$, giving the remainder

c $36 \div (13 - 4) + 8$ **f** $1429 \div 54$, giving the remainder

7 **a** Write in index form **i** $5 \times 5 \times 5 \times 5$ **ii** $7 \times 7 \times 7$

b Find the value of

i 3^4 **iii** $2^2 \times 3^2$ **v** $3^2 \times 5^3$

ii $2^3 \times 3^2$ **iv** $2^3 \times 7^2$ **vi** $2^3 \times 5^2$

c Express in index form **i** 32 **ii** 125 **iii** 72 **iv** 360

8 **a** Find the largest whole number that will divide exactly into

i 27 and 36 **ii** 42 and 70 **iii** 72 and 48

b Find the smallest whole number that

i 12 and 5 will divide into exactly

ii 6 and 9 will divide into exactly.

9 **a** Write down the next square number after **i** 36 **ii** 100

b Write down the prime numbers between 30 and 50.

c Which of the numbers 8, 11, 15, 22, 28, 30, 35, 36, 42, 45

are **i** prime numbers **iii** triangular numbers

ii rectangular numbers **iv** square numbers?

10 **a** Estimate the value of each of the following multiplications, then use a calculator to find the exact value.

i 53×472 **ii** 137×63 **iii** 86×952 **iv** 393×32

b Find, without using a calculator, the value of

i $3 \times 4 \div 2 + 2 \times 5$ **iii** $12 \div 4 - 2 - 3 \times 2 + 7$

ii $3 \times 5 \times 4 - 6 \times 5 \div 2$ **iv** $4 \times 5 \div 2 + 15 \div 3 - 2$

REVISION EXERCISE 1.2 (Fractions)

1 Fill in the missing numbers to make equivalent fractions.

a $\frac{3}{4} = \frac{}{28}$ **b** $\frac{11}{20} = \frac{44}{}$ **c** $\frac{5}{13} = \frac{25}{}$ **d** $\frac{4}{5} = \frac{}{60}$

2 Put either > or < between each of the following pairs of fractions.

a $\frac{9}{10} \quad \frac{7}{8}$ **b** $\frac{7}{10} \quad \frac{2}{3}$ **c** $\frac{1}{4} \quad \frac{3}{13}$ **d** $\frac{3}{7} \quad \frac{4}{9}$

3 Change into an improper fraction

a $3\frac{5}{7}$ **c** $7\frac{3}{4}$ **e** $1\frac{4}{9}$ **g** $9\frac{1}{3}$ **i** $5\frac{2}{3}$

b $4\frac{2}{5}$ **d** $5\frac{1}{5}$ **f** $3\frac{4}{5}$ **h** $7\frac{4}{7}$ **j** $4\frac{8}{9}$

4 Give as a mixed number

a $\frac{38}{5}$ **c** $\frac{14}{3}$ **e** $\frac{14}{5}$ **g** $\frac{31}{6}$ **i** $\frac{87}{12}$

b $\frac{18}{7}$ **d** $\frac{15}{2}$ **f** $\frac{27}{4}$ **h** $\frac{55}{9}$ **j** $\frac{51}{8}$

5 Find

a $\frac{2}{7}+\frac{3}{7}$ **g** $\frac{1}{4}+\frac{5}{6}$ **m** $\frac{5}{12}-\frac{1}{3}$

b $\frac{2}{5}+\frac{3}{10}$ **h** $\frac{3}{4}+\frac{1}{2}$ **n** $\frac{5}{8}-\frac{5}{12}$

c $\frac{3}{8}+\frac{5}{8}$ **i** $\frac{4}{5}+\frac{1}{6}$ **p** $\frac{3}{7}-\frac{3}{8}$

d $\frac{4}{5}+\frac{1}{7}$ **j** $\frac{11}{13}-\frac{2}{13}$ **q** $\frac{7}{8}-\frac{1}{2}$

e $\frac{5}{9}+\frac{2}{7}$ **k** $\frac{7}{12}-\frac{5}{12}$ **r** $\frac{11}{12}-\frac{3}{4}$

f $\frac{1}{4}+\frac{1}{3}$ **l** $\frac{3}{4}-\frac{1}{2}$ **s** $\frac{5}{9}-\frac{5}{18}$

6 Find

a $2\frac{3}{5}+1\frac{3}{4}$ **d** $3\frac{2}{3}+5\frac{5}{6}$ **g** $6\frac{7}{8}+5\frac{2}{7}$

b $5\frac{3}{4}-2\frac{1}{3}$ **e** $7\frac{6}{7}-3\frac{1}{4}$ **h** $9\frac{4}{5}-5\frac{7}{8}$

c $3\frac{7}{10}-2\frac{1}{5}$ **f** $5\frac{7}{12}+2\frac{3}{8}$ **i** $4\frac{1}{3}-1\frac{4}{5}$

7 Find

a $\frac{1}{2}\times\frac{2}{5}$ **e** $\frac{2}{5}\times 10$ **i** $1\frac{1}{2}\times\frac{1}{3}$

b $\frac{2}{3}\times\frac{1}{4}$ **f** $\frac{3}{4}\times 15$ **j** $\frac{2}{5}\times 2\frac{1}{2}$

c $\frac{1}{5}\times\frac{2}{3}$ **g** $\frac{1}{2}\times 9$ **k** $1\frac{1}{2}\times 1\frac{1}{4}$

d $\frac{3}{4}\times\frac{4}{5}$ **h** $6\times\frac{2}{9}$ **l** $3\frac{1}{2}\times 1\frac{1}{5}$

8 **a** Find **i** $\frac{1}{2}$ of 36 **iii** $\frac{2}{3}$ of 36 **v** $\frac{5}{9}$ of 108

ii $\frac{3}{4}$ of 48 **iv** $\frac{5}{6}$ of 60 **vi** $\frac{3}{7}$ of 112

b Which is the larger: $\frac{3}{5}$ of $\frac{7}{12}$ or $\frac{4}{9}$ of $\frac{2}{3}$?

9 Find

a $\frac{3}{8}$ of 48 miles **e** $\frac{5}{8}$ of £4 in pence

b $\frac{5}{7}$ of 2 weeks **f** $\frac{2}{5}$ of 3 m in centimetres

c $\frac{3}{8}$ of 72 gallons **g** $\frac{7}{9}$ of 171 francs

d $\frac{3}{4}$ of £60 **h** $\frac{7}{12}$ of 216 minutes

10 **a** Find as an improper fraction

i $\frac{5}{12} \times 40$ **ii** $66 \times \frac{2}{9}$ **iii** $\frac{7}{10} \times 55$

b Find **i** 72 p as a fraction of £2
ii 63 cm as a fraction of 3 metres

c There are 36 cars in the school car park and 8 of them are red. What fraction of the cars in the school car park are not red?

d Find **i** 36 cm as a fraction of 144 cm
ii 24 p as a fraction of £5

REVISION EXERCISE 1.3 (Decimals)

1 Find, without using a calculator

a $2.4 + 6.1$ **e** $5.1 - 1.874$ **i** $3 - 0.44$
b $5.23 + 3.44$ **f** $6.2 - 5.66$ **j** $12 - 6.89$
c $6.86 - 4.55$ **g** $5.99 + 2.94$ **k** $3.65 + 2.008$
d $13.73 + 4.96$ **h** $45.2 - 16.49$ **l** $16.03 - 9.474$

2 Give each number correct to the number of decimal places referred to in the bracket.
a 6.498 (1) **b** 0.0945 (2) **c** 34.7089 (3) **d** 2.009 (2)

3 Find, without using a calculator

a 0.05×6 **h** 500×3.7 **p** 33.6×0.08
b 0.6×0.34 **i** 10×4.52 **q** 0.8×100
c 100×1.8 **j** 0.45×0.07 **r** 24×0.7
d 7000×0.02 **k** 150×1.5 **s** 600×0.05
e 0.05×0.06 **l** 0.4×0.05 **t** 5000×4.7
f 13×0.9 **m** 2.6×0.04 **u** 3.88×0.05
g 0.4×0.8 **n** 10×0.06 **v** 1.63×0.08

4 Find, without using a calculator and correct to 2 decimal places if necessary

a $6.09 \div 9$ **h** $4.56 \div 0.8$ **p** $0.08 \div 0.05$
b $0.5 \div 0.2$ **i** $8.05 \div 0.11$ **q** $13.2 \div 7$
c $16.3 \div 0.06$ **j** $0.042 \div 0.08$ **r** $1.12 \div 0.2$
d $0.0047 \div 0.04$ **k** $0.0143 \div 0.11$ **s** $5.96 \div 6$
e $0.0093 \div 0.05$ **l** $24.3 \div 9$ **t** $4.2 \div 0.5$
f $0.0045 \div 0.5$ **m** $0.0077 \div 0.07$ **u** $16.8 \div 0.6$
g $0.0036 \div 0.07$ **n** $5 \div 0.03$ **v** $0.62 \div 0.8$

5 Arrange each set of decimals in order of size, with the smallest first.

a 3.6, 3.08, 3.61 **b** 8.28, 8.09, 8.2

6 Which is larger? Do not use a calculator.

a 32.4×0.7 or 4.67×5 **c** $4.5 \div 0.03$ or $9.4 \div 7$

b 8.29×1.3 or 6.31×1.7 **d** $56.2 \div 0.08$ or $14.2 \div 0.009$

7 Which is the smaller, and by how much?

a 54.2×0.076 or $4.78 \div 1.2$ **b** $9.004 \div 0.56$ or 27.3×0.7

8 Express each fraction as a decimal, correct to 2 decimal places if necessary. Do not use a calculator.

a $\frac{3}{5}$ **c** $\frac{7}{40}$ **e** $\frac{47}{50}$ **g** $\frac{1}{11}$ **i** $\frac{5}{12}$

b $\frac{9}{25}$ **d** $\frac{5}{11}$ **f** $\frac{2}{9}$ **h** $\frac{27}{100}$ **j** $\frac{5}{8}$

9 Express each decimal as a fraction in its lowest terms, expressing the fraction as a mixed number where necessary.

a 0.35 **e** 0.125 **i** 0.175 **m** 2.6

b 0.66 **f** 0.375 **j** 0.095 **n** 6.25

c 0.45 **g** 0.75 **k** 0.1025 **p** 3.06

d 0.06 **h** 0.55 **l** 1.8 **q** 2.375

10 Use your calculator to find, correct to 2 decimal places

a $0.045 + 0.645 \times 0.66$ **c** $9.034 \times (4.992 - 3.367)$

b $57 \times 0.0854 - 1.895$ **d** $(2.17 + 0.738) \times 2.45$

REVISION EXERCISE 1.4 (Percentages)

1 Express each percentage as a fraction in its lowest terms.

a 150% **c** 47% **e** 120% **g** 12%

b 75% **d** 64% **f** 360% **h** 40%

2 Express each percentage as a fraction in its lowest terms.

a $62\frac{1}{2}\%$ **b** $7\frac{1}{2}\%$ **c** $3\frac{3}{5}\%$ **d** $4\frac{3}{4}\%$

3 Express each percentage as a decimal. Do not use a calculator.

a 80% **c** 17% **e** $4\frac{1}{2}\%$ **g** $5\frac{2}{5}\%$

b 126% **d** 335% **f** 475% **h** 2345%

4 Express each percentage as a decimal correct to 3 decimal places where necessary.

a $6\frac{3}{4}\%$ **c** $3\frac{1}{4}\%$ **e** $9\frac{3}{4}\%$ **g** $10\frac{3}{8}\%$

b $17\frac{1}{2}\%$ **d** $7\frac{7}{12}\%$ **f** $15\frac{1}{3}\%$ **h** $9\frac{5}{8}\%$

5 Express each decimal as a percentage.

a 0.7 **c** 0.255 **e** 0.36 **g** 0.035

b 0.65 **d** 1.75 **f** 1.175 **h** 0.005

6 Express each fraction or mixed number as a percentage. Give answers that are not exact correct to 2 decimal places.

a $\frac{3}{5}$ **c** $\frac{42}{3}$ **e** $1\frac{27}{50}$ **g** $2\frac{4}{9}$

b $\frac{7}{10}$ **d** $\frac{3}{8}$ **f** $\frac{23}{56}$ **h** $\frac{172}{59}$

7 Find the value of

a 30% of £500 **d** 25% of 30 m **g** 13.6% of 50 cm

b 90% of 5400 cm^2 **e** 37% of 800 kg **h** 2.25% of £140

c 60% of 85 g **f** 64% of 200 litres **i** 34.4% of 750 litres

REVISION EXERCISE 1.5 (Metric and Imperial units)

In questions **1** to **18** express each given quantity in terms of the units in brackets.

1 7240 m (km) **7** 2 m 45 cm (cm) **13** 48 in (ft)

2 500 g (kg) **8** 6450 mm (m) **14** 65 in (ft and in)

3 340 mm (cm) **9** 0.0426 m (mm) **15** 150 ft (yd and ft)

4 87 cm (m) **10** 2.4 g (mg) **16** 3 lb 4 oz (oz)

5 0.04 kg (g) **11** 3 ft 4 in (in) **17** 12 st 3 lb (lb)

6 1.09 m (cm) **12** 4 yd 2 ft (ft) **18** 186 lb (stones and lb)

In questions **19** to **27** write the given quantity, roughly, in terms of the unit in brackets.

19 5 kg (lb) **22** 50 km (miles) **25** 2 in (cm)

20 9 lb (kg) **23** 10 ft (m) **26** $\frac{1}{2}$ in (mm)

21 50 miles (km) **24** 250 g (oz) **27** 20 cm (in)

Find, giving your answer in the unit in brackets

28 3 m + 60 cm (m)

29 5 kg + 500 g (kg)

30 116 g + 0.04 kg + 3940 mg (g)

31 2 m + 84 cm + 142 mm (cm)

32 1.6 t − 490 kg (kg)

33 0.9 m − 426 mm (cm)

34 Copy and complete the following sentences inserting the appropriate unit

a The weight of an aspirin pill is about 750 __ .

b The diameter of a household cake tin is about 20 __ .

c The capacity of a tea cup is about 0.1 __ .

35 Copy and complete the following sentences with a suitable number.

a The height of our kitchen door is about __ m.

b A 10-year-old weighs about __ kg.

c The area needed to stand a double bed on is about __ m^2.

REVISION EXERCISE 1.6 (Geometry)

1 State whether each of the following angles is acute, obtuse or reflex.

a 93° **b** 216° **c** 34° **d** 254° **e** 310° **f** 89°

2 Find the sizes of the marked angles.

a

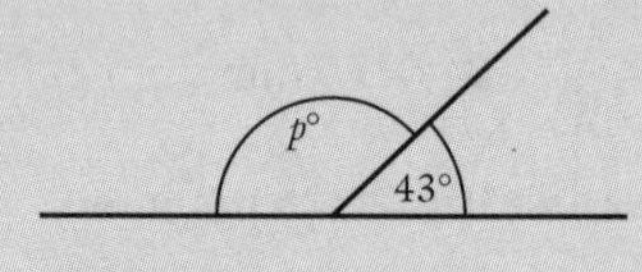

d

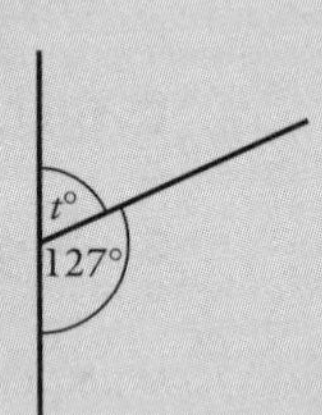

b

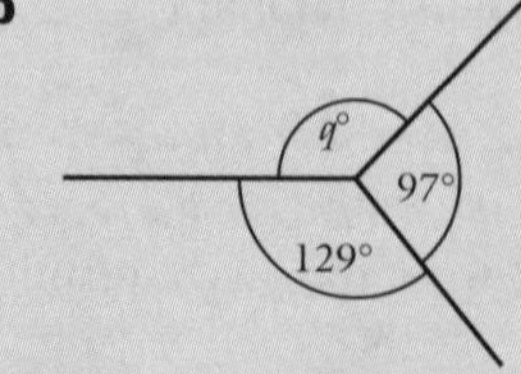

e

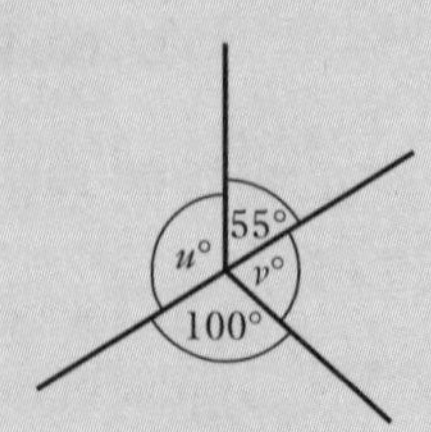

c

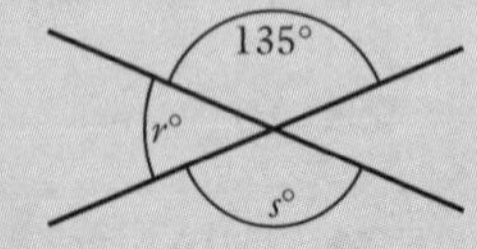

f

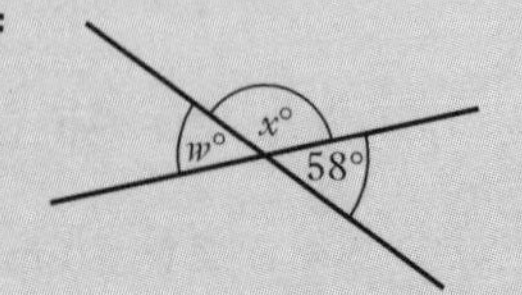

3 Find

a the supplement of **i** 48° **ii** 126°

b the third angle in a triangle in which the sizes of the other two angles are 67° and 45°

c the angles in a quadrilateral if all the angles are the same size.

4 If you stand facing west and turn clockwise through $\frac{3}{4}$ of a revolution, in which direction are you facing?

5 Find the sizes of the angles marked with a letter.

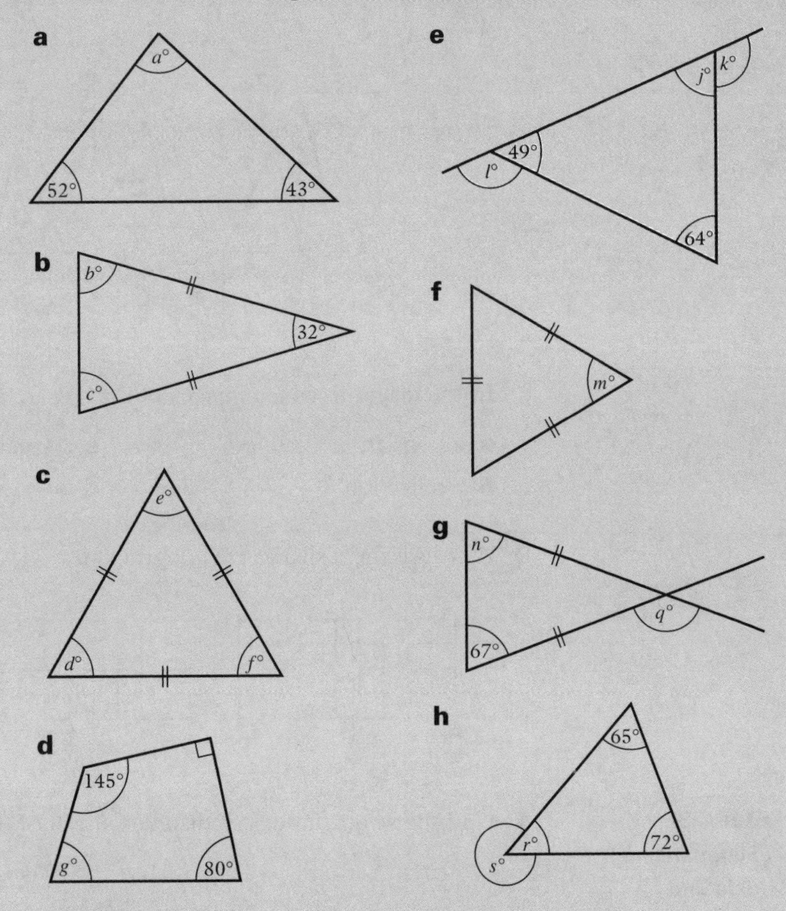

6 What special name do we give to each quadrilateral?

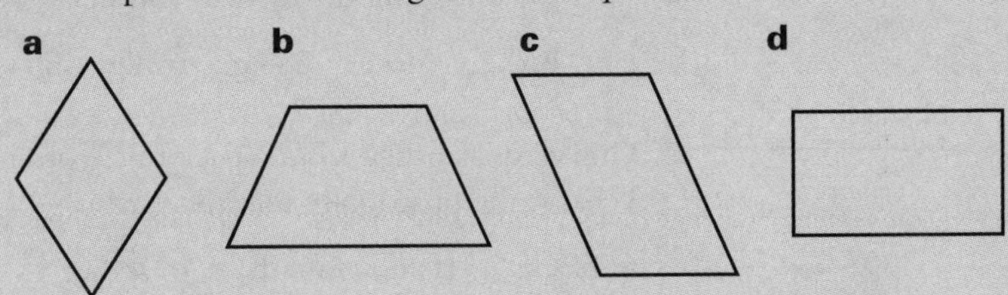

7 For each shape state

a the number of lines of symmetry

b whether or not the shape has rotational symmetry.

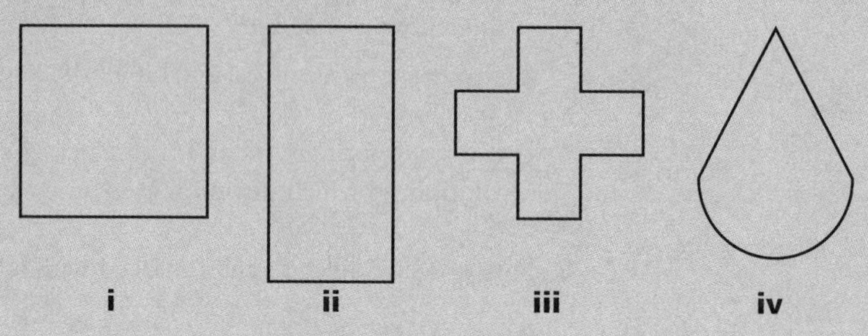

8

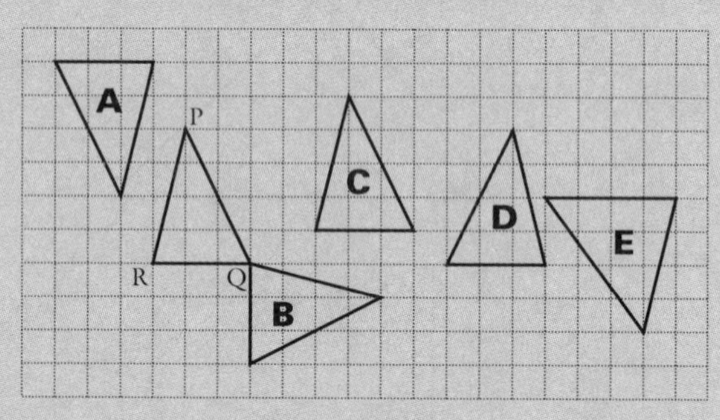

In the diagram, which images of $\triangle PQR$ are given by

a a translation

b a reflection

c a rotation

d none of these ?

9 Which of these shapes are congruent ?

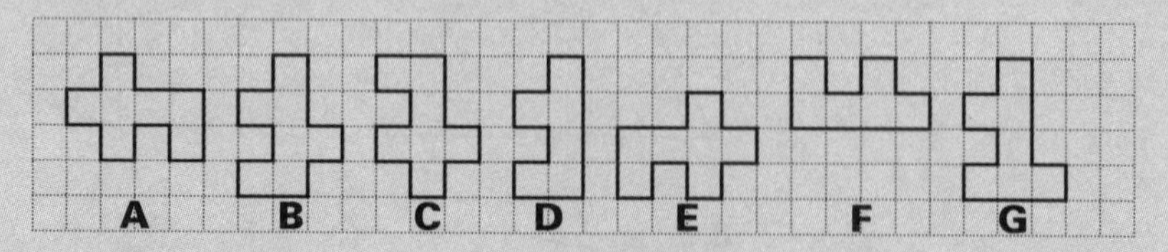

EXERCISE 1.7 (Summarising data and probability)

1 Find the range, mode, median and mean of the lengths

15 cm, 3 cm, 14 cm, 10 cm, 12 cm, 13 cm, 10 cm.

2 Find the range, mode, median and mean of the weights

66 kg, 56 kg, 54 kg, 62 kg, 59 kg, 62 kg, 61 kg.

3 One card is chosen from a pack of 52 ordinary playing cards. What is the probability that the card is

a black **b** a diamond **c** an ace **d** the king of spades ?

4 A dice is rolled. What is the probability that the number of spots uppermost is

a 4
b an even number
c a prime number
d a number that is both prime and odd?

5 A bag contains 3 red counters, 4 blue counters and 7 white counters. One counter is taken from the bag. What is the probability that this counter is

a blue **b** red or white **c** not red?

6

Mark	0	1	2	3	4	5
Frequency	1	0	4	7	10	3

The table shows the marks obtained by the pupils in Class 9G in a spelling test.

a How many pupils took the test?
b What was the modal mark?
c Find the median mark.
d Calculate the mean mark.

7 The table shows the number of goals scored by the first team in a hockey club last season.

Number of goals	0	1	2	3	4	5	6
Frequency	13	17	8	5	3	1	2

a How many games did they play?
b Find **i** the mode
ii the median
iii the mean number of goals scored per match.
c What is the range?
d Illustrate the distribution with a bar chart.

8 This pie chart shows how the crowd at an international match was divided into men, women, boys and girls.

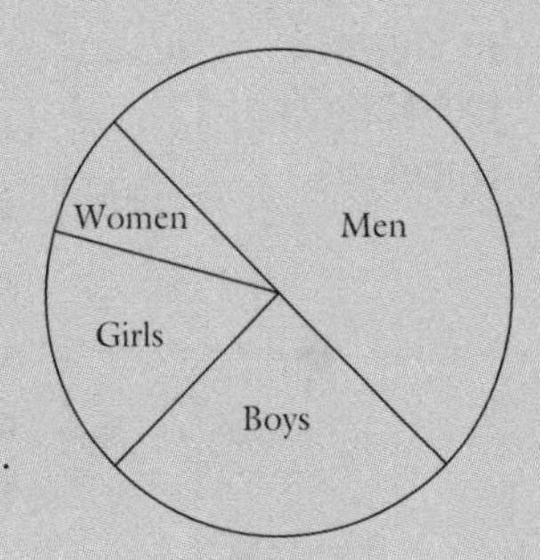

Estimate the percentage of the crowd that were

a male **b** female **c** boys **d** women.

REVISION EXERCISE 1.8 (Area and volume)

1 Find the perimeter and area of each shape, clearly stating the units involved.

a A square of side 4 in.
b A rectangle measuring 3 ft by 2 ft.
c A square of side 200 mm.
d A rectangle measuring 12 cm by 16 cm.
e A square of side 15 cm.
f A rectangle measuring 2.4 m by 1.7 m.

2 Find, giving your answer in the unit in brackets, the volume of a cuboid measuring

a 3 cm by 6 cm by 8 cm (cm^3)
b 8 cm by 4 cm by 1.4 m (cm^3)
c 1.5 m by 2 m by 1.5 m (m^3)
d 50 mm by 70 mm by 80 mm (mm^3)
e 4.5 cm by 5.4 cm by 6 cm (cm^3)

3 Find the volume of a cube of side

a 7 cm **b** $\frac{3}{4}$ m **c** $\frac{5}{8}$ in **d** 1.5 cm **e** 0.3 m

4 Express

a 3 cm^2 in mm^2 **d** 2 km^2 in m^2 **g** 8000 mm^3 in cm^3
b 3000 cm^2 in m^2 **e** 12 cm^3 in mm^3 **h** 1.5 litres in cm^3
c 0.4 m^2 in cm^2 **f** 0.003 m^3 in cm^3 **i** 3 m^3 in litres

5 Give roughly

a the number of pints in 10 litres
b the equivalent in litres of $2\frac{1}{2}$ gallons
c the number of litres in 6 pints
d the equivalent of 8 gallons in litres.

REVISION EXERCISE 1.9 (Algebra)

1 Simplify

a $3a - 2a + 5a$
b $4b + 6b - 5b$
c $3b - 6 + 4b - 7$
d $3c + 8c - 5c + 2c$
e $5c - 8 - 3c - 4$
f $9a + 3b - 4b + 3a$
g $2a - 4 + 5a - 7 + 3a$
h $5x - 7y - 2x + 4y$
i $3x + 4y - 4x + 5y$
j $8b - 2c - 6c - 3b$
k $5x - 10y - 4x + 12y$
l $3x - 5y + 5x + 2y$

2 Solve the equations.

a $x+8=14$
b $x-4=16$
c $6y=36$
d $3x-5=7$
e $7+4x=23$
f $x-0.8=1$
g $5x-7=2x+8$
h $15-4x=3$
i $3a=2$
j $9x-11-3x-13=0$
k $5y=45$
l $x+7=20$
m $x-9=8$
n $2x-3=11$
p $5a=2$
q $11-3x=3$
r $4x-13=2x-3$
s $x-0.4=2$
t $11x-13-4x-12=0$
u $7+3x=16$

3 Put < or > between the numbers in each of the following pairs.

a 8 5
b −7 5
c 6 −5
d −4 −6
e −3 4
f −9 −3

4 Find

a $-3-4+9$
b $8-4-7$
c $(+3)-(+4)-(+5)$
d $3-(-7)$
e $-6-(+2)$
f $-5-(+3)-(-6)$
g $7+(3-5)$
h $(8-12)-(7-11)$
i $-10-(+5)$
j $(7-2)-(9-12)$
k $-5-6+2$
l $6-(5-9)$
m $(8+7)-20$
n $(9-11)-(5-10)$
p $(4-2)-(6-11)$
q $(7-12)-(3-9)$

5 Find

a $(-7)\times 2$
b $(-8)\div 2$
c $(-4)\times(+4)$
d $18\div(-3)$
e $(-42)\div 6$
f -8×3
g $(-6)\div(-3)$
h $-(-5)$
i $(-12)\div 4$
j $(-25)\times 3$
k $(-6)\times(-2)$
l $\frac{24}{-8}$
m $8\times\left(-\frac{1}{2}\right)$
n $-\frac{3}{4}\times\frac{4}{5}$
p $\left(-\frac{1}{2}\right)\times\left(-\frac{1}{4}\right)$
q $(-1.5)\div 0.5$

6 **a** Find the sum of −5 and +3.
b Subtract (−4) from 1.
c Divide (−15) by (−3).
d Multiply (−6) by 4.

REVISION EXERCISE 1.10 (Coordinates and straight lines)

Copy the diagram and use it to answer questions **1** to **4**.

1 Write down the coordinates of the points A, B, C and D.

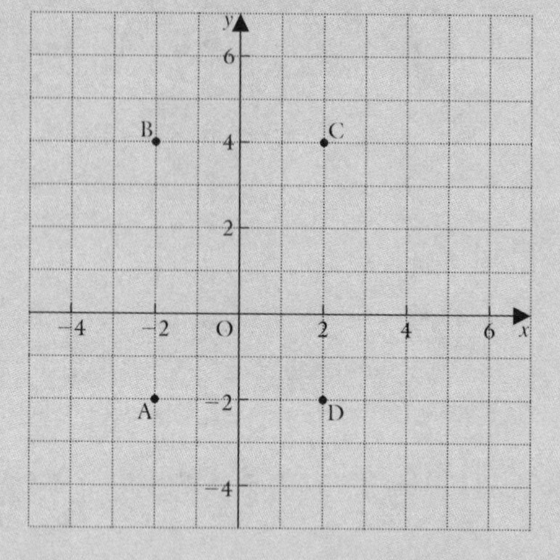

2 Join AB, BC, CD and DA. What name do you give to this shape?

3 Mark the point E so that ACED is a parallelogram. Write down the coordinates of E.

4 **a** Write down the coordinates of M, the middle point of AE.

b Write down the coordinates of N, the middle point of CD.

c How are M and N related?

5 Draw a set of axes and scale each one from −6 to 6. Mark the points A(2, −3), B(−3, 5), C(6, 5) and D(6, −3) and draw the quadrilateral ABCD. What name do you give to this type of quadrilateral?

6 **a** Write down the coordinates of A, B and C.

b D, E, F and G are other points on this line. Find the missing coordinates:
D(2, □), E(−1, □),
F(□, 9), G(□, −5).

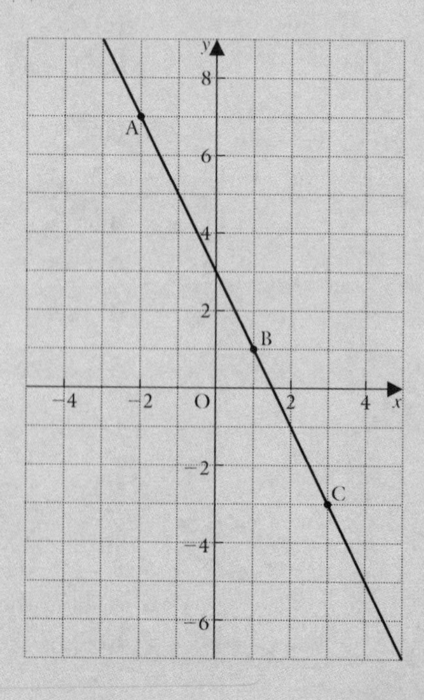

7 The equation of a straight line is $y = 3x$.

a Find the y-coordinate of the point on the line that has an x-coordinate of **i** 2 **ii** 5 **iii** -5

b Find the x-coordinate of the point on the line that has a y-coordinate of **i** 12 **ii** -9 **iii** 24

c Does the point $(3, -9)$ lie on the line? Justify your answer.

8 The table shows the conversion from United States dollars to pounds sterling for various amounts of money.

US dollars ($)	47	78	156
Pounds sterling (£)	30	50	100

Plot these points on a graph and draw a straight line through them. Let 1 cm represent $10 on the horizontal axis and 2 cm represent £10 on the vertical axis.
Use your graph to convert

i £80 into dollars
ii $120 into pounds
iii $64 into pounds
iv £65 into dollars.

SIGNIFICANT FIGURES

Rachel took 47 young people on a skiing trip.
After they had returned home, she found that £374 was left in the kitty.
Rachel used pencil and paper to calculate $374 \div 47$ to find the refund to each of the 47 members. Her result was £9.53.
She then checked the result by using a calculator and this time got £5.05.
Rachel was not confident that either answer was correct so she asked Dave to check them.

Dave quickly estimated $374 \div 47$ as about $400 \div 50$ i.e. 8, so recognised that £5.05 was very likely to be wrong, and that £9.53 was also probably wrong.

- There are situations when accurate answers to calculations matter. In Rachel's case, getting it right first time would avoid having to rectify the situation later – if a mistake results in overpayment, it may not be easy to sort out! In other cases inaccuracy can be much more serious – imagine the consequences if an engineer calculates the load that a bridge will carry as being ten times what the safe load should be.
- The first line of defence against inaccurate answers is to *start* by estimating the answer. If the calculated answer is very different from the estimate, you have a warning that something is wrong.

EXERCISE 1A

1 When Rachel entered $374 \div 47$ in her calculator and the display showed 5.05 . . . , she made a mistake that all of us can make sometimes. Find and describe her mistake.

2 Jackie and Dilip's kitchen floor is rectangular and measures 1.42 metres by 2.08 metres. To compare roughly how much it will cost them to cover this floor using different types of flooring, they start by finding the area of the floor.

a Discuss whether they need to calculate 1.42×2.08 accurately.

b Dilip estimates the area by rounding 1.42 metres to 1 metre and 2.08 metres to 2 metres. Jackie uses 1.5 metres and 2 metres for her estimate. Discuss which of these estimates is likely to result in a truer picture of the total cost.

3 Discuss some situations where an accurate calculation is

a vital **b** desirable, but not essential

c not necessary – an estimate is good enough.

4 Tim used his calculator to find $9.45 \div 0.35$. Discuss different methods he can use to check his answer.

5 Measure the width of your desk. Take measurements in at least three different places. Discuss whether it is possible to give such a measurement exactly.

SIGNIFICANT FIGURES

Discussion from the last exercise illustrates that, in many situations, we need to round numbers. Sometimes it is sufficient to round to the first figure in a number. In other situations rounding to the first figure is too coarse so we need to round to the second figure, or third figure, and so on.

Consider this situation: Danny measured her height as 1678 mm. She measured it again to make sure; this time the reading was 1676 mm.

- Try measuring your own height in millimetres three times. You will almost certainly find that you have three different measurements.
- Because it is not possible to measure height exactly, we need to round the measurement.

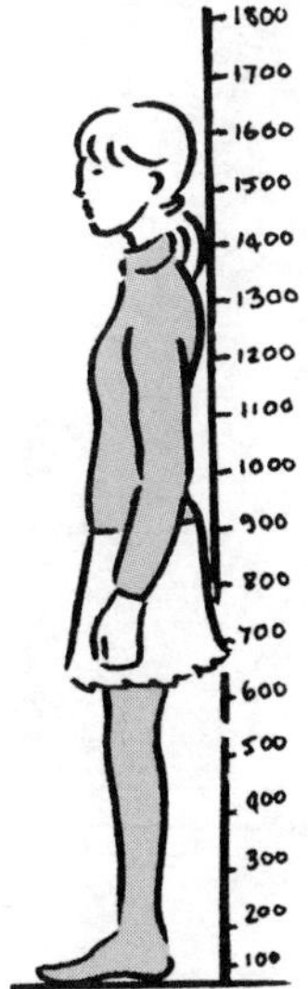

It should be possible to measure your height to the nearest 10 mm, that is, to the nearest centimetre. In Danny's case, it is reasonable to give her height as 1680 mm to the nearest 10 mm, that is, to the nearest centimetre.

If Danny used a measure graduated in centimetres, her first measurement would be 167.8 cm; this is 168 cm to the nearest centimetre.

If the ruler were graduated in metres, the reading would be 1.678 m. Correcting this to 2 decimal places gives a rounded height of 1.68 m. Now $1.68\text{ m} = 168\text{ cm}$, so 1.68 m is also correct to the nearest centimetre.

We could also give this measurement to the same degree of accuracy in kilometres,
i.e. 0.001 68 km correct to 5 decimal places (d.p.).

So, depending on which unit is chosen, Danny could give her height as

1680 mm to the nearest 10 mm,
168 cm to the nearest centimetre,
1.68 m correct to 2 d.p.,
0.001 68 km correct to 5 d.p.

Notice that the three figures 1, 6 and 8 occur in all four numbers and that it is the 8 that has been corrected in each case.

The figures 1, 6, and 8 are called the *significant figures* and in all four cases the number is given correct to 3 significant figures.

Using significant figures rather than decimal places has advantages. For example, if you are asked to measure your height and give the answer correct to 3 significant figures (s.f.), then you can choose any convenient unit. You do not need to be told which unit to use.

Reading from left to right, the *first significant figure* in a number is *the first non-zero figure*.
So 1 is the first significant figure in 170.6,
and 2 is the first significant figure in 0.025 09.

The *second significant figure* is the *next* figure to the right, *whether or not it is zero*, (7 in the case of 170.6 and 5 in the case of 0.025 09).

The *third significant figure* is the next figure to the right again (0 in both cases), and so on.

EXERCISE 1B

For 0.001 503 write down **a** the first significant figure
b the third significant figure

a The first s.f. is 1
b The third s.f. is 0

The first significant figure is always the first non-zero figure, the second significant figure is the next figure to the right whether or not it is zero, and so on.

In each of the following numbers write down the significant figure specified in the bracket.

1 36.2 (1st) **4** 3.786 (3rd) **7** 34.807 (4th)

2 378.5 (3rd) **5** 47.632 (2nd) **8** 0.076 03 (3rd)

3 0.0867 (2nd) **6** 5.083 (3rd) **9** 54.06 (3rd)

Give **a** 475 correct to 2 significant figures
b 32 685 correct to 1 significant figure

a To correct to 2 s.f. we look at the third s.f.: if it is less than 5 we leave the 2nd s.f. alone. In this case the third s.f. is 5 so we add 1 to the 7 to give 480. Notice that the 2nd s.f. in 475 is a number of tens, so by correcting to 2 s.f. we are giving the number to the nearest ten.

47|5 = 480 (correct to 2 s.f.)

b 3|2 685 = 30 000 (correct to 1 s.f.)

This is correct to the nearest ten thousand.

Always check that your corrected number is the same sort of size as the original number.

Give the following numbers correct to 1 significant figure.

10 59 727 **14** 80 755 **18** 667 505

11 4164 **15** 476 **19** 908

12 4 396 185 **16** 51 488 **20** 26

13 586 359 **17** 4099 **21** 980

Give the following numbers correct to 2 significant figures.

22 4673

23 57 341

24 72 601

25 444

26 59 700

27 892 759

28 50 047

29 53 908

30 6992

31 9973

32 476

33 597

Give 0.021 94 correct to 3 significant figures.

0.0219|4 = 0.0219 (correct to 3 s.f.)

The fourth s.f. is 4 so we leave the third s.f. alone.

Give the following numbers correct to 3 significant figures.

34 0.008 463

35 0.825 716

36 5.8374

37 78.49

38 46.8451

39 0.007 854 7

40 7.5078

41 369.649

42 0.989 624

43 53.978

Give each of the following numbers correct to the number of significant figures indicated in the bracket.

44 46.931 06 (2)

45 0.006 845 03 (4)

46 576 335 (1)

47 497 (2)

48 7.824 38 (3)

49 4537 (1)

50 37.856 72 (3)

51 6973 (2)

52 0.070 865 (3)

53 0.067 34 (1)

Find $50 \div 8$ correct to 2 significant figures.

To find an answer correct to 2 s.f. we first work to 3 s.f.

$$8\overline{)50.0|0}\quad = 6.2|5$$

So $50 \div 8 = 6.3$ (correct to 2 s.f.)

Without using a calculator find, correct to 2 significant figures

54 $20 \div 6$

55 $10 \div 6$

56 $25 \div 2$

57 $53 \div 4$

58 $125 \div 9$

59 $143 \div 5$

60 $0.7 \div 3$

61 $0.23 \div 9$

62 $0.0013 \div 7$

Depending on the circumstances, we may have to round numbers to a given number of significant figures or to a particular place value.
The next exercise contains a mixture of rounding questions. Make sure that you read each one carefully.

EXERCISE 1C

Round each number to the accuracy given in brackets.

1 1547 (nearest 10)

2 2.578 (nearest unit)

3 73.79 (2 s.f.)

4 8.896 (2 d.p.)

5 2993 (nearest 100)

6 55.575 (1 d.p.)

7 16.903 (nearest 10)

8 0.0527 (3 d.p.)

9 4.0579 (3 s.f.)

10 2022 (nearest 10)

11 0.000 357 (1 s.f.)

12 36 835 (nearest 1000)

13 Bella gave her weight as 51.2 kg correct to 1 decimal place. To how many significant figures did she correct her weight?

14 Greg gave his height as 65 cm correct to the nearest centimetre. To how many significant figures did he give his height?

15 Sally gave her height as 1.56 m correct to 2 decimal places. Leroy said, 'That means you are 160 cm tall to the nearest centimetre.' Why is he wrong?

16 Peter said that he took 30 minutes, to the nearest minute, to get to school this morning.
Jana said, 'That means you have corrected the time to 1 significant figure.'
Why is she wrong?

17 Martin was asked how far, roughly, he had to walk to school.
Being the proud owner of a new pedometer, he said 1563 metres.
What do you think a reasonable answer to this question would be and why?

18 A 10 metre length of string is cut into 7 equal pieces. How long is each piece? Round your answer to an appropriate degree of accuracy.

19 Jenni used a tape measure to find the length of her bedroom. She wrote down 254.5 cm for the length. Why is her room unlikely to be 254.5 cm long? What is a reasonable length to give for her room?

20 A rectangular table is 1.5 m long and 2.7 m wide, both measurements being correct to 1 decimal place. The table needs varnishing. The area of the table has to be known in order to work out how much varnish to buy. Find the area, rounding your answer to an appropriate degree of accuracy and explain why you have chosen that degree of accuracy.

21 Helen measured the width of a space in her kitchen correct to the nearest centimetre. She measured the width of a unit correct to the nearest centimetre. They both were 45 cm wide but the unit would not fit in the space. Why?

22 Claire is going to travel by train from London to Birmingham. She wants to know how long the train journey will be. Explain, with reasons, which of the following answers is sensible.

A $1\frac{1}{2}$ to 2 hours

B 1 hour 41 minutes

C $1\frac{3}{4}$ hours to the nearest $\frac{1}{4}$ hour

FINDING THE GREATEST AND LEAST VALUES

Tom needed to buy enough plastic spoons for 247 desserts. He bought this packet of plastic spoons.

When Tom laid out the spoons he found that he was 2 short.
If Tom had been thinking, he would have realised 'Average contents: 250' does not state the actual number of spoons in the packet; to be sure that there were enough he needed to know what the minimum number was.

EXERCISE 1D

> A building firm stated that, to the nearest 100, it built 2600 homes last year. What is the greatest number of homes that it could have built and what is the least number of homes that it could have built?
>
> **The smallest number that can be rounded up to 2600 is 2550.**
>
> **The biggest number that can be rounded down to 2600 is 2649.**
>
> **So the firm built at most 2649 homes and at least 2550 homes.**

1 A bag of marbles is said to contain 50 marbles to the nearest 10. What is the greatest number of marbles that could be in the bag and what is the least number?

2 To the nearest thousand, the attendance at a particular Premier League football match was 45 000. What is the largest number of spectators who could have been there and what is the smallest number who could have attended?

3 1500 people came to the school fête. If this number is correct to the nearest hundred, give the maximum and the minimum number of people who could have come.

4 The annual accounts of Scrub plc (soap manufacturers) gave the company's profit as £3 000 000 to the nearest million. What is the smallest profit that the company could have made ?

5 The chairman of A. Brick (Builders) plc says that they employ 2000 people. If this number is correct to the nearest 100, what is the least number of employees that the company can have ?

6 To the nearest metre, Vicky's garden is 12 m long. Vicky ran the length of her garden. What is the shortest length she may have run ?

7 To the nearest centimetre, Michael's handspan is 9 cm.

a What is the greatest width that Michael's handspan could be ?

b By how much could Michael's handspan be shorter than 9 cm ?

8 One side of the playground at school is 30 m long to the nearest metre. Mark ran up and down this side 20 times.

a Find the least distance he may have run.

b What is the difference between the least distance he may have run and the distance he thinks he has run using the given measurement ?

ESTIMATING ANSWERS TO CALCULATIONS

Discussion at the start of this chapter shows that knowing the rough size of the answer to a calculation warns us when the actual calculation is very wrong. It is important that estimating the result of a calculation becomes such a habit that we do it instinctively; the following situation illustrates why.

A harassed doctor in a busy casualty department has to calculate $9.25 \div 8.16$ to get the correct drug dose for a patient. She uses her calculator and the display shows 11.33 . . . but this is ten times larger than it should be. For the sake of the patient, let us hope that she instinctively recognises that this answer cannot be right.

The instinctive recognition that an answer is suspect comes about by

- *always* estimating *before* doing any calculations so that it becomes a habit
- simplifying the numbers involved to those we can work with in our heads, that is correcting them to 1 significant figure
- knowing the addition and multiplication facts (for whole numbers from 1 to 10) so well that we do not have to think, for example, about what 5×6 is equal to; the answer should be instantly in our heads.

The worked examples in the next exercise illustrate some of the thought processes involved.

EXERCISE 1E

Write down an estimate for $9.25 \div 8.16$

$9.25 \div 8.16 \approx 1$

Correct each number to 1 significant figure:
$9.25 \div 8.16 \approx 9 \div 8 = 1. \ldots$

Write down an estimate for each calculation. Do all working in your head.

1 2.4×1.8

2 $3.6 \div 1.7$

3 4.2×1.9

4 $6.8 \div 2.1$

5 $4.4 + 2.99$

6 $8.4 - 3.9$

7 $2.9 + 8.3$

8 $7.8 + 9.1$

9 7.6×5.7

10 $7.3 + 9.2$

11 7.3×9.2

12 $9.2 \div 7.3$

Write down an estimate for $136.27 \div 25.9$

$136.27 \div 25.9 \approx 3$

$136.27 \div 25.9 \approx 100 \div 30$.
Divide by 10, then by 3:
$100 \div 30 = 10 \div 3 = 3. \ldots$

Write down an estimate for each calculation. Do all working in your head.

13 15.6×12.13

14 $97.5 \div 4.8$

15 97.5×4.8

16 $156 + 3904$

17 $596 \div 9.12$

18 $876 - 241$

19 577×21.5

20 $7994 + 587$

21 31.6×8.3

22 $31.6 \div 8.3$

23 $294 + 149$

24 $389 - 291$

Write down an estimate for $\frac{2.97}{0.18}$

$\frac{2.97}{0.18} \approx 15$

$\frac{2.97}{0.18} \approx \frac{3}{0.2}$ make the denominator a whole number so multiply top and bottom by 10.

$= \frac{30}{2}$ this means $30 \div 2$

$= 15$

Write down an estimate for each calculation. Do all working in your head.

25 0.37×0.14

26 $0.37 \div 0.14$

27 $1.39 \div 0.045$

28 $24.7 \div 0.37$

29 $\frac{1.97}{2.95}$

30 $\frac{0.432}{0.208}$

31 4.49×0.75

32 $23.66 \div 0.92$

<u>33</u> $\frac{5.39}{0.045}$

<u>34</u> 0.43×0.27

<u>35</u> $\frac{0.027}{0.52}$

<u>36</u> $5.21 \div 0.049$

Write down an estimate for $(0.723)^2$

$(0.723)^2 \approx 0.5$

$(0.723)^2$ means 0.723×0.723

so $(0.723)^2 \approx 0.7 \times 0.7 = 0.49 \approx 0.5$

Write down an estimate for each calculation.

37 $(4.9)^2$

38 $(0.178)^2$

39 $27.2 \div 0.92$

40 45.87×12.36

41 $\frac{51.7}{0.031}$

42 $(0.037)^2$

43 $5892 \div 23.6$

44 $\frac{891}{47}$

<u>45</u> $(0.54)^2$

<u>46</u> 29.9×0.029

<u>47</u> $29.9 \div 0.029$

<u>48</u> $\frac{0.812}{2.04}$

49 Which of the numbers given are obviously *not* equal to 2.09×15.26?

A 3.189 **B** 31.89 **C** 45.72 **D** 0.0663

50 Which of the numbers given are obviously *not* equal to $(2.09)^2$?

A 0.436 81 **B** 437 **C** 25.9 **D** 4.37

51 Which of the numbers given are obviously *not* equal to $\frac{25.4}{2.8}$?

A 9.07 **B** 0.907 **C** 102.5 **D** 0.0102

52 Which of the numbers given are obviously *not* equal to $25 \times 42 \times 34$?

A 357 **B** 35 700 **C** 35.7 **D** 357 000

53 Which of the numbers given are obviously *not* equal to $345 + 24 + 552$?

A 930 **B** 1146 **C** 46 897 920 **D** 93

MAKING BETTER ESTIMATES

Finding an accurate answer to a calculation is not always necessary; sometimes an estimated answer is all that is required. However an estimate obtained by correcting each number to 1 significant figure can be so rough that it may mislead.

For example, Gita is buying a car and is about to sign the contract. She has to decide whether to pay for it with Option 1: 24 monthly payments of £249.85, or with Option 2: 36 monthly payments of £169.36.
To help with the decision, Gita can estimate the total cost of each option.
Option 1 gives a total cost of $24 \times £249.85$. If Gita estimates this by correcting each number to 1 significant figure, she gets
$20 \times £200 = £4000$. However, $24 \times £249.58 = £5996.40$ so the estimate is very low.
Option 2 gives a total cost of $36 \times £169.36$ $(= £6096.96)$. Correcting each number to 1 significant figure gives an estimate of
$40 \times £200 = £8000$. This is an overestimate.
These estimates suggest that the cost of paying over 36 months is double that of paying over 24 months whereas the real difference is about £100.

The reason for this is that the two numbers used in each estimate were rounded so that

for Option 1, they are both less than their true values,
for Option 2, they are both greater than their true values.

Also the changes in their values are fairly big because each number is close to a borderline where they would have been rounded the other way.

We see from this example that, when we make estimates, we should

- be aware of whether we are overestimating or underestimating
- make judgements about how to simplify the numbers, for example, use more than 1 significant figure for some of the numbers, round some numbers up instead of down, or vice-versa.

EXERCISE 1F

Do not use a calculator for this exercise.

1 Jim's lawn measures 24.5 metres by 12.6 metres. He wants to estimate its area so that he can judge how much fertiliser he needs.

a Estimate the area of the lawn by correcting each number to 1 significant figure.

b Is your estimate greater or less than the true area? Give a reason for your answer.

c Do you think your estimate is likely to be good enough for Jim's purposes? If your answer is yes, say why. If your answer is no, give a better estimate and say why it is closer than the first estimate.

2 Sarah intends to save £1.48 a week. Estimate how much she hopes to save in 52 weeks. Explain how you got your estimate and whether you think it is reasonably close to the real value.

3 David wants to save £1850 by putting the same amount into a savings account each week for 26 weeks.

a Estimate how much he should save each week.

b Is your estimate too large or too small and why?

c Is your estimate reliable enough to decide whether, if David deposits £75 each week, he will save enough?

4 Fran has to repay a debt of £3550 by paying an equal amount each week for 52 weeks.

a Estimate the amount she has to pay each week by correcting each number to 1 significant figure.

b Say, with reasons, whether your estimate is greater or less than the true weekly payment.

c Suggest how you can improve the estimate.

5 Gita had to decide quickly whether to pay for a car using
Option 1: 24 monthly payments of £249.85, or
Option 2: 36 monthly payments of £169.36.
Estimate the total cost of each option and say whether you think your estimate is good enough for Gita to be able to make a sensible decision.

CHECKING ANSWERS

An estimate cannot tell us whether an answer is correct; to be sure that a calculation is accurate, we must check it. The best way is to use a method *different* from the first one used (because when a method is repeated, we nearly always repeat the mistakes as well). When answers obtained from two different methods agree, you can be fairly certain that the calculation is correct. If they do not agree, there is a mistake in one or both methods; try a third method.

For example, if we need to calculate 24×6, we can use a calculator and check by using a non-calculator method, i.e.

$$\begin{array}{r} 24 \\ \times\ 6 \\ \hline 144 \end{array}$$

If the answers do not agree, we can use the fact that division is the opposite of multiplication,

i.e. if 24×6 comes to 144, then $144 \div 6$ should be equal to 24; so work out $144 \div 6$.

Addition can be checked by adding the numbers in the opposite order. Remember also that subtraction is the opposite of addition, that is, if $36 + 24 = 60$, then $60 - 24 = 36$

EXERCISE 1G

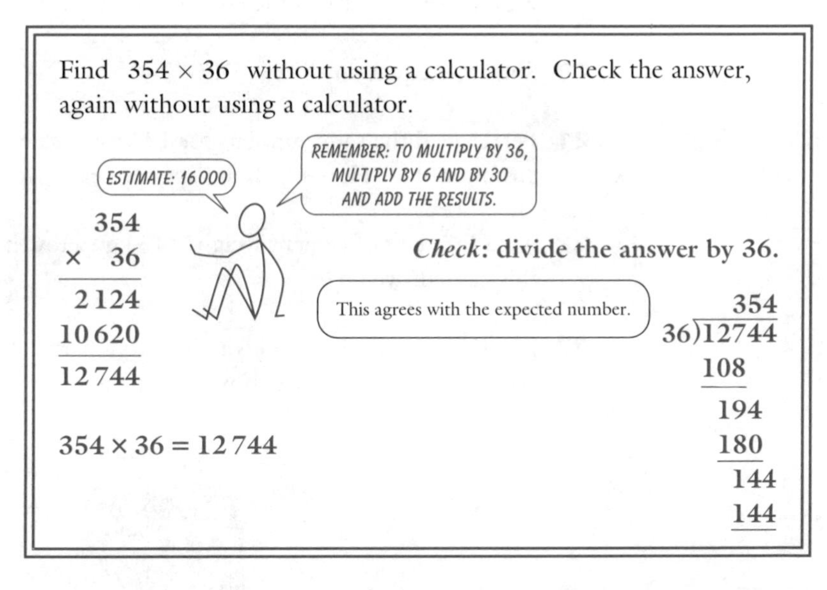

Without using a calculator, work out each calculation and check your answer. If your answers do not agree, use your calculator. Remember to start by estimating the result.

1 $2996 - 1059$

2 $13\,329 + 98\,827$

3 297×21

4 $884 \div 26$

5 $527 \div 17$

6 $\dfrac{8500}{170}$

7 535×15

8 $527 \div 31$

9 $213 - 186$

10 $4455 + 65\,441$

11 $4115 - 399$

12 29×177

13 $2550 + 59\,499$

14 $945 \div 21$

15 $\frac{1620}{36}$

Solve each problem and check your answer. Show all your working and state when you use a calculator.

16 Twenty-nine people in a syndicate won £513. How much did each person win?

17 The area of a sheet of paper is $375\,\text{cm}^2$. It is 15 cm wide. How long is it?

18 Jennifer makes picture frames. She sells each frame for £42. How much does she receive for a box of 36 frames?

19 Peter bought a box of 48 Mars Bars for £8.64 from a discount warehouse. What was the cost of each bar?

20 Solve the equation $83x = 747$

21 Petra saved the same amount for 19 weeks to buy a computer costing £855. How much did she save each week?

22 A 25 litre bag of cement weighs 115 kg. How much does 1 litre of this cement weigh?

23 Morris wants to post 49 invitations to a party. How much will it cost him to use first class post at 26 p each?

24

In a garage sale, Sally sold Mr. Peters a chair for £49, a spade for £2, a bookcase for £36 and a work bench for £127. How much should she have charged him?

PUZZLES

1 When second class post was 6 p and first class post was 7 p, 100 items of post were sent out for £6.20. Find how many of each class were posted using arithmetic only.

2 Some people make curious mistakes when working with numbers. Can you describe the mistakes that resulted in these wrong answers?

a $696 \div 29 = 38.66\ldots$

b $156 + 249 = 3915$

c $342 \times 63 = 6156$

d $354 + 37 = 724$

INVESTIGATION

My grandmother used 'casting out nines' to check her arithmetic. Each number is replaced by the remainder when it is divided by 9:

For example, to check whether 21×37 is equal to 777, find the remainder when 21 is divided by 9 (it is 3) and the remainder when 37 is divided by 9 (it is 1) so that 21×37 becomes $3 \times 1 = 3$ Now find the remainder when 777 is divided by 9; if it is also 3, the original calculation is probably correct.

Try this method on some other multiplications. Does it always work? Can you say why it works?
Will this method work on additions?

PARALLEL LINES

2

Two straight lines that are always the same distance apart, however far they are drawn, are called parallel lines.

The lines in your exercise books are parallel. You can probably find many other examples of parallel lines; for example, the edges on many buildings.

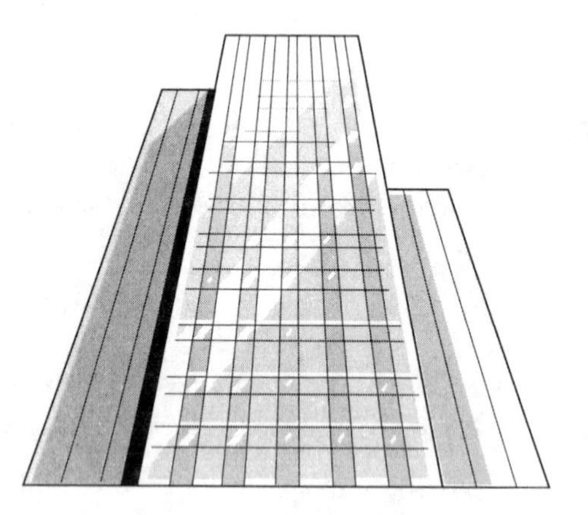

EXERCISE 2A

1 Discuss with your group, examples of parallel lines that

a are horizontal and you can see them in the room

b are vertical and you can see them in the room

c do not look parallel

2 Using the lines on your paper, draw three lines that are parallel. Do not make them all the same distance apart. For example

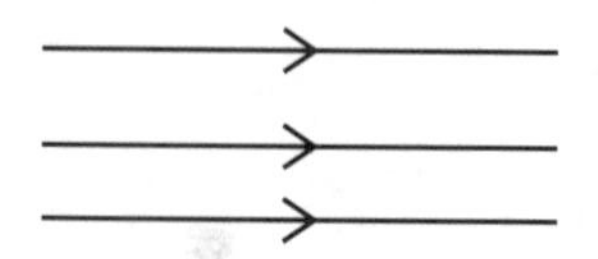

(We use arrows to mark lines that are parallel.)

3 Using the lines on your paper, draw two parallel lines. Make them far enough apart to be able to use a protractor. Now draw a slanting line across them. For example

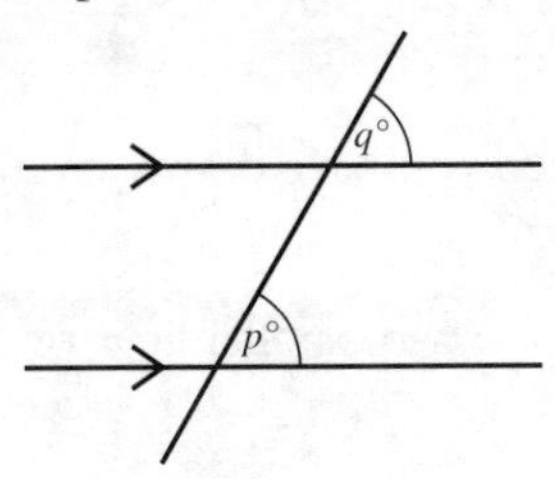

Mark the angles in your drawing that are in the same position as those in the diagram.

Measure your angles marked $p°$ and $q°$.

4 Draw a grid of parallel lines like the diagram below. Use the lines on your paper for one set of parallels and use the two sides of your ruler to draw the slanting parallels.

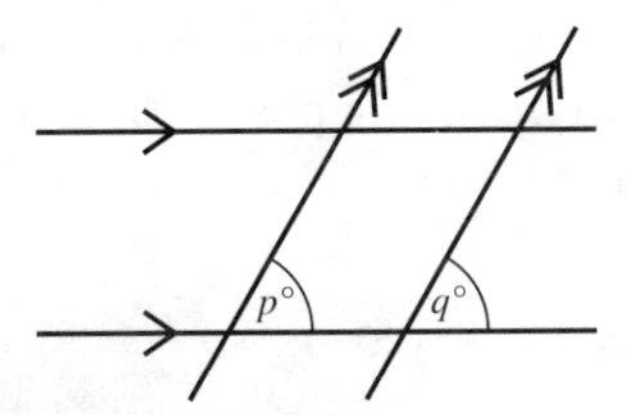

Mark your drawing like the diagram.

Measure your angles $p°$ and $q°$.

5 Repeat question **4** but change the direction of your slanting lines.

6 Draw three slanting parallel lines like the diagram below with a horizontal line cutting them. Use the two sides of your ruler and move it along to draw the third parallel line.

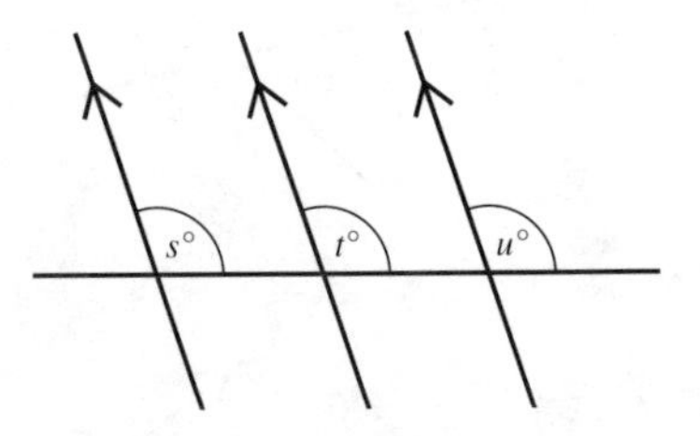

Mark your drawing like the diagram.

Measure the marked angles.

7 Repeat question **6** but change the slope of your slanting lines.

CORRESPONDING ANGLES

In the last exercise, lines were drawn that crossed a set of parallel lines.

> A line that crosses a set of parallel lines is called a *transversal.*

When you have drawn several parallel lines you should notice that

> two parallel lines on the same flat surface will never meet however far they are drawn

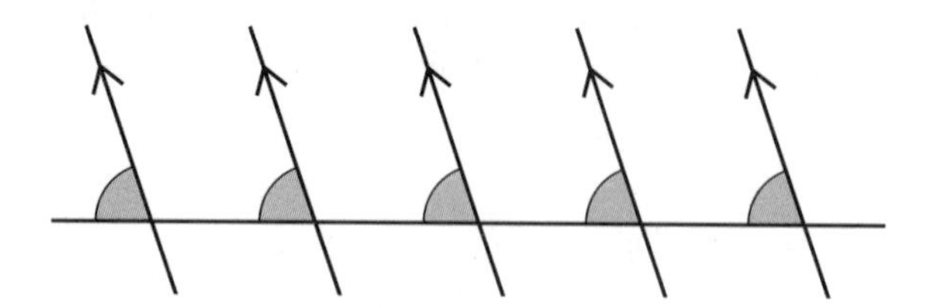

If you draw the diagram above by moving your ruler along you can see that all the shaded angles are equal. These angles are all in corresponding positions: they are all above the transversal and to the left of the parallel lines. Angles like these are called *corresponding angles*.

> When two parallel lines are cut by a transversal, the corresponding angles are equal.

EXERCISE 2B

In the diagrams below write down the angle that corresponds to the shaded angle.

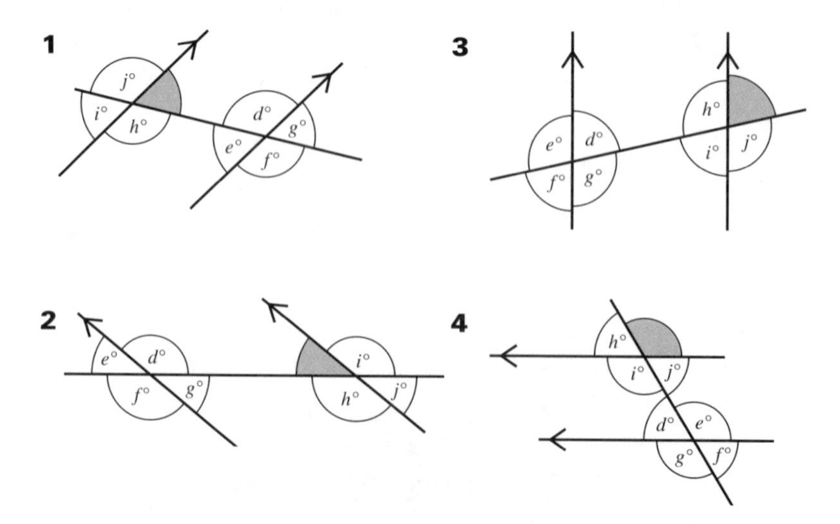

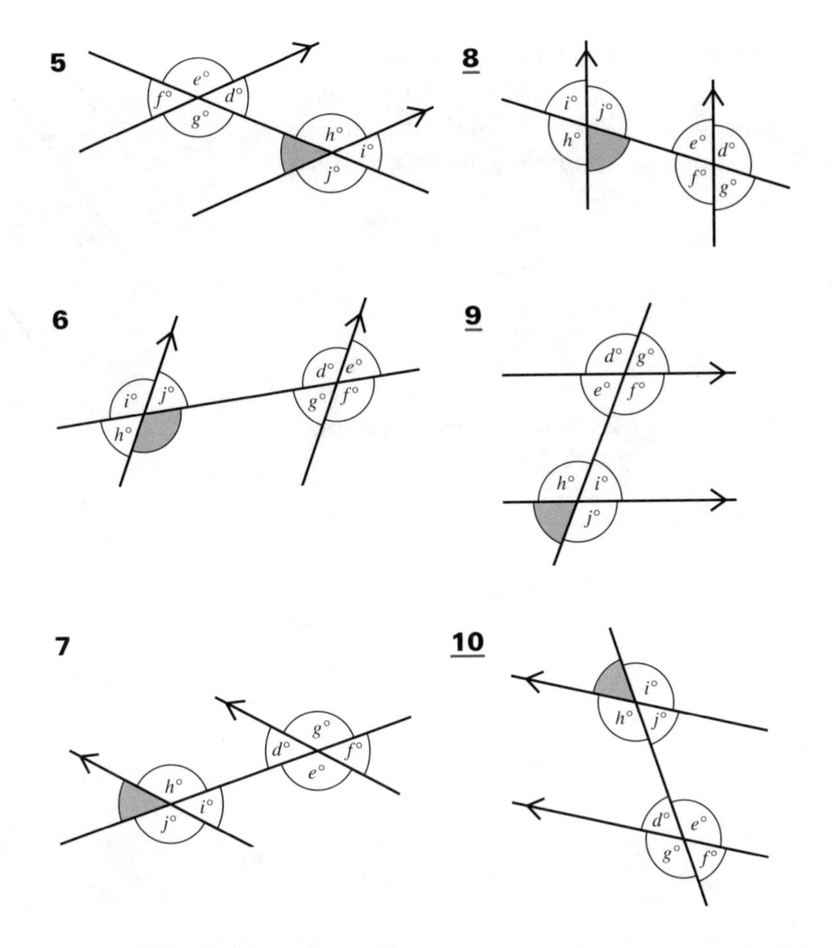

DRAWING PARALLEL LINES (USING A PROTRACTOR)

The fact that the corresponding angles are equal gives us a method for drawing parallel lines.

If you need to draw a line through the point C that is parallel to the line AB, first draw a line through C to cut AB.

Use your protractor to measure the shaded angle. Place your protractor at C as shown in the diagram. Make an angle at C the same size as the shaded angle and in the corresponding position.

You can now extend the arm of your angle both ways, to give the parallel line.

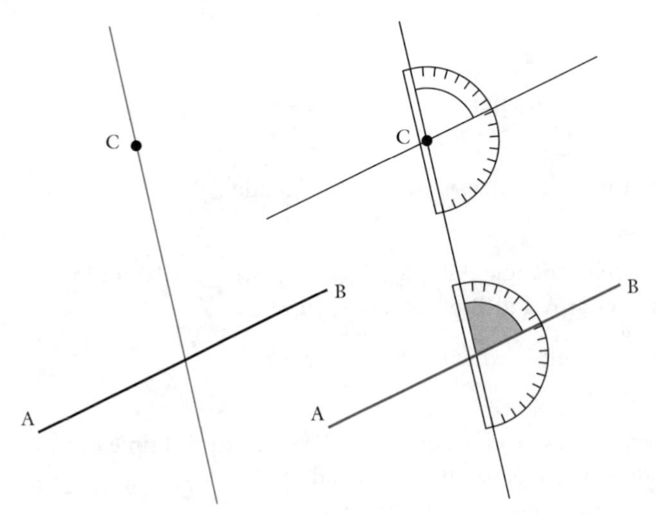

EXERCISE 2C

1 Using your protractor draw a grid of parallel lines like the one in the diagram. (It does not have to be an exact copy.)

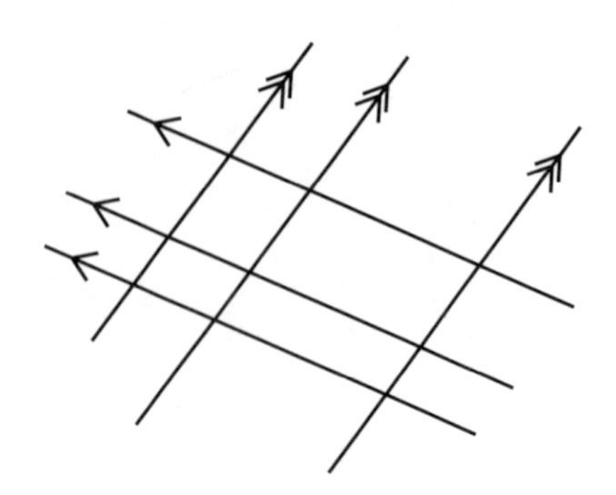

2 Trace the diagram below.

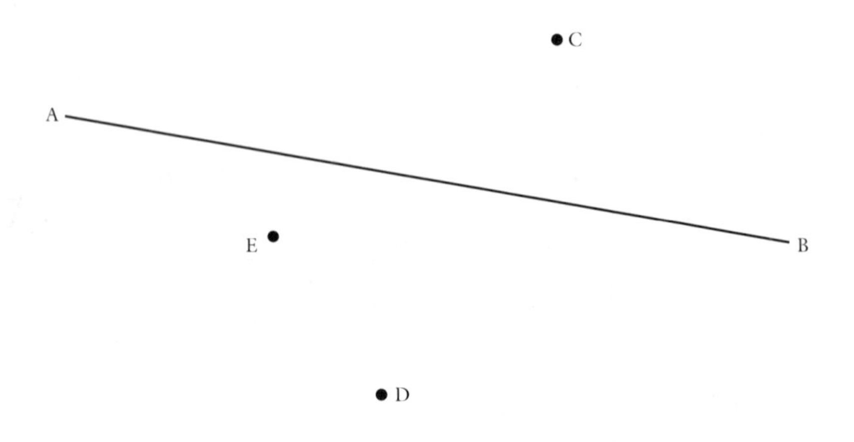

Now draw lines through the points C, D and E so that each line is parallel to AB.

In questions **3** to **6** draw a rough sketch before doing the accurate drawing.

3 Draw an equilateral triangle with sides each 8 cm long. Label the corners A, B and C.

Draw a line through C that is parallel to the side AB.

4 Draw an isosceles triangle ABC with base AB which is 10 cm long and base angles at A and B which are each 30°.

Draw a line through C which is parallel to AB.

5 Draw the triangle as given in question **4** again and this time draw a line through A which is parallel to the side BC.

6 Make an accurate drawing of the parallelogram below where the side AB is 7 cm, the side AD is 4 cm and $\hat{A} = 60°$

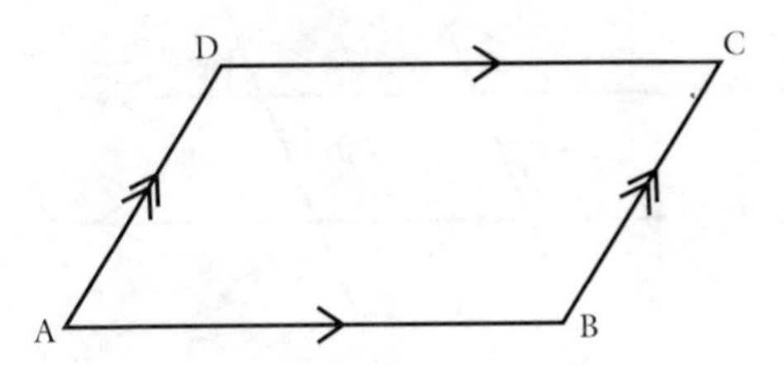

PROBLEMS INVOLVING CORRESPONDING ANGLES

The simplest diagram for a pair of corresponding angles is an F shape.

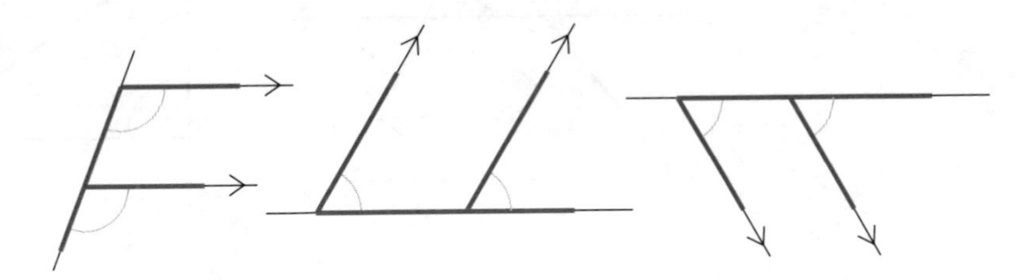

Looking for an F shape may help you to recognise the corresponding angles.

EXERCISE 2D

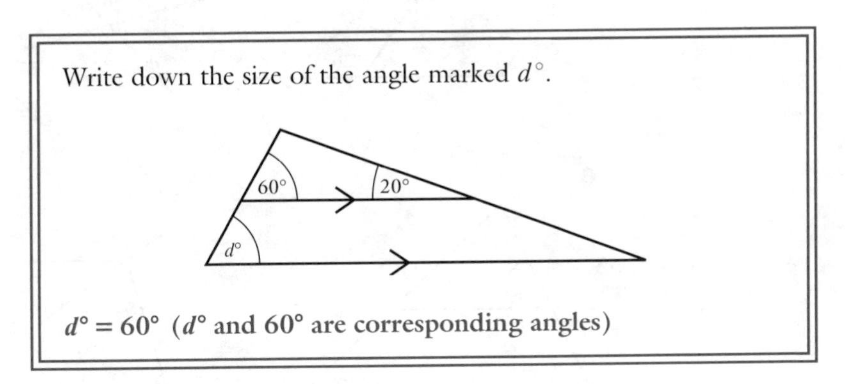

Write down the size of the angle marked $d°$.

$d° = 60°$ ($d°$ and $60°$ are corresponding angles)

Write down the size of the angle marked $d°$ in each of the following diagrams.

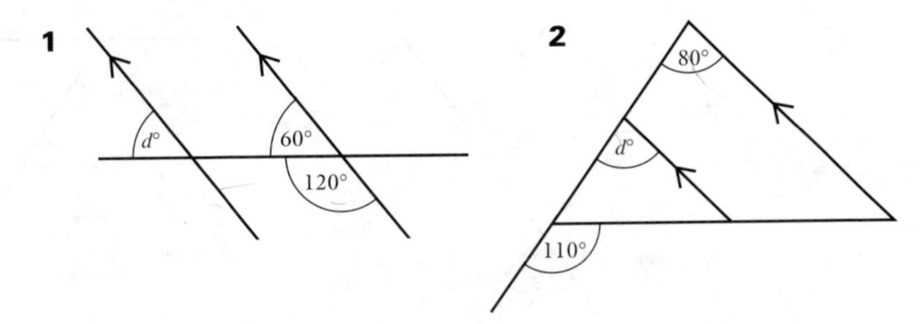

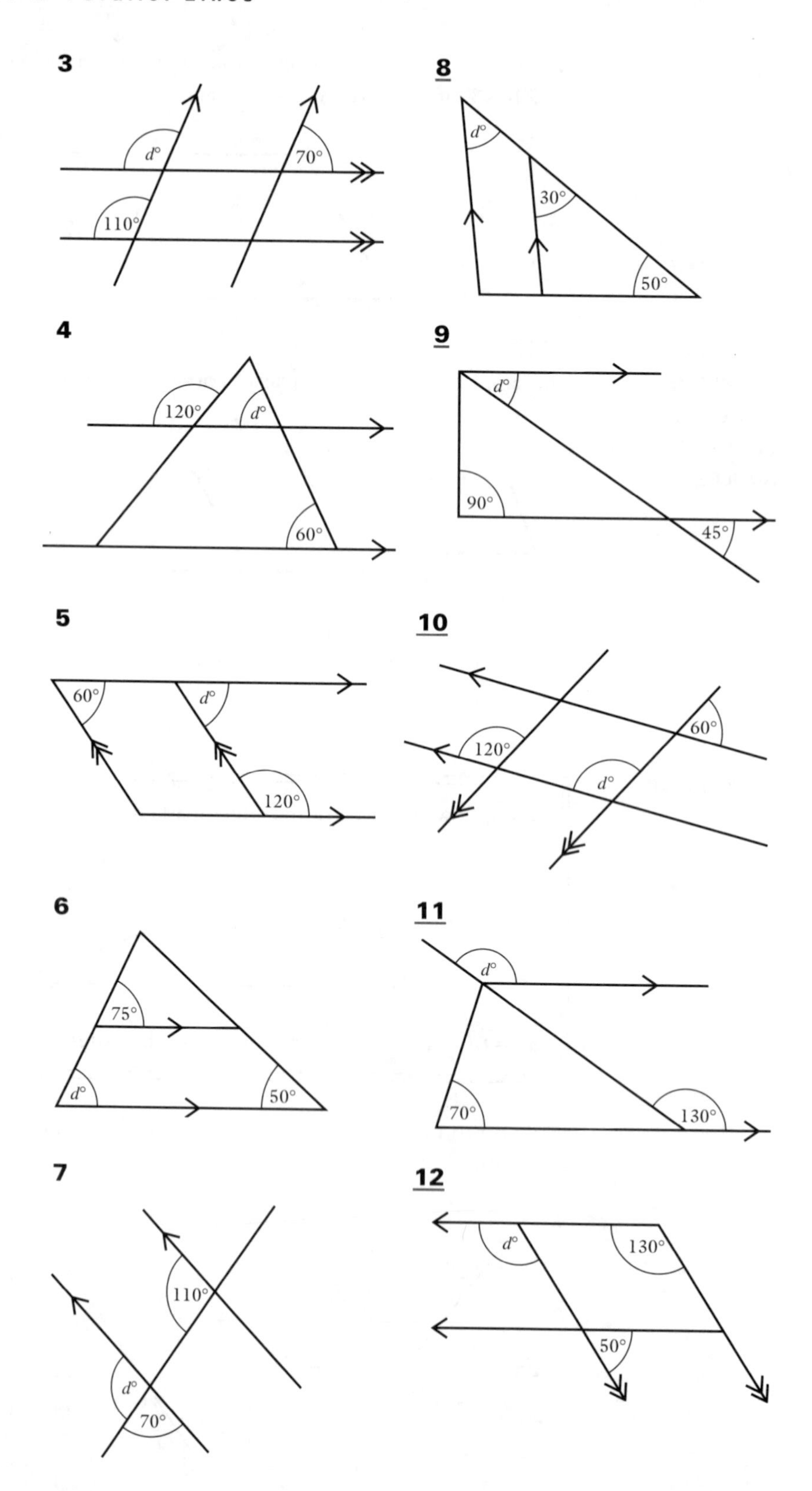
3
d°
70°
110°
8
d°
30°
50°
4
120°
d°
60°
9
d°
90°
45°
5
60°
d°
120°
10
120°
60°
d°
6
75°
d°
50°
11
d°
70°
130°
7
110°
d°
70°
12
d°
130°
50°

You will need to use the angle facts in the following questions. You can remind yourself about these facts by reading page 10 in the summary at the front of this book.

Find the size of each marked angle.

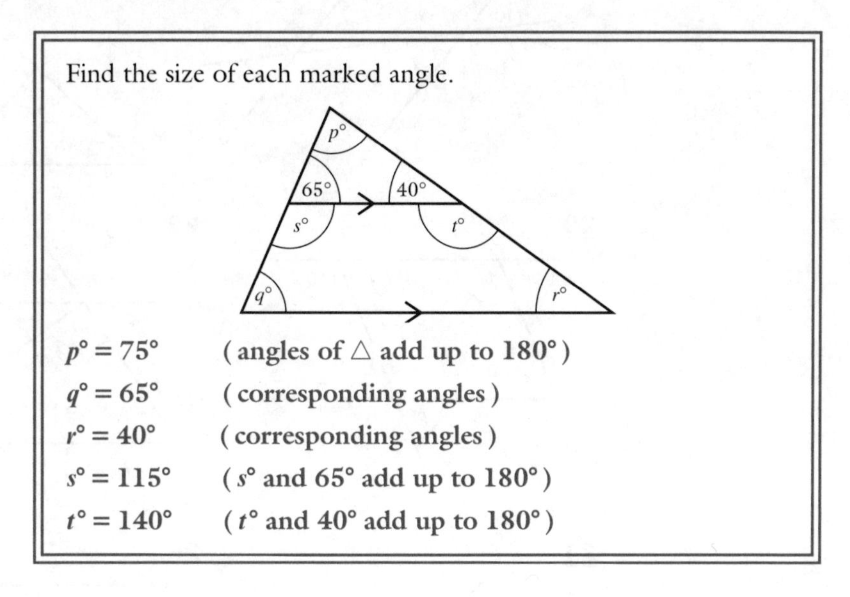

$p° = 75°$ (angles of △ add up to 180°)
$q° = 65°$ (corresponding angles)
$r° = 40°$ (corresponding angles)
$s° = 115°$ ($s°$ and 65° add up to 180°)
$t° = 140°$ ($t°$ and 40° add up to 180°)

Find the size of each marked angle. Give reasons for any statements that you make.

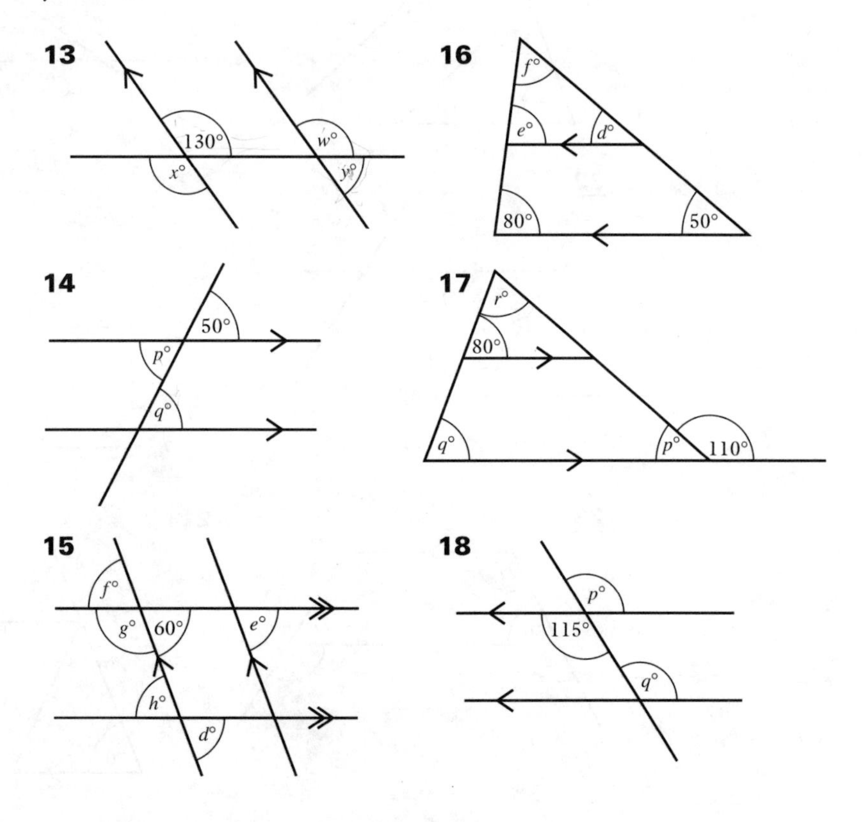

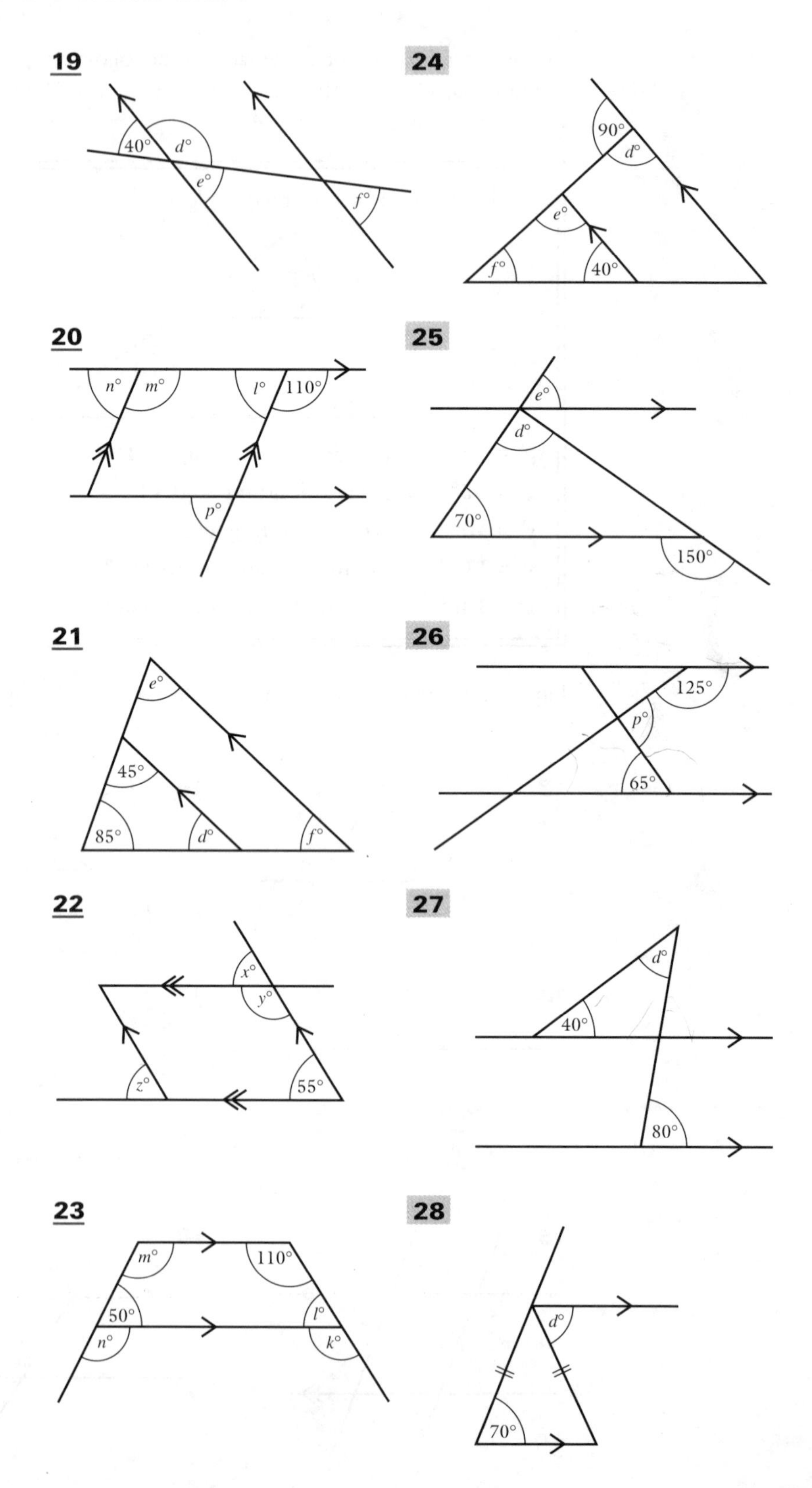

19
40°
d°
e°
f°
24
90°
d°
e°
f°
40°
20
n°
m°
l°
110°
p°
25
e°
d°
70°
150°
21
e°
45°
85°
d°
f°
26
125°
p°
65°
22
x°
y°
z°
55°
27
d°
40°
80°
23
m°
110°
50°
l°
n°
k°
28
d°
70°

Find the size of angle $d°$ in questions **29** to **32**.

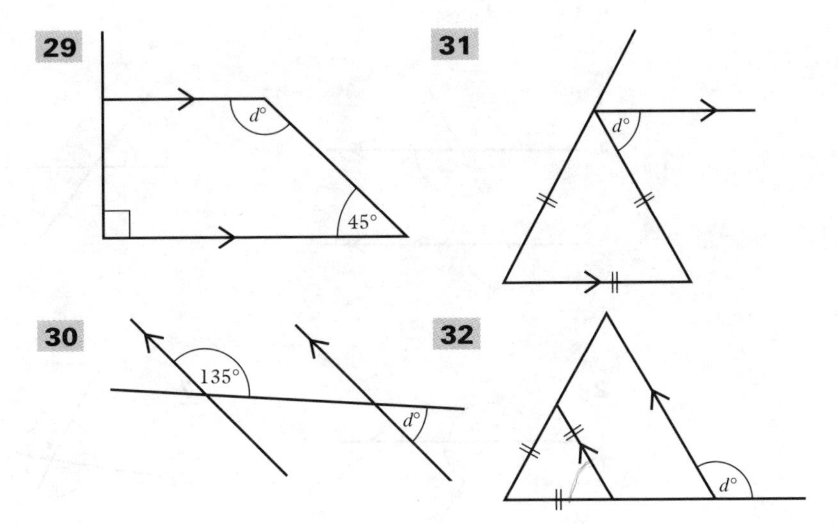

ALTERNATE ANGLES

This letter Z has rotational symmetry about the point marked with a cross. This means that the two shaded angles are equal.

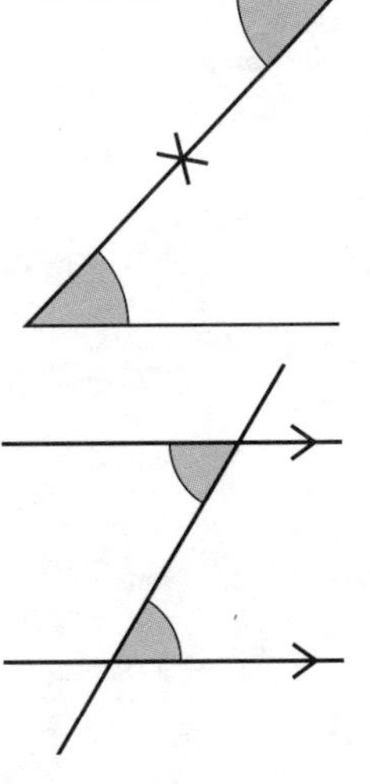

The pairs of shaded angles like those in Z are between the parallel lines and on alternate sides of the transversal.
Angles like these are called *alternate angles*.

When two parallel lines are cut by a transversal, the alternate angles are equal.

The simplest diagram for a pair of alternate angles is a Z shape.

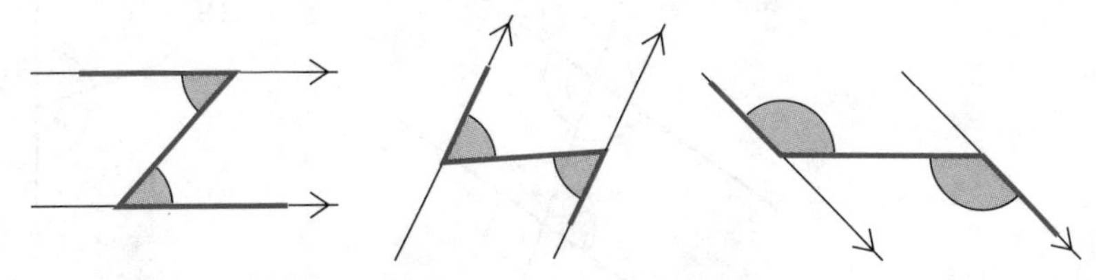

Looking for a Z shape may help you to recognise the alternate angles.

EXERCISE 2E

Write down the angle which is alternate to the shaded angle in the following diagrams.

1

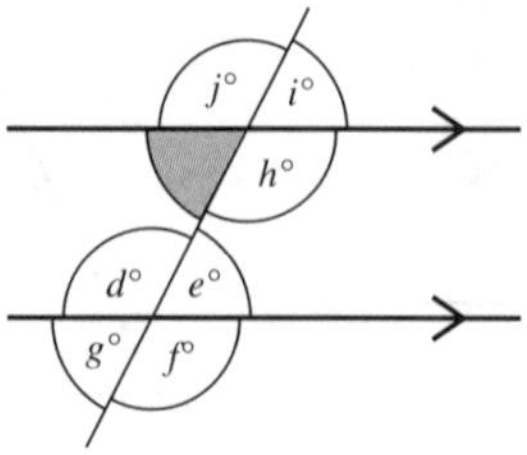

2

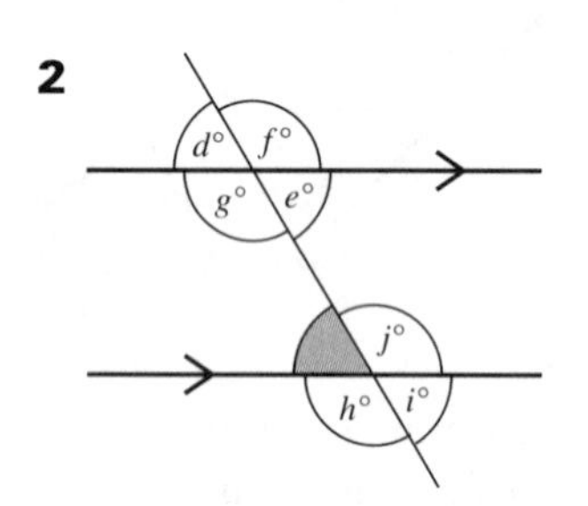

3

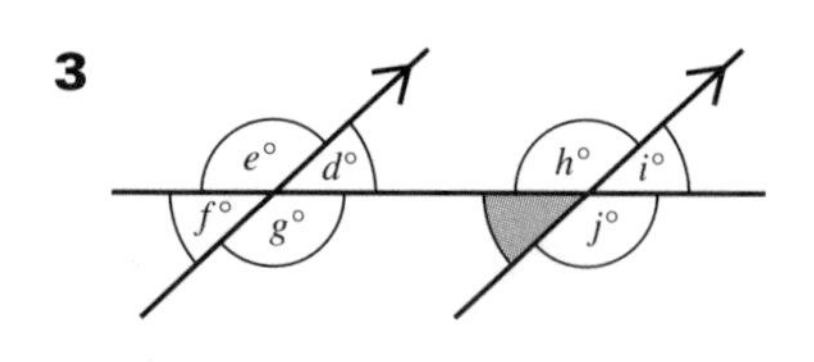

4

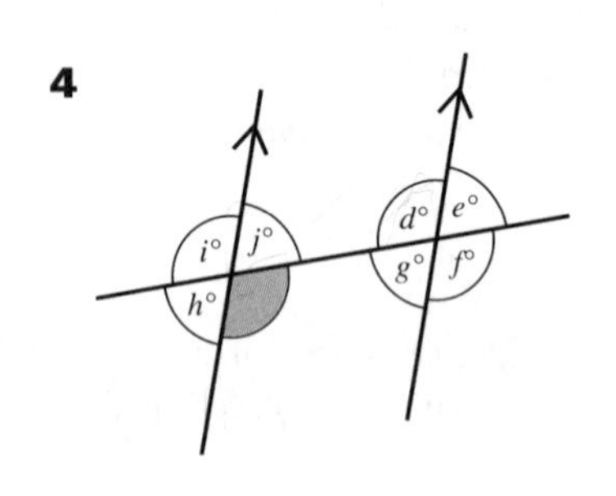

5

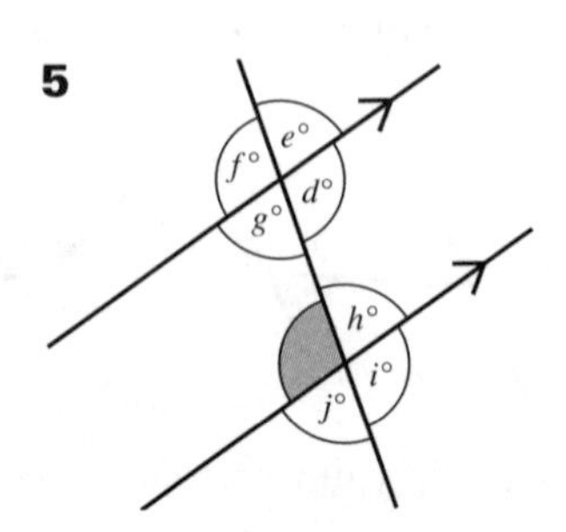

6

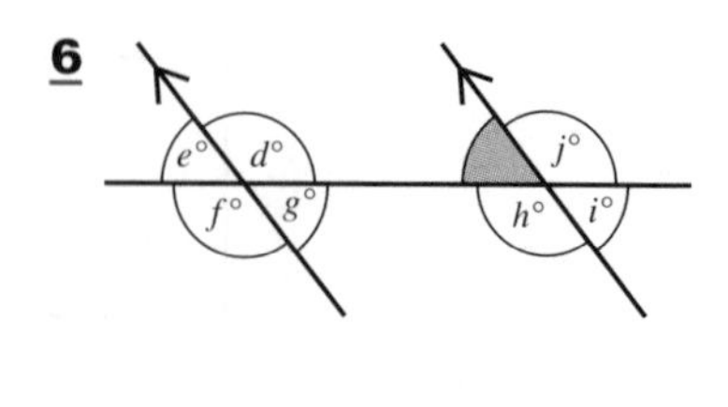

7

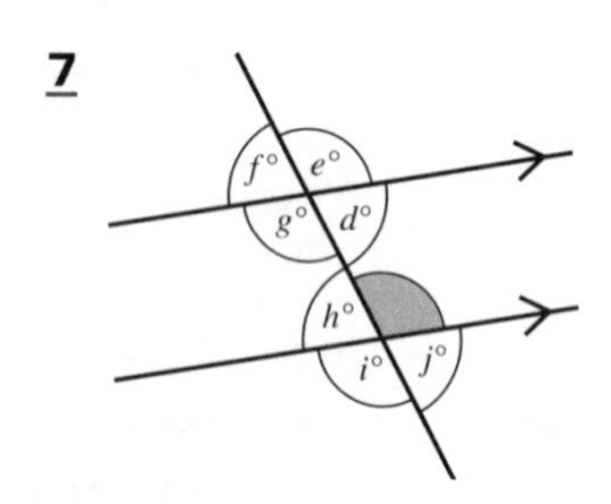

8

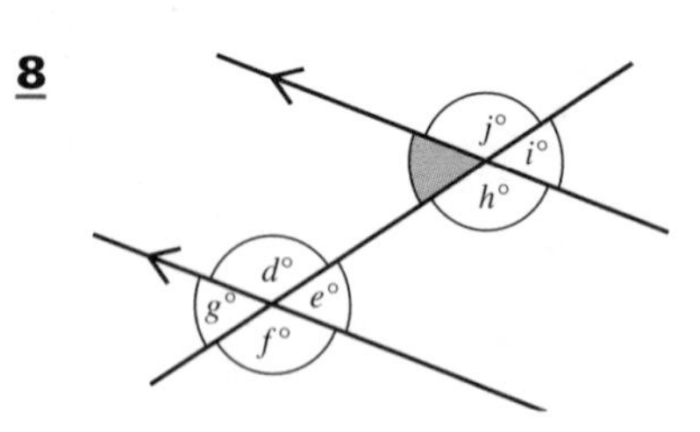

9

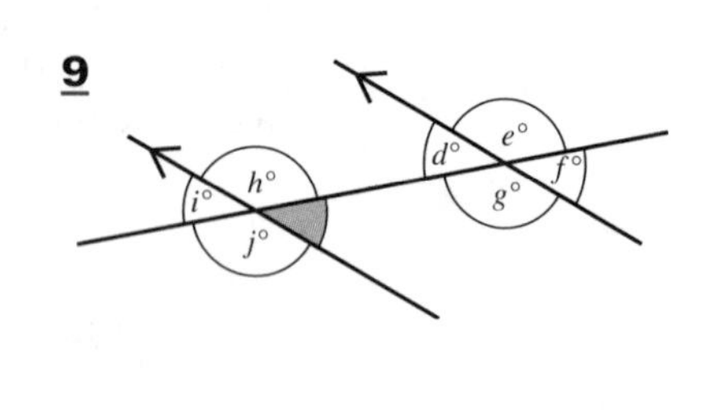

10

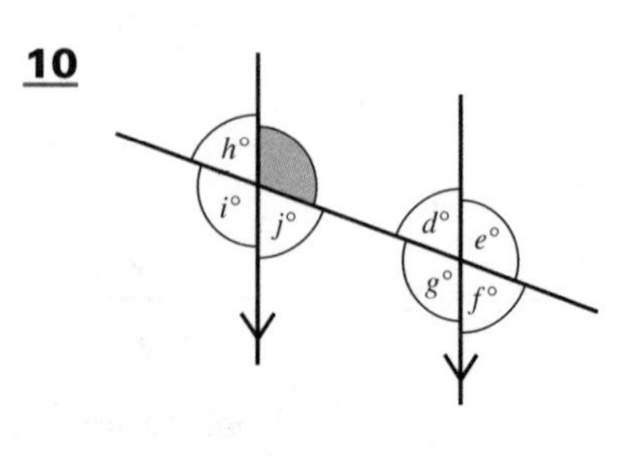

PROBLEMS INVOLVING ALTERNATE ANGLES

Without doing any measuring we can show that alternate angles are equal by using the facts that we already know:

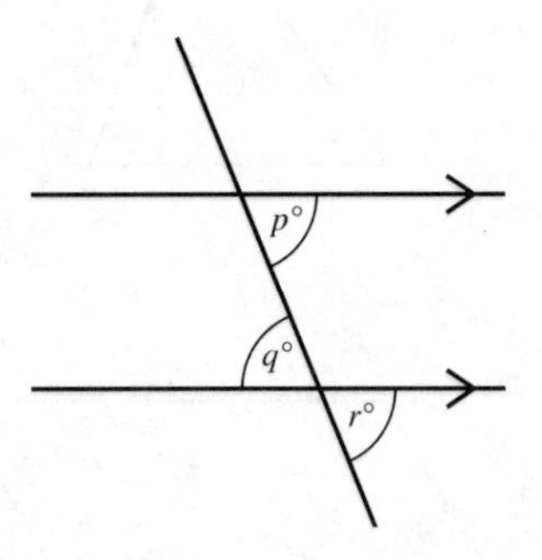

$p^\circ = r^\circ$ because they are corresponding angles

$q^\circ = r^\circ$ because they are vertically opposite angles

$\therefore$ $p^\circ = q^\circ$ and these are alternate angles

EXERCISE 2F

Find the size of each marked angle.

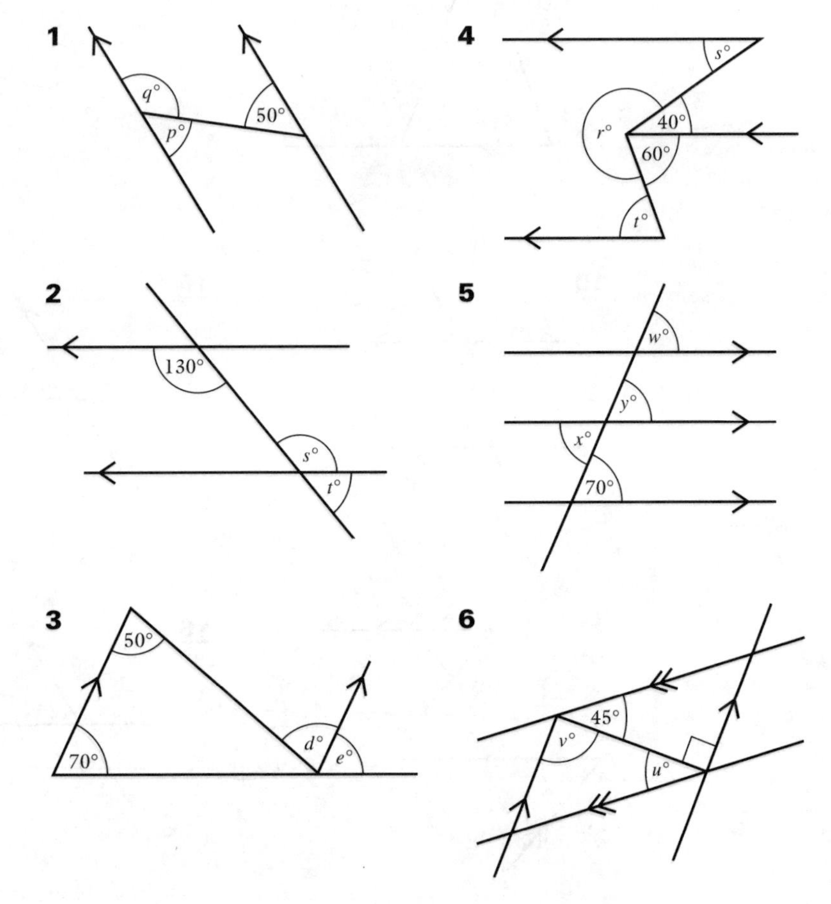

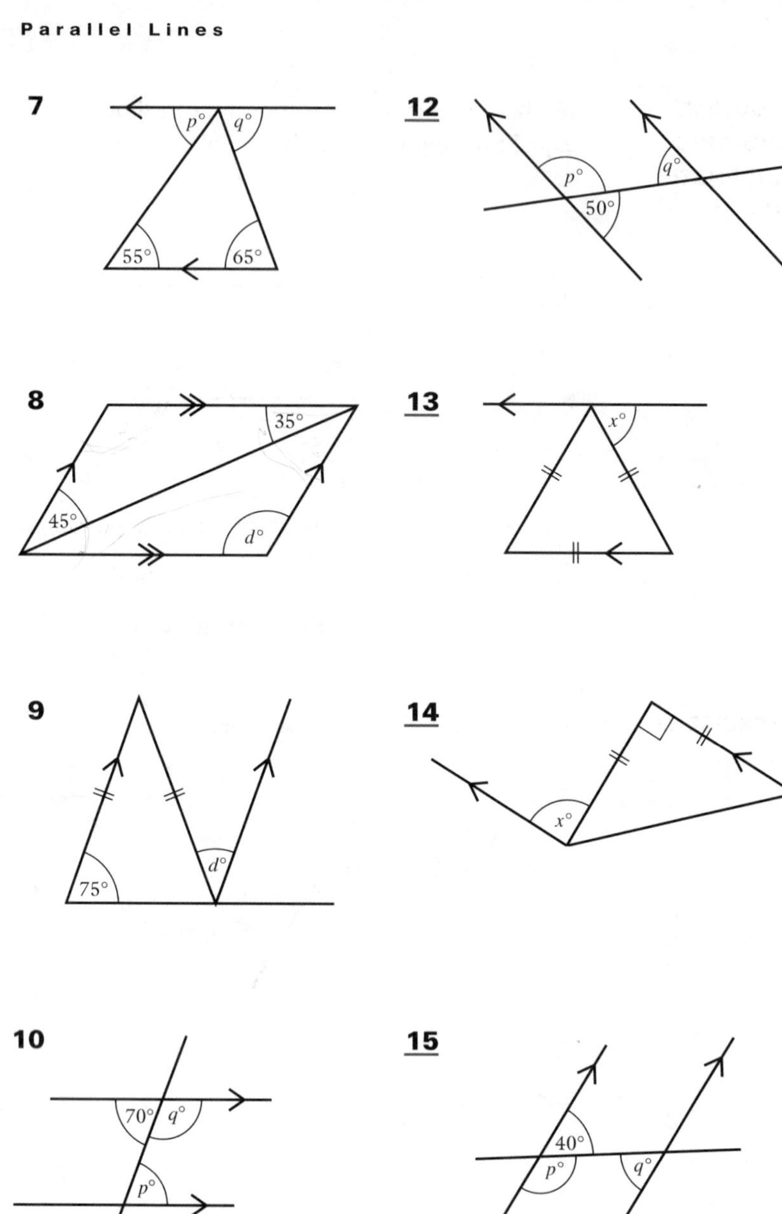
7
$p°$
$q°$
55°
65°
12
$p°$
$q°$
50°
8
35°
45°
$d°$
13
$x°$
9
75°
$d°$
14
$x°$
10
70°
$q°$
$p°$
15
40°
$p°$
$q°$

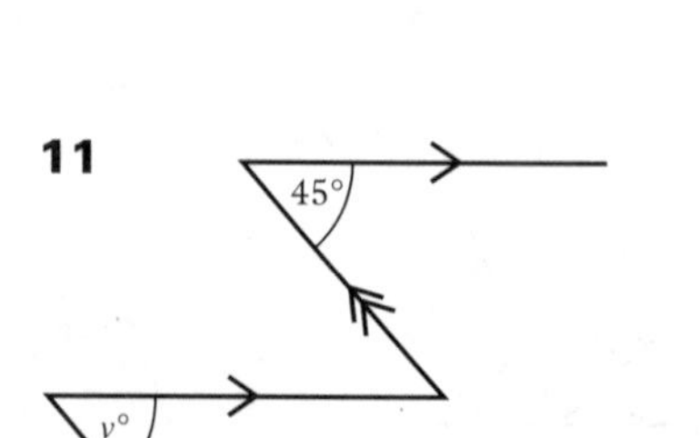
11
45°
$v°$

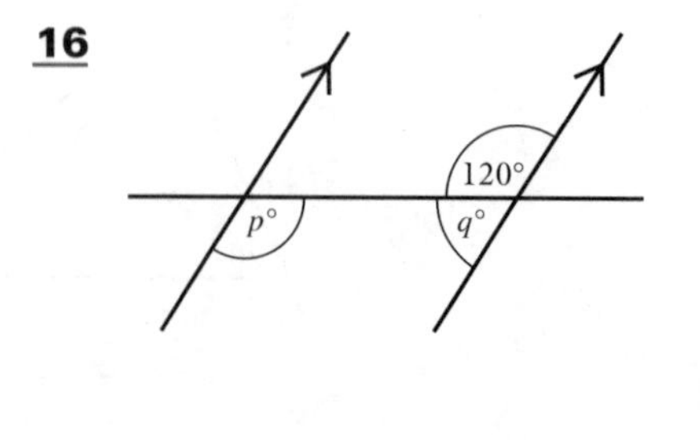
16
120°
$p°$
$q°$

Find the size of the angle marked $d°$.

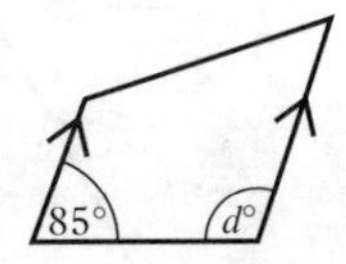

There are no pairs of corresponding angles or alternate angles marked in this diagram. On your own copy you can add lines and angles to help with the solution. In the diagram below we have extended the base and marked angle $e°$ to give a pair of corresponding angles.

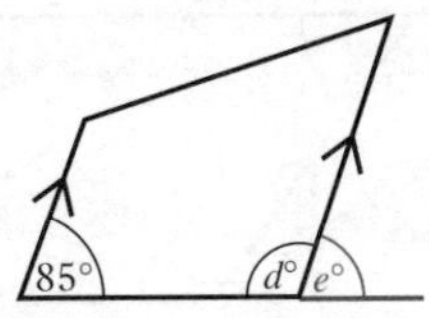

$e° = 85°$ (corresponding angles)

$d° = 180° - 85°$ (angles $d°$ and $e°$ add up to $180°$)

$= 95°$

Find the size of each marked angle.

17

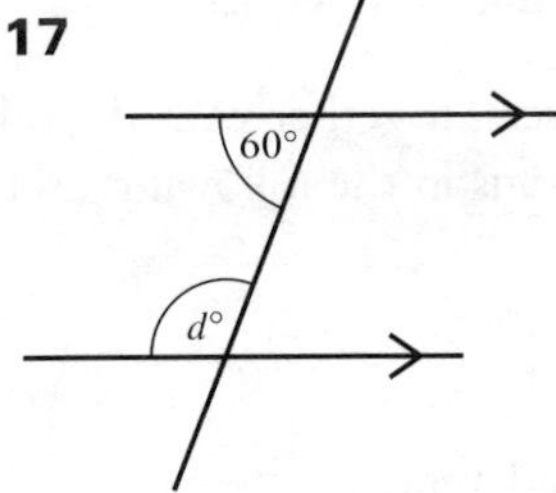

20

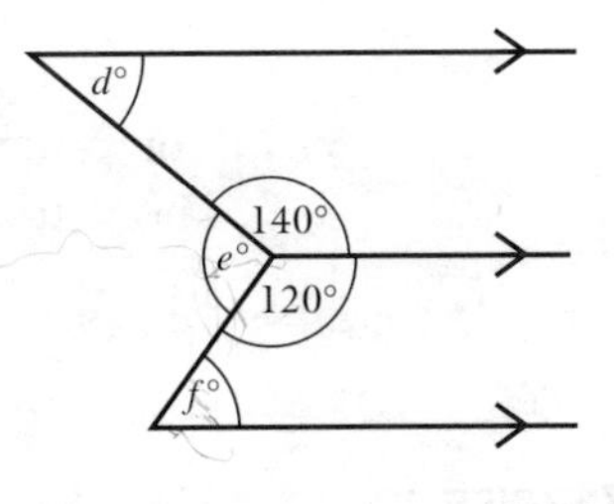

18

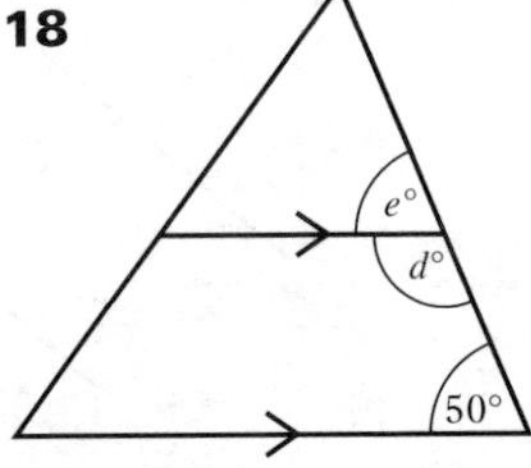

21

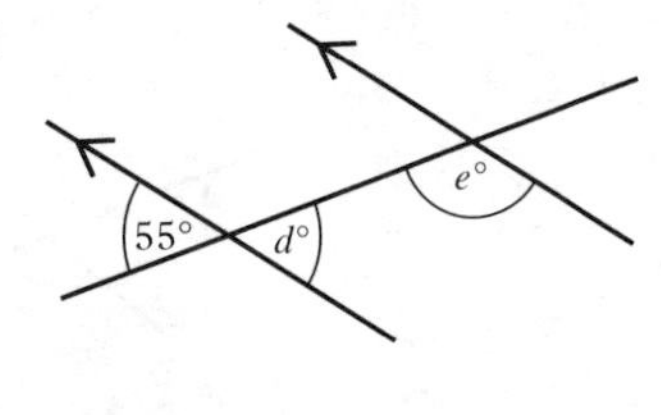

19

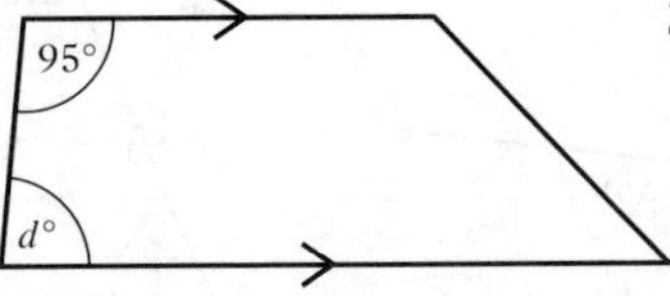

22

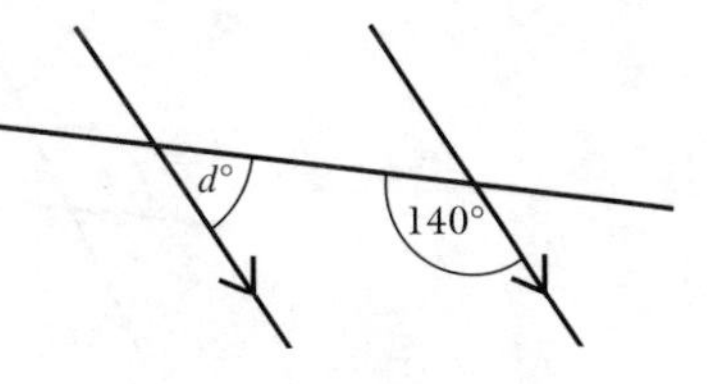

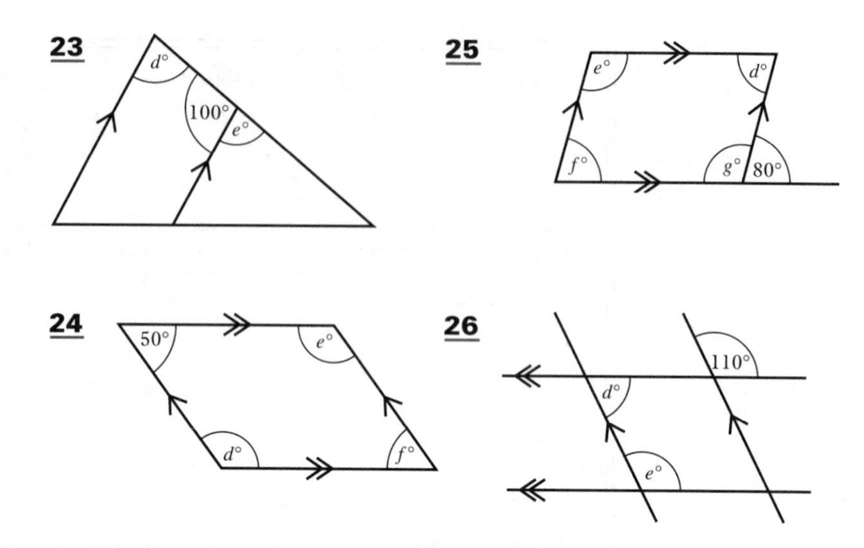

MIXED EXERCISE

You now know that when a transversal cuts a pair of parallel lines

the corresponding (F) angles are equal

the alternate (Z) angles are equal

You can use any of these facts, together with the other angle facts you know, to answer the questions in the following exercise.

EXERCISE 2G

Find the size of each marked angle.

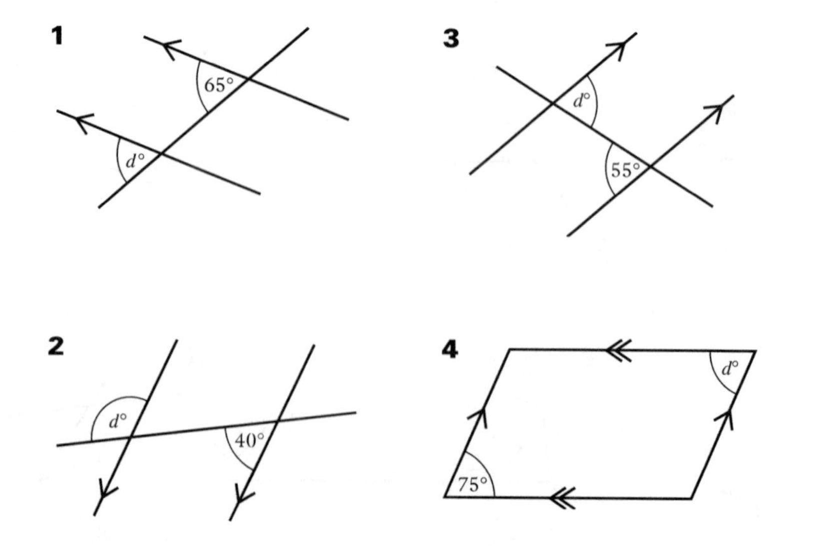

5

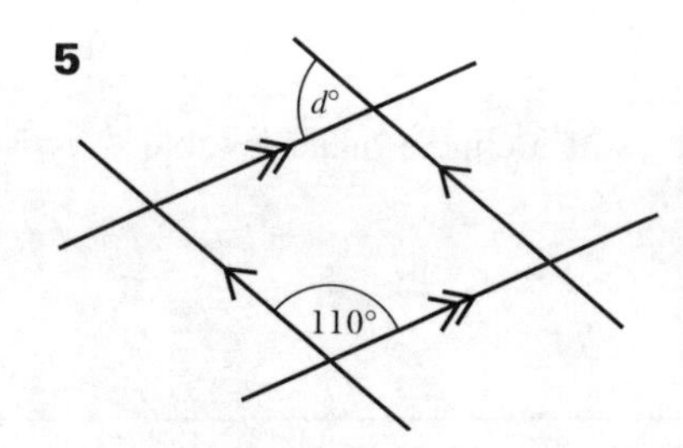

6

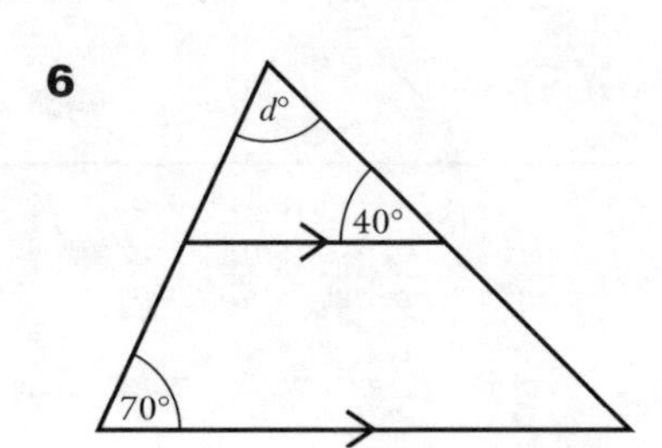

7

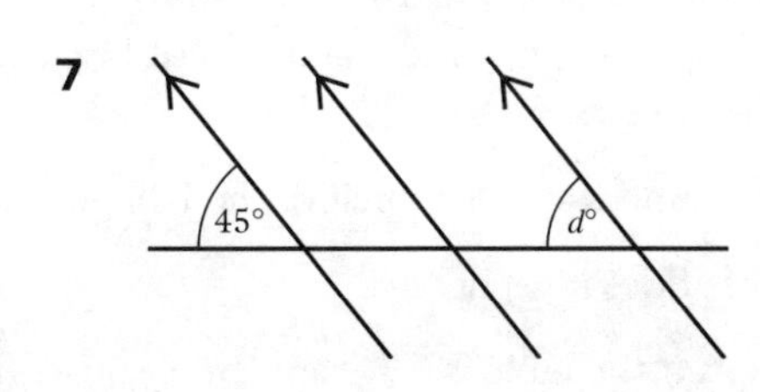

8

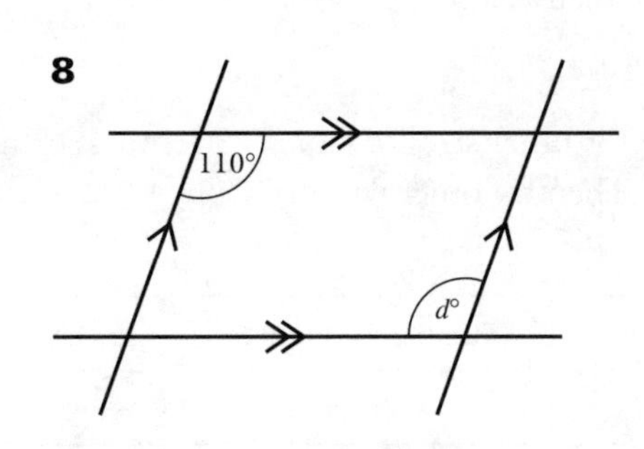

9

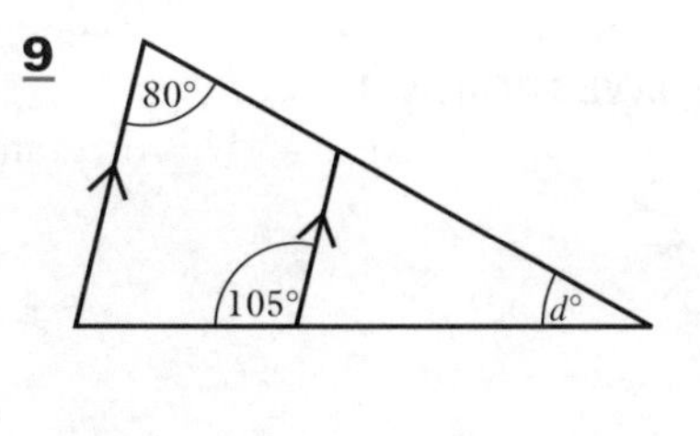

10

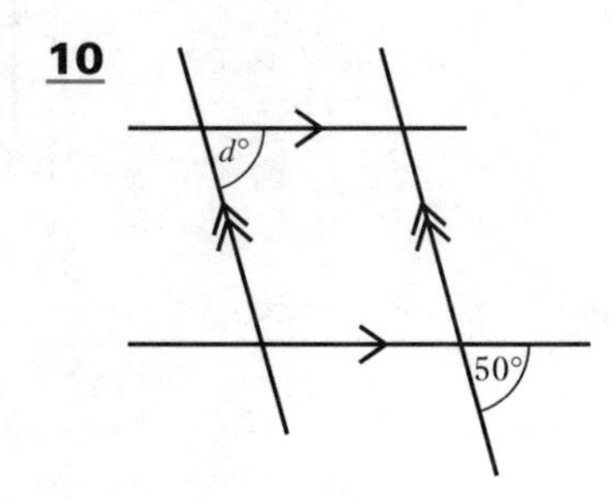

11

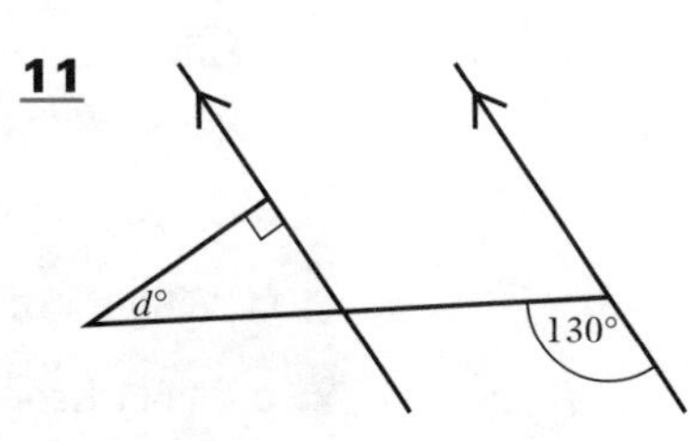

12

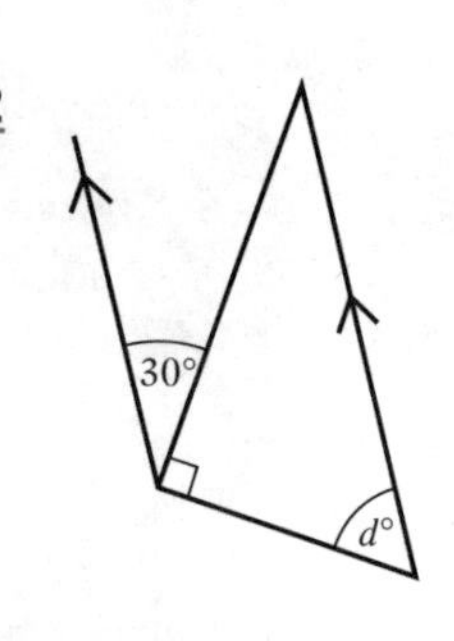

13 Construct a triangle ABC in which AB = 12 cm, BC = 8 cm and AC = 10 cm.
Find the midpoint of AB and mark it D.
Find the midpoint of AC and mark it E.
Join ED.
Measure $A\hat{D}E$ and $A\hat{B}C$.
($A\hat{D}E$ means the angle at D formed by the lines AD and DE.)
What can you say about the lines DE and BC?

INVESTIGATION

This diagram represents a child's billiards table.

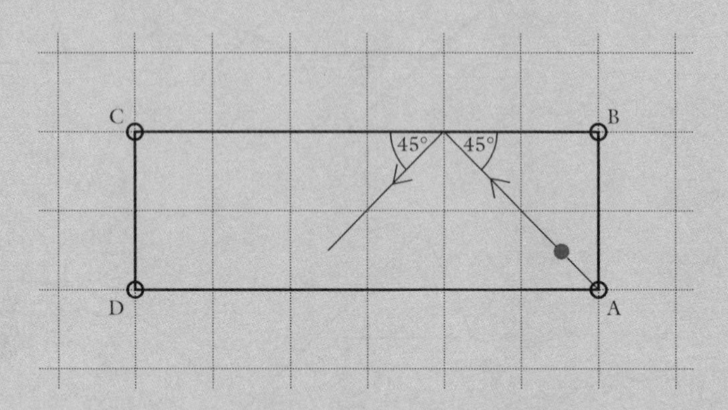

There is a pocket at each corner.
The ball is projected from the corner A at 45° to the sides of the table.
It carries on bouncing off the sides at 45° until it goes down a pocket.
(This is a very superior toy – the ball does not lose speed however many times it bounces!)

a How many bounces are there before the ball goes down a pocket?

b Which pocket does it go down?

c What happens if the table is 2 squares by 8 squares?

d Can you predict what happens for a 2 by 20 table?

e Now try a 2 by 3 table.

f Investigate for other sizes of tables. Start by keeping the width at 2 squares. Then try other widths. Copy this table and fill in the results.

Size of table	Number of bounces	Pocket
2×6		
2×8		
2×3		
2×5		

g Can you predict what happens with a 3×12 table?

FRACTIONS, DECIMALS AND PERCENTAGES

3

Jack needs twenty $\frac{3}{8}$-inch lengths of wire which have to be cut from longer lengths. He has a piece that is $5\frac{1}{2}$ inches long.

- To find out whether the wire he has is long enough, Jack can subtract $\frac{3}{8}$ from $5\frac{1}{2}$, subtract $\frac{3}{8}$ from the answer, and so on until there is not enough left to subtract again. This will take a long time, and with all those subtractions there are plenty of opportunities to make mistakes.

- When we want to find how many 6s there are in 84, we calculate $84 \div 6$. In the same way, to find out how many $\frac{3}{8}$s there are in $5\frac{1}{2}$ more quickly than using repeated subtraction, we need to know how to calculate $5\frac{1}{2} \div \frac{3}{8}$, that is how to divide by a fraction.

DIVIDING BY A FRACTION

We can use this diagram to find the number of $\frac{1}{2}$s in 4, that is, to find $4 \div \frac{1}{2}$.

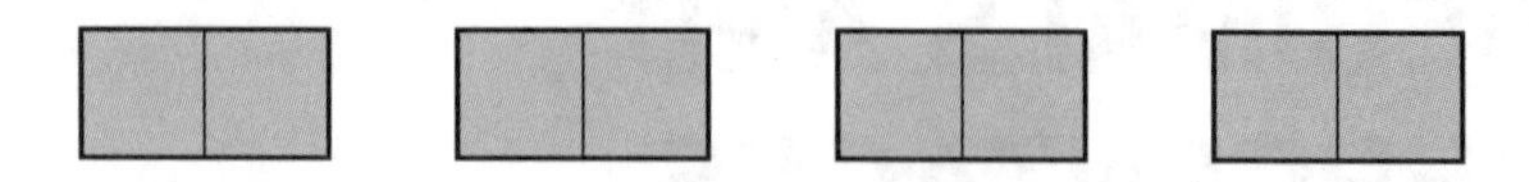

This shows that there are 8 halves in 4, that is, $4 \div \frac{1}{2} = 8$.

Now we know that $4 \times 2 = 8$,

and that 4 can be written as $\frac{4}{1}$ and 8 as $\frac{8}{1}$, so

$$\frac{4}{1} \div \frac{1}{2} = \frac{4}{1} \times \frac{2}{1},$$

i.e. '4 divided by $\frac{1}{2}$' is the same as '4 multiplied by $\frac{2}{1}$'.

Consider next the number of $\frac{3}{8}$s in $1\frac{1}{2}$, that is, the value of $1\frac{1}{2} \div \frac{3}{8}$.

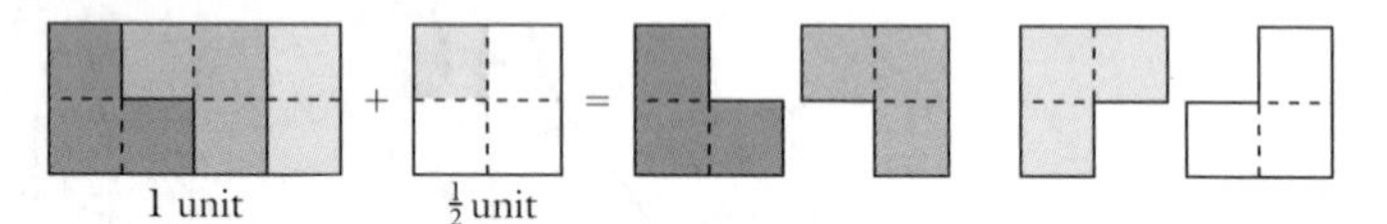

From the diagram we see that $1\frac{1}{2}$ bars can be divided into 4 pieces, each of which is $\frac{3}{8}$ of a bar, so $1\frac{1}{2} \div \frac{3}{8} = 4$, i.e. $\frac{3}{2} \div \frac{3}{8} = 4$.

Now $\frac{\cancel{3}^1}{\cancel{2}_1} \times \frac{\cancel{8}^4}{\cancel{3}_1} = 4$, so $\frac{3}{2} \div \frac{3}{8}$ is the same as $\frac{3}{2} \times \frac{8}{3}$.

These two examples demonstrate the rule that

> to divide by a fraction
> we turn that fraction upside down
> and multiply by it.

EXERCISE 3A

Find the value of $36 \div \frac{3}{4}$

$$\frac{36}{1} \div \frac{3}{4} = \frac{\cancel{36}^{12}}{1} \times \frac{4}{\cancel{3}_1}$$

$$= \frac{48}{1}$$

$$= 48$$

Remember, to multiply fractions, multiply the numerators and then multiply the denominators.

1 How many $\frac{1}{2}$s are there in 7?

2 How many $\frac{1}{4}$s are there in 5?

3 How many times does $\frac{1}{7}$ go into 3?

4 How many $\frac{3}{5}$s are there in 9?

5 How many times does $\frac{2}{3}$ go into 8?

Find

6 $8 \div \frac{4}{5}$

7 $18 \div \frac{6}{7}$

8 $40 \div \frac{8}{9}$

9 $72 \div \frac{8}{11}$

10 $28 \div \frac{14}{15}$

11 $15 \div \frac{5}{6}$

12 $14 \div \frac{7}{8}$

13 $35 \div \frac{5}{7}$

14 $44 \div \frac{4}{9}$

15 $27 \div \frac{9}{13}$

16 $36 \div \frac{4}{7}$

17 $34 \div \frac{17}{19}$

Divide $\frac{7}{16}$ by $\frac{5}{8}$

$$\frac{7}{16} \div \frac{5}{8} = \frac{7}{{}_2\cancel{16}} \times \frac{\cancel{8}^1}{5}$$

$$= \frac{7}{10}$$

Find

18 $\frac{21}{32} \div \frac{7}{8}$

19 $\frac{9}{25} \div \frac{3}{10}$

20 $\frac{3}{56} \div \frac{9}{14}$

21 $\frac{21}{22} \div \frac{7}{11}$

22 $\frac{8}{75} \div \frac{4}{15}$

23 $\frac{35}{42} \div \frac{5}{6}$

24 $\frac{28}{27} \div \frac{4}{9}$

25 $\frac{22}{45} \div \frac{11}{15}$

26 $\frac{15}{26} \div \frac{5}{13}$

27 $\frac{49}{50} \div \frac{7}{10}$

28 $\frac{8}{21} \div \frac{4}{7}$

29 $\frac{9}{26} \div \frac{12}{13}$

Find $3\frac{1}{8} \div 8\frac{3}{4}$

$$3\frac{1}{8} \div 8\frac{3}{4} = \frac{25}{8} \div \frac{35}{4}$$

$$= \frac{\cancel{25}^{5}}{_{2}\cancel{8}} \times \frac{\cancel{4}^{1}}{\cancel{35}_{7}}$$

$$= \frac{5}{14}$$

When mixed numbers are involved, they must first be changed into improper fractions,

i.e. $3\frac{1}{8}$ must be changed to $\frac{25}{8}$

and $8\frac{3}{4}$ must be changed to $\frac{35}{4}$.

Calculate

30 $5\frac{4}{9} \div \frac{14}{27}$

31 $3\frac{1}{8} \div 3\frac{3}{4}$

32 $7\frac{1}{5} \div 1\frac{7}{20}$

33 $4\frac{2}{7} \div \frac{9}{14}$

34 $5\frac{5}{8} \div 6\frac{1}{4}$

35 $6\frac{4}{9} \div 1\frac{1}{3}$

36 Divide $8\frac{1}{4}$ by $1\frac{3}{8}$

37 Divide $6\frac{2}{3}$ by $2\frac{4}{9}$

38 Divide $5\frac{1}{4}$ by $2\frac{11}{12}$

39 Divide $7\frac{1}{7}$ by $1\frac{11}{14}$

Calculate

40 $10\frac{2}{3} \div 1\frac{7}{9}$

41 $8\frac{4}{5} \div 3\frac{3}{10}$

42 $9\frac{3}{4} \div 1\frac{5}{8}$

43 $12\frac{1}{2} \div 8\frac{3}{4}$

44 Divide $11\frac{1}{4}$ by $\frac{15}{16}$

45 Divide $9\frac{1}{7}$ by $1\frac{11}{21}$

46 Divide $10\frac{5}{6}$ by $3\frac{1}{4}$

47 Divide $8\frac{2}{3}$ by $5\frac{7}{9}$

48 The filling for one sandwich needs $1\frac{1}{2}$ ounces of cheese. How many sandwiches can be filled using 12 ounces of cheese?

49 Tim says 'Here is $6\frac{1}{2}$ in of wire. Cut it into $\frac{3}{8}$ in lengths – you should get at least 20 pieces out of it.'
Explain why Tim is wrong.

50 If $1\frac{1}{4}$ lb of apples cost 80 p, what is the cost of 1 lb of these apples?

51 One 2 p coin is $\frac{1}{8}$ in thick.
A pile of 2 p coins is $1\frac{1}{2}$ in high.

a How many coins are there in the pile?

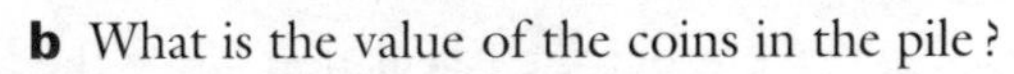

b What is the value of the coins in the pile?

52 Hassan read 30 pages of a book in $\frac{3}{4}$ hour.

a What fraction of an hour did it take him, on average, to read one page?

b How many minutes did it take him to read one page?

53 Which of these statements are true?

A $7 \div 3 = \frac{7}{3}$ **B** $\frac{2}{3} \div 2 = \frac{1}{3}$ **C** $\frac{4}{7} \div \frac{1}{2} = \frac{2}{7}$ **D** $\frac{5}{3} = 3 \div 5$

54 At Bertorelli's café, cakes are divided into eighths and each slice sold for £1.20. At Angelino's café they divide cakes of the same size into twelfths and sell each slice for 90 p.

a How many of Angelino's slices are equivalent to one of Bertorelli's slices?

b Which whole cake is more expensive?

55 This gift box has a volume of 49 cubic inches.
It is $3\frac{1}{2}$ inches wide by $3\frac{1}{2}$ inches deep.
How high is it?

56 This stack of \$100 bills is $25\frac{1}{2}$ mm high and is worth \$10 000.
What is the thickness of one bill as a fraction of a millimetre?

57 Simplify **a** $\frac{x}{2} \div \frac{1}{2}$ **b** $\frac{x}{3} \div \frac{3}{2}$

MIXED OPERATIONS WITH FRACTIONS

When a calculation involves brackets and a mixture of multiplication, division, addition and subtraction, remember the order in which these operations are performed:

> work out the calculation inside the brackets first, then do any multiplication and division before doing any addition and subtraction.

EXERCISE 3B

Calculate $4\frac{1}{3} \times 1\frac{1}{8} \div 2\frac{1}{4}$

$$4\frac{1}{3} \times 1\frac{1}{8} \div 2\frac{1}{4} = \frac{13}{3} \times \frac{9}{8} \div \frac{9}{4}$$

$$= \frac{13}{3} \times \frac{\not{9}^{1}}{\not{8}_{2}} \times \frac{\not{4}^{1}}{\not{9}_{1}}$$

$$= \frac{13}{6} = 2\frac{1}{6}$$

Remember that the sign before a number tells you what to do with just that number. So we divide by $\frac{9}{4}$, i.e. multiply by 4 over 9.

Find

1 $\frac{5}{8} \times 1\frac{1}{2} \div \frac{15}{16}$

2 $2\frac{3}{4} \times \frac{5}{6} \div \frac{11}{12}$

3 $\frac{2}{3} \times 1\frac{1}{5} \div \frac{12}{25}$

4 $\frac{2}{5} \times \frac{9}{10} \div \frac{27}{40}$

5 $\frac{3}{4} \times 2\frac{1}{3} \div \frac{21}{32}$

6 $3\frac{2}{5} \times \frac{4}{5} \div \frac{8}{15}$

7 $\frac{3}{5} \times \frac{9}{11} \div \frac{18}{55}$

8 $\frac{1}{4} \times \frac{11}{12} \div \frac{22}{27}$

9 $\frac{3}{7} \times \frac{2}{5} \div \frac{8}{21}$

Calculate $\frac{2}{5} - \frac{1}{2} \times \frac{3}{5}$

Multiplication must be done first, so we start by working out $\frac{1}{2} \times \frac{3}{5}$.

$$\frac{2}{5} - \frac{1}{2} \times \frac{3}{5} = \frac{2}{5} - \left(\frac{1}{2} \times \frac{3}{5}\right)$$

$$= \frac{2}{5} - \frac{3}{10}$$

$$= \frac{4}{10} - \frac{3}{10} = \frac{1}{10}$$

Remember that fractions can only be added or subtracted when they have the same denominator. Now $\frac{2}{5}$ is equivalent to $\frac{4}{10}$.

Calculate

10 $\frac{1}{2}+\frac{1}{4}\times\frac{2}{5}$

11 $\frac{2}{3}\times\frac{1}{2}+\frac{1}{4}$

12 $\frac{4}{5}-\frac{3}{10}\div\frac{1}{2}$

13 $\frac{2}{7}\div\frac{2}{3}-\frac{3}{14}$

14 $\frac{4}{5}+\frac{3}{10}\times\frac{2}{9}$

15 $\frac{1}{3}-\frac{1}{2}\times\frac{1}{4}$

16 $\frac{3}{4}\div\frac{1}{2}+\frac{1}{8}$

17 $\frac{1}{7}+\frac{5}{8}\div\frac{3}{4}$

18 $\frac{5}{6}\times\frac{3}{10}-\frac{3}{16}$

19 $\frac{3}{7}-\frac{1}{4}\times\frac{8}{21}$

Remember, work out the calculation in the bracket first.

20 $\left(\frac{4}{9}-\frac{1}{3}\right)\times\frac{6}{7}$

21 $\frac{3}{5}\times\left(\frac{2}{3}+\frac{1}{2}\right)$

22 $\frac{7}{8}\div\left(\frac{3}{4}+\frac{2}{3}\right)$

23 $\left(\frac{3}{10}+\frac{2}{5}\right)\div\frac{7}{15}$

24 $\left(\frac{5}{11}-\frac{1}{3}\right)\times\frac{3}{8}$

25 $\frac{3}{8}\div\left(\frac{2}{3}+\frac{1}{4}\right)$

26 $\left(\frac{4}{7}+\frac{1}{3}\right)\div 3\frac{4}{5}$

27 $\frac{5}{9}\times\left(\frac{2}{3}-\frac{1}{6}\right)$

28 $\left(\frac{6}{11}-\frac{1}{2}\right)\div\frac{3}{4}$

29 $\frac{9}{10}\div\left(\frac{1}{6}+\frac{2}{3}\right)$

State whether each of the following statements is true or false.

30 $\frac{1}{2}\times\frac{2}{3}+\frac{1}{3}=\frac{1}{3}+\frac{1}{3}$

31 $\frac{3}{4}-\frac{1}{2}\times\frac{2}{3}=\frac{1}{4}\times\frac{2}{3}$

32 Find $\frac{2}{3}$ of $\frac{3}{8}$ added to $1\frac{1}{2}$.

33 A pharmacist counts 58 tablets and puts them into a bottle. Each tablet weights $\frac{1}{4}$ gram and the empty bottle weighs $112\frac{1}{2}$ grams. What is the weight of the full bottle?

34 Nina usually walks to school in the morning and back home again in the afternoon. The distance from her home to school is $1\frac{1}{4}$ km. One week she was given a lift home from school on two afternoons and was given a lift halfway to school one morning. How far did she walk to and from school that week (5 days)?

35 Place +, −, ×, or ÷ in the space to make these calculations correct.

a $\frac{2}{3} \quad \frac{4}{5} = \frac{5}{6}$ **b** $\frac{3}{4} \quad \frac{8}{9} = \frac{2}{3}$ **c** $\frac{4}{5} \quad \frac{2}{3} = 1\frac{7}{15}$

36 Place < or > between each pair of calculations.

a $5 \times \frac{1}{2} \qquad 5 \times 2$ **b** $3\frac{1}{4} \times \frac{3}{5} \qquad 3\frac{1}{4} \div \frac{3}{5}$

37 The first four terms of a sequence are $\frac{2}{3}, \frac{4}{9}, \frac{8}{27}, \frac{16}{81}$.

a Write down the next two terms.

b Write down, as simply as possible, the rule for generating the sequence.

WORKING WITH FRACTIONS, DECIMALS AND PERCENTAGES

We can compare the 2 extra muffins in this special offer pack with the 8 muffins in a standard pack in several ways.

Using fractions, we can say that

the number of extra muffins is $\frac{1}{4}$ of the number in a standard pack,

or the number in this pack is $1\frac{1}{4}$ times the number in a standard pack.

Using percentages gives the same information in different ways, namely that

the number of extra muffins is 25% of the number in a standard pack.

or the number in this pack is 125% of the number in a standard pack.

Using decimals we can say that

the number in this pack is 1.25 of the number in a standard pack.

This example shows that part of a quantity can be expressed as a fraction, or as a percentage or as a decimal. Fractions, decimals and percentages are interchangeable. (If you need reminding about how to change from one form to another, use the Summary and Revision Exercise 1.4 at the front of this book.)

EXERCISE 3C

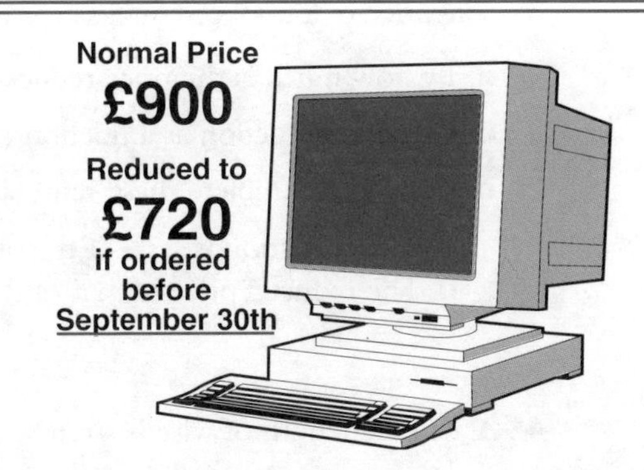

a What fraction is the reduced price of the normal price?

b What percentage is the reduced price of the normal price?

To find one quantity as a fraction of another, we put the first quantity over the second.

a The reduced price = $\frac{720}{900}$ **of the normal price**

$= \frac{4}{5}$ **of the normal price**

b The reduced price = $\frac{4}{5} \times 100\% = 80\%$ **of the normal price.**

Where answers are not exact, give them correct to 3 significant figures.

1

a Sally looked at this sale notice and said, 'Save 20% of what?' Discuss possible answers to Sally's question.

b What fraction is the percentage?

2 A standard pot of yoghurt contains 50 ml. A special offer pot contains 60 ml.

a How many extra ml of yoghurt are there in the special offer pot?

b What fraction of the normal contents is the extra quantity in the special offer pot?

c Copy and complete these sentences with fractions.

i The extra quantity is ... × the normal quantity.

ii The quantity in the larger pot is ... × the normal quantity.

3 The price of a bookcase in a sale is reduced from £42 to £35.

a By how much is the price reduced?

b Give the reduction as a fraction of the original price.

c Copy and complete these sentences.

i The reduction is . . . % of the original price.
ii The reduced price is . . . % of the original price.

4 A 1 metre length of wire is stretched to make it 20 cm longer.

a How long is the stretched length?

b Copy and complete this sentence with a decimal.
The new length is . . . × the original length.

5 A 300 g jar of coffee costs £2.70. A 250 g jar of coffee costs £2.50.

a What is the cost of 1 gram of coffee in
i the larger jar **ii** the smaller jar?

b What fraction is the cost per gram in the larger jar of the cost per gram in the smaller jar?

c Copy and complete this sentence.
The cost of 1 gram in the smaller jar is . . . % of the cost of 1 gram in the larger jar.

6 A supermarket promotion offers four of these cans for the price of three.

a Karen buys four of these cans. What fraction of the normal cost of four cans does she save?

b Max buys eight of these cans.
What percentage of the normal cost of eight cans does he save?

7 The sale price of all goods is 90% of the original price.

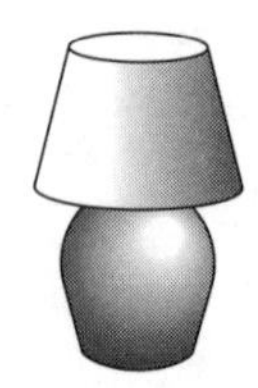

a The original price of this lamp is £18.
Copy and complete this sentence with a decimal.
The sale price = . . . × £18.

b What fraction of the original price is taken off in this sale?

8

Gold Travel Card

30% off all standard fares for up to 4 adults travelling together.

Dennis says, 'If two of us buy rail tickets we will save 60%.' Explain why he is wrong.

9 Hamish wanted to find 20% of £15.30.
He wrote: 20% of £15.30 = 20 × £15.30

a Why is Hamish wrong?

b Rewrite Hamish's sentence so that it is correct.

10 Write the first quantity
i as a fraction **ii** as a percentage, of the second quantity.

a 2 m, 5 m

b 2 cm, 8 cm

c 16 km, 25 km

d 8 pints, 40 pints

e £2, £25

f 56 miles, 35 miles

g 4.2 cm^2, 5.6 cm^2

h 42 p, £3.50

i 4025 seats, 3500 seats

PERCENTAGE INCREASE

Each of these sentences uses a percentage to describe an increase.

- Bus fares are to go up by 5% from the 1st of January.
- There will be 10% more people over the age of 80 by 2040.
- This year's wage increase will be 2.5%.
- Harry grew by 12% last year.
- Prices have inflated by 600% over the last 40 years.

> A percentage used to describe an increase is always a percentage of the quantity *before* it is increased.

Gemma's bus fare to school is 80 p now, and the fares are to increase by 5% next month.

REMEMBER, TO FIND A PERCENTAGE OF A QUANTITY, CHANGE THE PERCENTAGE TO A DECIMAL AND MULTIPLY THE QUANTITY BY THE DECIMAL.

She can use this information to work out the new fare.

The increase is 5% of 80 p, that is, 0.05 of 80 p
$= 0.05 \times 80\,\text{p} = 4\,\text{p}$

so the new fare is $80\,\text{p} + 4\,\text{p}$, i.e. 84 p.
Gemma can also work out the new fare directly without first finding the increase. The new fare is 5% *more* than the present fare, therefore the increased fare is $100\% + 5\% = 105\%$, of the present fare.
So the new fare is 105% of 80 p, i.e. $1.05 \times 80\,\text{p}$.
The number 1.05 is called the *multiplying factor*; it increases a quantity by 5%.

EXERCISE 3D

> If a price is increased by 12%, what percentage is the new price of the original price?
>
> **The new price is $(100 + 12)\%$ of the original price,**
> **i.e. 112% of the original price.**

Find the percentage that the new price is of the original price when the original is increased by

1 50% **4** 60% **7** 48% **10** 175%

2 25% **5** 8% **8** 300% **11** 57%

3 20% **6** 100% **9** $12\frac{1}{2}\%$ **12** 3%

> What multiplying factor increases a number by $17\frac{1}{2}\%$?
>
> **$(100 + 17.5)\% = 117.5\%$**
> **So the multiplying factor is 1.175.**

Give the multiplying factor that increases a number by

13 40% **16** 100% **19** 25% **22** 43%

14 8% **17** 35.5% **20** 250% **23** $11\frac{1}{2}\%$

15 37% **18** $6\frac{1}{2}\%$ **21** $2\frac{1}{2}\%$ **24** 400%

> Find the new length when 180 m is increased by 30%.
>
> **The new length is 130% of 180 m**
> **i.e. the new length is $1.3 \times 180\text{ m} = 234\text{ m}$.**

Find the new quantity when

25 £100 is increased by 40%

26 200 employees is increased by 85%

27 £340 is increased by 45%

28 500 m is increased by $36\frac{1}{2}$%

29 1600 cars is increased by 73%

30 745 cm^2 is increased by 14%

31 £64 is increased by $62\frac{1}{2}$%

32 111 boxes is increased by 66.7%

33 145 litres is increased by 120%

34 644 shops is increased by 275%

35 Tim's weight increased by 15% between his fifteenth and sixteenth birthdays.
He weighed 55 kg on his fifteenth birthday.
What did he weigh on his sixteenth birthday?

36 The water rates due for my house this year are 8% more than they were last year. Last year I paid £210. What must I pay this year?

37 There are 800 pupils in a school. It is expected that this number will rise by 5% next year. How many pupils are expected to be at the school next year?

38 Pierre is 20% taller now than he was 2 years ago. If he was 150 cm tall then, how tall is he now?

39 A factory employs 220 workers. Next year the work-force will be increased by 15%. How many workers will be employed next year?

40 In a sale a pair of trainers marked £40 is offered at a reduction of 30%. Because Paul is an employee he receives a discount of $12\frac{1}{2}$% off the sale price. How much does he have to pay for the trainers?

41 The management of AbleCable plc. offers its workforce a two-stage wage increase; 2% of this year's wage in January followed by 2% of the new wage in June. By what percentage will the present wage increase in June? (Start with a wage of £100.)

PERCENTAGE DECREASE

Percentages are also used to describe decreases.

- The number of reported burglaries in Wessex fell by 3% last year.
- The value of a car depreciated by 10% last year.
- The price of a shirt was reduced by 30% in a sale.
- A discount of $2\frac{1}{2}$% is offered to customers who pay their accounts within 10 days.

> A percentage used to describe a decrease is always a percentage of the quantity *before* it is decreased.

The value of a car is £4500 at the start of a year and it loses 10% of its value over that year. This means that at the end of the year its value is 10% *less* than the value at the beginning of the year.

Therefore the decreased value is $(100 - 10)\%$, that is, 90% of £4500
$= 0.9 \times £4500$

So to decrease a quantity by 10%
we find $(100 - 10)\% = 90\%$ or 0.9 of the original quantity,
so the multiplying factor is 0.9.
Similarly, to decrease a quantity by $2\frac{1}{2}\%$,
we find $(100 - 2.5)\% = 97.5\%$ of the original quantity
and the multiplying factor is 0.975.

EXERCISE 3E

> If a price is reduced by 65%, what percentage is the reduced price of the original price?
>
> **The reduced price is $(100 - 65)\%$ of the original price, i.e. 35% of the original price.**

What percentage is the new price of the original price when the original price is decreased by

1 50%	**4** 85%	**7** 35%	**10** 33.3%
2 25%	**5** 4%	**8** 42.2%	**11** 53%
3 70%	**6** $12\frac{1}{2}\%$	**9** $62\frac{1}{2}\%$	**12** $6\frac{1}{4}\%$

> What multiplying factor decreases a number by 30%?
>
> **$(100 - 30)\% = 70\%$**
> **So the multiplying factor is 0.7.**

What multiplying factor decreases a quantity by

13 40% **16** 12% **19** 34% **22** 45%

14 75% **17** 3% **20** 15.8% **23** 53%

15 20% **18** $5\frac{1}{2}\%$ **21** 6.5% **24** $17\frac{1}{2}\%$

Decrease a fleet of 250 lorries by 70%.

The decreased number of lorries is $(100 - 70)\%$, i.e. 30% of 250,
$\therefore$ the decreased number of lorries is $0.3 \times 250 = 75$

Decrease, giving your answer correct to the nearest whole number where necessary.

25 100 m by 30%

26 200 people by 15%

27 350 litres by 46%

28 £208 by 87.5%

29 £3400 by 8%

30 3450 books by 4%

31 93 cm by 33.3%

32 273 workers by 30%

33 750 light bulbs by 13%

34 248 ships by $37\frac{1}{2}\%$

35 Miss Kendall earns £120 per week from which income tax is deducted at 20%.
Find how much is left.

36 In a certain week a factory worker earns £150 from which income tax is deducted at 12%. Find his income after tax is deducted.

37 Mr Hall earns £1000 per month. If income tax is deducted at 20%, find his net pay after tax.

38 The number of children attending Croydly village school is 8% fewer this year than last year. If 450 attended last year, how many are attending this year?

39 The marked price of a man's suit is £125. In a sale the marked price is reduced by 12%. Find the sale price.

40 **Order this month and we will give you 10% discount**

Greg ordered £100 worth of goods from this company by phone. He expected to pay £80 but was charged £81.

a Why did Greg expect to pay £80?

b How does the company justify the charge of £81?

PERCENTAGE INCREASE AND DECREASE

The questions in the next exercise are about percentage change; they are a mixture of increase and decrease problems. Read each question carefully and decide whether you are asked to find the size of the change or the size of the changed quantity.

EXERCISE 3F

1 A bathroom suite is marked at £650 to which is added value added tax (VAT) at $17\frac{1}{2}\%$ of the marked price to give the selling price. How much does the suite actually cost the customer?

2 A CD costs £7 plus value added tax at 20% of the cost price. How much has to be paid for the CD?

3 In a sale all prices are reduced by 10%.

a What is the sale price of an article marked £40?

b How much is taken off the price of an article marked £85?

4 Last year in Blytham there were 75 reported cases of measles. This year the number of reported cases has dropped by 16%.

a How many cases have been reported this year?

b How many fewer cases is this than last year?

5 Due to predators the population of oyster-catchers on Stoka island is decreasing each year by 15% of the number of oyster-catchers on the island at the beginning of that year. The present population is estimated to be 12 000 pairs. What is the estimated population, in pairs, in

a a year's time **b** 2 year's time **c** 3 year's time?

(Give each answer correct to the nearest 100, but use the uncorrected result to work with.)

6

Wendy wants to buy a CD player. She shops around and comes to the conclusion that any one of the four listed above would suit her.

a By just thinking about the figures given above and without doing any calculations, which shop do you think sells the cheapest CD player?

b Calculate the asking price in each shop. In which shop can she buy the cheapest CD player? Does your answer agree with the thoughts you had in part **a**?

c How much more than the cheapest does the dearest CD player cost?

7 Mrs Murray has been allocated 250 tickets at £15 each for a performance of *The Mikado*. Because of the large number of tickets she bought she has been given a discount of 15%.

a How much would all the tickets cost without the discount?

b How much do these tickets cost Mrs Murray?

c Mrs Murray booked 5 coaches.
If each coach costs £120 + VAT at $17\frac{1}{2}$%, find the total cost of the coaches.

d The cost of the trip (tickets plus coaches) is divided equally among all those going.
How much should Mrs Murray collect from each person going on the trip?

8 A car is valued at £8000. It depreciates by 20% in the first year and thereafter each year by 15% of its value at the beginning of that year. Find its value

a after 1 year **b** after 2 years **c** after 3 years.

d By how much has the value decreased over the 3 years?

9 Mr Connah weighed 115 kg when he decided to go on a diet. He lost 10% of his weight in the first six months and a further 8% of his original weight in the second six months. How much did he weigh after 1 year of dieting?

10 In any year the value of a motorcycle depreciates by 10% of its value at the beginning of that year. What is its value after two years if the purchase price was £1800?

11 When John Short increases the speed at which he motors from an average of 40 mph to 50 mph, the number of miles travelled per gallon decreases by 25%. If he travels 36 miles on each gallon when his average speed is 40 mph, how many miles per gallon can he expect at an average speed of 50 mph?

12 When petrol was 50 p per litre I used 700 litres in a year. The price rose by 12% so I reduced my yearly consumption by 12%. Find

a the new price of a litre of petrol

b my new yearly petrol consumption

c the change in my petrol bill for the year as
 i a sum of money
 ii a percentage.

MIXED EXERCISE

EXERCISE 3G

1 Find **a** $\frac{1}{2} \div \frac{3}{4}$ **b** $\frac{2}{3} \div \frac{6}{7}$

2 Find **a** $4\frac{1}{2} \times 3\frac{1}{3}$ **b** $4\frac{1}{2} \div 3\frac{1}{3}$

3 Calculate **a** $5\frac{1}{4} - 1\frac{2}{3} \div \frac{2}{5}$ **b** $3\frac{3}{8} \times \left(8\frac{1}{2} - 5\frac{5}{6}\right)$

4 Find **a** $4\frac{1}{2} \times 3\frac{2}{3} - 10\frac{1}{4}$ **b** $3\frac{1}{2} \div \left(2\frac{1}{8} - \frac{3}{4}\right)$

5 When an area is increased by 25%, what percentage is the new area of the original area?

6 Increase 56 g by 75%.

7 Decrease £1200 by 20%.

8 A sculptor has a piece of wood weighing 6.6 kg when she begins work on a new statue. During her work she cuts away 55% of it. How much does the completed statue weigh?

INVESTIGATIONS

1 Newspaper articles

Work in groups for this investigation.

a The annual rate of inflation has fallen from 3.5% last month to 3.46% this month.
What does this sentence mean? Are prices rising, falling or standing still?

b The whole work-force is to get a pay rise of 4.5%. This gives the managing director an increase of £1350 a year, but the shelf-fillers get just £500 a year extra.
How can this be true if everyone gets 4.5%?

c Collect items from newspapers and magazines that contain references to percentages. Investigate what they mean.

2 Advertisements

This is part of an advertisement that appeared in a newspaper.

3 Year Guaranteed Growth Bond

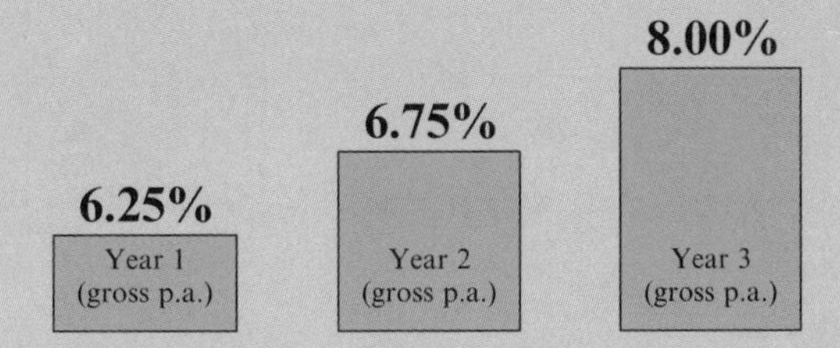

Whatever happens to interest rates over the next 3 years the new 3 Year Guaranteed Growth Bond guarantees an increasing return on your investment.
Invest from a minimum of £1,000 for 3 years and even if general interest rates fall, we guarantee gross rates of 6.25% in the first year, 6.75% in the second and 8.00% in the third.
You will appreciate that no withdrawals can be made during the three year term.

a Suppose that Avril invested £1000 in this offer.

i How much would her investment be worth after 1 year?

ii How much would her investment be worth after 2 years?

iii How much would her investment be worth after 3 years?

b Now look carefully at the illustration. Make as many criticisms of it as you can and back your comments with facts.

3 Continued fractions

a These are called continued fractions. Write down the next three patterns.

$$\frac{1}{1+1}, \quad \frac{1}{1+\frac{1}{1+1}}, \quad \frac{1}{1+\frac{1}{1+\frac{1}{1+1}}}$$

b Evaluate each of these fractions, giving your answers as

i a fraction in as simple a form as possible

ii as a decimal, correct to 5 decimal places when necessary.

c Investigate what happens as the pattern continues.

PROBABILITY

Sometimes we want to know what the chances are that an event will not happen.

For example, before Edward commits himself to spending 5 p, he is wondering what the chances are of not getting a red sweet out of this dispenser because he does not like red ones.

- If Edward judges that there are relatively few red sweets in this machine, he can estimate that the chances of getting one are fairly low, so the chances of not getting a red sweet are fairly high.

The next exercise explores the relationship between the probability that an event will happen and the probability that it will not.

EXERCISE 4A

1 An ordinary pack of 52 playing cards is well shuffled and then cut.

a What is the probability that the card showing is an ace?

b What is the probability that the card showing is *not* an ace?

c Write down the relationship between your answers to parts **a** and **b**.

2 A six-sided dice is thrown. Find the relationship between the probability of throwing a six and that of not throwing a six.

3 One card is drawn at random from an ordinary pack of 52 playing cards.

a What is the probability that the card is a club?

b What is the probability that the card is not a club?

c Write down the relationship between your answers to parts **a** and **b**.

4

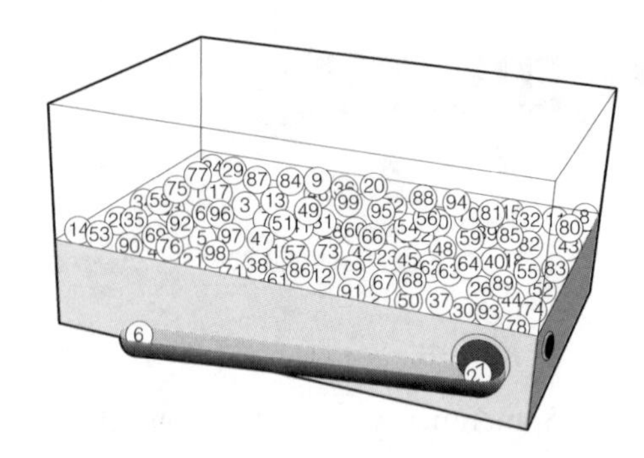

This Bingo machine contains 99 balls numbered from 1 to 99. One ball is ejected when the button is pressed.

a What is the probability that this ball has a single-digit number on it?

b What is the probability that this ball has a two-digit number on it?

c What is the relationship between your answers to parts **a** and **b**?

5 Mr. Impresario wants to book Wembley Stadium for a pop concert. He needs to do this one year in advance and has a choice of three dates; one in April, one in June and one in September. He wants to choose the date with the highest likelihood of it not raining. Discuss what information is needed to make a reasonably informed choice.

PROBABILITY THAT AN EVENT DOES NOT HAPPEN

The last exercise should convince you that the probabilities of an event happening and an event not happening add up to 1.

This relationship is always true because

$$\begin{pmatrix}\text{The number of}\\ \text{ways in which}\\ \text{an event, } A,\\ \text{can } \textit{not} \text{ happen}\end{pmatrix} = \begin{pmatrix}\text{The total}\\ \text{number of}\\ \text{possible}\\ \text{outcomes}\end{pmatrix} - \begin{pmatrix}\text{The number}\\ \text{of ways in}\\ \text{which } A\\ \text{can happen}\end{pmatrix}$$

i.e. $\quad \text{P}(A \text{ does not happen}) = 1 - \text{P}(A \text{ does happen})$

'A does not happen' is shortened to $\bar{A}$, where $\bar{A}$ is read as 'not A'.

Therefore $\quad \text{P}(\bar{A}) = 1 - \text{P}(A)$

For example, if the probability that I will pass my driving test is 0.7, then the probability that I will fail (that is, not pass) is $1 - 0.7$, i.e. 0.3.

EXERCISE 4B

One number is chosen at random from the whole numbers 1 to 50. What is the probability that it is not a multiple of 7?

The multiples of 7 are 7, 14, 21, 28, 35, 42, 49.

$$\text{P (a multiple of 7)} = \frac{\text{number of choices that are multiples of 7}}{\text{total number of possible choices}}$$

$$\textbf{P(a multiple of 7)} = \frac{7}{50}$$

$$\therefore \textbf{P(not a multiple of 7)} = 1 - \frac{7}{50}$$

$$= \frac{43}{50}$$

We could find this probability by listing the numbers from 1 to 50 that are not multiples of 7. There are a lot of these, so it is easier to list and then count the numbers that are multiples of 7.

1 The probability that Ann will have to wait more than five minutes for the next bus is 0.4. What is the probability that she will not have to wait more than five minutes?

2 Barry is not very good at getting his first serve in when playing tennis.

His long-term average is one in ten.

What is the probability that Barry's next first serve

a goes in

b does not go in?

3 A number is chosen at random from the first 20 positive whole numbers. What is the probability that it is not a prime number?

4 A card is drawn at random from an ordinary pack of playing cards. What is the probability that it is not a two?

5 One letter is chosen at random from the letters of the alphabet. What is the probability that it is not a vowel?

6 A box of 60 coloured crayons contains a mixture of colours, 10 of which are red. If one crayon is removed at random, what is the probability that it is not red?

7 A number is chosen at random from the first 10 whole numbers. What is the probability that it is not exactly divisible by 3?

8 One letter is chosen at random from the letters of the word

ALPHABET

What is the probability that it is not a vowel?

9 In a raffle, 500 tickets are sold. If you buy 20 tickets, what is the probability that you will not win first prize?

10 If you throw an ordinary six-sided dice, what is the probability that you will not get a score of 5 or more?

11 There are 200 packets hidden in a lucky dip. Five packets contain £1 and the rest contain 1 p. What is the probability that you will not draw out a packet containing £1?

12 Edward buys a sweet from a dispenser containing red, yellow, green, blue and orange sweets in equal numbers. What is the probability that Edward will not get a green sweet?

13 When an ordinary pack of playing cards is cut, what is the probability that the card showing is not a picture card? (The picture cards are the jacks, queens and kings.)

14 There are 100 sweets in this bag.
Carl took one sweet out of the bag at random, wrote down its colour, and then put it back in the bag.
He repeated this 100 times.
The table shows how many colours Carl found and how many times he took that colour out of the bag.

Red	15
Green	25
Yellow	44
Orange	16

a Is it correct to say that there are 25 green sweets in the bag? Justify your answer.

b If Carl takes another sweet out of the bag, can he use his results to find the probability that it will not be green?

15 A letter is chosen at random from the letters of the word

SUCCESSION

What is the probability that the letter is

a N **b** S **c** a vowel **d** not S?

16 A card is drawn at random from an ordinary pack of playing cards. What is the probability that it is

a an ace

b a spade

c not a club

d not a seven or an eight?

17 A bag contains a set of snooker balls (i.e. 15 red and 1 each of the following colours: white, yellow, green, brown, blue, pink and black). What is the probability that one ball removed at random is

a red

b not red

c black

d not red or white?

18 There are 60 cars in the station car-park. Of the cars, 22 were made in Britain, 24 were made in Japan and the rest were made in Europe but not in Britain. What is the probability that the first car to leave was

a made in Japan

b not made in Britain

c made in Europe but not Britain

d made in America?

19 One number is chosen at random from the whole numbers 1 to 100 inclusive.
What is the probability that the number

a is not a multiple of ten

b is a single digit number

c has two digits?

20 A train operator states that, over the last year, 3 out of every 10 trains that ran arrived early.

a Use this information to estimate the probability that, when you next travel on one of these trains, it will not arrive early.

b Jane said 'This means that there is a 7 in 10 chance that a train will arrive late.' Is she right? Give reasons for your answer.

c Say why the answer to part **a** can only be an estimate.

21 Royal Standard Company deals in car insurance. The company report for one year gave the number of accident claims for cars driven by its policy holders and included these details:

Make of car	Ford	Vauxhall	Jaguar
Claims	148	127	13

a Penny looked at these figures and said 'Jaguars must be safe cars to drive'. Eddy set out to prove that Penny didn't understand simple probability.
What other information does Eddy need to be able to do this?

b What information do you need to decide whether one make of car is safer than another make?

THE NUMBER OF TIMES AN EVENT IS LIKELY TO HAPPEN

We sometimes need to estimate how often an event might happen.
Suppose, for example, we are organising this stall at a school fête.
We will need to estimate how many wins to expect; we can then decide how many cans to provide.

If we lay out 40 cards, of which only 2 are aces, we know that, on one turn, the probability of winning a can is $\frac{1}{20}$, i.e. about 1 in every 20 turns will result in a win.
Estimating that there will be about 1000 turns, then we can see that there are likely to be about $1000 \div 20$ wins, that is about 50 wins, so we need about 50 cans.

> If p is the probability that an event happens once,
> when the situation is repeated n times
> we expect the event to happen about
> $p \times n$ times.

For example, if we toss a coin 20 times, we expect to get about $\frac{1}{2} \times 20$ heads.

EXERCISE 4C

1 **a** What is the probability of getting a head on one toss of a coin?

b How many heads would you expect to get if you tossed the coin 100 times?

c Will you get this number of heads? Give a reason for your answer.

d Explain what your reaction would be if you tossed a particular coin 100 times and got 10 heads.

2 On a sailing course for beginners, past experience shows that about 1 in 5 pupils capsize on their first solo sailing trip.
There are 20 pupils out sailing solo for the first time. How many are expected to capsize?

3 Jamestown airport has 500 flights leaving each day. On average, the departure of 1 plane in 25 is delayed. How many delayed flights are expected on one day?

4 An ordinary six-sided dice is thrown 24 times.

a How many sixes are expected?

b Is the number of sixes that are expected the same as the number of sixes that you will get if you throw a dice 24 times?

5 Mandy said 'If I toss a coin 10 times, I will get 5 heads.'
Explain why she was almost certainly wrong.

6 When the same symbol shows in each of the three windows on this slot machine, the machine pays out £5, otherwise it pays out nothing. The probability that the machine pays out is $\frac{1}{50}$.

a How many times is the machine likely to pay out in 100 turns?

b Each turn costs 10 p.
Lim starts with £10, and intends to have 100 turns on this machine; he says that 'It will cost me nothing because I will end up with £10.' Why is he very likely to be wrong?

POSSIBILITY SPACE FOR TWO EVENTS

When we toss two dice there are two events to consider: the way the first dice lands and the way the second dice lands.

When two events are involved it is not always easy to be sure that all the possible outcomes have been taken into account.

For example, before parting with her money at this stall, Sue wants to know what her chances are of winning a can. She knows that there is only one way that the dice can land showing two fives. To work out the probability of winning Sue needs to find how many other ways there are in which the dice can land. She should try listing the possible outcomes: 1,1 1,2 1,3 2,4 . . . but can she be sure that she hasn't missed any?

Situations like this need an organised approach to ensure that all the possible outcomes are listed. We will start by considering a simple case.

Suppose a 2 p coin and a 10 p coin are tossed together. One possibility is that the 2 p coin will land head up and that the 10 p coin will also land head up.

If we use H for a head on the 2 p coin and *H* for a head on the 10 p coin, we can write this possibility more briefly as the ordered pair (H, *H*).

To list all the possibilities, we use a table.

The possibilities for the 10 p coin are written across the top and the possibilities for the 2 p coin are written down the side. They could also go the other way; it does not matter which coin is placed along the top.

		10 p coin	
		H	*T*
2 p coin	H		
	T		

When both coins are tossed we can see all the combinations of heads and tails that are possible and then fill in the table.

		10 p coin	
		H	*T*
2 p coin	H	(H, *H*)	(H, *T*)
	T	(T, *H*)	(T, *T*)

Now we have all the possible outcomes when the two coins are tossed. All the possible outcomes of any experiment is called the *possibility space*.

EXERCISE 4D

1 Two bags each contain 3 white counters and 2 black counters. One counter is removed at random from each bag. Copy and complete the following possibility space for the possible combinations of the two counters.

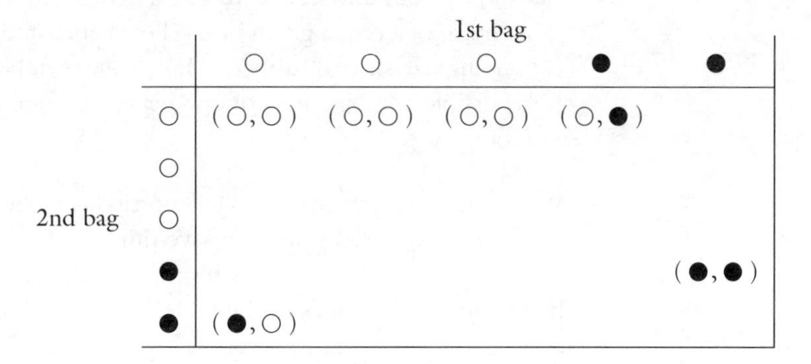

		1st bag				
		○	○	○	●	●
	○	(○,○)	(○,○)	(○,○)	(○,●)	
	○					
2nd bag	○					
	●					(●,●)
	●	(●,○)				

2 An ordinary six-sided dice is tossed and a 10 p coin is tossed. Copy and complete the following possibility space.

		Dice					
		1	2	3	4	5	6
10 p coin	H		(H, 2)				
	T				(T, 4)		

3 One bag contains 2 red counters, 1 yellow counter and 1 blue counter. Another bag contains 1 red counter, 2 yellow counters and 1 blue counter. One counter is taken at random from each bag. Copy and complete the following possibility space.

		1st bag			
		R	R	Y	B
	R		(R, R)		
2nd bag	Y				(Y, B)
	Y				
	B	(B, R)			

4 

A top like the one in the diagram is spun twice. Copy and complete the possibility space.

		1st spin		
		1	2	3
	1			
2nd spin	2			
	3			

5 A boy goes into a shop to buy a pencil and a rubber. He has a choice of a red, a green or a yellow pencil and a round, a square or a triangular-shaped rubber. Make your own possibility space for the possible combinations of one pencil and one rubber that he could buy.

When there are several entries in a possibility space it can take a long time to fill in the ordered pairs. To save time we use a cross in place of each ordered pair. We can see which ordered pair a particular cross represents by looking at the edges of the table.

Two ordinary six-sided dice are tossed. Draw up a possibility space showing all the possible combinations in which the dice may land. Use the possibility space to find the probability that a total score of at least 10 is obtained.

		1st dice					
		1	2	3	4	5	6
	1	×	×	×	×	×	×
	2	×	×	×	×	×	×
2nd dice	3	×	×	×	×	×	×
	4	×	×	×	×	×	⊗
	5	×	×	×	×	⊗	⊗
	6	×	×	×	⊗	⊗	⊗

We have ringed the entries giving a score of 10 or more. There are 36 entries (i.e. possibilities) in the table and 6 of them give a score of 10 or more.

$$\text{P(score of at least 10)} = \frac{6}{36} = \frac{1}{6}$$

6 Copy the possibility space in the example above and use it to find the probability of getting a score of

a 4 or less **b** 9 **c** a double

d Find the chance that Sue will win a can on the stall shown on page 88.

7 Use the possibility space for question **1** to find the probability that the two counters removed

a are both black **b** contain at least one black.

8 Use the possibility space for question **2** to find the probability that the coin lands head up and the dice gives a score that is less than 3.

9 Use the possibility space for question **3** to find the probability that the two counters removed are

a both blue

b both red

c one blue and one red

d such that at least one is red.

10 A 5 p coin and a 1 p coin are tossed together. Make your own possibility space for the combinations in which they can land. Find the probability of getting two heads.

11 One bag of coins contains three 10 p coins and two 50 p coins. Another bag contains one 10 p coin and one 50 p coin. One coin is removed at random from each bag. Make a possibility space and use it to find the probability that a 50 p coin is taken from each bag.

12 One bookshelf contains two story books and three text books. The next shelf holds three story books and one text book. Draw a possibility space showing the various ways in which you could pick up a pair of books, one from each shelf. Use this to find the probability that

a both books are story books **b** both are text books.

13 The four aces and the four kings are removed from an ordinary pack of playing cards. One card is taken from the set of four aces and one card is taken from the set of four kings. Make a possibility space for the possible combinations of two cards and use it to find the probability that the two cards

a are both black

b are both spades

c include at least one black card

d are both of the same suit.

14 A six-sided dice has two of its faces blank and the other faces are numbered 1, 3, 4 and 6. This dice is tossed with an ordinary six-sided dice (faces numbered 1, 2, 3, 4, 5, 6). Make a possibility space for the ways in which the two dice can land and use it to find the probability of getting a total score of

a 6 **b** 10 **c** 1 **d** at least 6.

TREE DIAGRAMS

Making a table is an easy way to show all the possibilities when two events are involved. Suppose, however, that we want to find all the possibilities when three coins are tossed. There is nowhere to place the third coin in the table, so we need a different way of listing possibilities. We use a 'tree' and we illustrate this with a simple example.

Suppose we have three coins, a 10 p coin, a 20 p coin and a 50 p coin.

Tossing the 10 p coin, the possible outcomes are a head or a tail. This information can be shown in the following diagram.

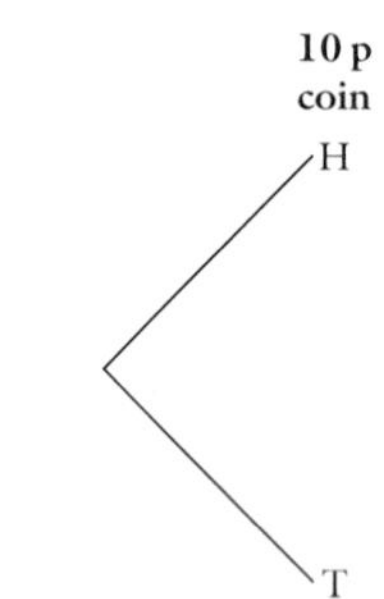

Suppose that the 10 p coin shows a head and we go on to toss the 20 p coin. The possibilities are that it will show a head or a tail. We can add this information to the diagram.

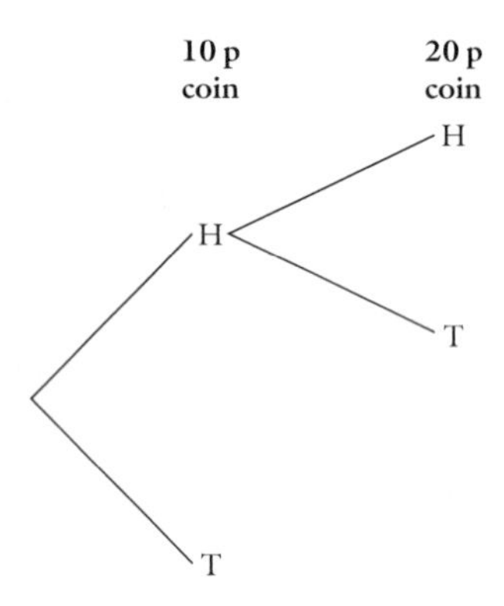

We now consider the possibilities if the 10 p coin shows a tail before we toss the 20 p, and add these to the diagram.

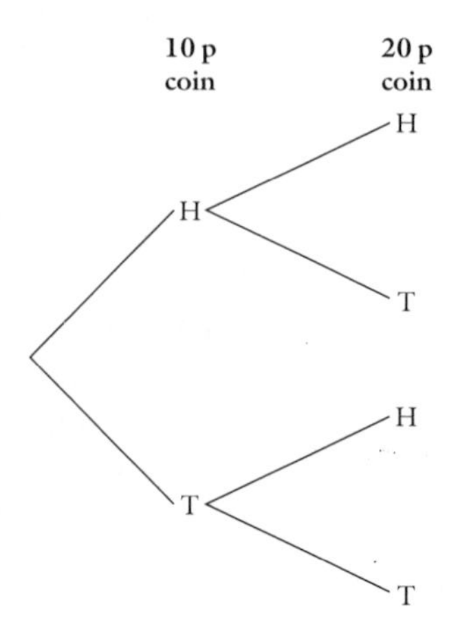

Now suppose that the 10 p coin and the 20 p coin both show a head and we go on to toss the 50 p coin. It will land showing either a head or a tail and we can add this information to the diagram. We complete the diagram by adding branches to show the possibilities for the 50 p coin to the end of each of the branches for the 20 p coin.

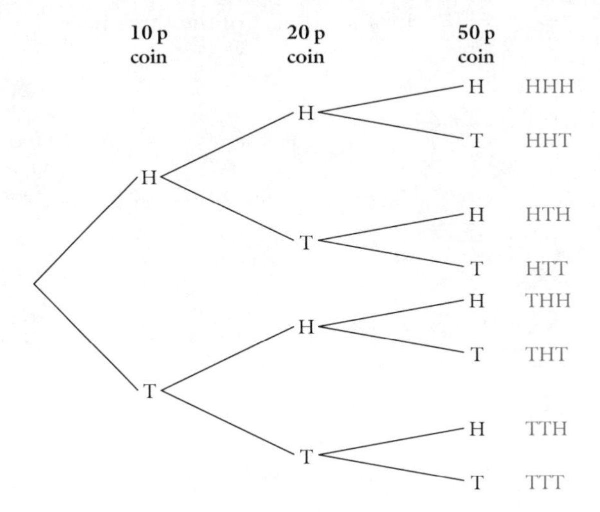

All the possible outcomes can now be listed by writing down the possibilities along each path from left to right,

i.e. HHH, HHT, HTH, HTT, THH, THT, TTH, TTT

Diagrams like this are called *tree diagrams* or *possibility trees*.

EXERCISE 4E

1 When a drawing pin falls to the ground it may land point up or point down.

a Two drawing pins fall one after the other.
Copy and complete the tree diagram and use it to list all the possible outcomes.

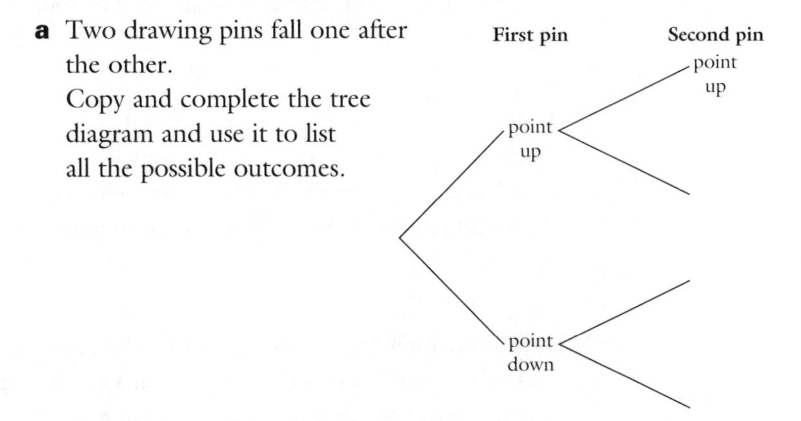

b A third pin is dropped. Extend your tree and list the possible outcomes.

2 The first of two boxes of tennis balls contains one white and one yellow ball. The second box contains one yellow and one green ball. The third box contains one white ball and one pink ball. A ball is taken at random from each box.

a Copy and complete the possibility tree to show all the possibilities for the colours of the three balls.

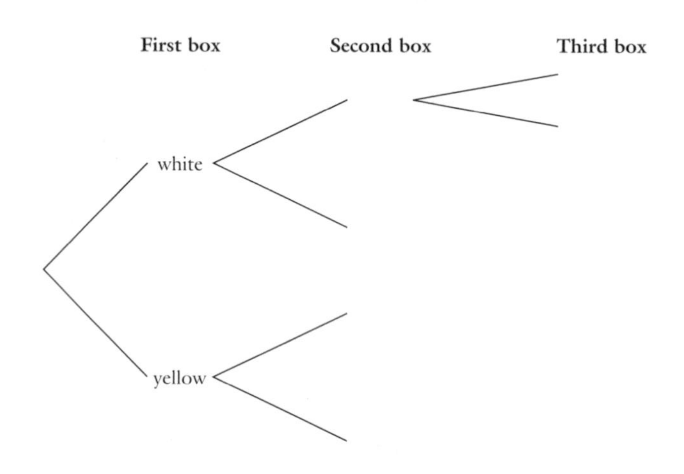

b Write down a list of all the possible orders of colours.

3 Three soldiers, Becker, Crossley and Davis, fire at a target. Each of them may hit or miss the target. Becker fires first then Crossley fires and Davis fires last.
Draw a tree diagram to show all the possibilities for hitting or missing the target.

4 Ran goes into a shop to buy a pencil, a rubber and a ruler. He has a choice of a red, green or yellow pencil, a square or round rubber and a 15 cm or 30 cm ruler. Draw a tree diagram to show all the possible combinations of one pencil, one rubber and one ruler that he could buy.

5 The weather forecast suggests that the probability that it will rain on Friday is 0.05, the probability that it will rain on Saturday is 0.07 and the probability that it will *not* rain on Sunday is 0.89.

a Lucy says that Sunday is likely to be the driest day.
Why is she wrong?

b Copy and complete this tree diagram.

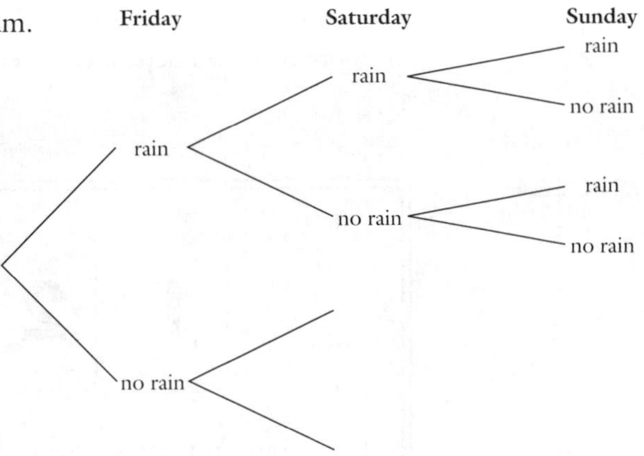

c Use your tree diagram to complete the following table showing the possible combinations of days when it rains or does not rain.

Friday	Saturday	Sunday
rain	rain	rain
rain	rain	no rain

DEPENDENT OUTCOMES

When we toss a 10 p coin and a 20 p coin, the 20 p coin may land head up or tail up whatever happens to the 10 p coin; the coins behave independently of each other.

If we take one disc from this pile and then take another disc *without putting the first disc back in the pile*, the possibilities for the colour of the second disc *depend* on the colour of the first disc.

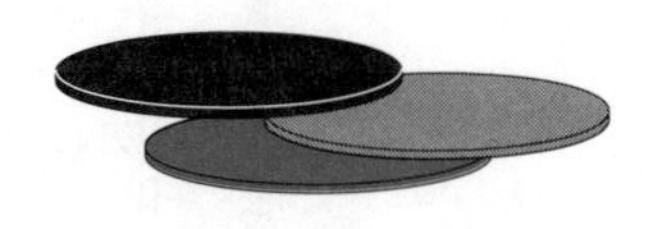

For example, if the first disc is grey, the second disc can only be red or black. We can use a tree to show all the possibilities in this case but it is important to be aware that the possibilities on the branches depend on what else has happened.

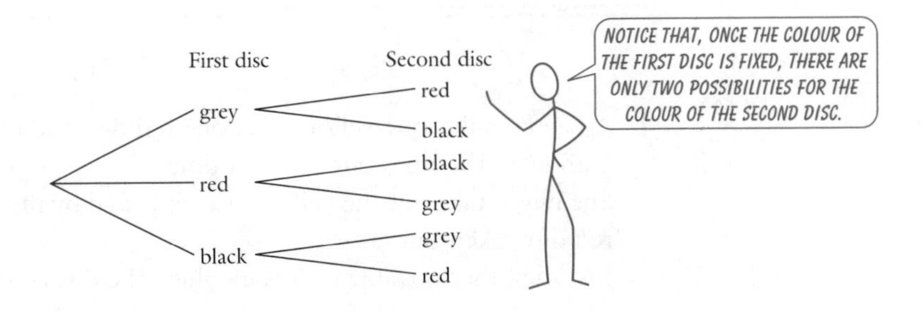

The worked example in the next exercise shows how trees can be used for more than two dependent events.

EXERCISE 4F

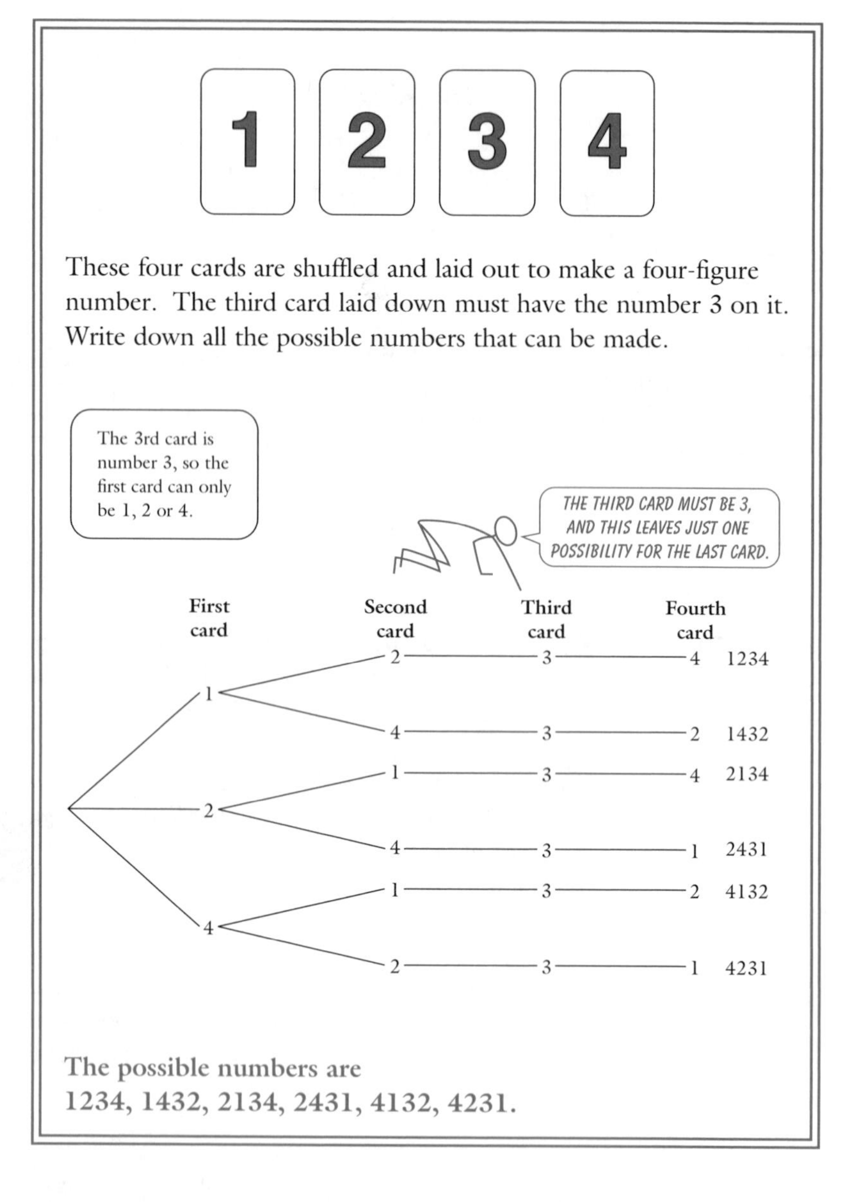

1 A bag contains one yellow disc, one red disc and one blue disc. Pam takes the discs out one at a time.
She might take out the yellow disc, followed by the blue disc with the red disc taken out last.
List the other possible orders in which the discs could be removed.

2 Repeat the worked example to show the numbers that are possible if

a the second card, not the third, is number 3

b the first card is number 3

c card number 3 can be in any position.

3 Jan, David and Mustafa are waiting outside the medical room to have a vaccination. Jan says she will go first.
Write down all the possible orders in which they may have their vaccinations, assuming that Jan is first.

4 This spinner is spun four times to make a number.
If the first spin gives 2, the second spin gives 0, the third spin gives 1 and the last spin gives 3, then the number is 2013.

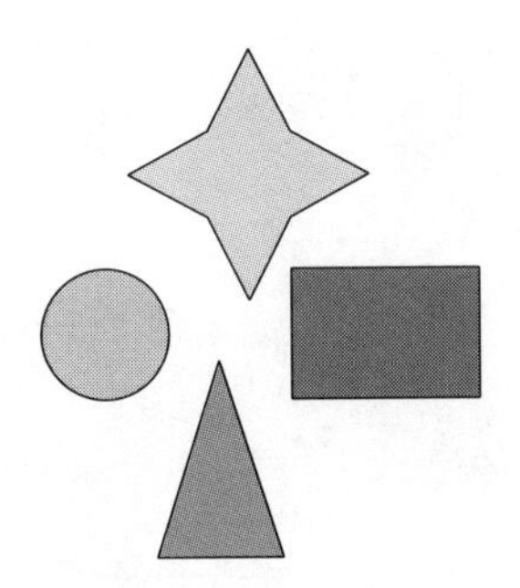

a How many numbers can be made ending in zero?

b List these numbers.

5 A young child is asked to place these shapes in a row.
How many different orders are possible with the circle first?
In how many of these is the star last?

6 Anne, Jim, Solly and Gita each choose one of these fruits.

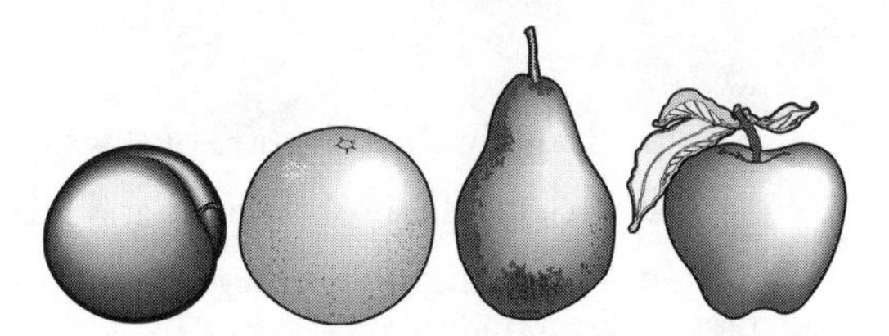

Gita says that she will have the pear as no one else wants it.
Copy and complete the table to show the possible fruits chosen by each person.

Anne	Jim	Solly	Gita
Orange	Apple	Peach	Pear

7

These cards are placed in a line to make a four-figure number. Make a possibility tree to find all the possible even numbers that can be made with these cards.

MIXED EXERCISE

EXERCISE 4G

1 The probability that it will snow tomorrow is $\frac{2}{7}$. What is the probability that it will not snow tomorrow?

2 A blue six-sided dice has two faces numbered 1, two faces numbered 2 and two faces numbered 3. A red six-sided dice has its faces numbered 0, 1, 2, 3, 4, and 5. Both dice are thrown.

a Make a table to show the possible outcomes.

b Use the table to find the probability that both dice show the same number.

3 There is a prize when the pointer on this board stops in the shaded area.

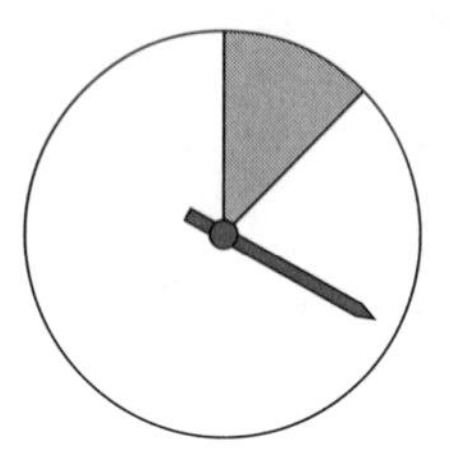

a Roughly what fraction of this board is shaded?

b What is the probability that a prize will be won with one spin?

c It is thought that there will be about 500 turns on this spinner. Roughly how many prizes are needed?

4 These cards are laid in a line to make a four-figure number.

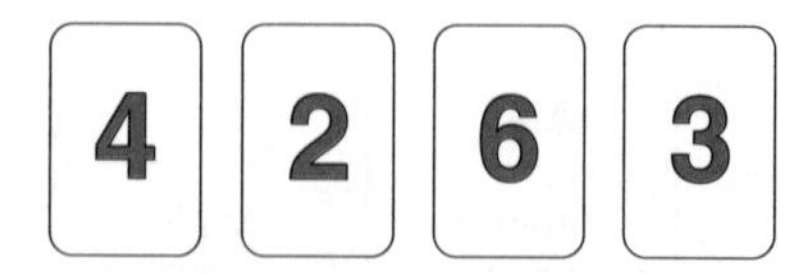

Make a possibility tree to find all the possible odd numbers and list them.

PRACTICAL WORK

1 This is an experiment to find out if you can see into the future!
You need to work in pairs and you need one coin.
One of you should toss and record while the other guesses.

a The guesser predicts whether the coin will land head up or tail up.
The other person then tosses the coin.
If the guesser has no special powers,

i what is the probability that he/she will guess the actual outcome?

ii when this experiment is repeated 100 times, about how many times do you expect the guesser to predict the actual outcome?

b Now perform the experiment described at least 100 times and record each result as right or wrong as appropriate.
Make an observation sheet in the form of a tally chart before you start.

c Compare what you expected to happen with what did happen, using appropriate diagrams. Comment on the likelihood of the guesser being able to predict which way the coin will land.

d Suggest ways in which you could make your results more reliable.

e Suggest other experiments that you could perform to test whether someone can see into the future.

2 Ten (very desirable) posters have been donated to your class.

You have to use these posters for a fund-raising activity to raise money for charity.

Plan a suitable activity and write a report. Give all your ideas, including any that you reject. Include the advantages and the disadvantages of each scheme that you consider.

FORMULAS AND SEQUENCES

Lyn finds a recipe for orange cake in her grandmother's old cookery book. The ingredients are:

8 oz plain flour, 6 oz butter, 6 oz caster sugar, 3 eggs,
$\frac{1}{4}$ teaspoon salt, $1\frac{1}{2}$ level teaspoons baking powder and 1 orange.

The mixture to be baked in a 7-inch circular tin at 350 °F.

She remembers how much she used to enjoy this cake when she was younger, but before she can make her own cake Lyn needs to

- change the quantities of the ingredients into metric units so that she can use her set of scales
- know if one of the circular baking tins she already has is a suitable tin in which to bake the cake
- solve the problem of what temperature to set her oven at since the dial on her oven marks temperature in degrees Celsius and the recipe gives the temperature in degrees Fahrenheit.

EXERCISE 5A

1 Discuss what information Lyn needs so that she can make an orange cake of her own.

2 John's grandfather is going to get petrol from the local garage. The petrol tank of his car holds 10 gallons. It is $\frac{1}{4}$ full at the moment and he does not want to spend more than £15. At the garage petrol is sold by the litre. Discuss what John's grandfather needs to know so that he does not draw more petrol from the pump than the tank will hold and so that he does not spend more than £15.

3 Don Padfield lives in Devon and wants to sell his farm. He is confident that several French farmers will be interested so he decides to advertise the farm in a French farming weekly as well as in a British magazine. Discuss how the two advertisements could differ and how the details should be given so that both advertisements are accurate.

SUBSTITUTING POSITIVE NUMBERS INTO FORMULAS

The formula $C = \frac{5}{9}(F - 32)$ can be used to convert a temperature in degrees Fahrenheit (°F) into a temperature in degrees Celsius (°C).

If Lyn must bake her orange cake at 350 °F we can find this temperature in degrees Celsius by putting $F = 350$ in the formula above.

i.e. $C = \frac{5}{9}(350 - 32)$

$= \frac{5}{9} \times 318$

$= 176.6\ldots$

$\therefore$ $C = 177$ correct to the nearest whole number.

Lyn should therefore set her oven temperature as near to 177 °C as possible.

In the work that follows remember that

$3a$ means $3 \times a$ and that pqr means $p \times q \times r$

EXERCISE 5B

If $v = u + at$, find v when $u = 2$, $a = \frac{1}{2}$ and $t = 4$.

$v = u + at$

When $u = 2$, $a = \frac{1}{2}$ and $t = 4$,

$v = 2 + \frac{1}{2} \times 4$

$= 2 + 2 = 4$

Remember that at means $a \times t$

Remember, do multiplication and division before addition and subtraction.

1 If $N = T + G$, find N when $T = 4$ and $G = 6$.

2 If $T = np$, find T when $n = 20$ and $p = 5$.

3 If $P = 2(l + b)$, find P when $l = 6$ and $b = 9$.

4 If $L = x - y$, find L when $x = 8$ and $y = 6$.

5 If $N = 4(I - s)$, find N when $I = 7$ and $s = 2$.

6 If $S = n(a + b)$, find S when $n = 20$, $a = 2.4$ and $b = 7.8$.

7 If $V = lbw$, find V when $l = 4$, $b = 3$ and $w = 0.8$.

8 If $W = pq + r$, find W when $p = 0.4$, $q = 0.5$ and $r = 1.2$.

9 If $H = a - bc$, find H when $a = 3.2$, $b = 2.1$ and $c = 0.8$.

10 If $I = \frac{PRT}{100}$, find I when $P = 100$, $R = 3$ and $T = 5$.

11 If $w = u(v - t)$, find w when $u = 5$, $v = 7$ and $t = 2$.

12 If $s = \frac{1}{2}(a + b + c)$, find s when $a = 5$, $b = 7$ and $c = 3$.

13 If $v = u + at$, find v when $u = \frac{2}{5}$, $a = \frac{1}{10}$ and $t = 3$.

14 If $S = \frac{1}{u} + \frac{1}{v}$, find S when $u = \frac{3}{4}$ and $v = \frac{9}{8}$.

SUBSTITUTING DIRECTED NUMBERS INTO FORMULAS

In some formulas one or more of the letters can have a negative value. For example, in the formula $C = \frac{5}{9}(F - 32)$ the value of F can be negative. Remember that

> when directed numbers are multiplied or divided,
> both signs the *same* gives a *positive* answer,
> *different* signs give a *negative* answer.

EXERCISE 5C

Find the value of

a $(-3) \times 6$ **b** $(-21) \div (-7)$ **c** $2(10 - (-6))$

a $(-3) \times 6 = -18$

b $(-21) \div (-7) = 3$

c $2(10 - (-6)) = 2(10 + 6) = 2 \times 16 = 32$

Find the value of

1 $-(+4)$

2 $-(-3)$

3 $+(-2)$

4 $4\times(-3)$

5 $4+(-3)$

6 $(-5)\times 6$

7 $\dfrac{(-8)}{4}$

8 $4-(-3)+(-5)$

9 $(-2)\times(+6)$

10 $(-4)\times(-5)$

11 $(+8)\div(-2)$

12 $3(3-(-4))$

13 $(-6)\div(-3)$

14 $\dfrac{12}{(-3)}$

15 $\dfrac{(-2)-(-3)}{4}$

If $v=u-at$, find v when $u=5$, $a=-2$, $t=-3$.

$$v = u - at$$

When $u=5,\ a=-2,\ t=-3,$

$$v = 5-(-2)\times(-3)$$
$$= 5-(+6)$$
$$= 5-6$$
$$= -1$$

Remember that at means $a\times t$

Notice that when negative numbers are substituted for letters they have been put in brackets. This makes sure that only one operation at a time is carried out.

---

16 If $N=p+q$, find N when $p=4$ and $q=-5$.

17 If $C=RT$, find C when $R=4$ and $T=-3$.

18 If $z=w+x-y$, find z when $w=4$, $x=-3$ and $y=-4$.

19 If $r=u(v-w)$, find r when $u=-3$, $v=-6$ and $w=5$.

20 Given that $X=5(T-R)$, find X when $T=4$ and $R=-6$.

21 Given that $P=d-rt$, find P when $d=3$, $r=-8$ and $t=2$.

22 Given that $v=l(a+n)$, find v when $l=-8$, $a=4$ and $n=-6$.

23 If $D=\dfrac{a-b}{c}$, find D when $a=-4$, $b=-8$ and $c=2$.

24 If $Q=abc$, find Q when $a=3$, $b=-7$ and $c=-5$.

25 If $I = \frac{2}{3}(x + y - z)$, find I when $x = 4$, $y = -5$ and $z = -6$.

26 If $P = q + 2r$, find P when $q = 8.7$ and $r = -2.3$.

27 If $Z = 3x - 4y$, find Z when $x = 5.34$ and $y = 2.26$.

28 Given that $N = 2(n - m)$, find N when

a $n = 6$ and $m = 4$ **b** $n = 7$ and $m = -3$

29 If $z = x - 3y$, find z when

a $x = 3\frac{1}{2}$ and $y = \frac{3}{4}$ **b** $x = \frac{3}{8}$ and $y = -1\frac{1}{2}$

30 If $P = 10r - t$, find P when

a $r = 0.25$ and $t = -10$ **b** $r = 0.145$ and $t = 15.6$

31 Copy and complete the table if $y = 4 - 2x$.

x	-2	-1	0	1	4
y		6			

32 Given that $P = 50R - 30$, copy and complete the following table.

R	-1	0	1	3
P				

33 The nth term of a sequence is given by the expression $10 - 3n$.
Copy and complete the following table.

n	1	2	3	4	5	6
nth term						

CONSTRUCTING A FORMULA

In Book 8B we constructed simple formulas connecting two given letters. As we continue that work we must remember the convention that letters stand for unknown *numbers*. For example if there is an unknown number of boxes on a shelf, we could use b for the number. We can say that there are b boxes, that is, b is the *number* of boxes. If we use b to stand for the boxes as well as the number of them, we would have to talk about b on the shelf and this would not describe the situation clearly.

Similarly, if a length is unknown, that is, it is an unknown number of units, we use a letter for the unknown number only. The letter does not include the units. We can then say that the length is l cm rather than talk about the length as l.

If we stick to this convention, any expression in letters is a relationship between numbers only, and the ordinary rules of arithmetic apply.

The next exercise includes formulas that involve more than two given letters.

EXERCISE 5D

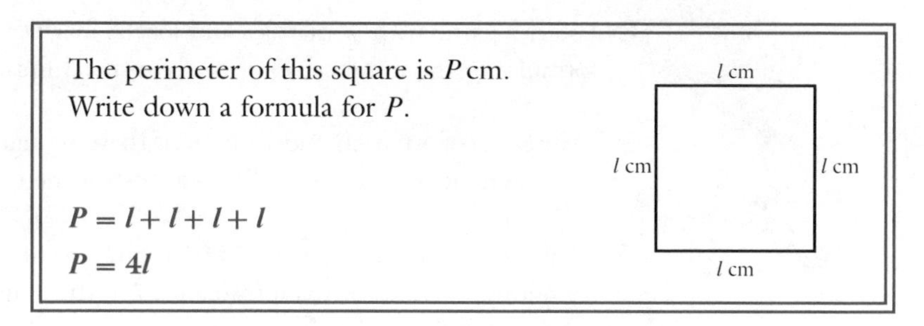

The perimeter of this square is P cm.
Write down a formula for P.

$P = l + l + l + l$

$P = 4l$

In each of the following diagrams the perimeter is P cm.
Write down a formula for P starting with $P =$.

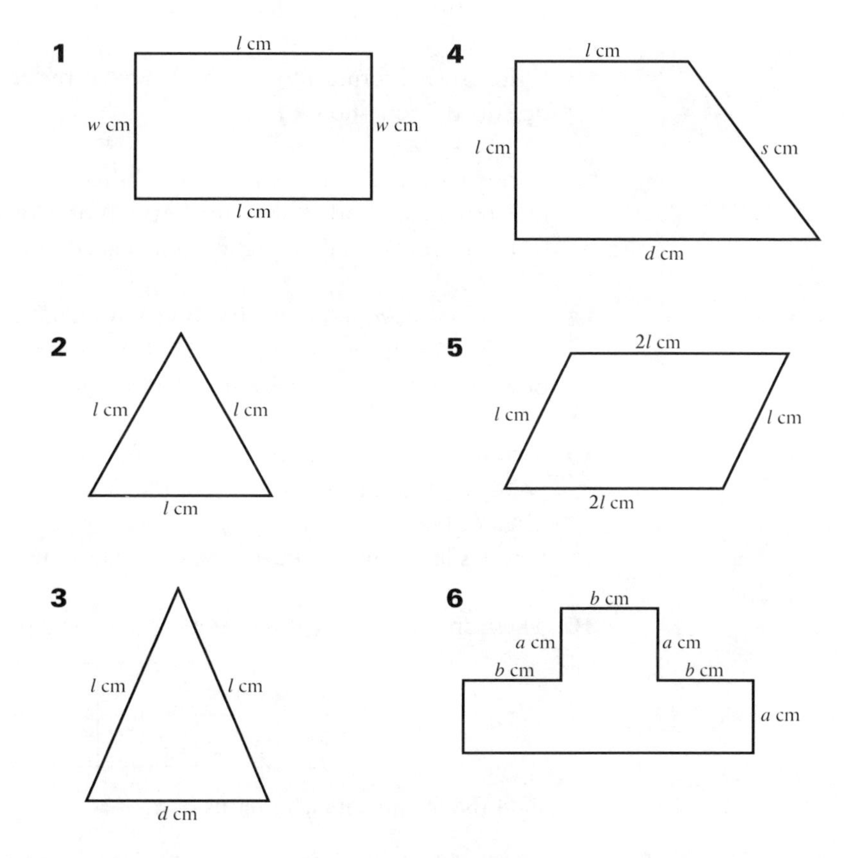

> If G is the number of girls in a class and B is the number of boys, write down a formula for the total number, T, of children in the class.
>
> $$T = G + B$$

7 I buy x lb of apples and y lb of pears. Write down a formula for W if W lb is the weight of fruit that I have bought.

8 I start a game with N marbles and lose L marbles. Write down a formula for the number, T, of marbles that I finish with.

9 Oranges cost x p each and I buy n of these oranges. Write down a formula for C where C p is the total cost of the oranges.

10 I have a piece of string which is l cm long. I cut off a piece which is d cm long. Write down a formula for L if the length of string which is left is L cm.

11 A rectangle is $2b$ m long and b m wide. Write down a formula for P where P m is the perimeter of the rectangle.

12 Write down a formula for A where $A\,\text{m}^2$ is the area of the rectangle described in question **11**.

13 A lorry weighs T tonnes when empty. Steel girders weighing a total of S tonnes are loaded on to the lorry. Write down a formula for W where W tonnes is the weight of the loaded lorry.

14 A train travels p km in one direction and then it comes back q km in the opposite direction. If it is then r km from its starting point, write down a formula for r. (Assume that p is greater than q.)

15 Two points have the same y-coordinate. The x-coordinate of one point is a and the x-coordinate of the other point is b. If d is the distance between the two points, write down a formula for d given that a is less than b. Draw a sketch to illustrate this problem.

16 These are the coordinates of some points on a straight line.

x-coordinate	1	2	3	4	5
y-coordinate	2	3	4	5	6

Find the formula for y in terms of x.

A letter costs x pence to post. The cost of posting 20 such letters is £q. Write down a formula for q in terms of x.

The cost of a letter is given in pence and the total cost is in £s.
Both quantities must be in the same unit.
We will work in the larger unit i.e. pounds.

Cost of 20 letters at x pence each is $20 \times x$ pence,

i.e. $$£\frac{20x}{100} = £\frac{x}{5}$$

The formula connecting p and q is therefore $q = \frac{x}{5}$

17 One grapefruit costs y pence. The cost of n such grapefruit is £L. Write down a formula for L.

18 A rectangle is l m long and b cm wide. The area is $A\text{ cm}^2$. Write down a formula for A.

19 On my way to work this morning the train I was travelling on broke down. I spent t hours on the train and s minutes walking. Write down a formula for T if the total time that my journey took was T hours.

20 Kiwi fruit cost n pence each and a box of 50 of these kiwi fruit costs £C.

a Write down a formula for C.

b Use your formula to find the cost of a box of kiwi fruit if each kiwi fruit costs 12 p.

21 A rectangular box is p cm long, q cm wide and r cm deep. The volume of the box is $V\text{ cm}^3$.

a Write down a formula for V.

b Use your formula to find the volume of a box which is 10 cm long, 5 cm wide and $2\frac{1}{2}$ cm deep.

22 A rectangle is a cm long and $(2a - 10)$ cm wide.

a Write down a formula for P if P cm is the perimeter of the rectangle.

b Use your formula to find the perimeter of a rectangle 6.9 cm long.

c What is the smallest integer that a can represent for the value of P to make sense?

23 The length of a rectangle is twice its width. The rectangle is x cm wide.

a Draw a diagram to show this information.

b Write down a formula for P if the perimeter is P cm.

c Use your formula to find the width of a rectangle that has a perimeter of 36 cm.

24 A roll of paper is L m long. N pieces each of length r m are cut off the roll. If the length of paper left is P m, write down a formula for P. A roll of paper 20 m long had 10 pieces, each of length 1.5 m cut from it. Use your formula to find the length of paper left.

FINDING THE *n*th TERM OF A SEQUENCE

In the sequence 6, 12, 18, 24, 30, ...
the 1st term is 6, the 2nd term is 12, the 3rd term is 18, and so on.
If we use n for the position number of a term, we can arrange the terms in a table

i.e.

n	1	2	3	4	5
nth term	6	12	18	24	30

Now we can see that the nth term is equal to 6 times n
i.e. $6 \times n$ or $6n$.

EXERCISE 5E

Find an expression, in terms of n, for the nth term of each sequence.

1

n	1	2	3	4	5
nth term	2	4	6	8	10

2

n	1	2	3	4	5
nth term	5	10	15	20	25

3

n	1	2	3	4	5
nth term	10	20	30	40	50

4

n	1	2	3	4	5
nth term	0.5	1	1.5	2	2.5

5

n	1	2	3	4	5
nth term	$\frac{1}{5}$	$\frac{2}{5}$	$\frac{3}{5}$	$\frac{4}{5}$	1

6

n	1	2	3	4	5
nth term	0.1	0.2	0.3	0.4	0.5

7 For each sequence given in questions **1** to **6**, write down, in words, the rule for generating the sequence.

The terms of a sequence are generated by following a rule.
In questions **8** to **11**

a write the first five terms in a table like those in questions **1** to **6**

b find an expression for the nth term in terms of n.

8 Start with 3 and add 2 each time.

9 Start with 9 and add 5 each time.

10 Start with 1 and add 3 each time.

11 Start with 5 and add 4 each time.

The nth term of a sequence is given by the formula

$$n\text{th term} = 2n + 5.$$

Give the first three terms and the 8th term.

nth term $= 2 \times n + 5$

$n = 1$ 1st term $= 2 \times 1 + 5 = 7$

$n = 2$ 2nd term $= 2 \times 2 + 5 = 9$

$n = 3$ 3rd term $= 2 \times 3 + 5 = 11$

$n = 8$ 8th term $= 2 \times 8 + 5 = 21$

In questions **12** to **17** write down the first four terms and the 8th term of the sequence for which the nth term is given.

12 $3n + 2$

13 $4n - 2$

14 $5n + 3$

15 $6n - 5$

16 $\frac{1}{2}n + 3$

17 $0.1n + 2$

Find a formula for the nth term of the sequence 2, 5, 8, 11, ...

Start by making a table.

Now see if we can spot the relationship between the term and its position number. The terms increase by 3 each time, so multiples of 3 are involved. Add another line to the table.

n	1	2	3	4
nth term	2	5	8	11
$3n$	3	6	9	12

These values are all 1 more than the given terms so we subtract 1 from $3n$.

i.e. nth term $= 3n - 1$

Check: $n = 1$ 1st term $= 3 \times 1 - 1 = 2$

$n = 2$ 2nd term $= 3 \times 2 - 1 = 5$

$n = 3$ 3rd term $= 3 \times 3 - 1 = 8$

$n = 4$ 4th term $= 3 \times 4 - 1 = 11$

Find an expression for the nth term of each of the following sequences.

18 7, 9, 11, 13, ...

19 4, 7, 10, 13, ...

20 7, 12, 17, 22, ...

21 1, 5, 9, 13, ...

22 11, 20, 29, 38, ...

23 3, 10, 17, 24, ...

24 Look at this pattern.

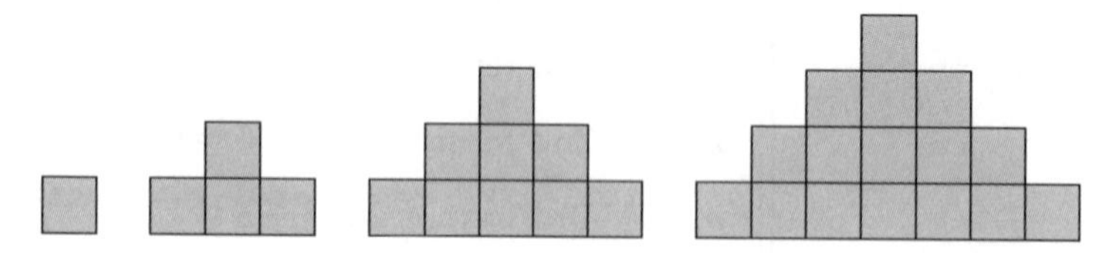

Copy and complete this table.

nth pattern	1	2	3	4	5
Number of squares	1	4			

a Find, in terms of n, a formula for the number of squares in the nth term of this pattern.

b If N is the number of squares in the 10th pattern, find N.

25 Look at this pattern using square tiles.

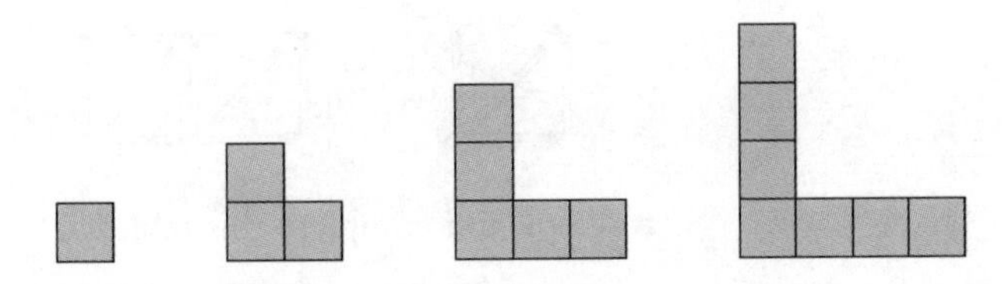

a Copy and complete this table.

nth pattern	1	2	3	4	5	6
Number of tiles						

b Find a formula, in terms of n, for the number of tiles in the nth term of this pattern.

c How many tiles are needed for the 12th term?

d If 27 tiles are needed for the Nth term in this pattern, find the value of N.

26

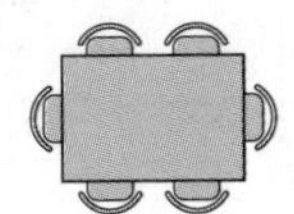

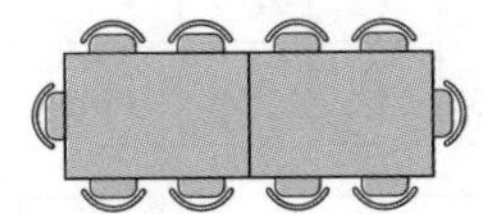

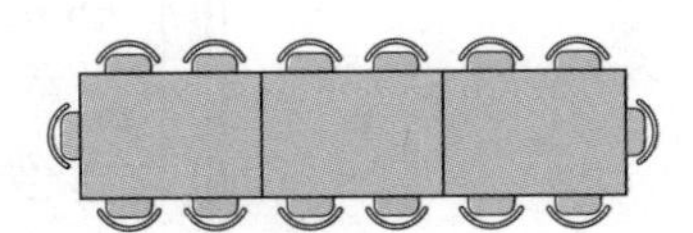

Ann arranges rectangular tables in a row for a Christmas Party.

a Copy and continue the table which shows the number of children that can be seated when a number of tables are arranged next to each other in a row.

Number of tables	1	2	3	4
Number of seats available	6			

b If there are n tables, find a formula in terms of n for the number, N, of children that can be seated.

c Use your formula to find how many children can be seated around 12 tables arranged in a row.

d If 30 children are to be seated, how many tables are needed?

e If 40 children are to be seated, how many tables are needed? Are there any spare seats? If so, how many?

27 These patterns are made from matchsticks.

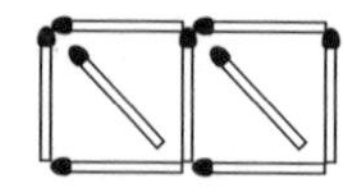
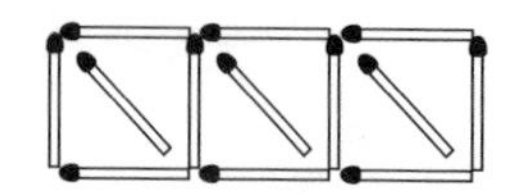

a Copy and complete this table.

*n*th pattern	1	2	3	4	5
Number of matchsticks					

b Find a formula, in terms of n, for the number of matchsticks needed for the nth pattern.

c How many matchsticks are needed for the 20th pattern?

d Colin uses 65 matchsticks for the Nth arrangement in this pattern. What is the value of N.

Find a formula for the nth term of the sequence 24, 18, 12, 6, . . .

n	1	2	3	4
nth term	24	18	12	6
$6n$	6	12	18	24

The terms decrease by 6 each time, so multiples of 6 are involved. Add another line to the table.

Entries in the second and third lines add up to 30 so if 6 is subtracted from 30 we get 24, i.e. the first term. If 12 is subtracted from 30 we get 18, i.e. the second term, and so on.

i.e. nth term $= 30 - 6n$

Check: $n = 1$ 1st term $= 30 - 6 \times 1 = 30 - 6 = 24$

$n = 2$ 2nd term $= 30 - 6 \times 2 = 30 - 12 = 18$

$n = 3$ 3rd term $= 30 - 6 \times 3 = 30 - 18 = 12$

$n = 4$ 4th term $= 30 - 6 \times 4 = 30 - 24 = 6$

Find an expression for the nth term of each sequence.

28 12, 10, 8, 6, . . .

29 17, 14, 11, 8, . . .

30 4, 2, 0, −2, . . .

31 5, 0, −5, −10, . . .

Find an expression for the nth term of the sequence

$$4, 7, 12, 19, 28, 39, \ldots$$

The differences between consecutive terms are 3, 5, 7, 9, 11, ... which are not the same multiples of n so we must try something different. Consider the square of each position number.

n	1	2	3	4	5	6
nth term	4	7	12	19	28	39
n^2	1	4	9	16	25	36

Comparing the values of n^2 with the terms in the given sequence we see that every term in the sequence is 3 more than the corresponding value of n^2.

i.e. n**th term** $= n^2 + 3$

Find an expression for the nth term of each of the following sequences.

32 1, 4, 9, 16, ...

33 6, 9, 14, 21, ...

34 3, 6, 11, 18, ...

35 0, 3, 8, 15, ...

36 1, 8, 27, 64, ...

37 7, 26, 63, 124, ...

MIXED EXERCISE

EXERCISE 5F

1 **a** If $P = 3(a + b)$, find P when $a = 5$ and $b = 7$.

b If $R = \frac{1}{2}(m + M)$, find R when $m = \frac{1}{3}$ and $M = \frac{1}{6}$.

2 Find the value of

a $-5(+2)$

b $-(-7)$

c $(-3) \times (-6)$

d $18 \div (-3)$

e $4 \times (-6)$

f $(-3) \times (+7)$

g $(-15) \div (-3)$

h $(-21) \div (-7)$

i $20 \div (-4)$

3 Given that $A = a(b - c)$, find A when

a $a = 3$, $b = 4$ and $c = -5$

b $a = 2$, $b = -2$ and $c = -7$

c $a = -4$, $b = 7$ and $c = -3$

4 Karin has a 1 kg bag of sugar. After using p grams to make some cakes she has Q grams left.
Find a formula for Q.

5 When a shop opened in the morning there were x boxes of Mornflakes on the premises. During the day they sold y boxes and took delivery of a carton containing 48 boxes. At the end of the day they had Z boxes of Mornflakes. Find a formula for Z.

6 Write down the first 4 terms and the 20th term of the sequence whose nth term is $5n - 3$.

7 Find a formula for the nth term of the sequence 4, 11, 18, 25, ...

INVESTIGATION

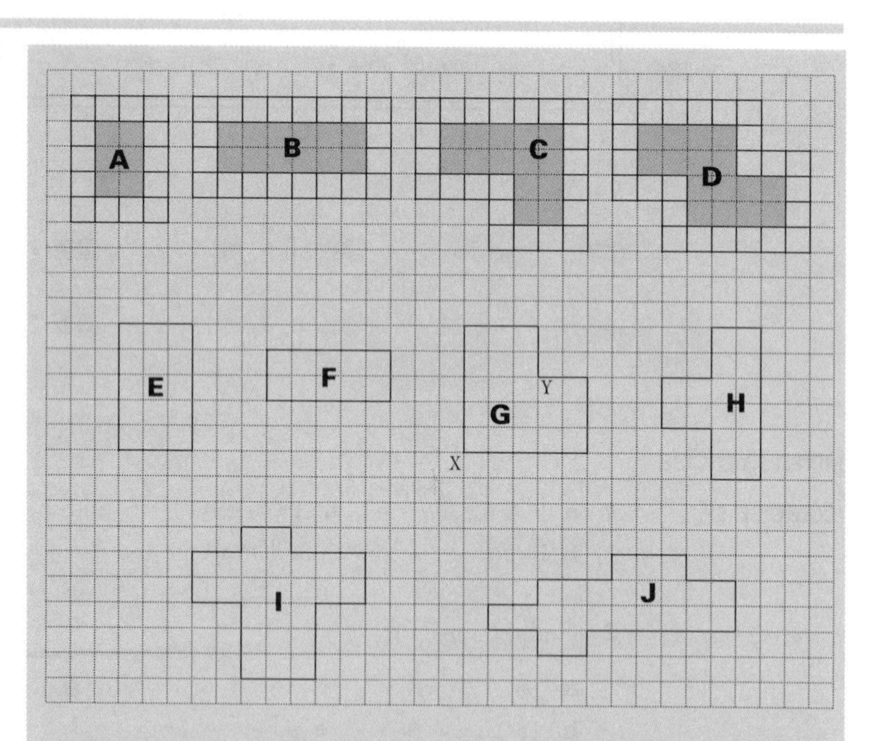

Paul works for a landscape gardener and specialises in laying paving slabs around lawns, flower beds and ponds. All the slabs he uses are square and have an area of one square foot. Different shapes of flower beds are shown in diagrams **A** to **J**.

a Bed **A** measures 3 ft by 2 ft. How many slabs does Paul need to go around its edge?

b For bed **B** write down:
 i its overall length and breadth
 ii the number of slabs needed to go all the way round it.

c For bed **C** the overall width of the bed is 4 ft and the overall length is 5 ft. What is its perimeter? How many slabs are needed to go all the way round?

d How many slabs touch an 'outside' corner like X, in bed **G**? How many slabs touch an 'inside' corner like Y? How many more slabs touch an outside corner than touch an inside corner?

e For flowerbed **D**,
 i what is its overall length and width?
 ii how many slabs are needed to go around its edge?
 iii how many outside corners does it have?
 iv how many inside corners does it have?

f Repeat part **e** for each of the beds from **E** to **J**.

g Copy the table given below and complete it using your answers to the previous parts.

	Overall					
Diagram	Width in feet	Length in feet	Perimeter, P, in feet	Number, a, of outside corners	Number, b, of inside corners	Total number, N, of slabs needed
A						
B						
C						
D						
E						
F						
G						
H						
I						
J						

h Construct a formula that gives the number, N, of slabs needed to go round a flower bed that has a perimeter of P ft, and has a outside corners and b inside corners.

i What can you say about the size of a compared to the size of b?

j Investigate whether or not an arrangement can be drawn for any values of P, a and b.

SUMMARY 2

SIGNIFICANT FIGURES

The first significant figure in a number is the first non-zero figure when reading from left to right.

The second significant figure is the next figure to the right, whether or not it is zero.

The third significant figure is the next figure to the right, whether or not it is zero, and so on.

For example, in 0.0205, the first significant figure is 2,
the second significant figure is 0,
the third significant figure is 5.

To correct a number to a given number of significant figures, look at the next significant figure; if it is 5 or more, add 1 to the previous figure, otherwise leave the previous figure alone.

For example, $0.020|5 = 0.021$ correct to 2 significant figures
$0.02|05 = 0.02$ correct to 1 significant figure.

PARALLEL LINES

When two parallel lines are cut by a transversal, the *corresponding angles* are equal,

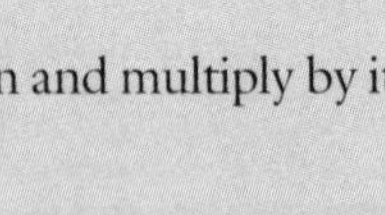

the *alternate angles* are equal,

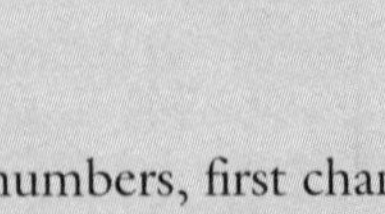

FRACTION

To divide by a fraction, we turn the fraction upside down and multiply by it,

e.g. $\frac{1}{2} \div \frac{5}{3} = \frac{1}{2} \times \frac{3}{5} = \frac{3}{10}$.

To multiply or divide with mixed numbers, first change the mixed numbers to improper fractions.

PERCENTAGE INCREASE

To increase a quantity by 15%,

we find *the increase* by finding 15% of the quantity, so we multiply by 0.15:

we find *the new quantity* by finding 100% + 15%, i.e. 115% of the original quantity, so we multiply by 1.15.

PERCENTAGE DECREASE

To decrease a quantity by 15%,
we find *the decrease* by finding 15% of the quantity,

We find *the new quantity* by finding 100% – 15%,
i.e. 85% of the original quantity, so we multiply by 0.85.

PROBABILITY

The probability that an event A does not happen is equal to one minus the probability that it does happen,

i.e. P(A does not happen) = 1 – P(A does happen).

If p is the probability that an event happens on one occasion, then we expect it to happen about np times on n occasions. For example, the probability that a coin lands head up on one toss is $\frac{1}{2}$, so if we toss the coin 50 times, we expect about (but are very unlikely to get exactly) 25 heads.

REVISION EXERCISE 2.1 (Chapters 1 to 3)

1 For each of the following numbers write down the significant figure referred to in the bracket.

a 73.4 (1st) **c** 0.004 27 (2nd)
b 60.24 (3rd) **d** 7004 (2nd)

2 Write down each number correct to the number of significant figures given in the bracket.

a 37 (1) **c** 84 392 (3)
b 2493 (2) **d** 0.349 54 (3)

3 a Write down an *estimate* for each of the following calculations. Do all the working in your head.
i $3.4 + 5.98$ **ii** $10.5 - 3.9$ **iii** 17.16×9.88 **iv** $37.4 \div 0.95$

b Which of the given numbers are obviously not equal to 3.05×13.26?

A 4.35 **B** 0.2300 **C** 40.44 **D** 35.13

4 Find the size of the marked angles.

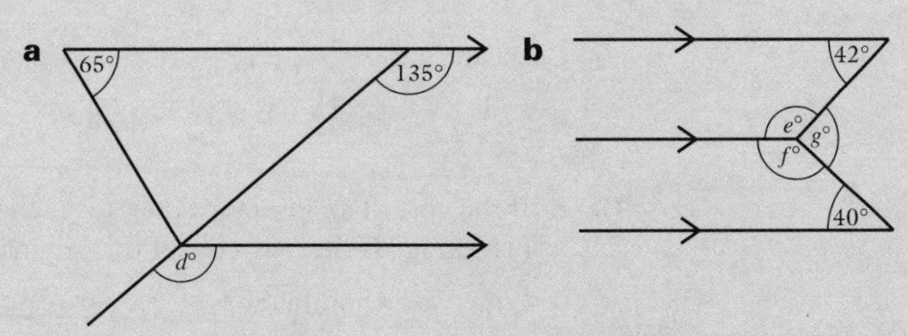

5

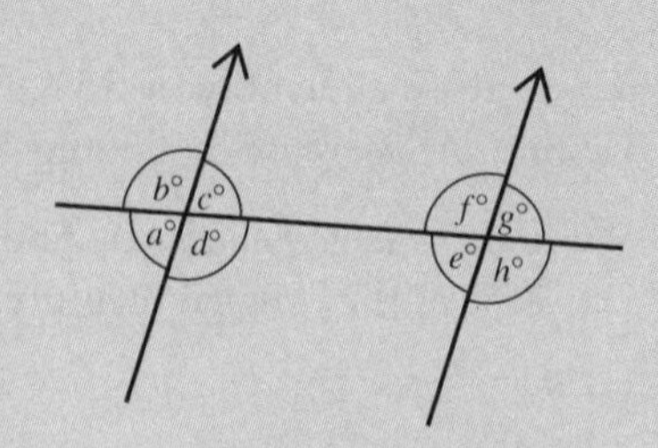

Use the letters marked in the diagram to give

a two angles that are corresponding angles, one of which is $d°$

b two angles that are supplementary angles, one of which is $d°$

c two angles that are alternate angles, one of which is $e°$.

6 Calculate

a $9 \div \frac{2}{3}$ **b** $32 \div 1\frac{3}{5}$ **c** $\frac{11}{21} \div \frac{6}{7}$

7 A special offer pack of rolls contains two extra rolls free. A normal pack contains 16 rolls.

a Copy and complete this sentence with a fraction.
The number of extra rolls is ... of the normal number of rolls.

b Copy and complete this sentence with a percentage.
The extra number of rolls is ... of the normal number of rolls.

c Copy and complete this sentence with a decimal.
The extra number of rolls = ... × the normal number.

8 A 500 g box of Mornwheat cereal costs £1.79. A special offer box contains 550 g.

a How many extra grams are there in the special box?

b What fraction of the normal contents is the extra in the special offer box?

c Copy and complete each sentence.
i The extra quantity is ... % × the normal quantity.
ii the quantity in the special offer box is ... % × the normal quantity.

9 Calculate

a $(2\frac{1}{4} - 1\frac{1}{3}) \div \frac{11}{24}$ **b** $(4\frac{1}{3} - 2\frac{2}{7}) \times \frac{49}{86}$ **c** $1\frac{1}{3} \times 1\frac{8}{9} \div 3\frac{7}{9}$

10 **a** If the cost of an insurance policy is increased by 55%, what percentage is the new cost of the original cost?

b **i** Increase £560 by 35% **ii** Decrease £650 by 24%

REVISION EXERCISE 2.2 (Chapters 4 and 5)

1 The probability that Tony will score a treble 20 with his next dart is 0.2. What is the probability that Tony will not score a treble 20 with his next dart?

2 In a sale 60 shirts are on offer at reduced prices. Of these, 15 are size 13, 20 are size 14, 12 are size 15 and the remainder are size 16. Ken chooses a shirt at random. What is the probability that the shirt he chooses is

a size 14

b not size 15

c size 15 or larger

d at least size 14?

3 Four kings and four queens are removed from an ordinary pack of playing cards. One card is taken from the set of kings and one card is taken from the set of queens. Make a table showing all of the possible combinations of the two cards and use it to find the probability that the two cards

a are both red

b include at least one red card

c are both hearts

d are of different suits.

4 Two ordinary six-sided dice are rolled together 360 times. About how many double sixes are there likely to be?

5 Checkley have to play home matches against Eastleigh, Blockley, Wayford and Monkton on four consecutive Saturdays. They decide the order in which they will play these matches by drawing the names of their opponents from a hat.

a If Eastleigh are drawn to play Checkley on the first Saturday write down all the possible orders in which the other matches can be played.

b Write down all the possible orders if Eastleigh play Checkley on the third Saturday.

6 a Calculate

i $(-4)+(-6)$

ii $(-4)\times(-6)$

iii $(-5)\times(+3)$

iv $(-12)\div(+4)$

b Oranges cost n pence each. Write down a formula for N if N pence is the cost of 5 oranges.

7 a If $v=u+at$ find v when $u=4$, $a=-3$ and $t=2$.

b The volume of this cuboid is $V\text{ cm}^3$. Find a formula for V.

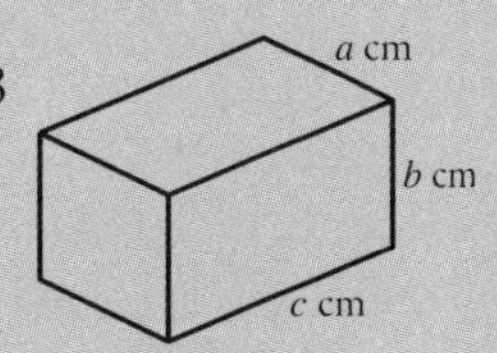

8 a A rectangle is l cm long and b cm wide. Write down a formula for P where P cm is the perimeter of the rectangle.

b Find a formula for the nth term in terms of n.

n	1	2	3	4	5
nth term	4	5	6	7	8

9 The perimeter of each shape is P cm. Write down a formula for P.

a

l cm

$(l + 2)$ cm

$(l + 1)$ cm

b

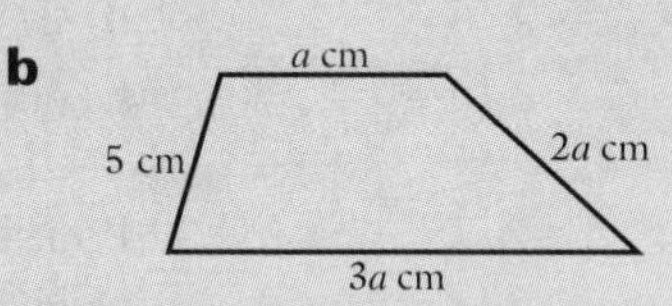

10 a Write down the first four terms of the sequence generated by starting with 5 and adding 3 each time. Find an expression for the nth term in terms of n.

b Write down the first four terms and the 10th term of the sequence for which the nth term is
i $3n + 7$ **ii** $30 - 2n$

REVISION EXERCISE 2.3 (Chapters 1 to 5)

1 a Write down each number correct to the number of significant figures given in the bracket.
i 92 143 (1) **iii** 3.141 59 (2)
ii 17.42 (3) **iv** 80 073 (3)

b Round each number to the accuracy given in brackets.
i 27 527 (nearest 1000) **iii** 3996 (nearest 100)
ii 5.8827 (2 d.p.) **iv** 5.0267 (3 s.f.)

2 a Write down an estimate for each of the following calculations.
i $7.3 + 4.776$ **iii** $(3.07)^2$
ii $60.09 \div 9.76$ **iv** 19.56×3.12

b The estimated seating capacity of a new stadium is 66 000, correct to the nearest 1000. What is the largest number of seats they expect to have and what is the smallest number?

3 Copy these statements and fill in the blanks.

a The . . . of the three angles of a triangle is 180°.

b Corresponding angles are . . . .

c 56° and . . . are supplementary angles.

4 Find the size of the marked angles.

a

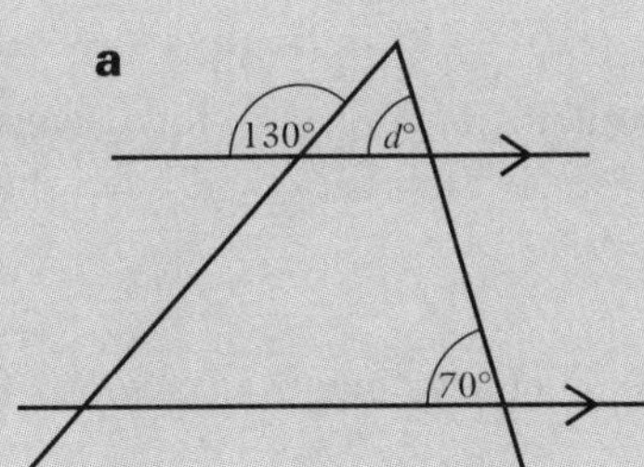

b

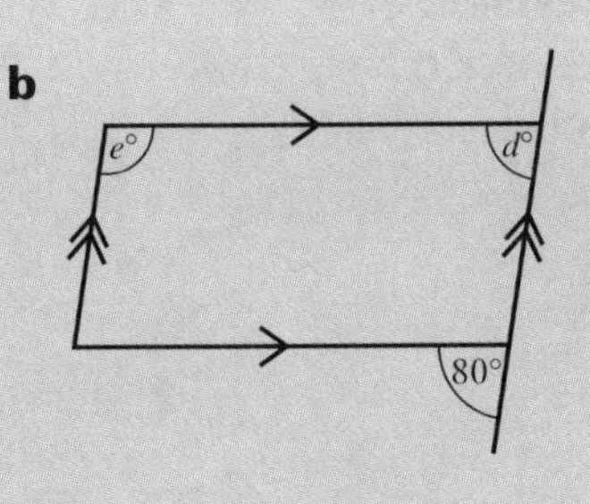

5 **a** Calculate

i $3\frac{1}{5} \div \frac{4}{7}$ **ii** $8\frac{1}{8} \div 7\frac{3}{7}$ **iii** $(4\frac{1}{2} - 2\frac{1}{10}) \div 1\frac{1}{3}$

b How many $\frac{2}{5}$s are there in 4?

c How many pieces of wire $\frac{3}{4}$ inch long can be cut from a length of $3\frac{1}{8}$ inches of wire?

6 **a** Give the multiplying factor when 200 kg is increased by 20%.

b Give the multiplying factor when 300 m is decreased by 30%.

c A stereo priced at £200 was reduced by 30% in a sale. What was the sale price?

d In 1990, 360 people lived in Lorke. By 1995 this number had increased by 30%. How many people lived in Lorke in 1995?

7 A number is chosen at random from the first twelve whole numbers. What is the probability that it is

a exactly divisible by 3 **b** not exactly divisible by 3?

8 At the Eastlee Fitness Centre it is normal for about 1 in 3 of the members of each new keep-fit class to leave within the first three weeks of enrolling. Thirty members enrol for one class. How many members are expected to attend the class held during the fourth week?

9 **a** If $s = \frac{1}{2}(a + b + c)$, find s when $a = 6$, $b = 2\frac{1}{2}$ and $c = 5\frac{1}{2}$.

b Use the formula $C = \frac{5}{9}(F - 32)$ to convert a temperature of 400 degrees Fahrenheit to degrees Celsius.

c If $I = \dfrac{PRT}{100}$ find I when $P = 300$, $R = 3$ and $T = 6$.

10 **a** Write down the first four terms and the 12th term of the sequence for which the nth term is

i $5n - 4$ **ii** $10 - 3n$

b Find an expression for the nth term of the sequence

i 8, 11, 14, 17, ... **ii** 13, 11, 9, 7, ...

REVISION EXERCISE 2.4 (Chapters 1 to 5)

1 a Without using a calculator find, correct to 2 significant figures
i $30 \div 7$ **ii** $61 \div 3$ **iii** $0.44 \div 9$ **iv** $0.002 \div 6$

b A car-park contains 1400 cars to the nearest 100. What is the greatest number of cars that could be in the car-park and what is the least number?

2 a Which of the given numbers are obviously not equal to 7.14×2.08?
A 3.43 **B** 14.85 **C** 13.82 **D** 0.29

b Round each number to the accuracy given in brackets.
i 7597 (nearest 100) **iii** 53 532 (nearest 1000)
ii 7.6666 (2 s.f.) **iv** 1.0846 (2 d.p.)

3 Find the marked angles.

a

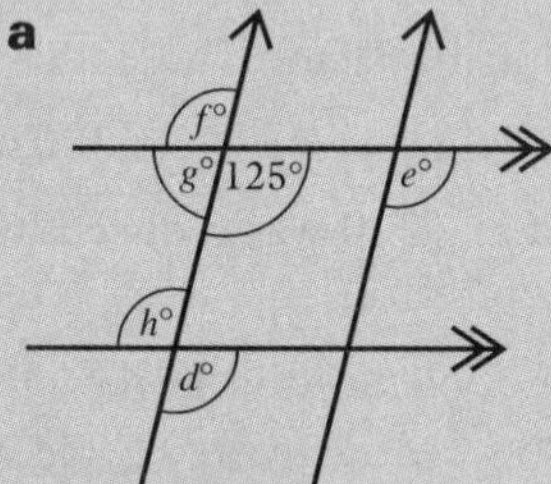

b

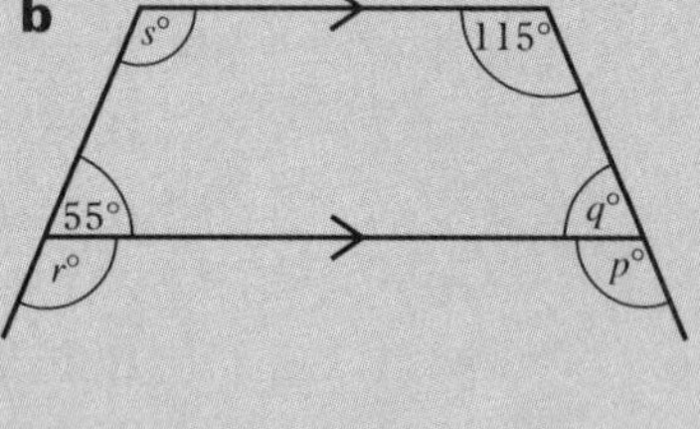

4 Copy these statements and fill in the blanks.

a Alternate angles are . . . .

b If the sum of two angles is 180° the angles are . . . .

5 a Find
i $3\frac{1}{2} \times 2\frac{1}{4}$ **iii** $1\frac{1}{3} \times 1\frac{8}{9} \div 3\frac{7}{9}$
ii $3\frac{1}{3} \div 2\frac{1}{4}$ **iv** $\frac{9}{14} \div (\frac{1}{2} - \frac{1}{14})$

b Which is the greater and by how much $2\frac{1}{2} \div \frac{2}{3}$ or $2\frac{1}{2} \times \frac{2}{3}$?

6 a Find the percentage that the new price is of the original price when the original price is increased by 40%.

b Find the percentage that the new price is of the original price when the original price is decreased by 25%.

7 A card is drawn at random from an ordinary pack of 52 playing cards. What is the probability that the card drawn is

a a 3 **c** the 3 of hearts

b a red 3 **d** not a red 3?

8 A 10 p coin and a 20 p coin are tossed together. Make your own possibility space for the combinations in which they can land. Find the probability of getting

a one head and one tail **b** two tails **c** at least one head.

9 a If $s = \frac{1}{2}(a + b + c)$, find s when $a = 6$, $b = 7$, $c = 9$.

b If $N = abc$ find N when $a = 5$, $b = -2$ and $c = -3$.

c If $Q = a - bc$ find Q when $a = 10$, $b = -2$ and $c = -3$.

10 a If $P = qr + w$ find P when $q = 0.5$, $r = 1.2$ and $w = 3.4$.

b Find a formula for the nth term in terms of n.

n	1	2	3	4	5
nth term	−1	0	1	2	3

POLYGONS

6

David attended pottery classes and made some tiles. He wanted to make a heat-proof mat with them, and decided that he liked this shape:

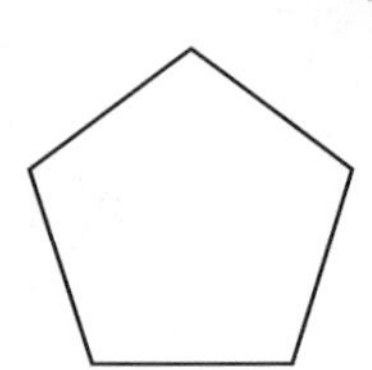

When he came to fit the tiles together he found that he could not get them to cover the mat without leaving gaps.

- If David had done a little research before he started he would have found that this shape could never be arranged so that it covered a flat surface completely without leaving any gaps.

- Shapes like these tiles are called polygons. If David had been familiar with their properties before he started it would have helped him to decide which shape of polygon to use for his tile.

In this chapter we look at polygons. By the end of the chapter you should be in a position to avoid David's mistake.

The summary on pages 10 and 11 will remind you of the angle facts and of the different classifications of triangles and quadrilaterals studied in Book 8B. Some of this knowledge is used in this chapter.

POLYGONS

A polygon is a plane (flat) figure bounded by straight lines.

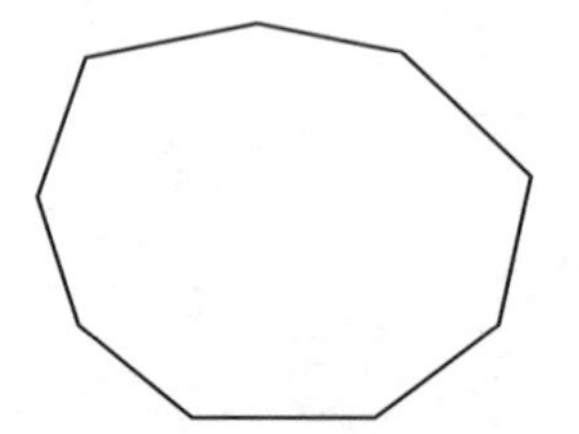

This is a nine-sided polygon.

Some polygons have names which you already know:

a three-sided polygon is a triangle

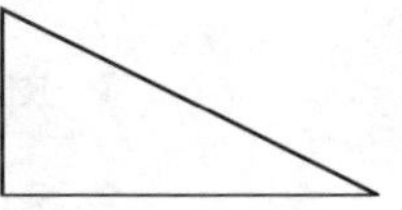

a four-sided polygon is a quadrilateral

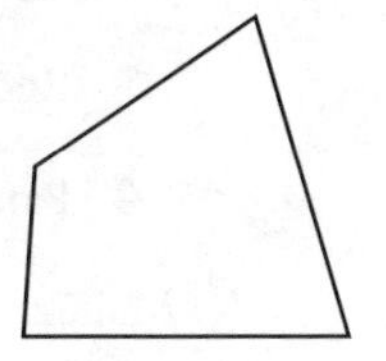

a five-sided polygon is a pentagon

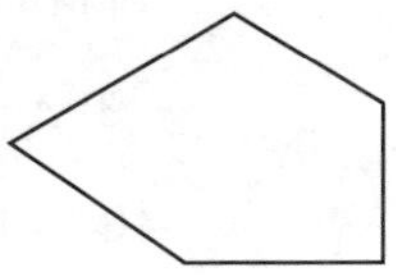

a six-sided polygon is a hexagon

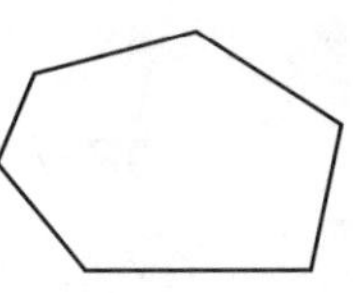

an eight-sided polygon is an octagon

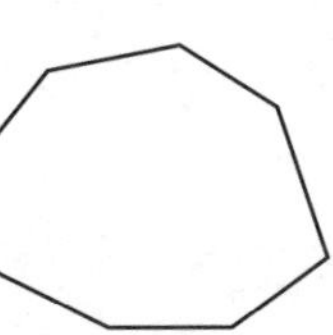

REGULAR POLYGONS

The polygons drawn above are not regular polygons.

> A polygon is called regular when all its sides are the same length *and* all its angles are the same size.

The polygons below are all regular:

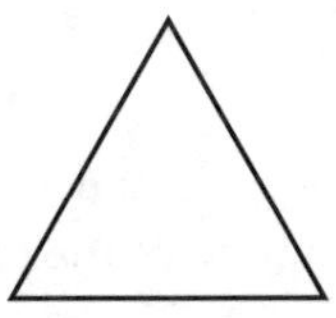
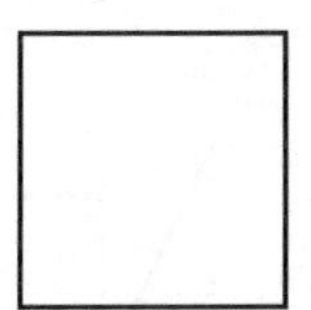
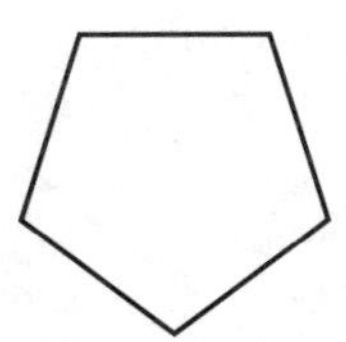
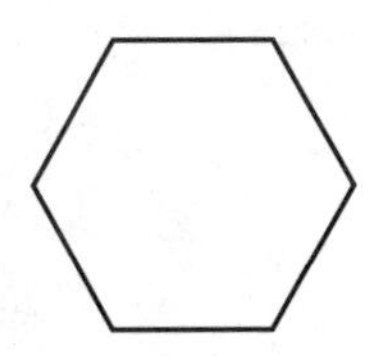

Regular polygons are quite commonplace in everyday life. For example:

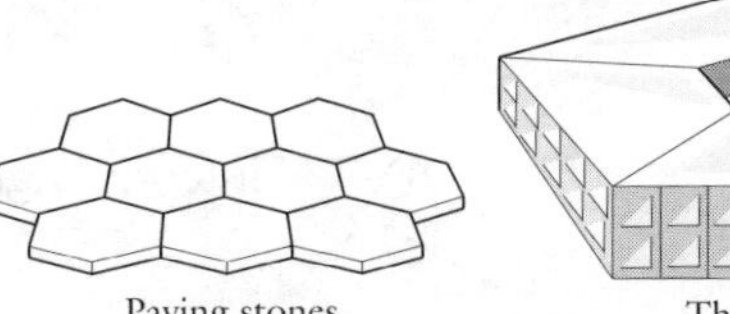
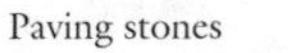

Paving stones

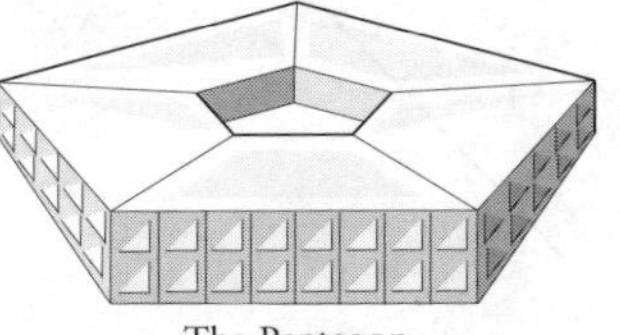

The Pentagon in Washington

An octagonal table

EXERCISE 6A

State which of the following figures are regular polygons and why. Give a brief reason for your answer.

1 Rhombus

2 Square

3 Rectangle

4 Parallelogram

5 Isosceles triangle

6 A triangle with one right angle

7 Equilateral triangle

8 Circle

Make a rough sketch of each of the following polygons. (Unless you are told that a polygon is regular, you must assume that it is *not* regular.)

9 A regular quadrilateral

10 A hexagon

11 A triangle

12 A regular triangle

13 A regular hexagon

14 A pentagon

15 A quadrilateral

16 A ten-sided polygon

When the vertices of a polygon all point outwards, the polygon is *convex*.

Sometimes one or more of the vertices point inwards, in which case the polygon is *concave*.

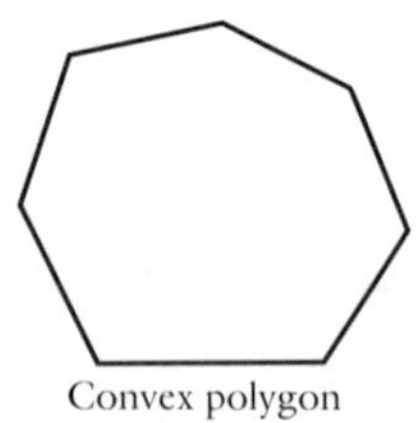

Convex polygon

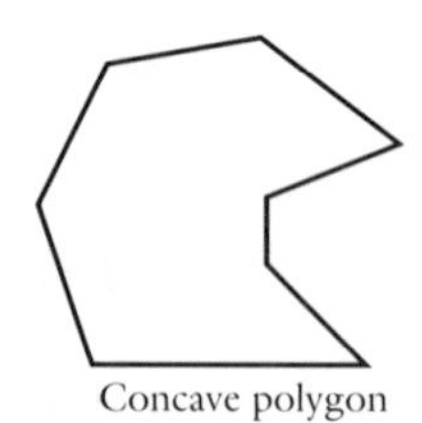

Concave polygon

In this chapter we consider only convex polygons.

INTERIOR ANGLES

The angles enclosed by the sides of a polygon are the interior angles. For example,

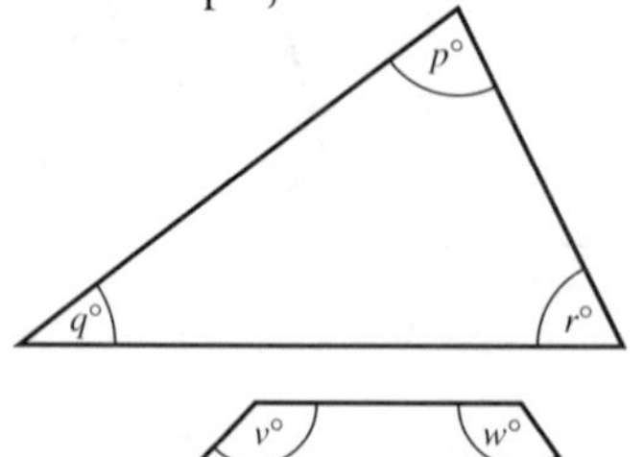

$p°$, $q°$, and $r°$ are the interior angles of the triangle,

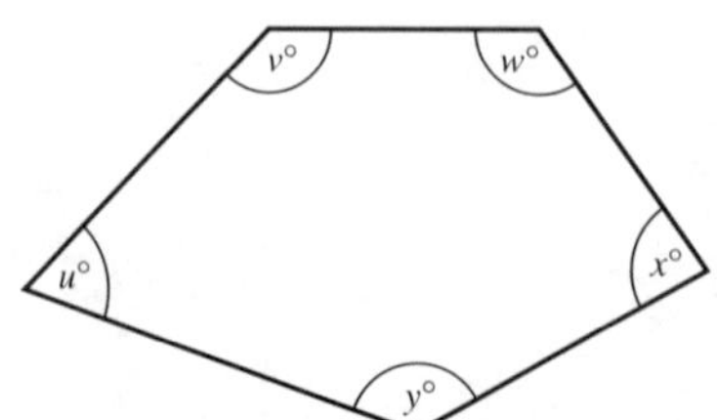

$u°$, $v°$, $w°$, $x°$ and $y°$ are the interior angles of the pentagon.

EXTERIOR ANGLES

If we extend one side of a polygon, an angle is formed outside the polygon. It is called an *exterior angle*.

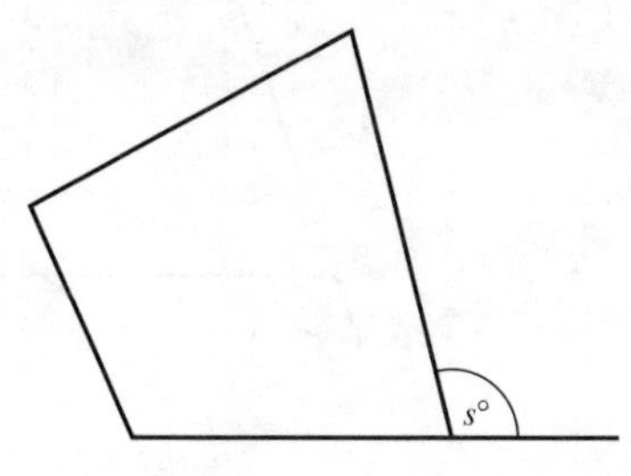

For example, $s°$ is an exterior angle of the quadrilateral.

If we produce (that is, extend) all the sides in order we have all the exterior angles.

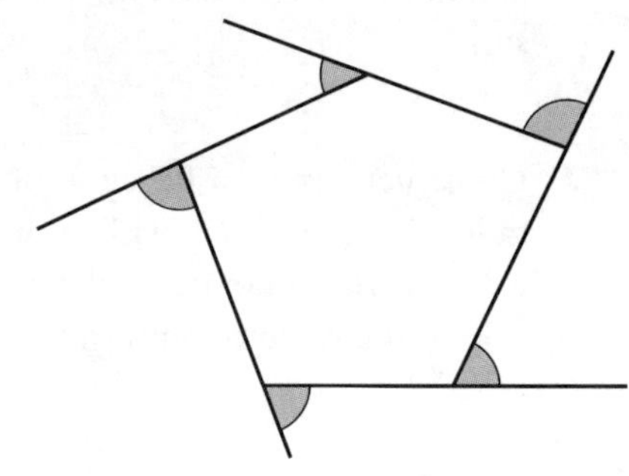

EXERCISE 6B

1 What is the sum of the interior angles of any triangle ?

2 What is the sum of the interior angles of any quadrilateral ?

3 In triangle ABC, find

a the size of each marked angle

b the sum of the exterior angles.

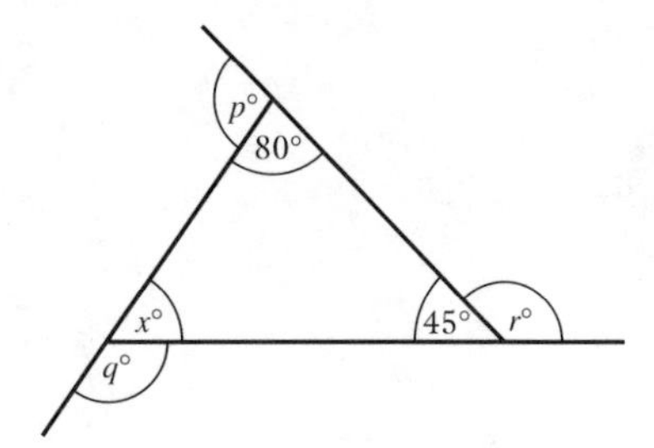

4

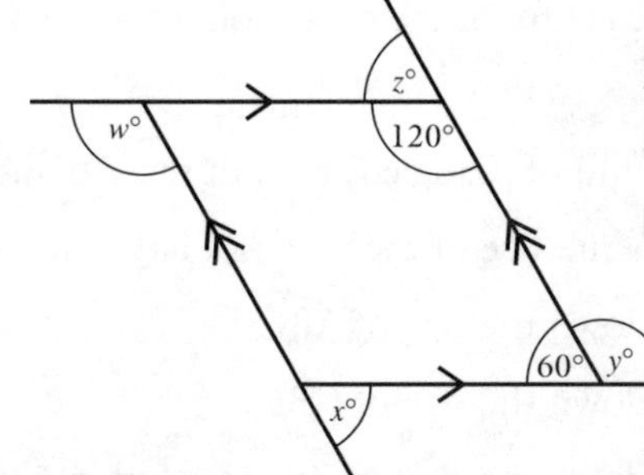

This is a parallelogram.

Find

a the size of each marked angle

b the sum of the exterior angles.

5 This is a trapezium. Find

a the size of each marked angle

b the sum of the exterior angles.

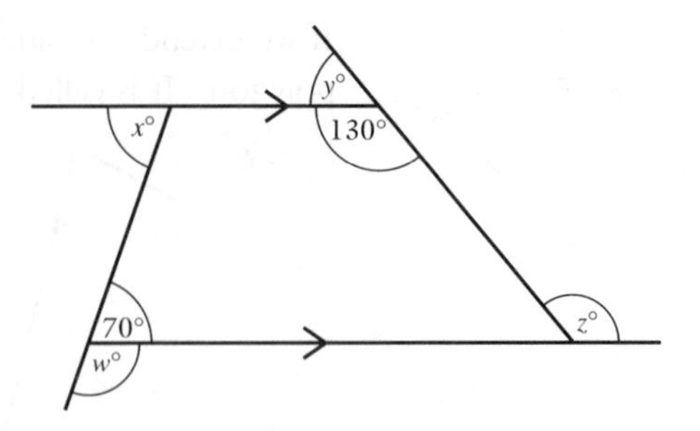

6 Draw a pentagon. Produce the sides in order to form the five exterior angles. Measure each exterior angle and then find their sum.

7 Construct a regular hexagon of side 5 cm. (Start with a circle of radius 5 cm and then with your compasses still open to a radius of 5 cm, mark off points on the circumference in turn.) Produce each side of the hexagon in turn to form the six exterior angles.

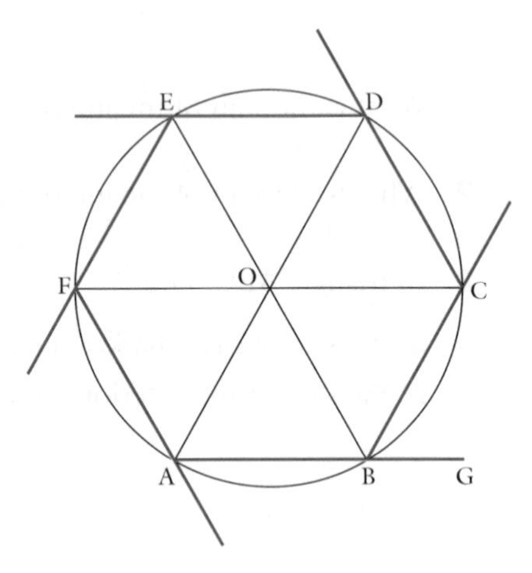

If O is the centre of the circle, join O to each vertex to form six triangles.

a What kind of triangle is each of these triangles ?

b What is the size of each interior angle in these triangles ?

c Write down the size of $A\hat{B}C$.

d Write down the size of $C\hat{B}G$.

e Write down the sum of the six exterior angles of the hexagon.

THE SUM OF THE EXTERIOR ANGLES OF A POLYGON

In the last exercise, we found that the sum of the exterior angles is 360° in each case. This is true of any polygon, whatever its shape or size, as we can demonstrate.

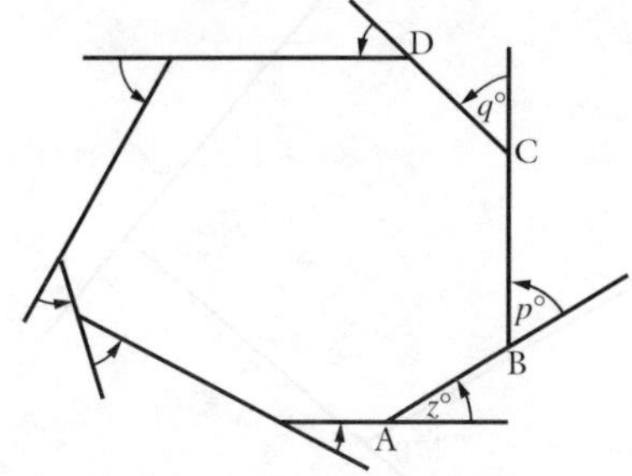

Consider walking round this polygon. Start at A and walk along AB. When you get to B you have to turn through angle $p°$ to walk along BC. When you get to C you have to turn through angle $q°$ to walk along CD,... and so on until your return to A. If you then turn through angle $z°$ you are facing in the direction AB again. You have now turned through all the exterior angles and have made just one complete turn, i.e.

the sum of the exterior angles of a polygon is 360°.

EXERCISE 6C

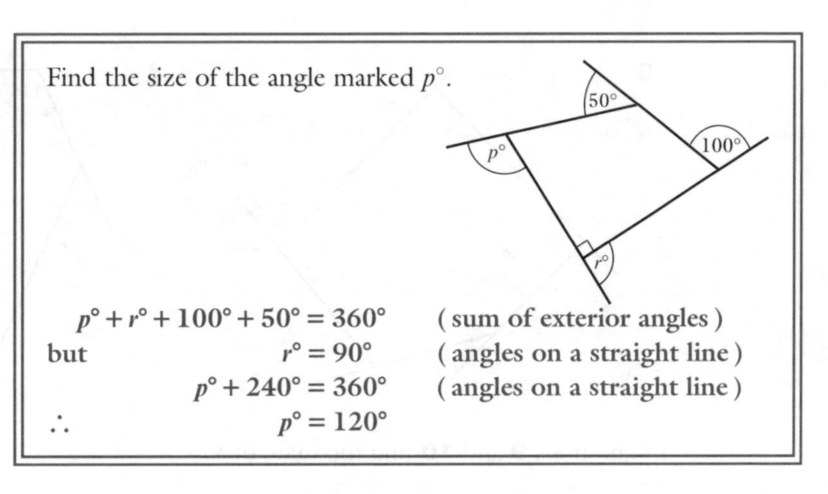

Find the size of the angle marked $p°$.

	$p° + r° + 100° + 50° = 360°$	(sum of exterior angles)
but	$r° = 90°$	(angles on a straight line)
	$p° + 240° = 360°$	(angles on a straight line)
∴	$p° = 120°$	

In each case find the size of the marked angle(s).

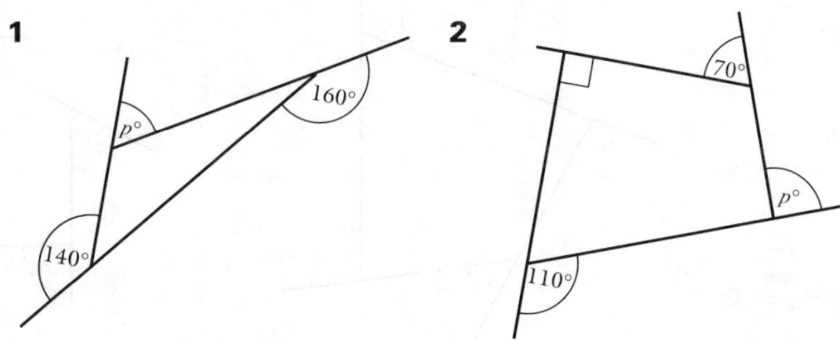

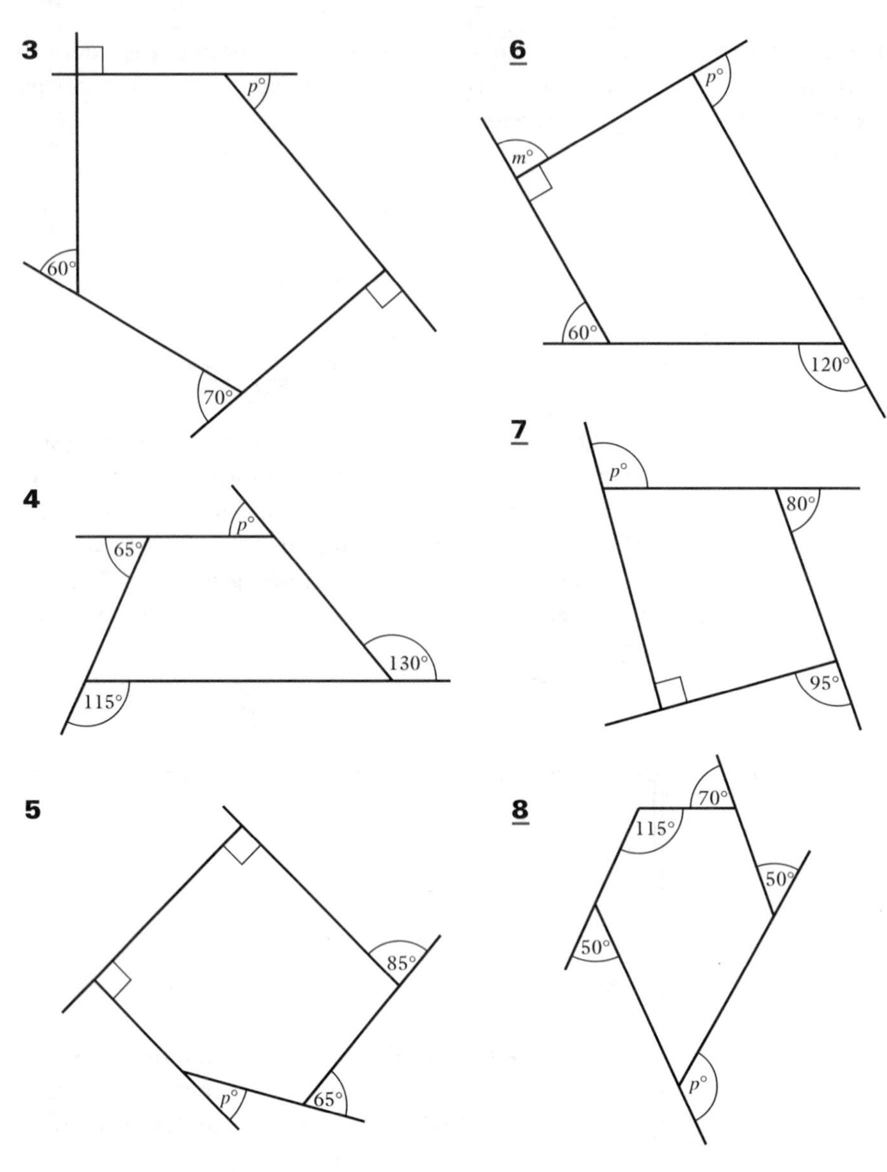

In questions **9** and **10** find the value of x.

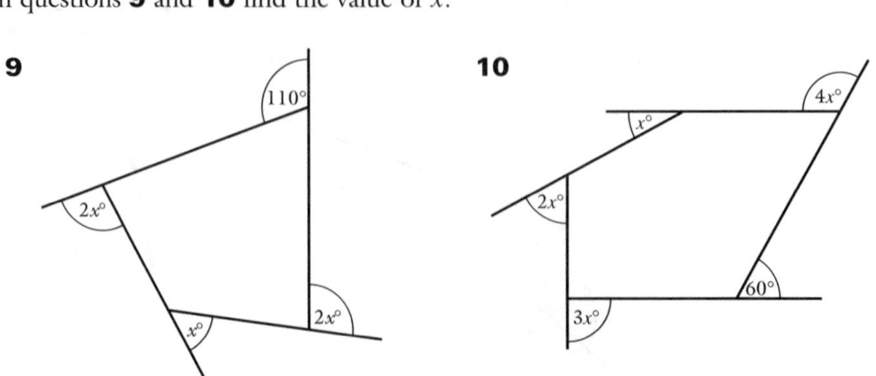

11 Find the number of sides of a polygon if each exterior angle is

a 72° **b** 45°.

THE EXTERIOR ANGLE OF A REGULAR POLYGON

If a polygon is regular, all its exterior angles are the same size. We know that the sum of the exterior angles is 360°, so the size of one exterior angle is easy to find; we just divide 360 by the number of sides of the polygon, i.e.

> in a *regular* polygon with n sides, the size of an exterior angle is
> $$\frac{360^\circ}{n}$$

EXERCISE 6D

Find the size of each exterior angle of a 24-sided regular polygon.

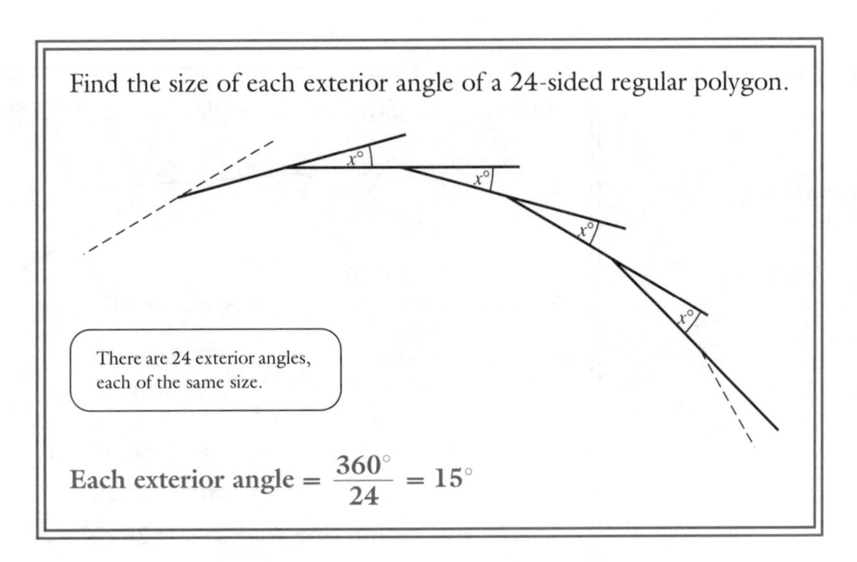

Each exterior angle $= \dfrac{360^\circ}{24} = 15^\circ$

Find the size of each exterior angle of a regular polygon with

1 10 sides

2 8 sides

3 12 sides

4 6 sides

5 15 sides

6 18 sides

7 9 sides

8 16 sides

9 20 sides

THE SUM OF THE INTERIOR ANGLES OF A POLYGON

This is an octagon.

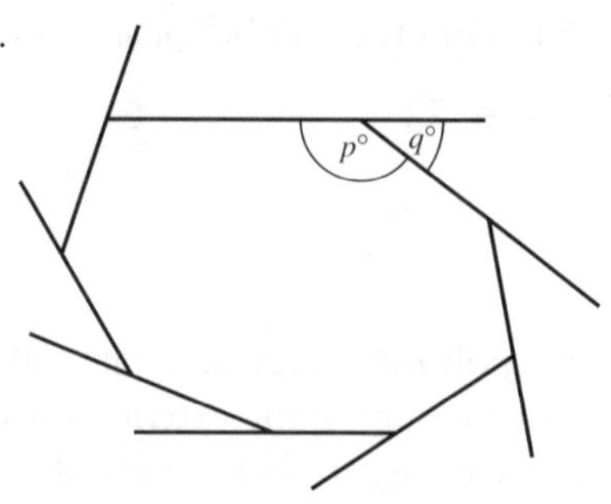

At each vertex there is an interior angle and an exterior angle and the sum of these two angles is 180° (angles on a straight line),
i.e. $p^\circ + q^\circ = 180^\circ$ at each one of the eight vertices.

Therefore the sum of the interior angles and exterior angles together is

$$8 \times 180^\circ = 1440^\circ$$

The sum of the eight exterior angles is 360°.

Therefore, the sum of the interior angles is

$$1440^\circ - 360^\circ = 1080^\circ$$

EXERCISE 6E

Find the sum of the interior angles of a 14-sided polygon.

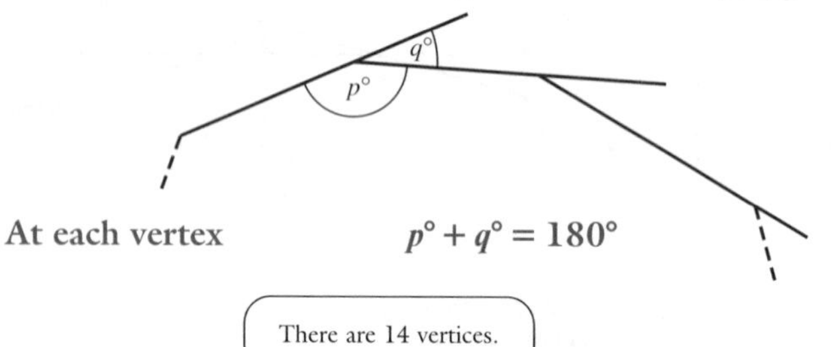

At each vertex $\qquad p^\circ + q^\circ = 180^\circ$

There are 14 vertices.

∴ **sum of interior angles and exterior angles is**

$$14 \times 180^\circ = 2520^\circ$$

∴ **sum of interior angles** $= 2520^\circ - 360^\circ$

$= 2160^\circ$

Find the sum of the interior angles of a polygon with

1 6 sides	**4** 4 sides	<u>**7**</u> 18 sides
2 5 sides	**5** 7 sides	<u>**8**</u> 9 sides
3 10 sides	**6** 12 sides	<u>**9**</u> 15 sides

10 List the results for questions **1** to **9** in a table. Find an expression for the sum of the interior angles of a polygon with n sides.

FORMULA FOR THE SUM OF THE INTERIOR ANGLES

If a polygon has n sides, then the sum of the interior and exterior angles together is $n \times 180° = 180n°$

so the sum of the interior angles only is $180n° - 360°$ which,

as $180° = 2$ right angles and $360° = 4$ right angles, can be written as $(2n - 4)$ right angles

i.e. in a polygon with n sides, the sum of the interior angles is $(180n - 360)°$ or $(2n - 4)$ right angles.

EXERCISE 6F

1 Find the sum of the interior angles of a polygon with

a 20 sides **b** 16 sides **c** 11 sides.

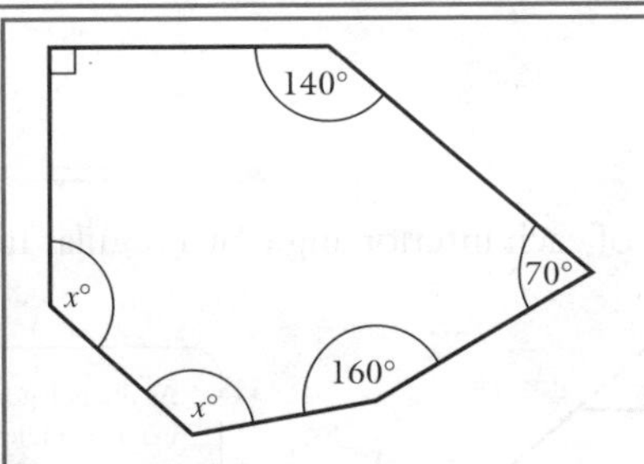

In a hexagon the angles marked $x°$ are equal. Find the value of x.

The sum of the interior angles is $180n° - 360°$

i.e. when $n = 6$,

the sum of the interior angles is $180° \times 6 - 360° = 720°$

$$\therefore \quad 90 + 140 + 70 + 160 + 2x = 720$$

$$460 + 2x = 720$$

$$2x = 260$$

$$x = 130$$

In questions **2** to **7** find the size of the marked angle(s).

2

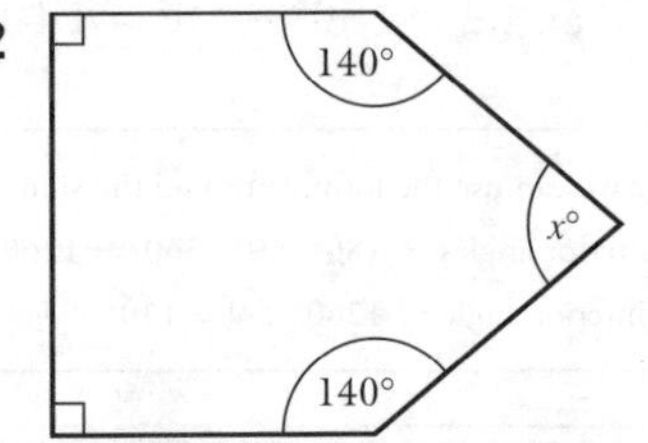

3

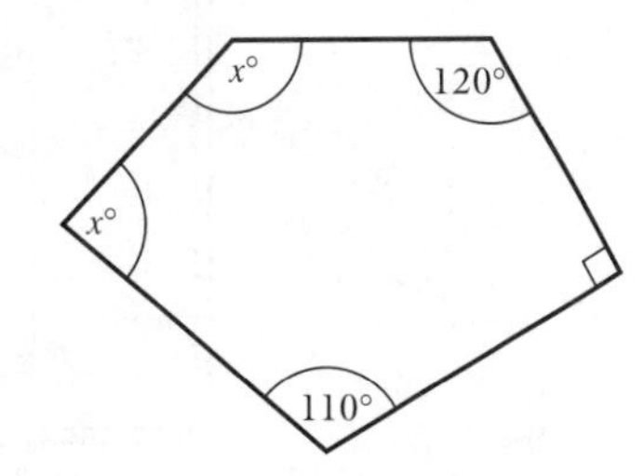

4

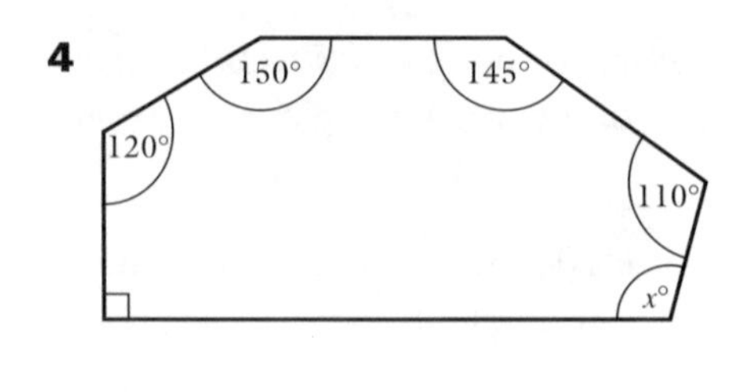

6

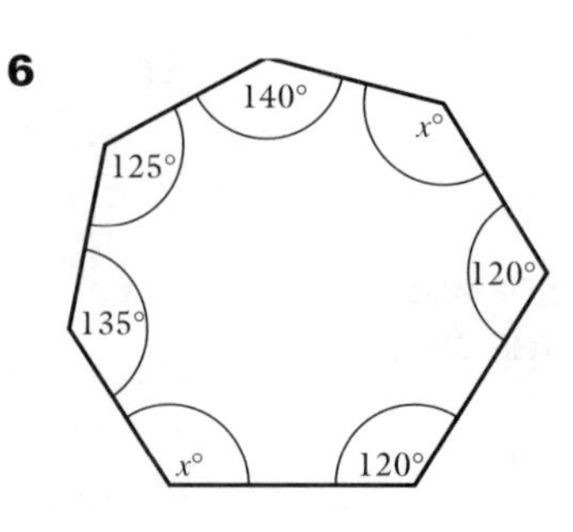

5

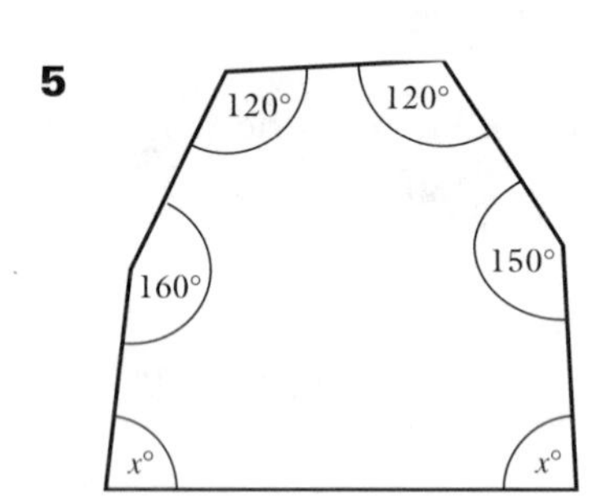

7

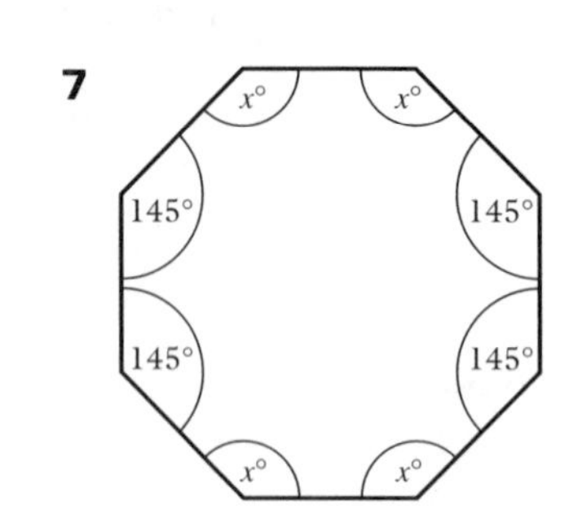

Find the size of each interior angle of a regular nine-sided polygon.

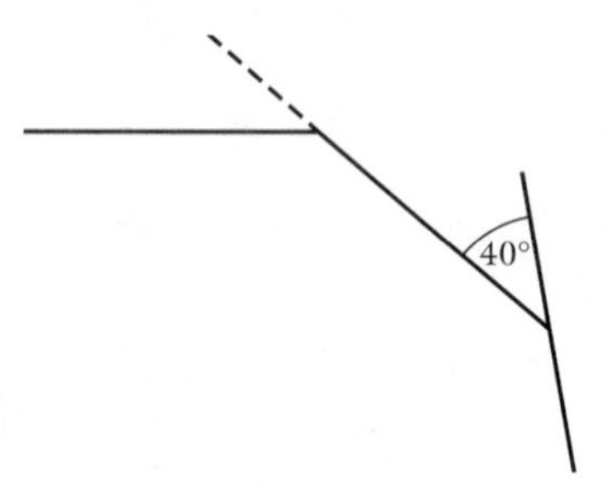

As the polygon is regular, all the exterior angles are equal and all the interior angles are equal.

We can find the size of one exterior angle and then use this to find the size of an interior angle.

Sum of exterior angles = 360°

$\therefore$ each exterior angle = 360° ÷ 9 = 40°

$\therefore$ each interior angle = 180° − 40° = 140°

Alternatively we can use the formula to find the sum of the interior angles.

Sum of interior angles = 180° × 9 − 360° = 1260°

$\therefore$ each interior angle = 1260° ÷ 9 = 140°

Find the size of each interior angle of

8 a regular pentagon

9 a regular hexagon

10 a regular ten-sided polygon

11 a regular 12-sided polygon

12 How many sides has a regular polygon if each exterior angle is

a 20° **b** 15°?

13 How many sides has a regular polygon if each interior angle is

a 150° **b** 162°?

(Find the exterior angle first.)

14 Is it possible for each exterior angle of a regular polygon to be

a 30° **c** 50° **e** 70°

b 40° **d** 60° **f** 90°?

In those cases where it is possible, give the number of sides.

15 Is it possible for each interior angle of a regular polygon to be

a 90° **c** 180° **e** 170°

b 120° **d** 175° **f** 135°?

In those cases where it is possible, give the number of sides.

16 Construct a regular pentagon with sides 5 cm long.
(Calculate the size of each interior angle and use your protractor.)

17 Construct a regular octagon of side 5 cm.

ABCDE is a pentagon in which the interior angles at B and E are $4x^\circ$ and the interior angle at D is $2x^\circ$. The sides EA and CB are extended until they meet at F and FD is a line of symmetry. Find $\widehat{AFB}$.

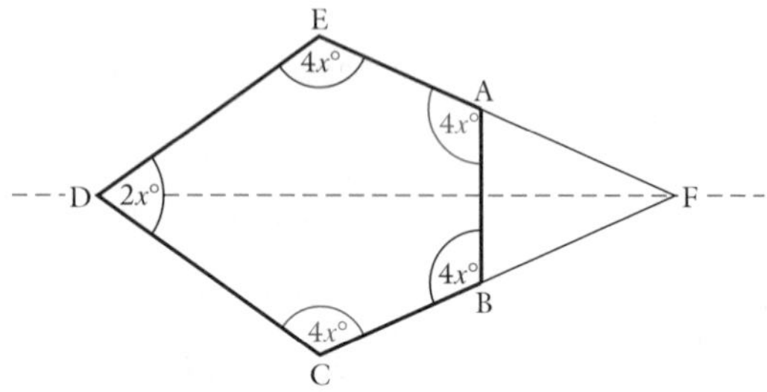

Since FD is a line of symmetry the interior angles at A and C are both $4x^\circ$. We can find the sum of the interior angles (using the formula) and then form an equation and solve it to find x.

Sum of the interior angles of a pentagon $= 180^\circ \times 5 - 360^\circ$

$= 540^\circ$

$\therefore \quad 2x + 4x + 4x + 4x + 4x = 540$

$18x = 540$

$x = 30$

Now that we know x, we can find $\widehat{ABC}$ and hence $\widehat{AFB}$.

$\widehat{ABC} = 4 \times 30^\circ = 120^\circ$ **and** $\widehat{EAB} = 120^\circ$

$\therefore \quad \widehat{FBA} = 60^\circ$ **and** $\widehat{BAF} = 60^\circ$ **(angles on a straight line)**

$\therefore \quad \widehat{AFB} = 180^\circ - 2 \times 60^\circ$ **(angle sum of $\triangle$ ABF)**

$= 60^\circ$

In questions **18** to **21** find the value of x. A broken line is a line of symmetry.

18

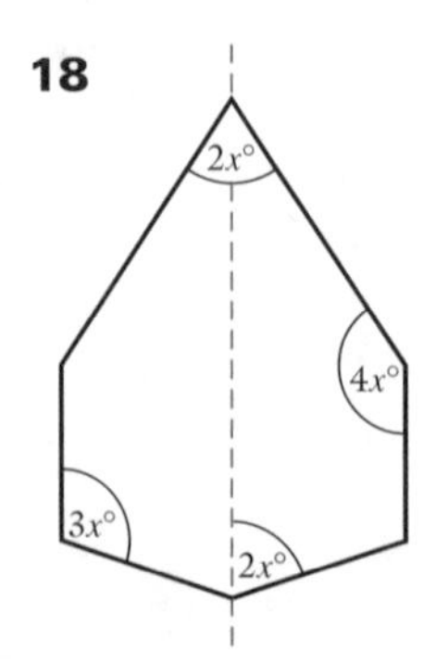

19

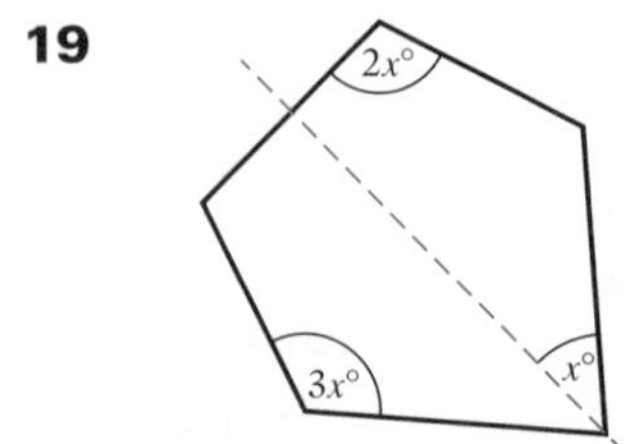

20

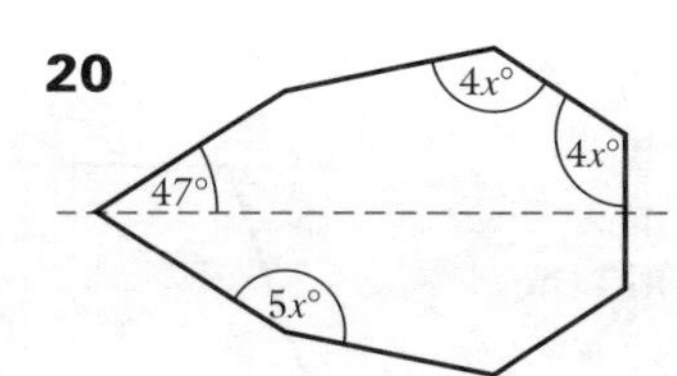

21

22 ABCD is a pentagon which has one line of symmetry through B. If $B\widehat{A}E = 130°$ and $A\widehat{B}C = 50°$ find the size of the angles $p°$, $q°$ and $r°$.

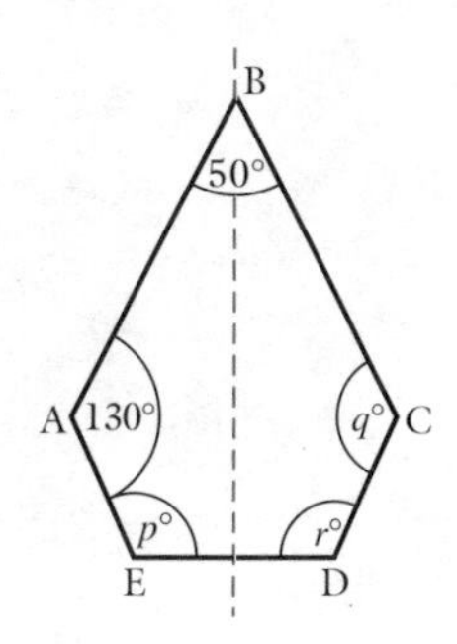

23

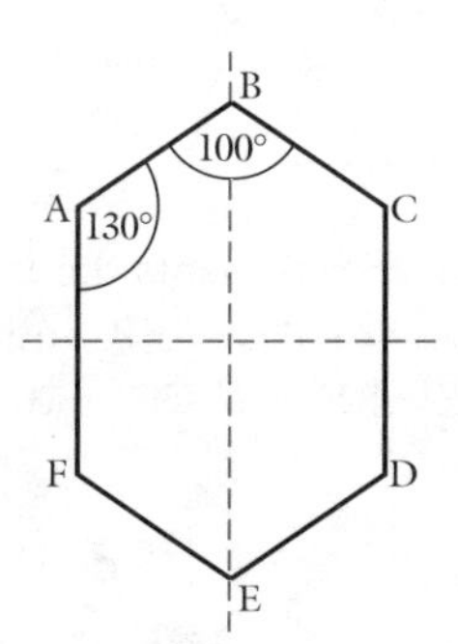

A hexagon ABCDEF has two axes of symmetry which are shown on the diagram. If $F\widehat{A}B = 130°$ and $A\widehat{B}C = 100°$ find the size of all the angles in trapezium BCDE.

24 The diagram shows a regular pentagon with two of its lines of symmetry.

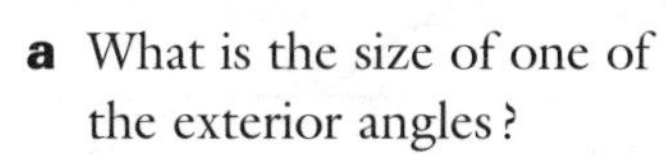

a What is the size of one of the exterior angles?

b Find the size of the angles marked $p°$, $q°$ and $r°$.

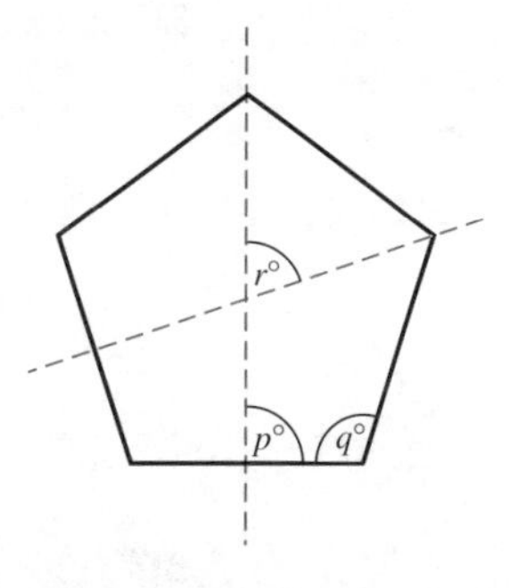

25

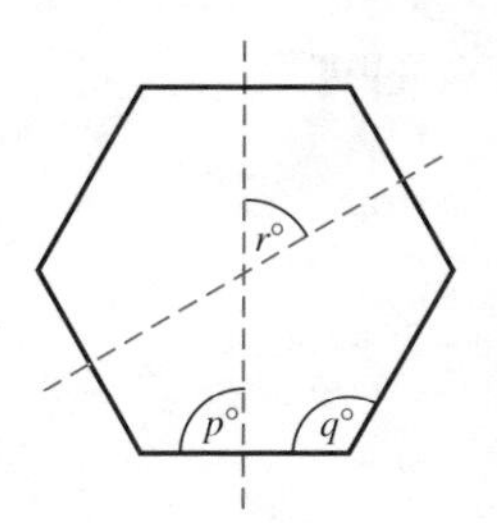

Two of the lines of symmetry for this regular hexagon are marked.

a What is the size of one of the exterior angles?

b Find the size of the angles marked $p°$, $q°$ and $r°$.

26 ABCD is a trapezium which is symmetrical about the coloured broken line.
If $A\hat{B}C = 125°$ find the marked angles.

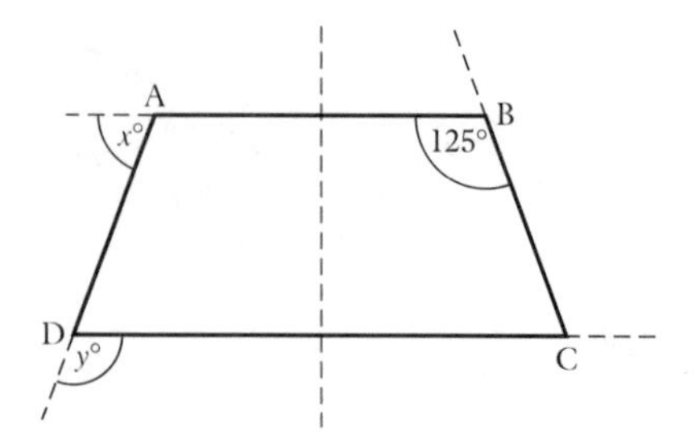

27

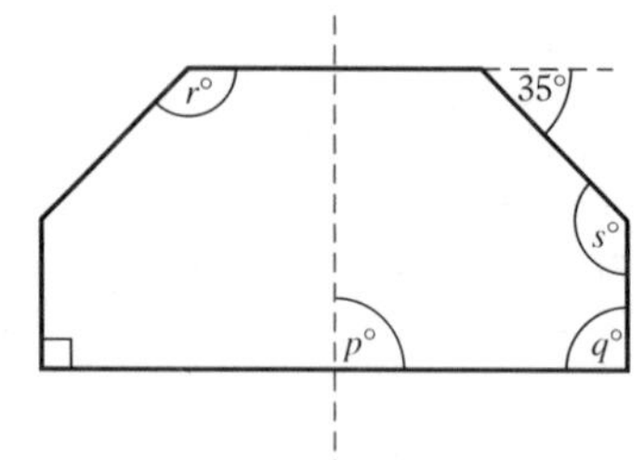

This hexagon is symmetrical about the red broken line. Find the size of the marked angles.

28

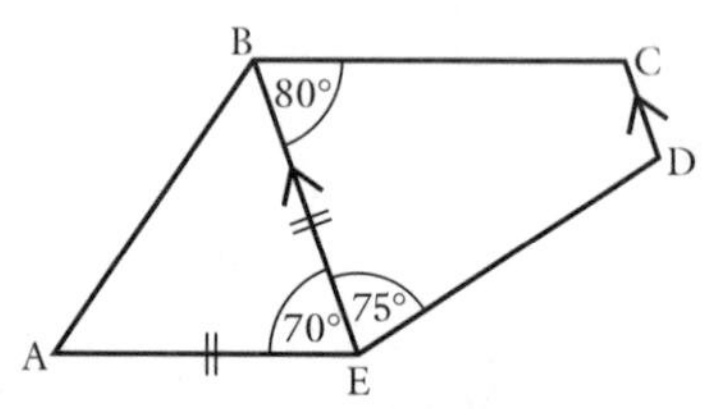

The pentagon ABCDE represents the frame for Ken's bike. ABE is an isosceles triangle with $AE = EB$ and $A\hat{E}B = 70°$. In the quadrilateral BCDE, $B\hat{E}D = 75°$ and $C\hat{B}E = 80°$.
Find the size of

a $A\hat{B}E$ **b** $B\hat{C}D$ **c** $E\hat{D}C$

29

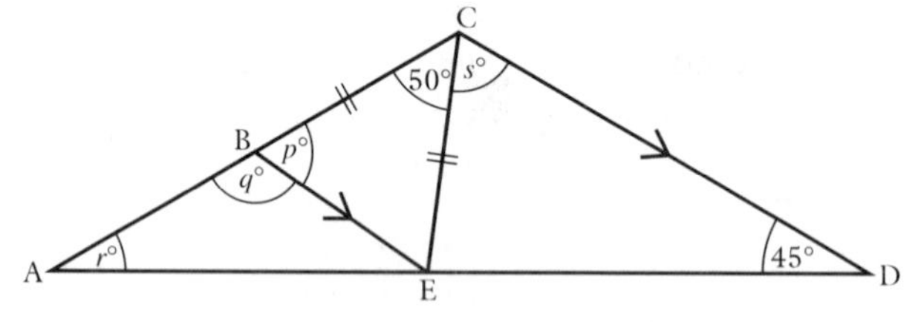

The diagram shows a roof truss in which $BC = CE$ and BE is parallel to CD. If $B\hat{C}E = 50°$ and $C\hat{D}E = 45°$ find the marked angles.

30 This shape is used as a character in a simple computer game.
It is a regular octagon with the side AH missing.
Find $A\hat{E}H$.

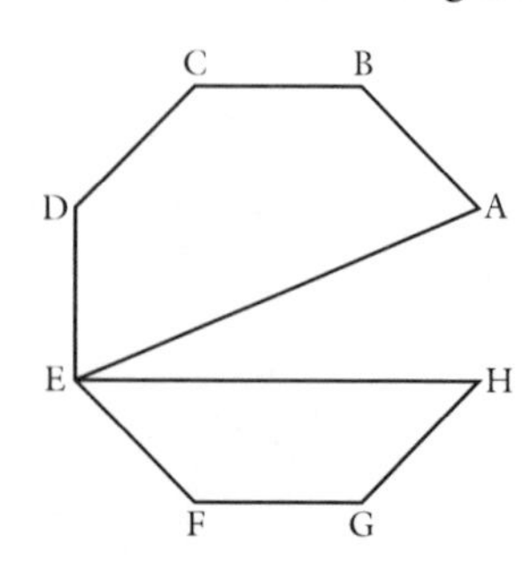

31 The sketch shows part of a spanner for regular octagonal nuts.
Find angle $B\hat{J}D$.

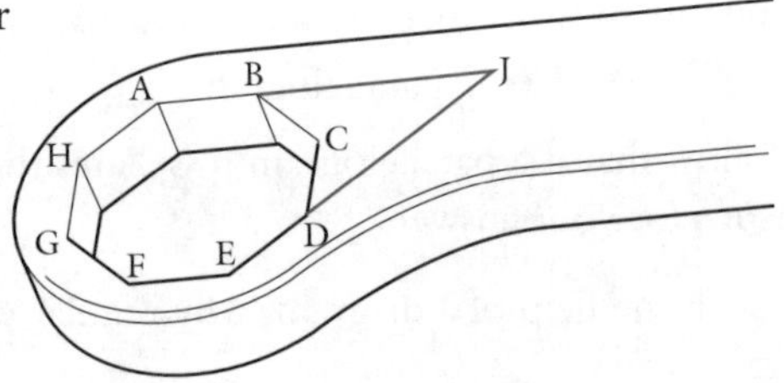

CONSTRUCTING REGULAR POLYGONS

All regular polygons have rotational symmetry. For example, a regular pentagon has rotational symmetry of order 5 because we can rotate it by $\frac{1}{5}$ of a revolution, i.e. $360° \div 5 = 72°$, about its centre and it still looks the same.

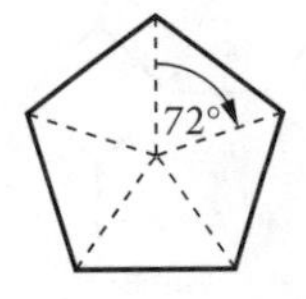

We can use this fact to construct a regular pentagon.
Start by drawing a circle with a radius of at least 6 cm;
then use a protractor to draw five angles, each of 72°, at the centre.
Join the points where the arms of the angles cut the circumference.

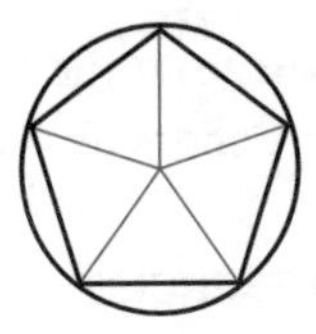

Use this idea to draw

a a regular octagon
b a regular polygon with nine sides
c an equilateral triangle
d a regular polygon with 12 sides

PATTERN MAKING WITH REGULAR POLYGONS

Regular hexagons fit together without leaving gaps, to form a flat surface.
We say that they *tessellate*.

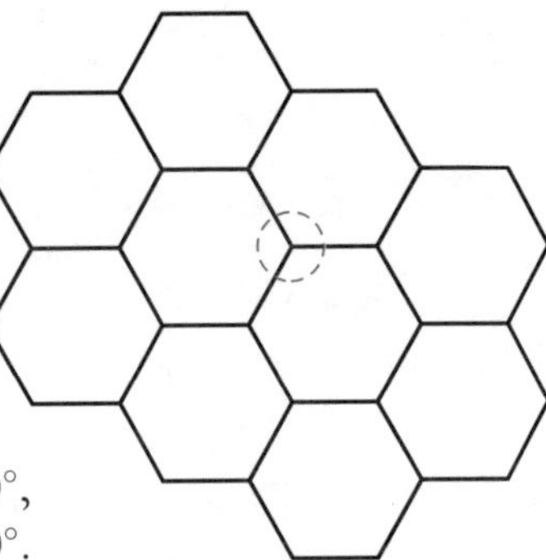

The hexagons tessellate because each interior angle of a regular hexagon is 120°, so three vertices fit together to make 360°.

EXERCISE 6G

1 Draw a tessellation using this tile shaped like a kite.
Trace it onto card, cut it out and use it as a template.
In how many different ways can you position the tiles?
If the tiles can be of different colours, what is the smallest number of different colours needed if no two tiles with touching edges are to be the same colour.

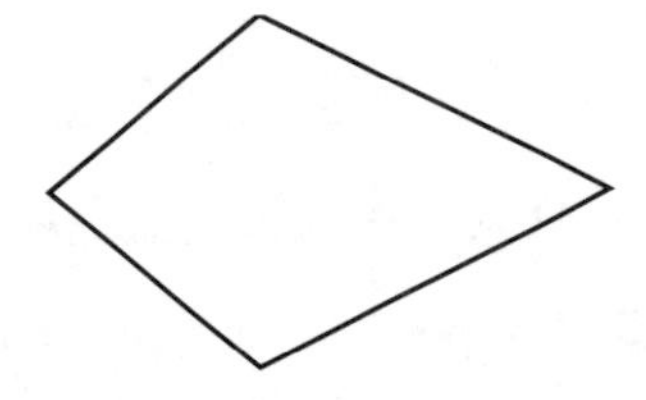

2 Draw diagrams to show that the following shapes tessellate.

a a square **b** a parallelogram **c** any triangle with three unequal sides

Does it follow that if a parallelogram tessellates then every triangle must also do so? Give reasons for your answer.

3 Explain, with the help of a diagram, why regular pentagons do not tessellate.

4 This is a pattern using regular octagons. They do not tessellate:

a Explain why they do not tessellate.

b What shape is left between the four octagons?

c Continue the pattern. (Trace one of the shapes above, cut it out and use it as a template.)

5 Apart from the hexagon, there are two other regular polygons that tessellate. Which are they, and why do they tessellate?

MIXED EXERCISE

EXERCISE 6H

1 Find the size of each marked angle.

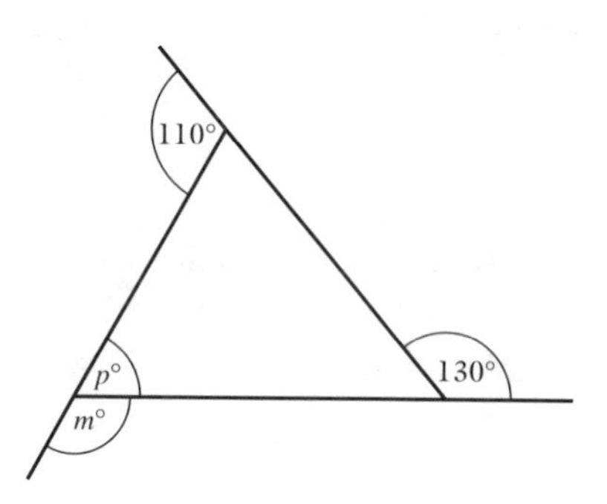

2 Find the size of each exterior angle of a regular polygon with 12 sides. What is the size of each interior angle?

3 The broken line is a line of symmetry. Find the size of the angle marked $x°$.

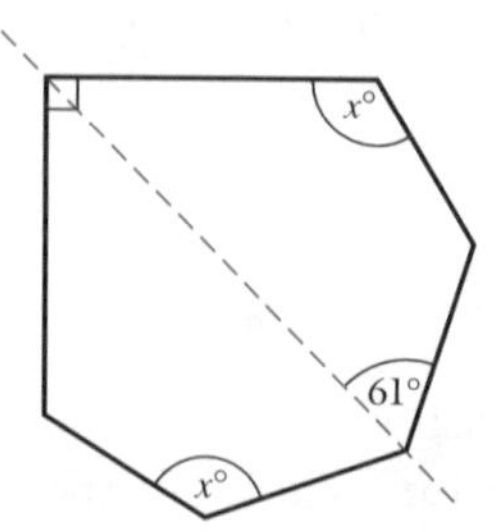

4 How many sides has a regular polygon if each interior angle is 168°?

5 Is it possible for each exterior angle in a regular polygon to be **a** 45° **b** 75°? Explain your answers.

6 Find the size of the marked angle.

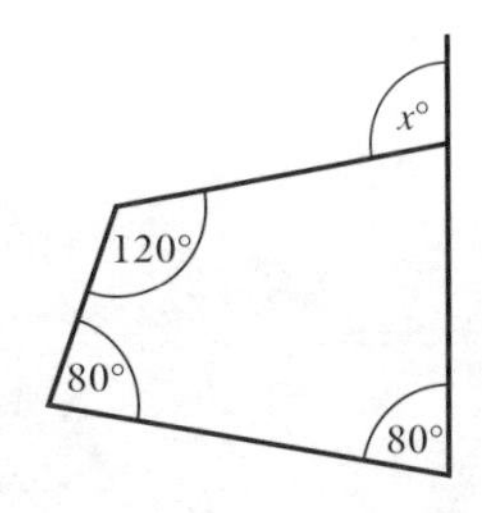

7 Which of the following statements are true and which are false?
Try to justify the statement you think is true. Illustrate any statement with a sketch.

a Every triangle tessellates.

b Some quadrilaterals tessellate and some do not.

c A rhombus does not tessellate.

d Some shapes with curved edges tessellate.

e Every regular polygon tessellates.

f It is possible to draw a hexagon that is not regular that tessellates.

PUZZLE

This is an old Chinese puzzle, called a 'tangram'.
Draw a square of side 8 cm and divide it into five right-angled isosceles triangles, a square and a parallelogram as shown in the diagram.
(As a first step join the midpoints of two adjacent sides of the square. Then draw the other lines.)
Mark the regions 1 to 7 as shown.

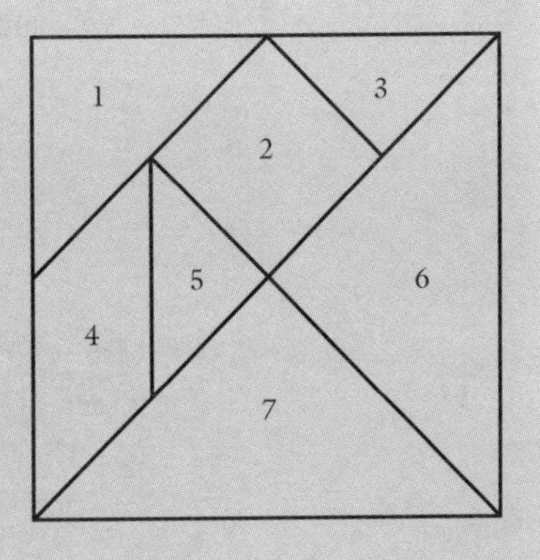

a Arrange the two larger triangles to form a square.

b Arrange the remaining five pieces to form an identical square to the square you arranged in part **a**.

c Arrange all seven pieces to form a rectangle.

d Remove one piece from the rectangle formed in part **c** and place it in a new position so that the resulting shape is a parallelogram.

e Change the position of one piece so as to form a trapezium.

f Using all seven pieces, can you arrange them to form
  i a regular hexagon **ii** a hexagon that is not regular?

If you can, show with a sketch how this can be done.

PRACTICAL WORK

1 Trace this regular pentagon and use it to cut out a template.

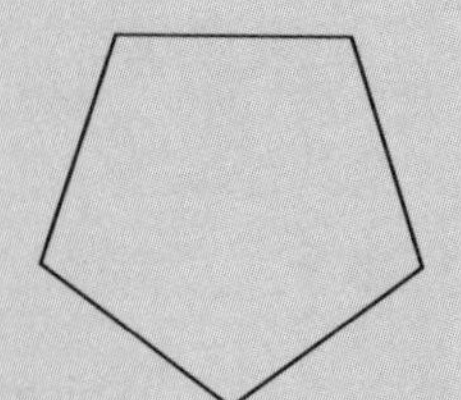

a Will pentagons tessellate?

b Use your template to copy and continue this pattern until you have a complete circle of pentagons.
What shape is left in the middle?

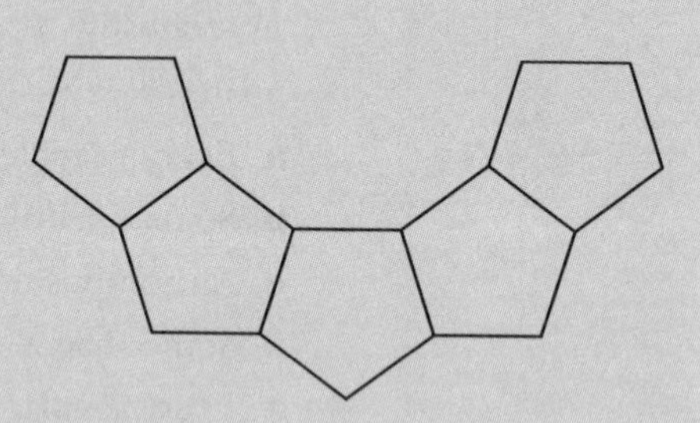

c Make up a pattern using pentagons.

2

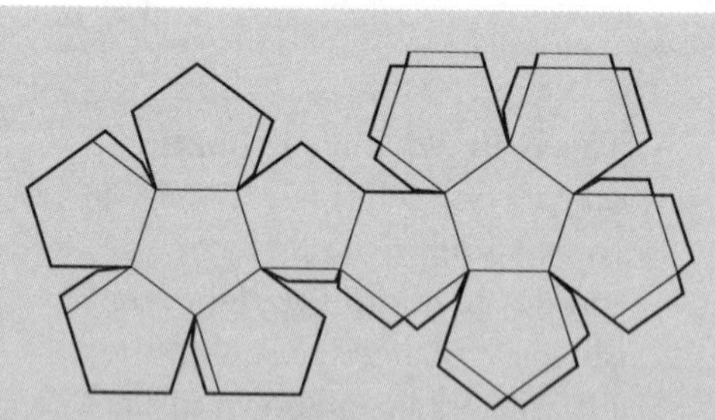

Use your template from question **1** to copy this net onto thick paper. Cut it out and fold along the lines. Stick the edges together using the flaps. You have made a regular dodecahedron (a solid with 12 equal faces).

3 Regular hexagons, squares and equilateral triangles can be combined to make interesting patterns. Some examples are given below.

Copy these patterns and extend them. Can you find other patterns? (If you make templates to help you, make each shape of side 2 cm.)

4 Bricklayers sometimes make very interesting patterns when building a wall.

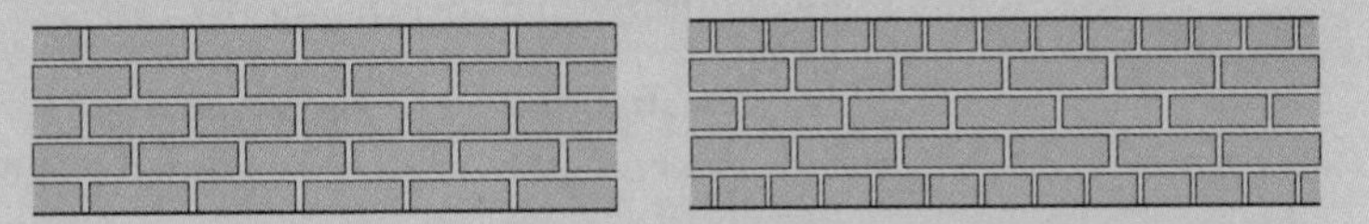

Show some designs that you have seen and try to find the different names for each pattern. (A brick is twice as long as it is wide.)

INVESTIGATIONS

Pattern making using tessellating designs can be quite fascinating.

1 The simplest shape that is used to cover a flat surface completely, without any gaps, is the square. We can see examples around us – square floor tiles, square ceramic tiles on a bathroom wall and square paving slabs.
However, starting with a square we can remove a piece from one edge and attach it to the opposite edge so that the resulting shape will still tessellate.
In each of the following pairs of diagrams the shaded area is removed and placed in the position shown.

a Starting with a square tile remove a shape of your own choice from one side and place it on the opposite side. Draw about 10 of these shapes to show that they tessellate.

b Now remove another shape from the shape you finished with in part **a** and attach it to the opposite side. Draw at least 6 of these to show that they tessellate.

c Continue the process to make more interesting shapes that tessellate.

2 Starting with other shapes that tessellate, such as a rhombus, a parallelogram or a regular hexagon, repeat the instructions you followed in the first investigation.

This illustration, by M C Escher, starts with equilateral triangles and shows how they can be developed to give interesting artwork.

TRANSFORMATIONS

John is using a computer to design a logo.

He starts with this basic pattern.

He then reflects, rotates and translates exact copies of the basic pattern to make this shape.

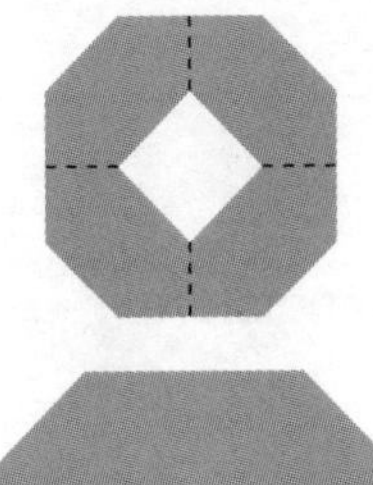

Finally he enlarges the shape to give this logo.

We last studied transformations in Chapter 9 of Book 8B. It is time to revise that work and progress a little further.

EXERCISE 7A

1 Copy the circular traffic sign. Discuss the symmetries you can find. How many lines of symmetry does it have? Does it have rotational symmetry? If so, what is the order of this symmetry?

2

Several road traffic signs are shown above. Discuss which signs have line symmetry, which have rotational symmetry, which have both and which have neither. Draw sketches to show any lines of symmetry and, where there is rotational symmetry, state the order.

3

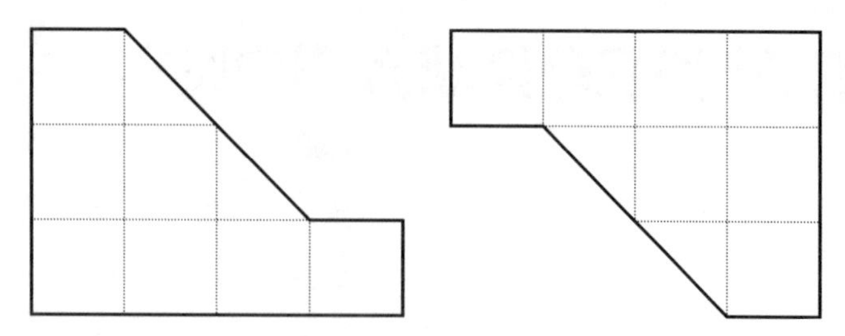

Each of these two identical six-sided shapes is made from 8 equal squares. Discuss whether or not they can be placed together, without turning either shape over, so that they touch along complete edges to give a shape that has

a rotational symmetry but not line symmetry

b line symmetry and rotational symmetry.

EXERCISE 7B

1 Copy the objects and mirror lines (indicated by dashed lines) onto squared paper, and draw the reflection of each object.

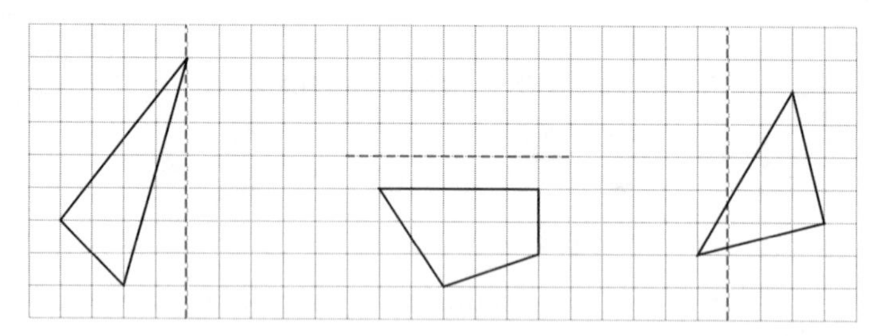

2 Draw axes, for x from -8 to 8 and for y from 0 to 8. Draw $\triangle$ABC by plotting A(2, 1), B(5, 7) and C(7, 3). Draw the image A′B′C′ when ABC is reflected in the y-axis.

3 In the diagram, which images of $\triangle$LMN are given by

a a translation **b** a reflection **c** a rotation ?

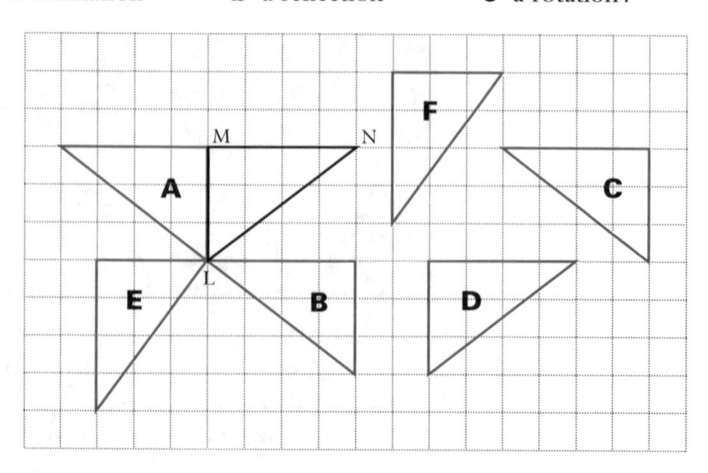

4 Which of these shapes have

a rotational symmetry **b** line symmetry **c** neither?

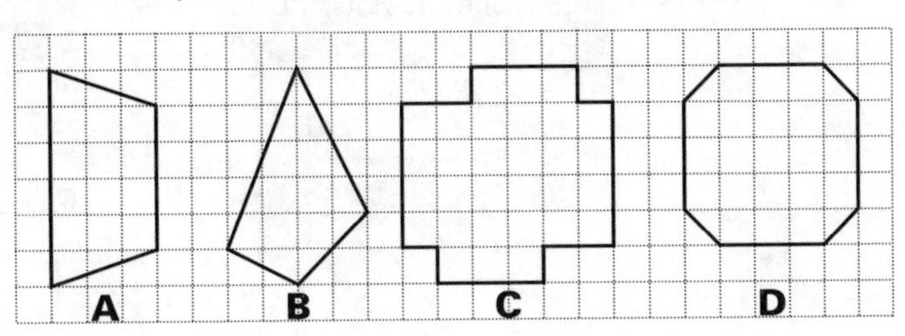

5

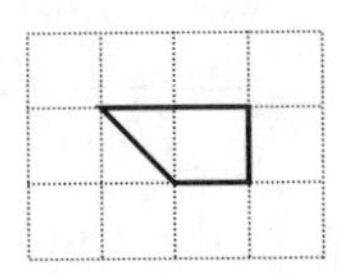

This shape was obtained by folding another shape along a line of symmetry.
Possible shapes that it could come from are

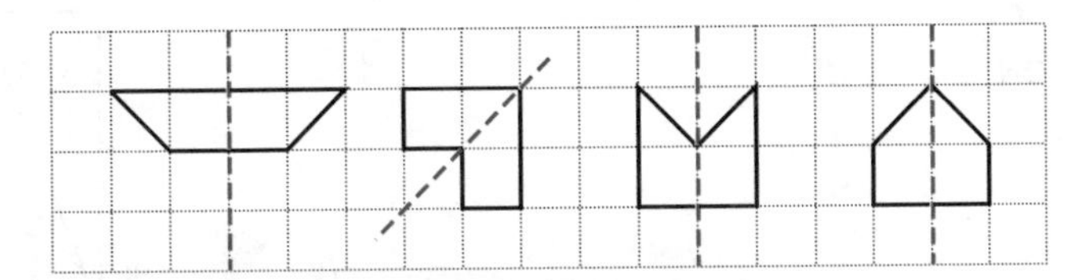

Find all the different shapes from which the given shape can come by being folded along a line of symmetry.

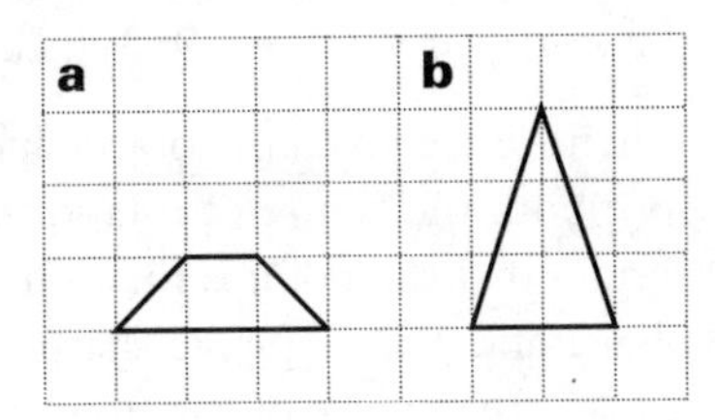

6 Give the angle of rotation when △ABC is mapped onto △A′B′C′ by rotating △ABC about A.

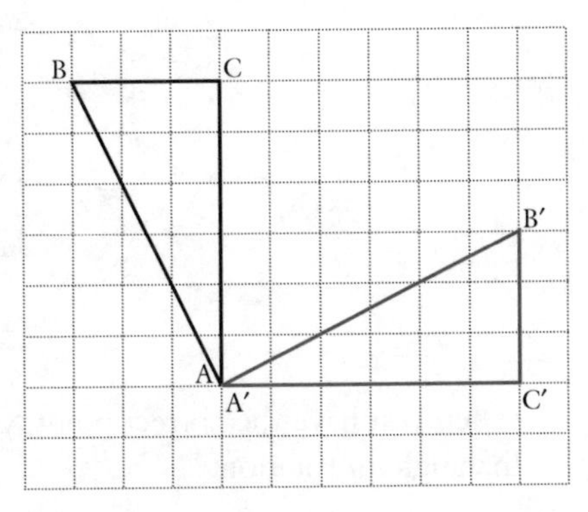

7 Copy the diagram and draw the image of rectangle ABCD given by a rotation of 90° anticlockwise about the point (2, 1). Label the image rectangle A′B′C′D′.

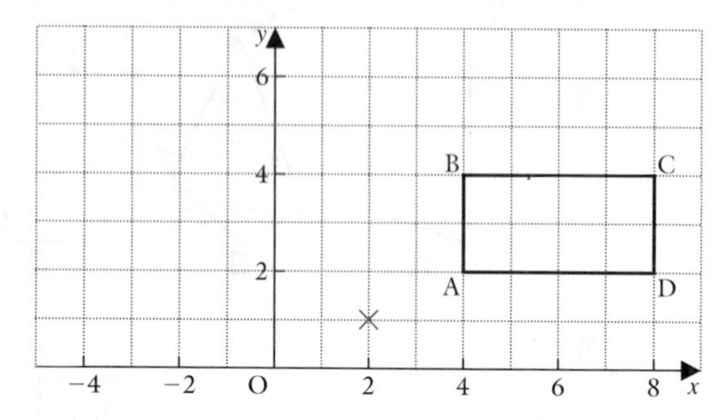

8 Copy the diagram for question **7** and draw the image of rectangle ABCD when it is translated 5 squares to the left and 2 squares down. Give the coordinates of the image of A.

CENTRE OF ROTATION

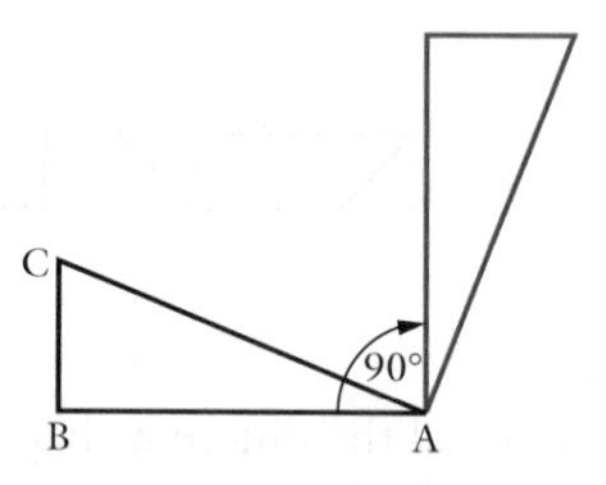

When we rotate △ABC about A through 90° clockwise (↻), we call A the *centre of rotation*; '90° clockwise' is the *angle of rotation*.

When we are given the object and its image after a rotation, we can often spot both the centre of rotation and the angle of rotation. To make certain that the point is the right one, we can use tracing paper: trace the object and place a pin (a sharp pencil will do) on the point that you think is the centre of rotation, then rotate the tracing about your 'pin' and see if it 'lands' on the image.

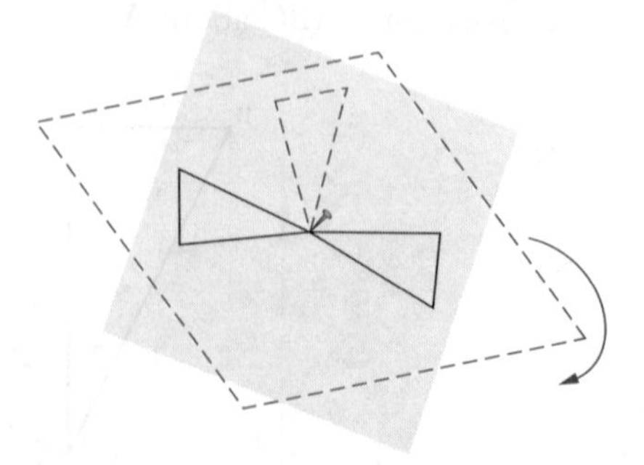

When you have the correct point, you can also use your tracing to find the angle of rotation.

EXERCISE 7C

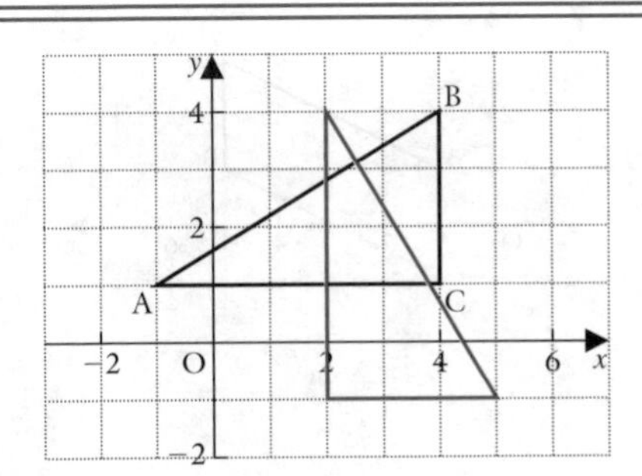

The diagram shows $\triangle ABC$ and its image after it has been rotated about a point.

a Give the coordinates of the centre of rotation.

b State the angle of rotation.

a If necessary make a tracing of $\triangle ABC$ to help you find the centre of rotation.

The centre of rotation is the point (2, 1).

b **The angle of rotation is 90° clockwise.**

For the questions in this exercise state the centre of rotation and the angle of rotation. $\triangle ABC$ is the object in each case.

1

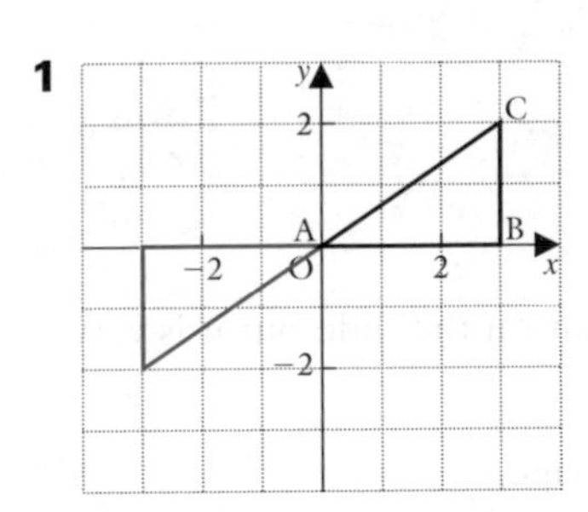

3

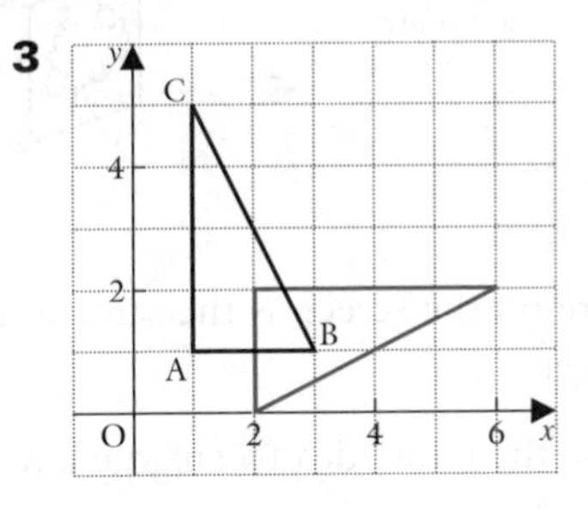

5

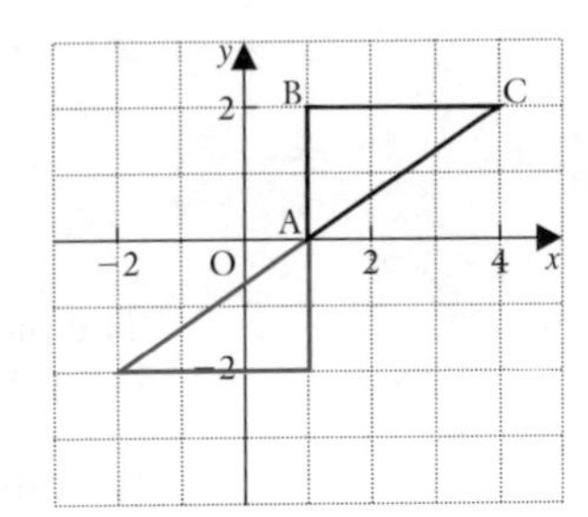

2

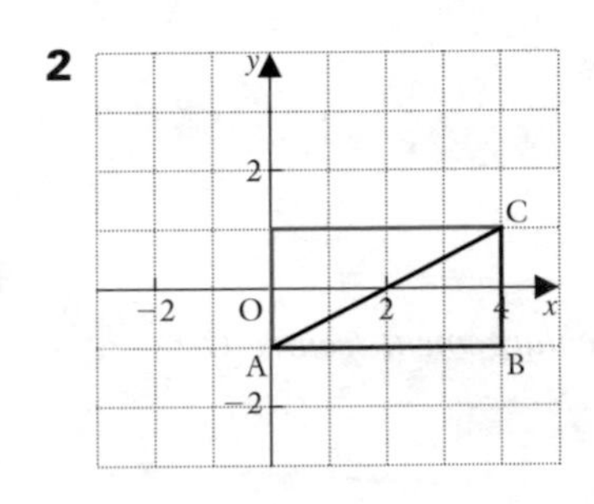

4

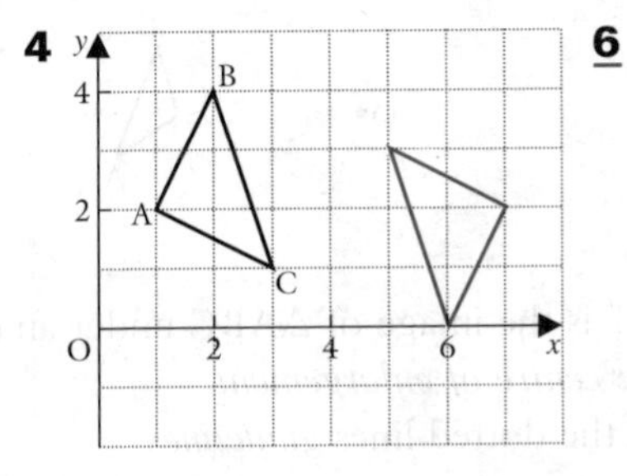

6

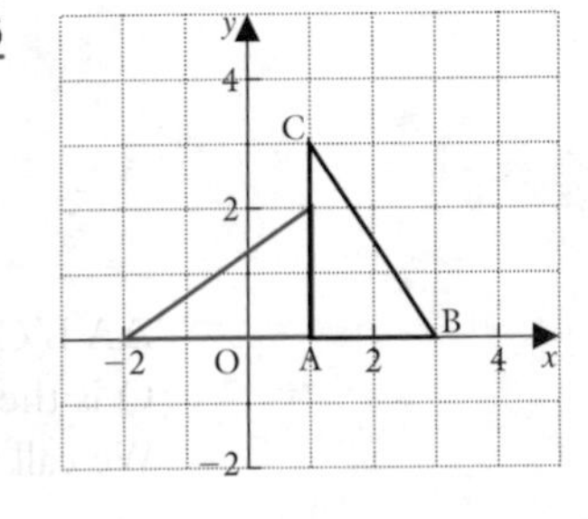

7

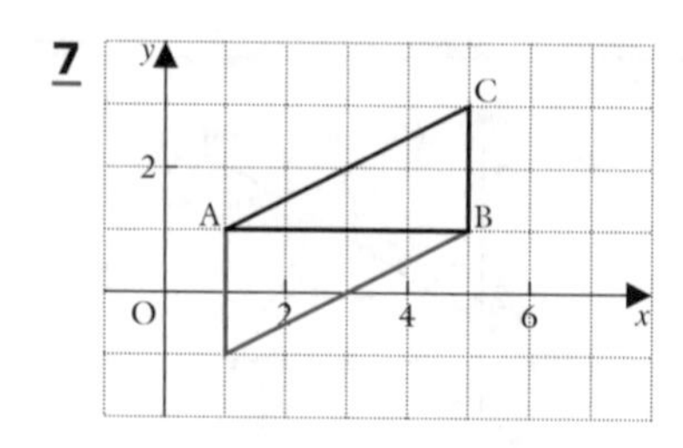

8

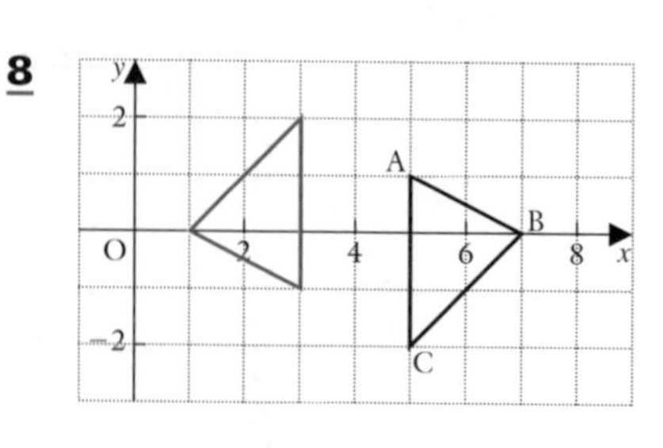

ENLARGEMENTS

All the transformations we have used so far (reflections, translations and rotations) have moved the object or turned it over to produce the image, but they have not changed the shape and size, that is the image and the object are congruent. Now we consider a different transformation, an enlargement, that keeps the shape but alters the size.

EXERCISE 7D

Discuss which of the following people use enlargement in their work.

1 photographer **3** architect **5** social worker

2 doctor **4** automotive engineer **6** travel agent

Think of the picture thrown on the screen when a slide projector is used.

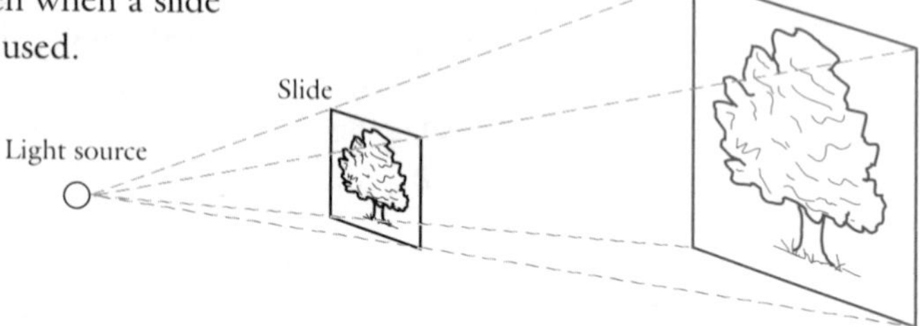

The picture on the screen is the same as that on the slide but it is very much bigger.

We can use the same idea to enlarge any shape.

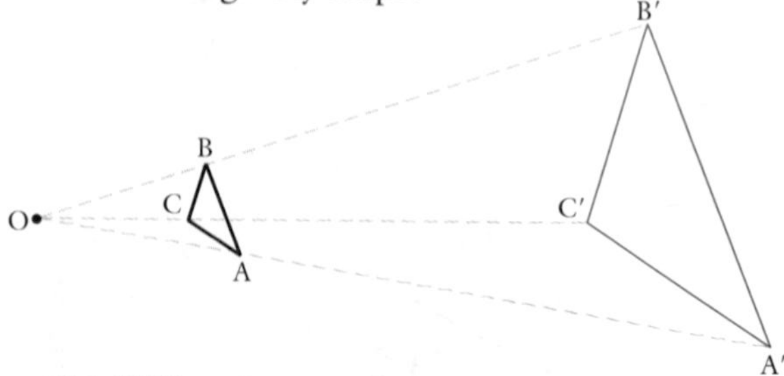

$\Delta A'B'C'$ is the image of ΔABC under an *enlargement, centre O.*
O is the *centre of enlargement.*
We call the dotted lines *guidelines.*

CENTRE OF ENLARGEMENT

In the next exercise we investigate how to find the centre of enlargement when we are given the original shape and its image.

EXERCISE 7E

In all these questions, one shape is an enlargement of the other.

1 Copy the diagram using 1 cm to 1 unit. Draw A′A, B′B, C′C, and D′D and continue all four lines until they meet.
The point where the lines meet is called the centre of enlargement.

a Give the coordinates of the centre of enlargement.

b Consider the sides and angles of the two squares. What do you notice?

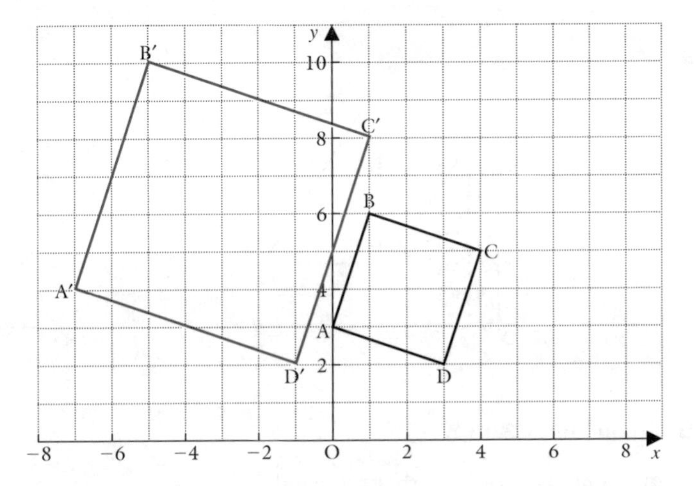

2 Repeat question **1** using this diagram.

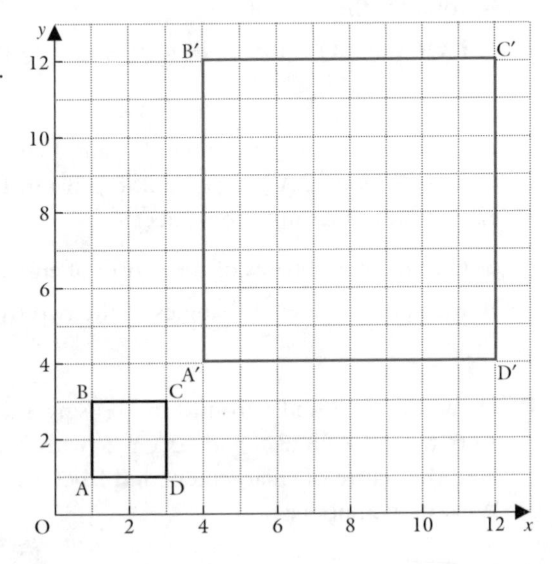

3 Copy the diagram using 1 cm to 1 unit. Draw P′P, Q′Q and R′R and continue all three lines until they meet.

Give the coordinates of the centre of enlargement.

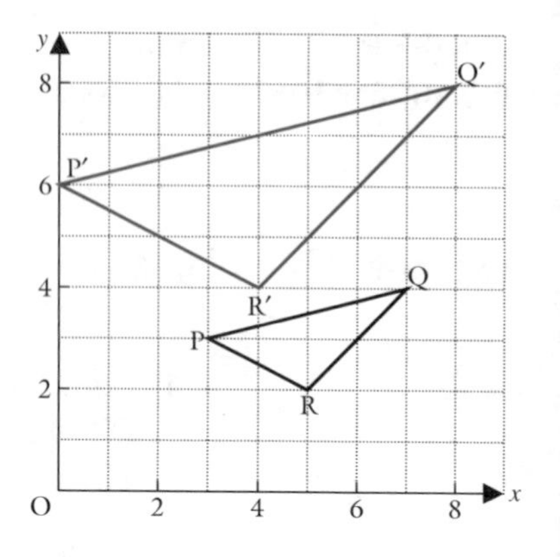

Repeat question **3** using the diagrams in questions **4** and **5**.

4

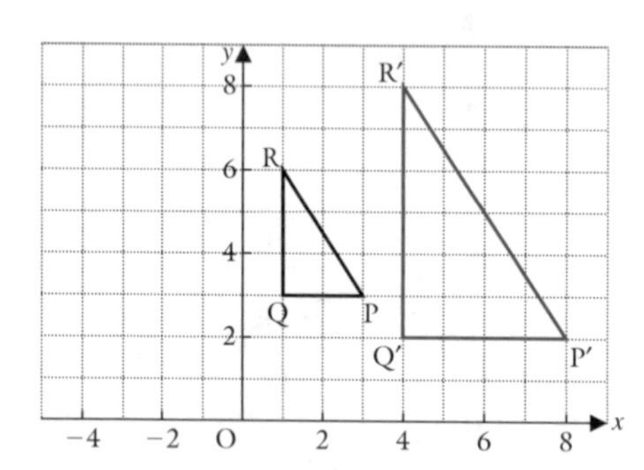

5

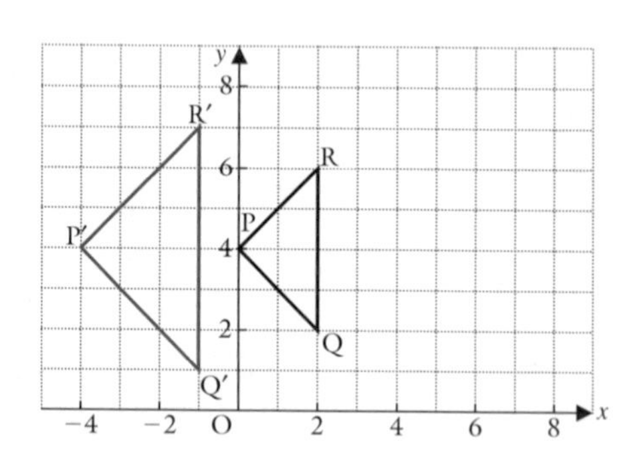

6 In questions **3** to **5**

a name pairs of lines that are parallel

b compare the sizes of

i $Q\hat{P}R$ and $Q'\hat{P}'R'$ **ii** $R\hat{Q}P$ and $R'\hat{Q}'P'$ **iii** $P\hat{R}Q$ and $P'\hat{R}'Q'$

7 Draw axes for x and y from 0 to 9 using 1 cm as 1 unit. Draw ΔABC: A(2, 3), B(4, 1), C(5, 4). Draw ΔA′B′C′: A′(2, 5), B′(6, 1), C′(8, 7). Draw A′A, B′B and C′C and extend these lines until they meet.

a Give the coordinates of the centre of enlargement.

b Measure the sides and angles of the two triangles. What do you notice?

8 Draw axes for x and y from 0 to 10 using 1 cm as 1 unit. Draw ΔXYZ with X(8, 2), Y(6, 6) and Z(5, 3) and ΔX′Y′Z′ with X′(6, 2), Y′(2, 10) and Z′(0, 4). Find the centre of enlargement and label it P. Measure PX, PX′, PY, PY′, PZ, PZ′. What do you notice?

The centre of enlargement can be anywhere, including a point inside the object or a point on the object.

The centres of enlargement in the diagrams below are marked with a cross.

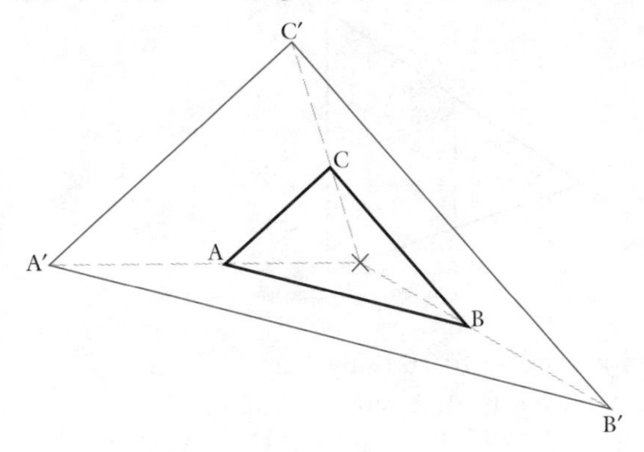

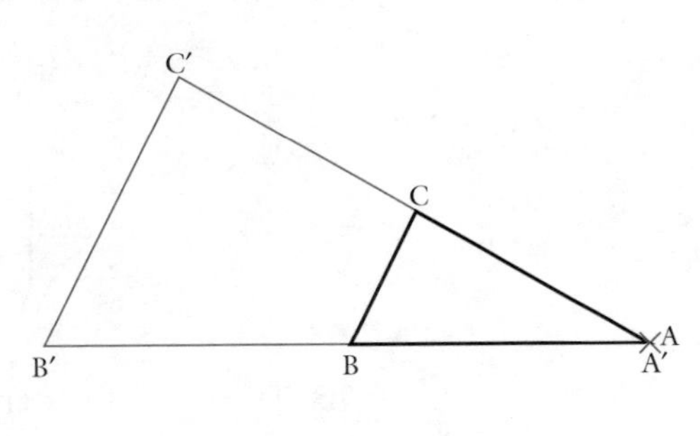

9 Copy the diagram using 1 cm as 1 unit. Draw A′A, B′B, C′C and D′D and extend the lines until they meet. Give the coordinates of the centre of enlargement.

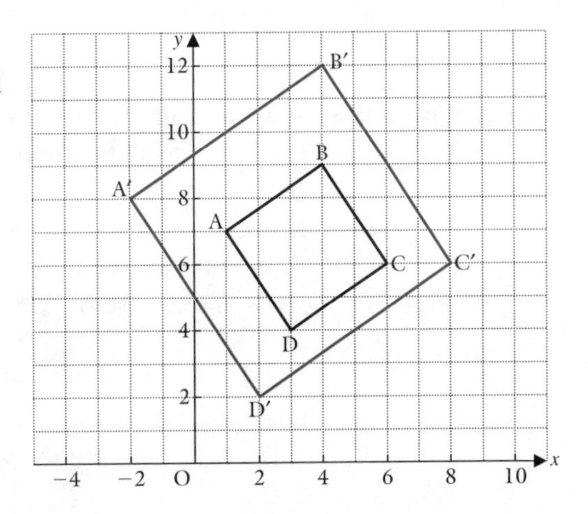

10 In the diagram which point is the centre of enlargement?

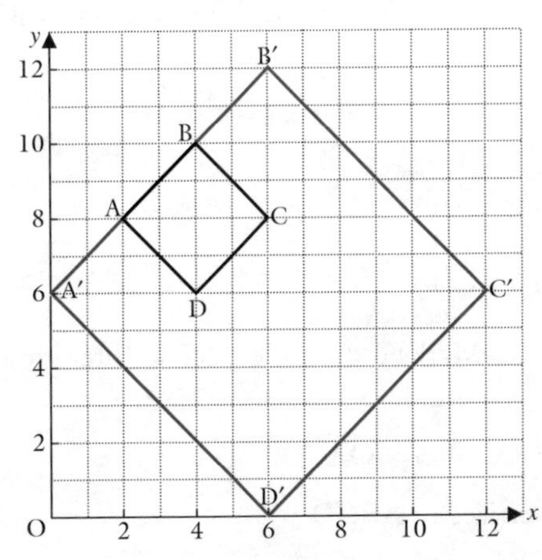

11 Copy the diagram using 1 cm as 1 unit. Draw A′A, B′B and C′C and extend the lines until they meet. Give the coordinates of the centre of enlargement.

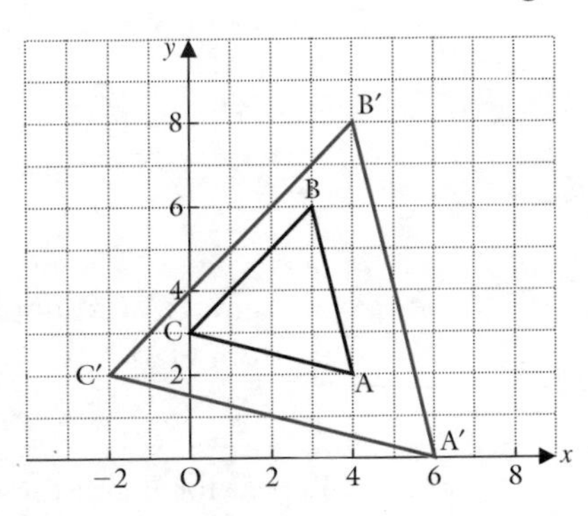

12 In the diagram below which point is the centre of enlargement?

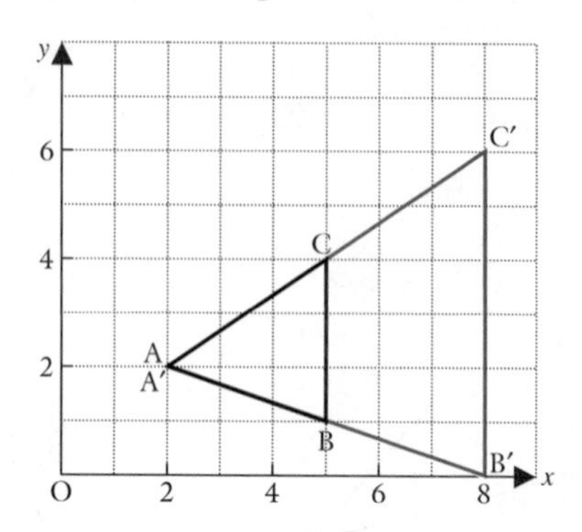

13 Draw axes for x and y from -3 to 10 using 1 cm as 1 unit.
Draw $\triangle ABC$ with $A(4, 0)$, $B(4, 4)$ and $C(0, 2)$.
Draw $\triangle A'B'C'$ with $A'(5, -2)$, $B'(5, 6)$ and $C'(-3, 2)$.
Find the coordinates of the centre of enlargement.

SCALE FACTORS

If we measure the lengths of the sides of the two triangles PQR and P′Q′R′ and compare them, we find that the lengths of the sides of $\triangle P'Q'R'$ are *three* times those of $\triangle PQR$.

We say that $\triangle P'Q'R'$ is the image of $\triangle PQR$ under an enlargement, centre O, with *scale factor 3*.

FINDING AN IMAGE UNDER ENLARGEMENT

If we measure OR and OR′ in the diagram above, we find OR′ is three times OR. This enables us to work out a method for enlarging an object with a given centre of enlargement (O, say) and a given scale factor (3, say).

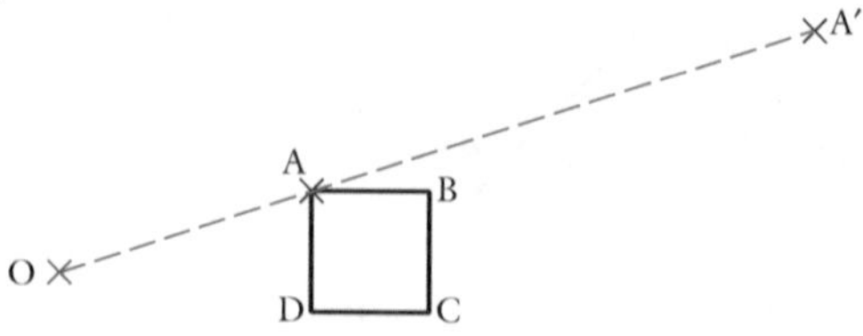

Measure OA. Multiply it by 3. Mark A′ on the guideline three times as far from O as A is,

i.e. $$OA' = 3 \times OA$$

Repeat for B and the other vertices of ABCD.

Then A′B′C′D′ is the image of ABCD.
To check, measure A′B′ and AB.
A′B′ should be three times as large as AB.

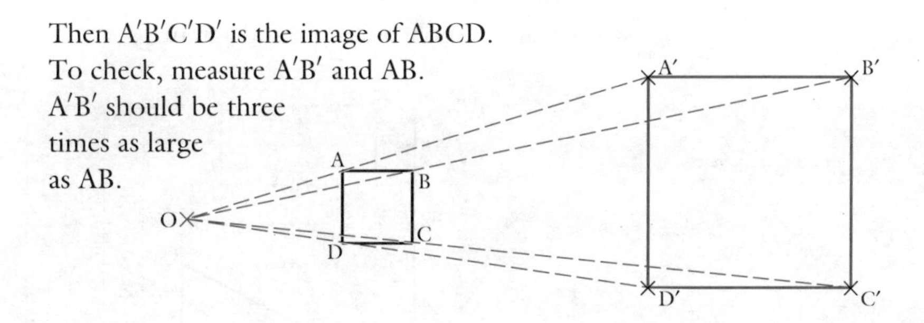

EXERCISE 7F

1 Find the scale factor used for each of questions **1** to **5** in **Exercise 7E**.

2 Copy the diagram using 1 cm as 1 unit. P is the centre of enlargement. Draw the image of the square ABCD under an enlargement, scale factor 2.

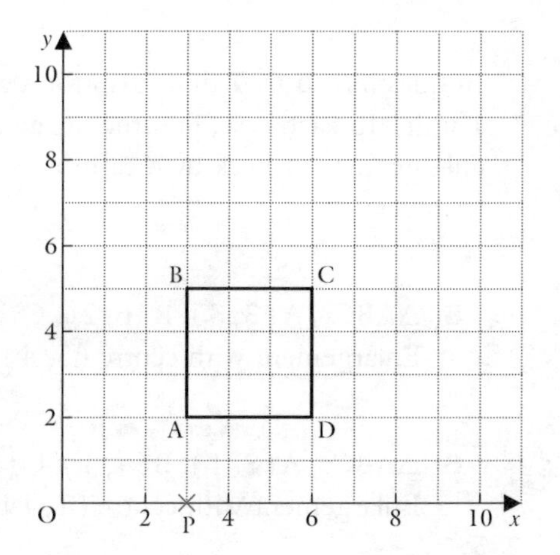

3 Copy the diagram using 1 cm as 1 unit. P is the centre of enlargement. Draw the image of Δ ABC under an enlargement, scale factor 2.

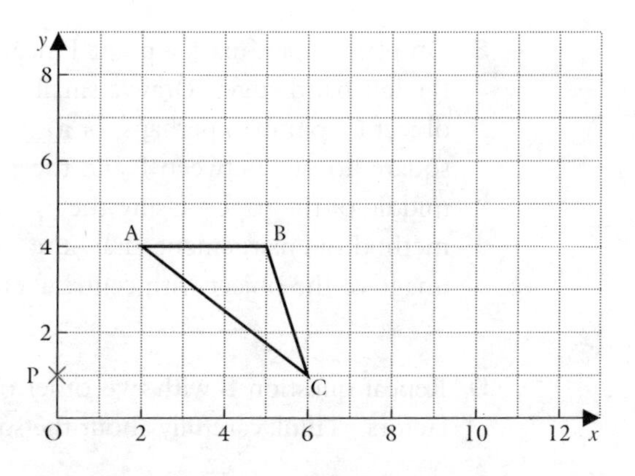

4 Repeat question **3** using this diagram.

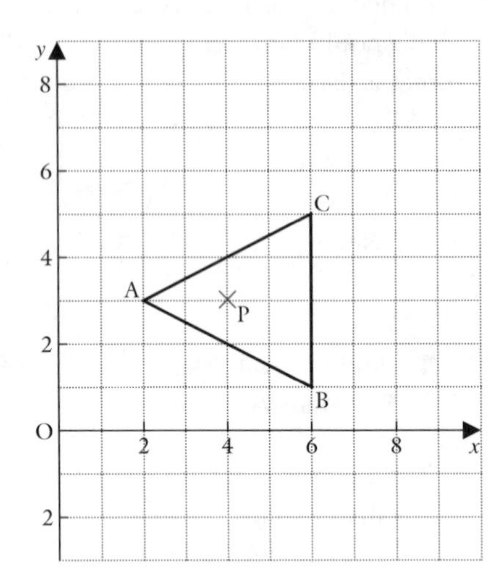

In questions **5** to **7** draw axes for x and y from 0 to 10, using 1 cm as 1 unit. In each case, find the image A′B′C′ of ΔABC using the given enlargement. Check by measuring the lengths of the sides of the two triangles.

5 ΔABC: A(3, 3), B(6, 2), C(5, 6).
Enlargement with centre (5, 4), and scale factor 2.

6 ΔABC: A(2, 1), B(4, 1), C(3, 4).
Enlargement with centre (1, 1), and scale factor 3.

7 ΔABC: A(1, 2), B(7, 2), C(1, 6).
Enlargement with centre (1, 2), and scale factor $1\frac{1}{2}$.

8 On plain paper, mark a point P near the left-hand edge. Draw a small object (a pin man perhaps, or a square house) between P and the middle of the page. Using the method of enlargement, draw the image of the object with centre P and scale factor 2.

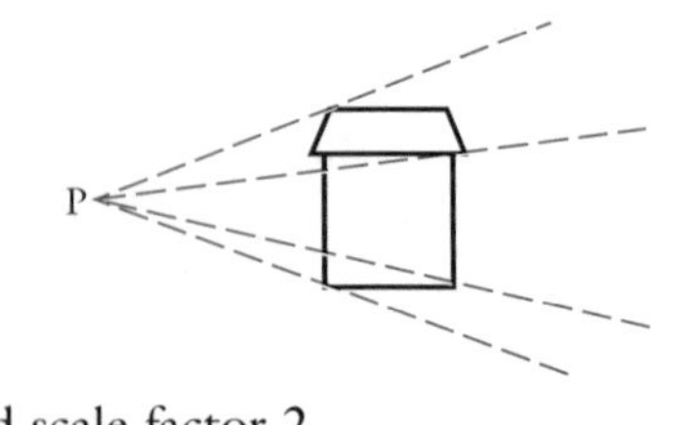

9 Repeat question **8** with two other objects and two other scale factors. Think carefully about the space you will need for the image.

10 Draw axes for x and y from 0 to 10 using 1 cm as 1 unit. Draw the square ABCD with A(5, 7), B(6, 9), C(8, 8) and D(7, 6). Taking the point P(10, 9) as the centre of enlargement and a scale factor of 2, draw the image of ABCD by counting squares and without drawing guidelines.

11 Draw axes for x and y from 0 to 10 using 1 cm as 1 unit. Draw ΔABC with A(2, 2), B(5, 1) and C(3, 4). Taking the origin as the centre of enlargement and a scale factor of 2, draw the image of ΔABC by counting squares and without drawing guidelines.

12 Draw axes for x and y. Scale the x-axis from 0 to 16 and the y-axis from 0 to 24, using 5 mm as 1 unit. Plot the following points and join them in order by straight lines:

(3, 0), (3, 3), (0, 3), (2, 6), (1, 6), (3, 9), (2, 9), (4, 12), (6, 9), (5, 9), (7, 6), (6, 6), (8, 3), (5, 3) and (5, 0).

What shape have you drawn?

Take the origin as the centre of enlargement and a scale factor of 2, draw the image of this shape by counting squares. Do not draw guidelines.

How are the coordinates of the image related to the coordinates of the object?

COMPOUND TRANSFORMATIONS

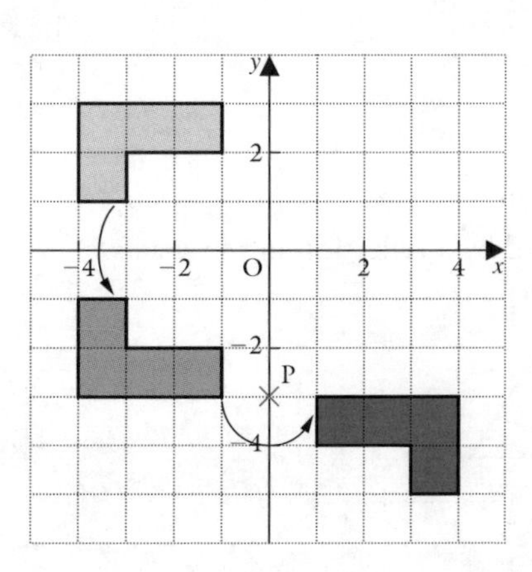

If we reflect any object in the x-axis and then rotate it by 180° about P we are carrying out one example of a compound transformation.

EXERCISE 7G In questions **1** to **6** copy the diagram and carry out the given compound transformation. Label the final image P. You may find it useful to use tracing paper.

1 A reflection in the x-axis followed by a reflection in the y-axis.

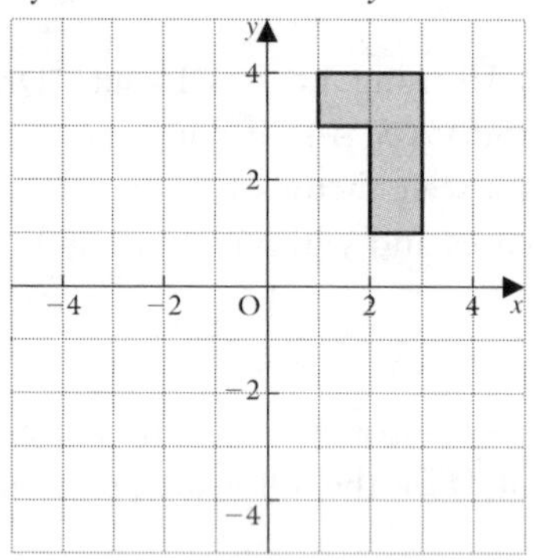

2 A reflection in the y-axis followed by a reflection in the x-axis.

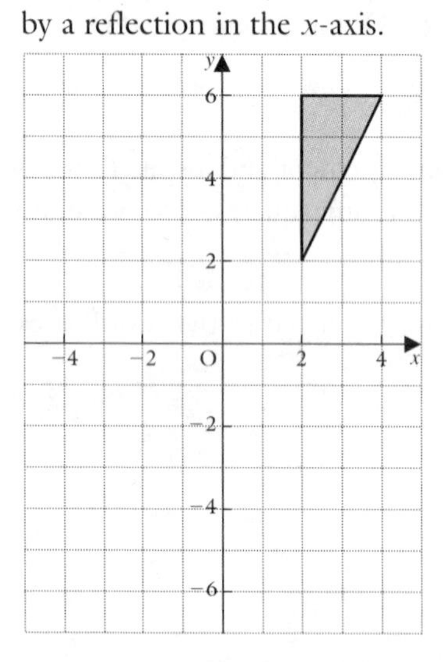

3 A rotation of 90° clockwise about the point (3, 2) followed by a reflection in the x-axis.

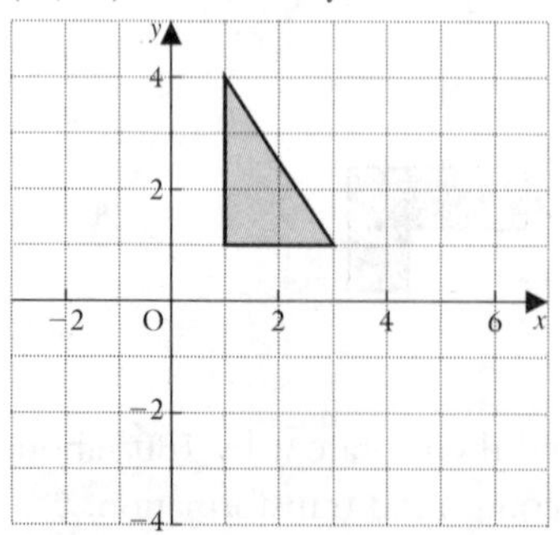

4 A reflection in the y-axis followed by a rotation of 90° clockwise about the origin.

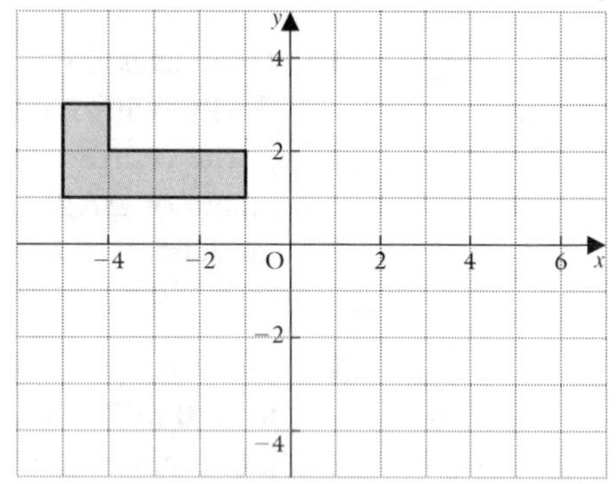

5 A reflection in the y-axis followed by a rotation of 90° anticlockwise about (4, 1).

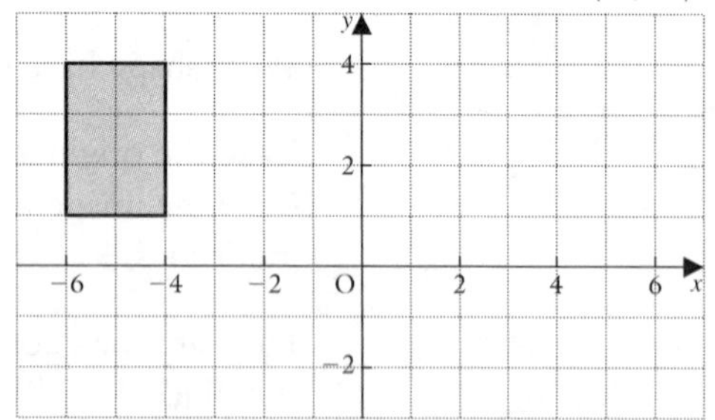

6 A reflection in the x-axis followed by a translation 4 units parallel to the x-axis to the right and 1 unit parallel to the y-axis up.

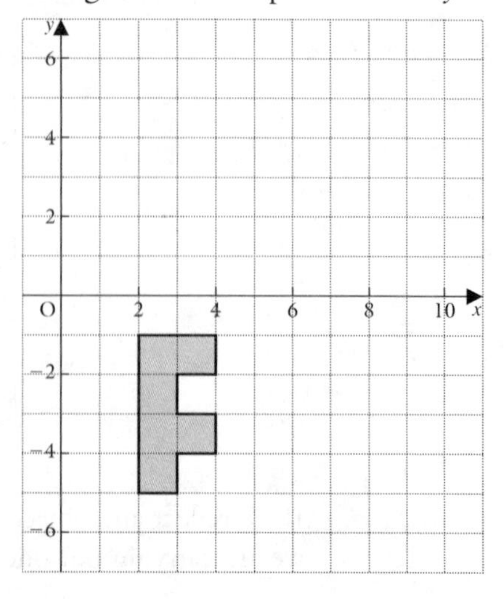

USING A COMPUTER

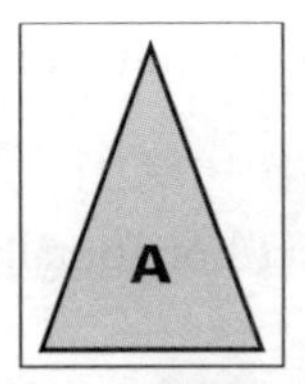

The shape labelled **A** can be drawn on a computer screen by using a drawing program.

A particular program has two commands to transform a shape:

Flip Top–bottom and Rotate 90° clockwise

If the Flip Top–bottom command is used

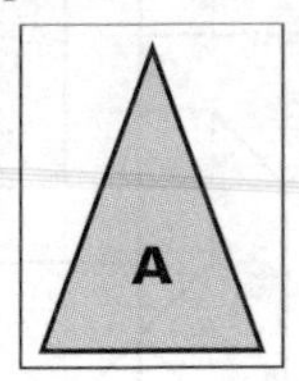

becomes

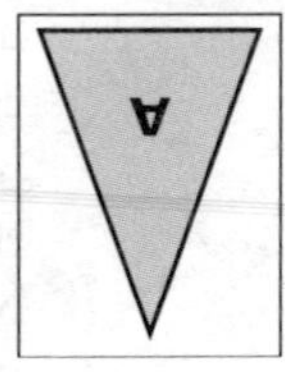

and if the Rotate 90° clockwise command is used

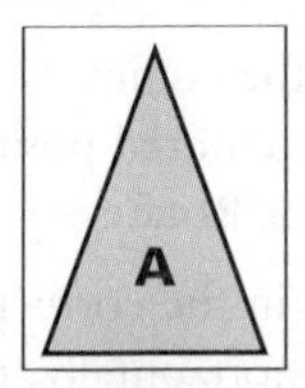

becomes

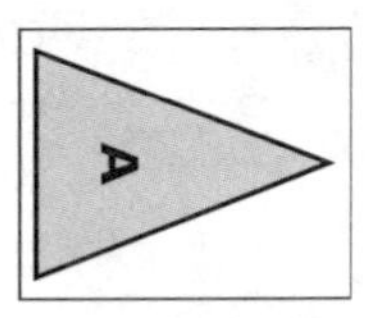

If the Flip Top–bottom command is followed by the Rotate 90° clockwise command

then

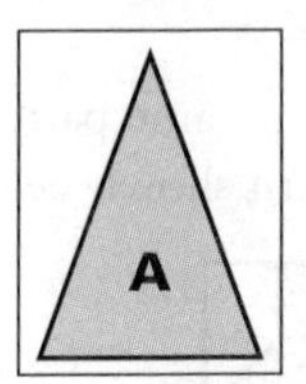

→ →

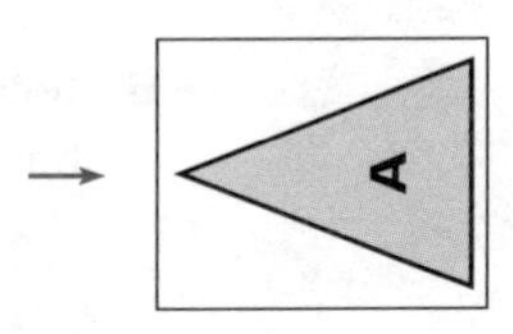

This shows how a compound transformation can be achieved by using a computer program.

EXERCISE 7H

In questions **1** to **4** copy the given shape and draw its image after carrying out the two commands in the order given. (It doesn't matter where the image is drawn.)

1

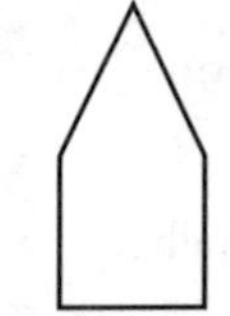

Flip Top–bottom
Rotate 90° clockwise

2

Rotate 90° clockwise
Rotate 90° clockwise

3

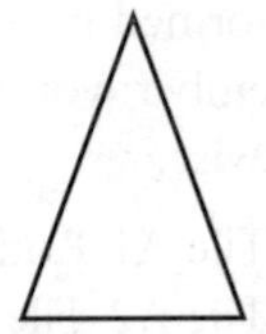

Rotate 90° clockwise
Flip Top–bottom

4

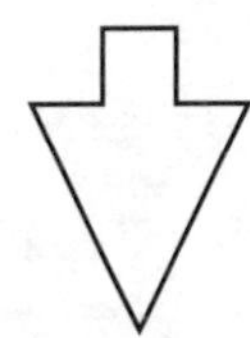

Rotate 90° clockwise
Rotate 90° clockwise

5 On a computer drawing Kim has two commands available:

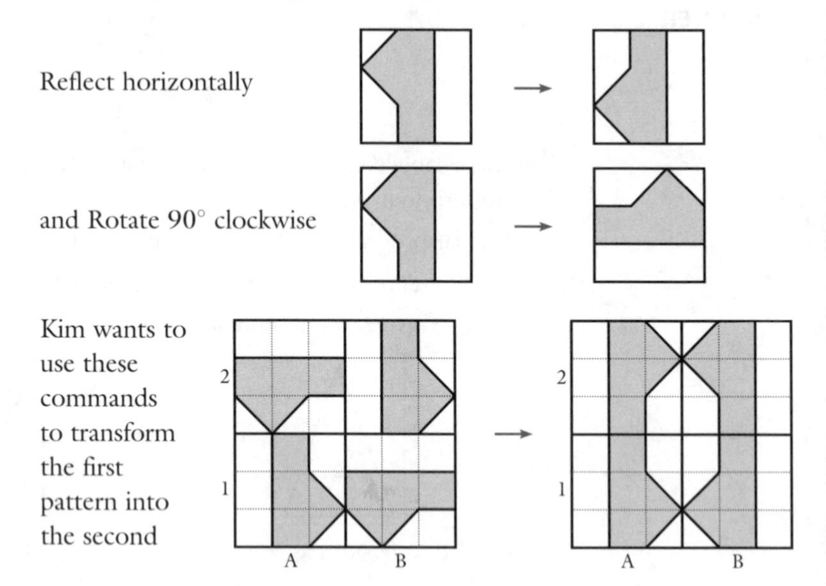

Copy and complete the commands so that the four tiles are transformed to their required positions. Remember: you can only Reflect horizontally or Rotate 90° clockwise.

Tile A1 Already in the correct position.
Tile A2 Reflect horizontally, then Rotate 90° clockwise.
Tile B1 Rotate 90° clockwise, then . . .
Tile B2 . . .

6 Joe wants to start with the same pattern and use the same program but get the second pattern shown below.

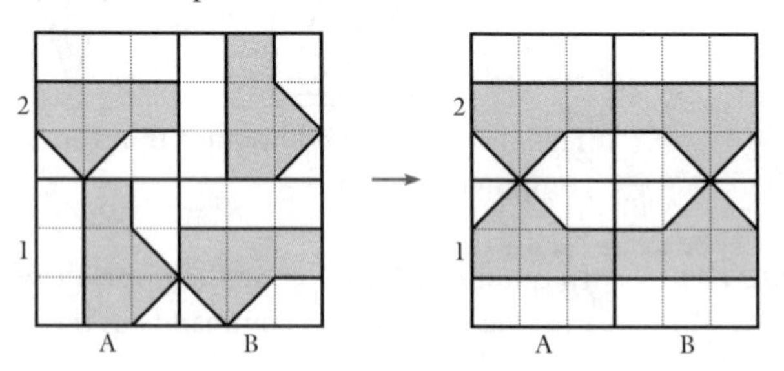

Copy and complete the commands so that the first pattern is transformed into the second pattern.
Remember: you can only Reflect horizontally or Rotate 90° clockwise.

Tile A1 Rotate 90° clockwise, then Reflect horizontally.
Tile A2 Tile is in the correct position.
Tile B1 . . .
Tile B2 . . .

MIXED EXERCISE

EXERCISE 7I

1 Which of these shapes have **a** rotational symmetry **b** line symmetry **c** neither?

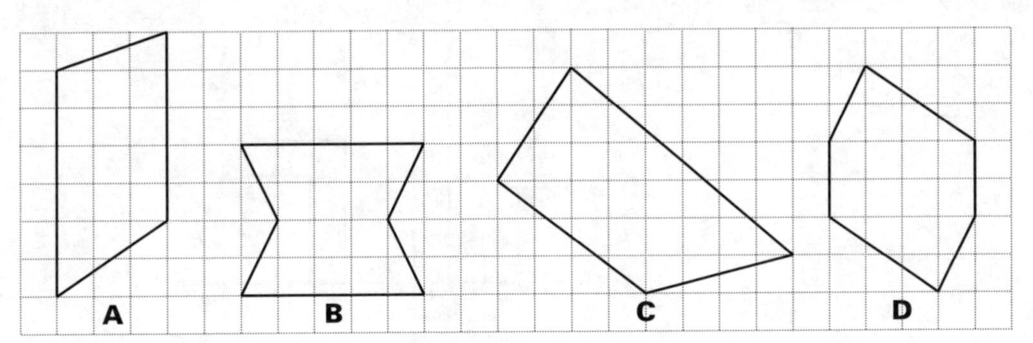

2 The diagrams shows △ABC and its image after it has been rotated about a point.

a Give the coordinates of the centre of rotation.

b State the angle of rotation.

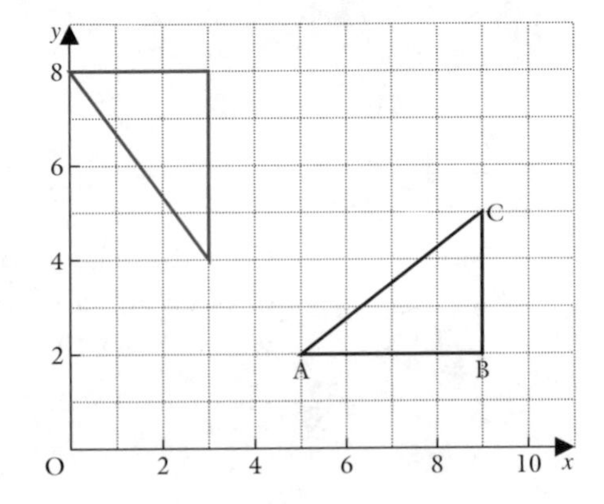

3

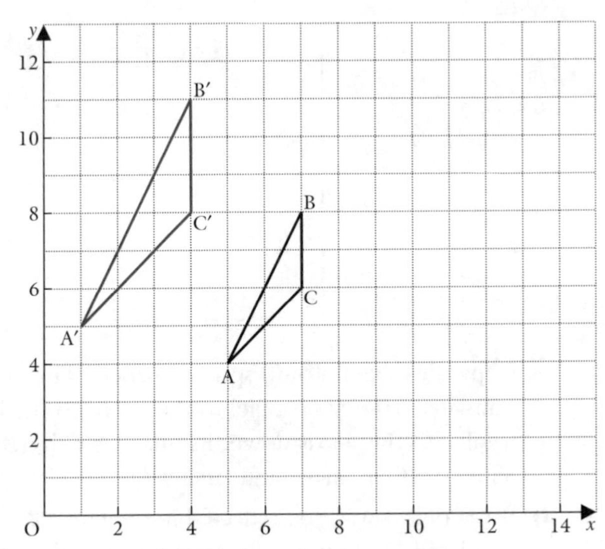

Copy the diagram using 1 cm to 1 unit. Draw AA′, BB′ and CC′ and extend them until they meet. Give the coordinates of the centre of enlargement.

4 Draw x- and y-axes from 0 to 14, using 1 cm as 1 unit. Plot the points A(10, 1), B(9, 4) and C(12, 3). Find the image $\triangle A'B'C'$ when $\triangle ABC$ is enlarged using the point (13, 0) as the centre of enlargement and a scale factor of 3. Write down the coordinates of A′, B′ and C′.

5

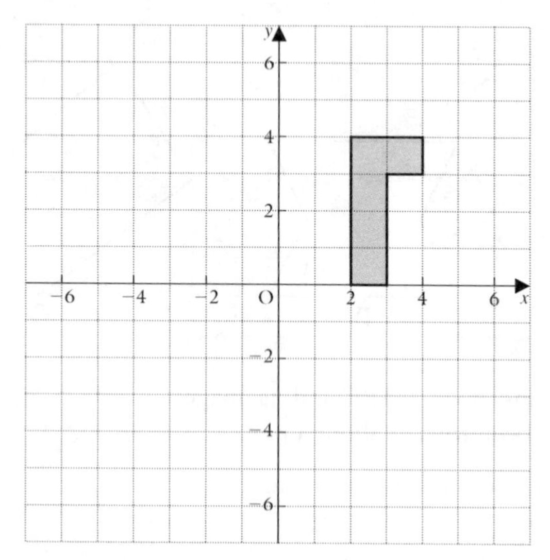

Copy the diagram onto squared paper. The given shape is rotated through 90° clockwise about the origin and its image reflected in the y-axis. Show the final image and label it P.

6

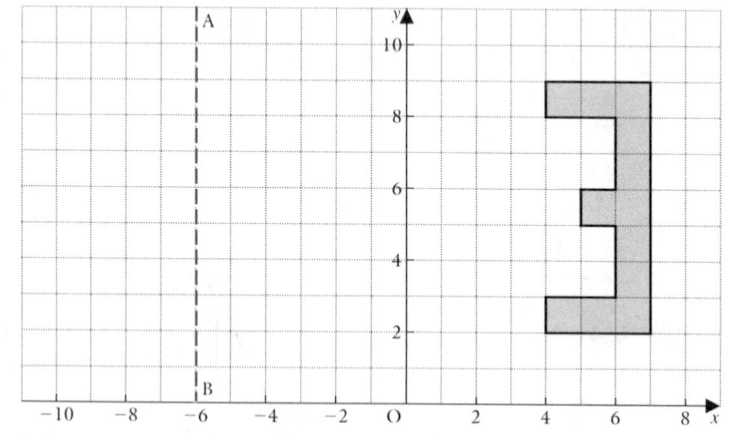

a Copy the diagram onto squared paper. The given object is translated 10 units parallel to the x-axis to the left and 1 unit parallel to the y-axis down; its image is reflected in the line AB. Show the final image and label it Q.

b If the object was first reflected in the line AB and its image was translated 10 units parallel to the x-axis to the left and 1 unit parallel to the y-axis down, would the final image be the same as the image labelled Q in part **a**?

INVESTIGATION

a Make a pattern by following these instructions:

> From any starting point, S, and facing up the page,
> go **1** square forward and turn 90° clockwise.
> Next go **2** squares forward and turn 90° clockwise
> and then go **4** squares forward and turn 90° clockwise.

Repeat these three instructions until you get back to your starting point.
This is called pattern 124 because it follows the instructions using the digits 1, 2, 4 in that order.

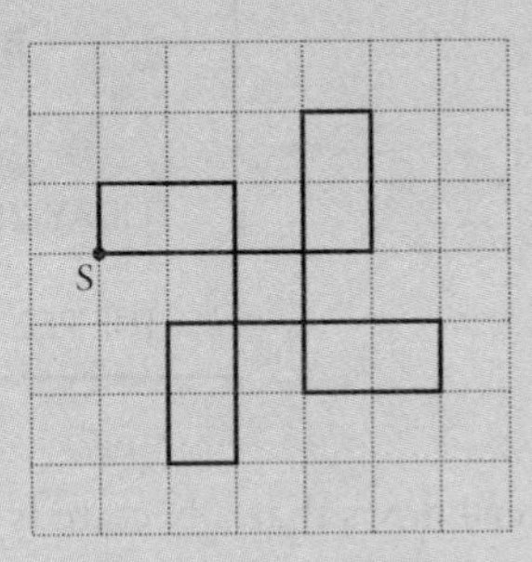

b Does this shape have line symmetry? If so, draw the mirror line.

c Does this shape have rotational symmetry? If so, state the order of rotational symmetry.

d Repeat parts **a** to **c** but putting the same three digits in a different order.
For example, 2, 4, 1 or 4, 2, 1.
How many different shapes do you get?

e Repeat parts **a** to **d** for other triples of digits, for example 2,5,2; 2,4,3; 2,6,7.

f **i** Some sets of digits lead to shapes that have both line symmetry and rotational symmetry. List those sets you have found.

ii Some sets of digits lead to shapes that have rotational symmetry only. List those sets.

iii Find a rule about the digits which allows you to forecast the symmetry of the shapes and test it on new sets of digits.

AREAS

Peter Brown sees this advertisement.

> **FOR SALE BY PRIVATE AUCTION**
> **BROCKLEY FARM**
> 265.4 hectares
> on
> FRIDAY 28th MARCH 1997, 11 a.m.
> at
> THE RED LION HOTEL, SHEPSTON

Peter knows that a hectare is a unit of area, but he does not know how big it is. To understand this advertisement Peter needs to know

- what a 'hectare' is
- how to convert hectares into units that he is familiar with.

A hectare is a metric unit of area and an acre is an Imperial unit of area. We start this chapter by looking at metric and Imperial units of area.

METRIC UNITS OF AREA

In the metric system the units of area we have used so far are the square millimetre (mm^2), the square centimetre (cm^2), the square metre (m^2) and the square kilometre (km^2), where

$$1\ cm^2 = 100\ mm^2$$

$$1\ m^2 = 10\,000\ cm^2$$

and $$1\ km^2 = 1\,000\,000\ m^2$$

Which of these units should be used depends on the size of area being measured, for example the area of a country could be given in km^2, a garden in m^2, a sheet of paper in cm^2 and a small coin in mm^2.

Another metric unit which is used to measure an area of land is the *hectare*. On the continent, and increasingly in this country, the area of a farm is given in hectares.

A hectare, which is abbreviated to ha, is the area of a square that has a side of 100 metres

i.e. $1\ \text{ha} = 100 \times 100\ \text{m}^2 = 10\,000\ \text{m}^2$

EXERCISE 8A

Copy and complete the following sentences adding the appropriate unit or number.

1 The area of a standard postage stamp is about 5 __ .

2 The area of the top of a single bed is about 2 __ .

3 The area of the top of a washing machine is about __ cm^2.

4 The area of one side of a standard door is about __ m^2.

Find the area of each shape, clearly stating the units involved.

5 A square of side 4.5 m

6 A rectangle measuring 1.8 mm by 2.6 mm

7 A paving slab measuring 50 cm by 50 cm

8 A football pitch measuring 105 m by 85 m

Express $45\,600\ \text{cm}^2$ in m^2.

Since $1\ \text{m} = 100\ \text{cm}$, $1\ \text{m}^2 = 100 \times 100\ \text{cm}^2 = 10\,000\ \text{cm}^2$

i.e. to change cm^2 to m^2 we divide by 10 000.

$$45\,600\ \text{cm}^2 = \frac{45\,600}{10\,000}\ \text{m}^2 = 4.56\ \text{m}^2$$

9 Express

a $600\ \text{mm}^2$ in cm^2

b $3500\ \text{cm}^2$ in m^2

c $0.06\ \text{m}^2$ in cm^2

d $6500\ \text{cm}^2$ in m^2

e $75\ \text{mm}^2$ in cm^2

f $1.05\ \text{km}^2$ in m^2

g $80\,000\ \text{m}^2$ in km^2

h $55\ \text{cm}^2$ in mm^2

10 Jane said that the area of the top of her lunchbox in her bag was $0.5\ \text{m}^2$. Explain why she was wrong.

A rectangular field is 0.5 km long and 350 m wide.
Find the area of the field **a** in m^2 **b** in hectares.

0.5 km

350 m

a To find the area of the rectangle in square metres both dimensions must be in metres, so we change kilometres into metres.

$$0.5\text{ km} = 0.5 \times 1000\text{ m}$$
$$= 500\text{ m}$$

$$\text{Area of field} = \text{length} \times \text{breadth}$$
$$= 500 \times 350\text{ m}^2$$
$$= 175\,000\text{ m}^2$$

b 1 hectare = $10\,000\text{ m}^2$ so we divide by 10 000 to change from m^2 to hectares.

$$\text{Area of field} = 175\,000\text{ m}^2$$
$$= \frac{175\,000}{10\,000}\text{ ha}$$
$$= 17.5\text{ ha}$$

11 A roll of wallpaper is 10 m long and 55 cm wide. Find its area in square metres.

12 A kitchen top is 3.5 m long and 60 cm wide. Find its area in cm^2.

13 A pavement is 1.2 km long and 2.5 m wide. Find its area in square metres.

14 A rectangular field is 0.2 km long and 0.05 km wide. Find its area in square metres.

15 It is recommended that a particular grass seed is sown at the rate of 75 grams to the square metre.
What weight of seed is needed to cover an area measuring 40 m by 35 m? Give your answer in **a** grams **b** kilograms.

16 A square floor tile measures 30 cm by 30 cm. How many of these tiles would be needed to cover a floor measuring 9 m by 6 m?

17 A rectangular park is 550 m long and 425 m wide. Find the area of the park in hectares.

18 The area of a smallholding is 4.35 ha. What is this in square metres?

19 A builder buys 9.6 ha of land for building houses. If each house is to be built on a rectangular plot measuring 80 m by 25 m or on a plot with the same area, what is the largest number of houses he could build?

20 How much larger, in square metres, is a square field of side 0.18 km than a rectangular field that has an area of 2.85 ha?

IMPERIAL UNITS OF AREA

The Imperial units of length we have used so far are the inch, the foot, the yard and the mile, where 12 inches (in) = 1 foot (ft), 3 feet = 1 yard (yd) and 1760 yards = 1 mile.

It follows that the units of area are the square inch, the square foot, the square yard and the square mile

where $1\,\text{ft}^2 = 12 \times 12\,\text{in}^2 = 144\,\text{in}^2$ and $1\,\text{yd}^2 = 3 \times 3\,\text{ft}^2 = 9\,\text{ft}^2$

The Imperial unit used for the areas of fields and farms is the *acre*, where

1 acre = 4840 square yards

Acres and hectares can be interchanged using the approximate relationship

1 hectare = 2.5 acres

(This relationship is correct to 2 significant figures. For a more accurate conversion use 1 hectare = 2.471 acres which is correct to 4 significant figures.)

EXERCISE 8B

Find the area of each shape, stating clearly the units involved.

1 A square of side 8 inches

2 A rectangle measuring 9 ft by 4 ft

3 A rectangular allotment which is 60 yd long and 20 yd wide

4 A rectangular car park measuring 240 yd by 120 yd

5 Express

a $5\frac{1}{2}$ sq ft in square inches **c** 36 sq ft in sq yd

b 27 sq yd in sq ft **d** 504 sq in in sq ft

6 A rectangular field is 85 yd long and 54 yd wide. Find its area in

a square yards **b** square feet

7 A rectangular table is $3\frac{1}{2}$ ft long and $2\frac{1}{2}$ ft wide. Find its area in square feet. How much larger or smaller is the area of this table than a square table of side 1 yard?

8

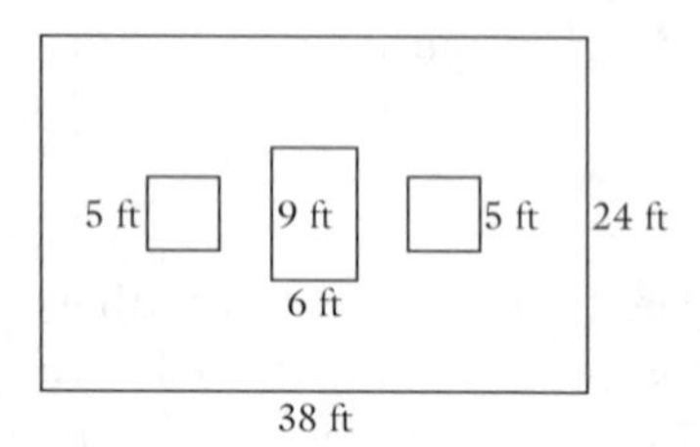

Two square flower beds of side 5 ft and a rectangular flower bed measuring 9 ft by 6 ft are cut out of a rectangular lawn measuring 38 ft by 24 ft. What area of lawn remains?

9 Express

a 2.5 sq yd in square feet **b** 1.5 sq ft in square inches.

10 A rectangular field measures 250 yards by 130 yards. How many acres does the field cover?

11 A house in France is advertised for sale with 2.6 hectares of ground. How many acres is this?

12 Solve Peter Brown's problem as stated at the beginning of the chapter. What is the area of Brockley Farm in acres?

13 The area of the United Kingdom is 94 214 square miles. Express this area in

a acres **b** hectares **c** square kilometres.

14 The area of Scotland is 30 405 square miles. Use the relationship 1 mile = 1.6093 km correct to 4 decimal places, to give the area of Scotland in square kilometres to the nearest square kilometre. State with reasons whether your answer is accurate.

15 This is part of a map showing a wood. The scale of the map is 2 cm = 1 km.
Estimate the area of the wood **a** in hectares **b** in acres.

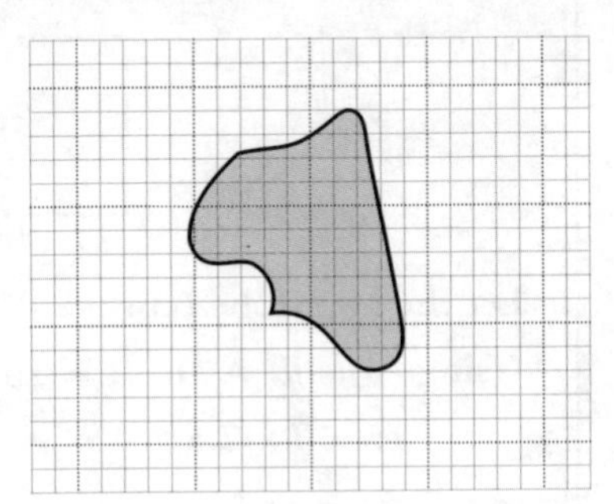

FINDING THE MISSING MEASUREMENTS

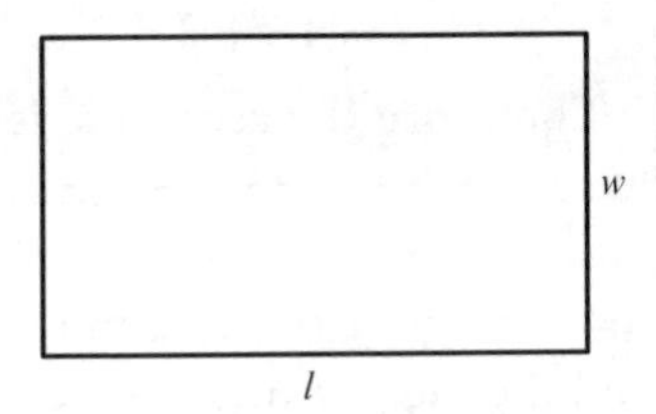

We know the formula for finding the area of a rectangle.
If A square units is the area of this rectangle, then

$$A = l \times w$$

If we know the area of a rectangle and the length of one side we can use this formula to find the length of the unknown side.

Suppose, for example, we are told that the area of a rectangular patio is 25 m^2 and that it is 10 m long. If we let the width be b m, and use $A = l \times b$ with $A = 25$ and $l = 10$, we can find b, and hence the width of the patio.

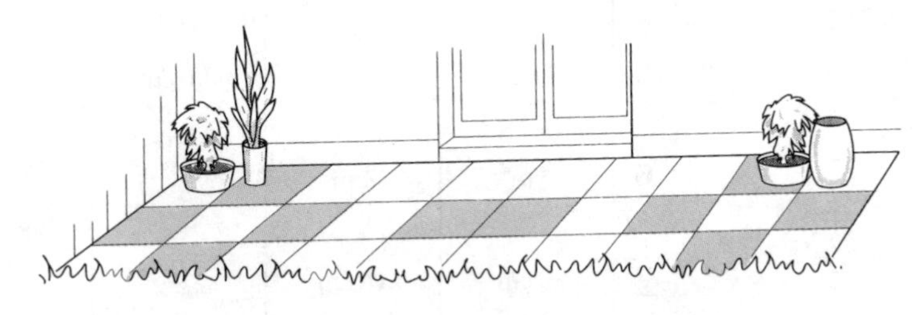

So $A = l \times b$ gives $25 = 10 \times b$

This is a simple equation that we can solve to find b.

$$10b = 25$$

$$b = 25 \div 10 = 2.5$$

Therefore the width of the patio is 2.5 m.

EXERCISE 8C

The area of a rectangle is 15 cm^2 and the width is 2.5 cm.
Find the length of the rectangle.

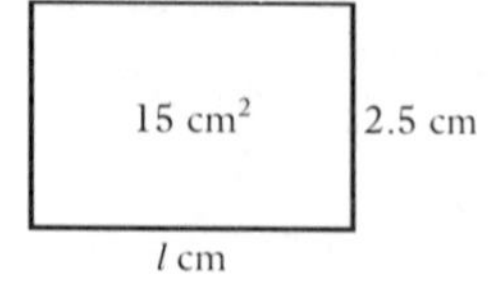

Let the length be l cm.

Using $A = lb$ with $A = 15$ and $b = 2.5$ gives

$$15 = l \times 2.5$$

i.e. $2.5l = 15$

$$l = 15 \div 2.5 = 6$$

Therefore the rectangle is 6 cm long.

The table gives the area and one measurement for various rectangles. Find the missing measurements.

	Area	Length	Width
1	2.4 cm^2	6 cm	
2	20 cm^2		4 cm
3	36 m^2		3.6 m
4	108 mm^2	27 mm	
5	3 cm^2		0.6 cm
6	6 m^2	4 m	
7	20 cm^2	16 cm	
8	7.2 m^2		2.4 m
9	4.2 m^2		0.6 m
10	14.4 cm^2		2.4 cm

FINDING SQUARE ROOTS

Suppose we have a square tablecloth whose area is known to be $4\,\text{m}^2$. The area of a square is found by multiplying the length of a side by itself. To find the length of a side of this cloth, we have to find a number which, when it is multiplied by itself, is equal to 4.

Now $2 \times 2 = 4$, so the sides of the cloth are 2 m long.

If a square carpet has an area of $20\,\text{m}^2$, then, to find the length of a side of this carpet we have to find a number which, when it is multiplied by itself, is equal to 20. We call this number the *square root* of 20.

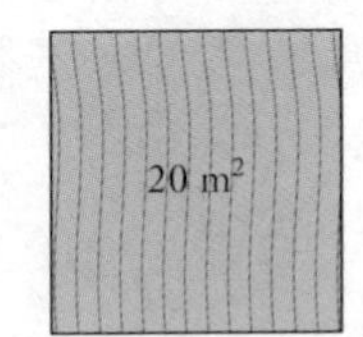

The symbol $\sqrt{\ }$ is used to mean 'the square root of', so $\sqrt{20}$ means the square root of 20.

We know that $4 \times 4 = 16$ and that $5 \times 5 = 25$,

i.e. $4^2 = 16$ and $5^2 = 25$, so $\sqrt{16} = 4$ and $\sqrt{25} = 5$

Now we can see that $\sqrt{20}$ is a number between 4 and 5.

The $\sqrt{\ }$ button on a calculator can be used to find $\sqrt{20}$ correct to as many significant figures as the display will show.

Enter √ 2 0 = the display will show 4.472135 ...

so $\sqrt{20} = 4.47$ correct to 3 s.f.

Therefore, correct to 3 s.f., the length of a side of the square is 4.47 m.

(If this does not work on your calculator, try 2 0 √)

EXERCISE 8D

Find the square root of each number without using a calculator.

1 9 **3** 4 **5** 49 **7** 64

2 36 **4** 81 **6** 121 **8** 144

Without using a calculator, find the value of

9 $(0.1)^2$ **13** $(0.07)^2$ **17** $(1.2)^2$ **21** 7^2

10 $(0.2)^2$ **14** $(0.06)^2$ **18** 20^2 **22** 70^2

11 $(0.01)^2$ **15** $(0.12)^2$ **19** 400^2 **23** 700^2

12 $(0.5)^2$ **16** $(1.1)^2$ **20** 40^2 **24** 7000^2

Find $\sqrt{74.5}$ correct to 3 significant figures.

$\sqrt{74.5} = 8.63|1\ldots$

$= 8.63$ (correct to 3 s.f.) Press √ 7 4 · 5 =

Check: $(8.63)^2 \approx 9^2 = 81$

Use your calculator to find the square root of each number correct to 3 significant figures. Remember to check your answer by squaring it.

25 38.4	**29** 32	**33** 650	**<u>37</u>** 80
26 19.8	**30** 9.8	**34** 10 300	**<u>38</u>** 11.2
27 428	**31** 67	**35** 4 012 000	**<u>39</u>** 24
28 4230	**32** 5.7	**36** 8000	**<u>40</u>** 728

41 Find the square root of

a 6 **b** 600 **c** 60 000 **d** 60 **e** 6000

What do you notice?

42 Find the square root of

a 5 **b** 0.5 **c** 0.05 **d** 5000 **e** 500

What do you notice?

43 Without using a calculator, explain why Simon is wrong when he says 'The square root of 90 is equal to 30.'

Find the side of the square whose area is $50\,\text{m}^2$.

$50\,\text{m}^2$

Length of the side $= \sqrt{50}$ m

Length of the side $= 7.07|1\ldots$ m

$= 7.07$ m (correct to 3 s.f.)

Check: $(7.07)^2 \approx 7^2 = 49$

Find the sides of the squares whose areas are given below. Give your answers correct to 3 significant figures.

44 $85\ \text{cm}^2$ **47** $32\ \text{m}^2$ **50** $749\ \text{mm}^2$

45 $120\ \text{cm}^2$ **48** $0.06\ \text{m}^2$ **51** $84\,300\ \text{km}^2$

46 $50\ \text{m}^2$ **49** $15.1\ \text{cm}^2$ **52** $0.0085\ \text{km}^2$

USING AREAS

The walls of this house need painting.

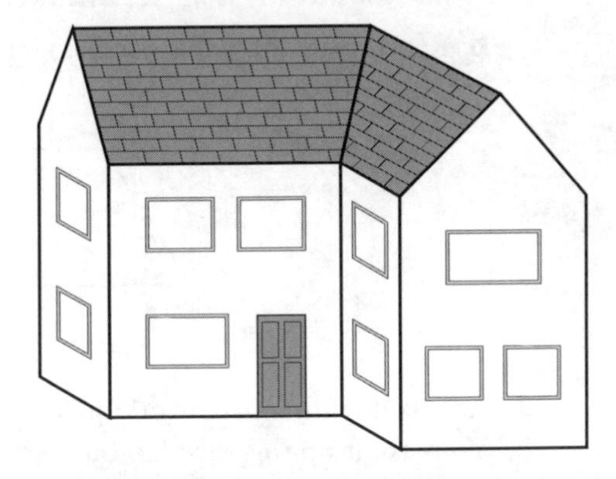

The colour of paint varies slightly from batch to batch, so it is sensible to buy all the paint needed at the same time. This means that we want a reasonably accurate estimate of the amount of paint required. To find this, we first have to work out the area that needs painting.

The shapes involved are all squares or rectangles except for the gables which are triangular. Assuming that we know all the measurements, we can find the area to be painted

- by making an accurate scale drawing of the shape on squared paper and then counting the squares. The disadvantage of doing this is that it is very time consuming.
- by calculation using formulas. We have a formula for the area of a square and a rectangle and we now need a formula that gives the area of a triangle.

EXERCISE 8E

1 A pack has to be designed to hold six of these crayons. The ends of the crayons are equilateral triangles. Part of the design activity involves costing the packaging. Discuss what you need to know to be able to do this costing.

2 a

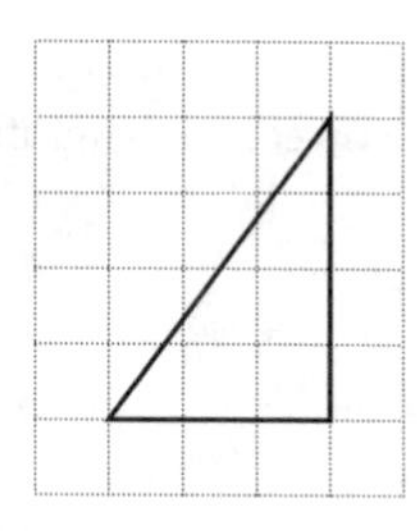

Copy this diagram onto 1 cm squared paper.
Discuss how you can find the area of this triangle using what you know about finding the area of a rectangle. Can you adapt your methods to any triangle, whatever its shape or size?

b Repeat part **a** for this parallelogram.

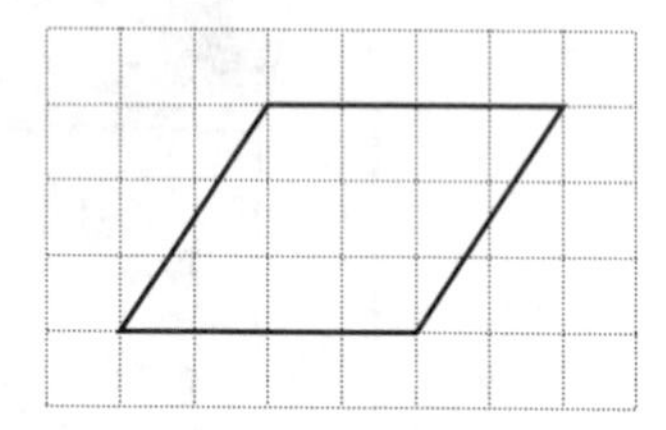

3 Angela designs a patchwork quilt. This is part of her design. To make it up she needs to buy enough material of each colour.

a What are the names of the shapes used in this design?

b Discuss what Angela needs to know, and what she must do, in order to buy about the right amount of material.

4 Rob is designing a pattern using floor tiles of different shapes. Part of his design is shown below.

a What are the names of the two shapes used?

b Discuss what Rob needs to know so that he buys enough of each shape of tile to cover a floor of a particular size.

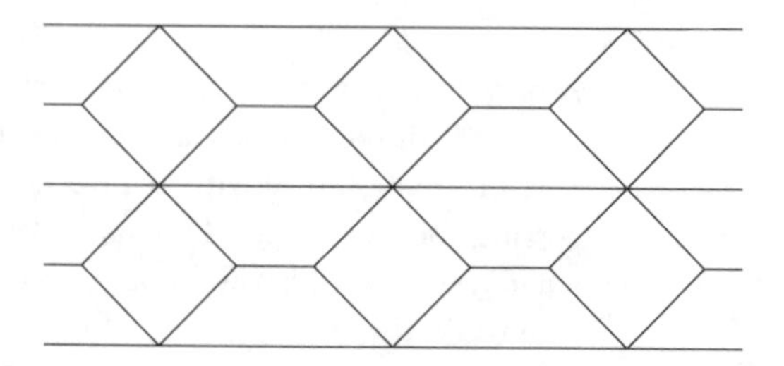

AREA OF A PARALLELOGRAM

Discussion of the examples in **Exercise 8E** shows that triangles and parallelograms are shapes that appear in many everyday situations and that we need a simple way of working out their areas.

Consider this parallelogram.

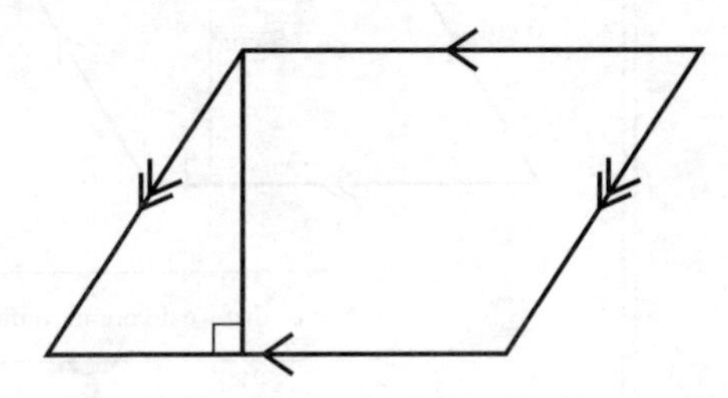

If we cut off the triangle shown above and move it to fit on the right-hand side as shown, we have transformed the parallelogram into a rectangle without changing the area.

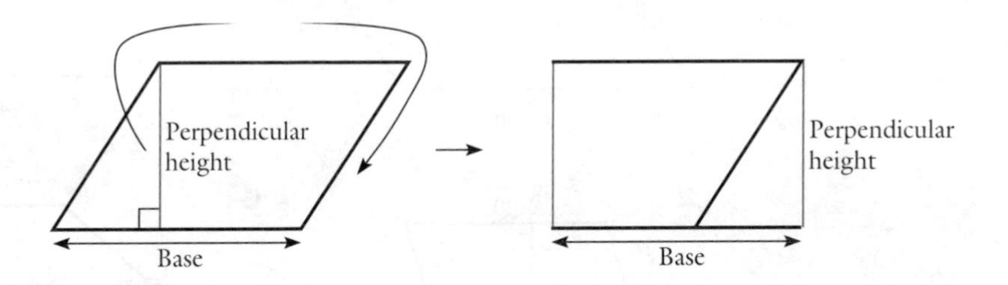

Therefore the area of the parallelogram is equal to the area of the rectangle.

Now the area of the rectangle is given by length $\times$ width which, using the labels in the diagram, is the same as base $\times$ height

The height of the rectangle is equal to the perpendicular height of the parallelogram; so

$$\text{area of parallelogram} = \text{base} \times \text{perpendicular height}$$

Provided that we know the length of the base and the perpendicular height, we can use this formula to find the area of any parallelogram.

Note that when we talk about the *height of a parallelogram* we mean the *perpendicular height*.

EXERCISE 8F

Find the area of a parallelogram of base 7 cm, height 5 cm and slant height 6 cm.

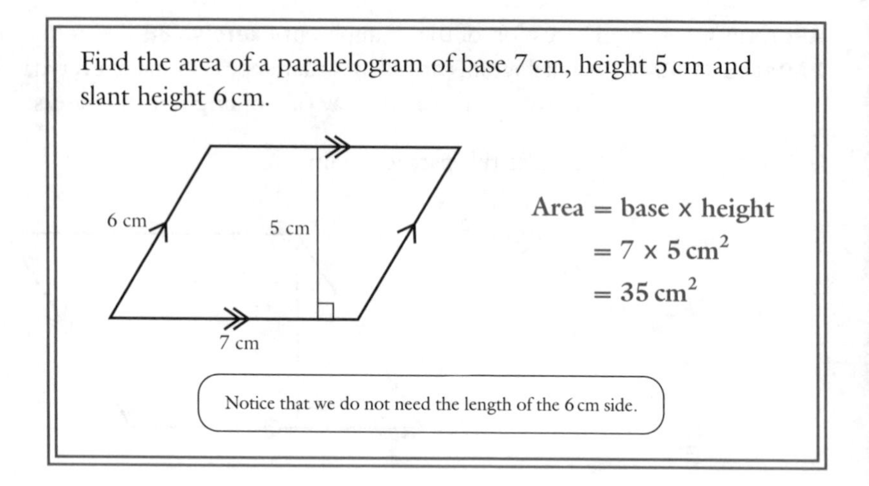

Find the areas of the parallelograms.

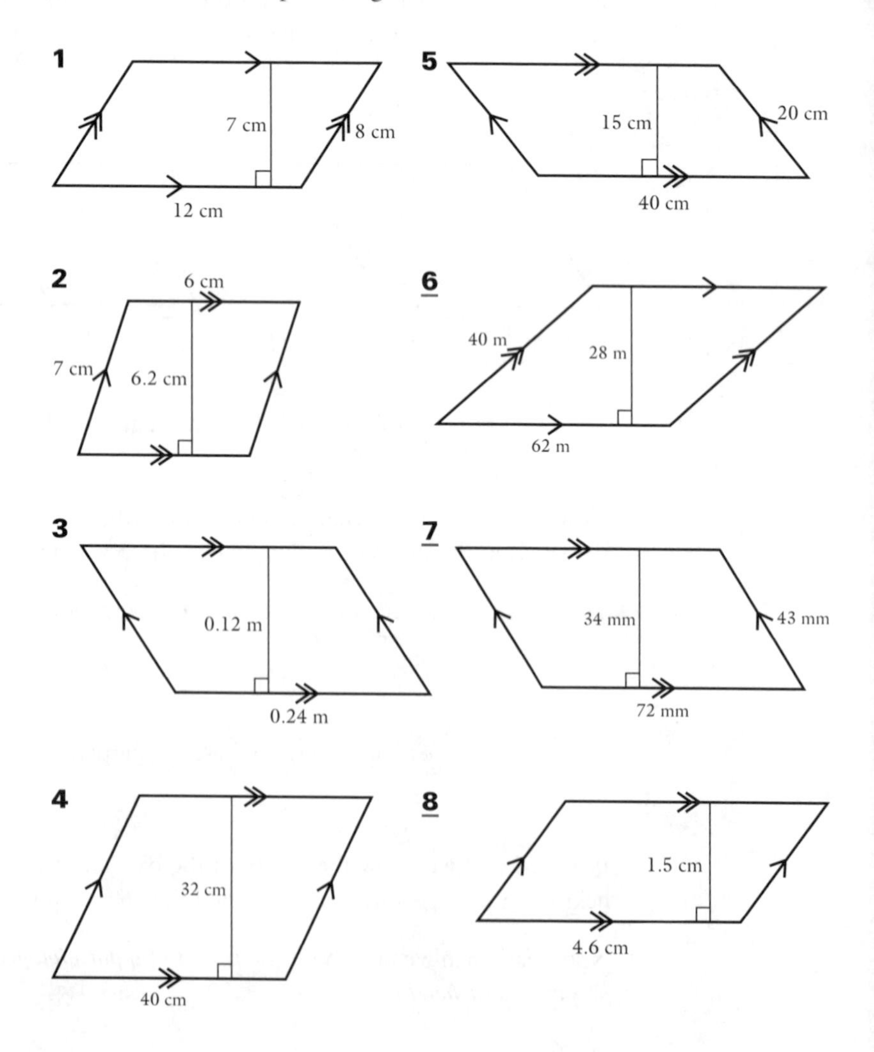

Find the area of the parallelogram.

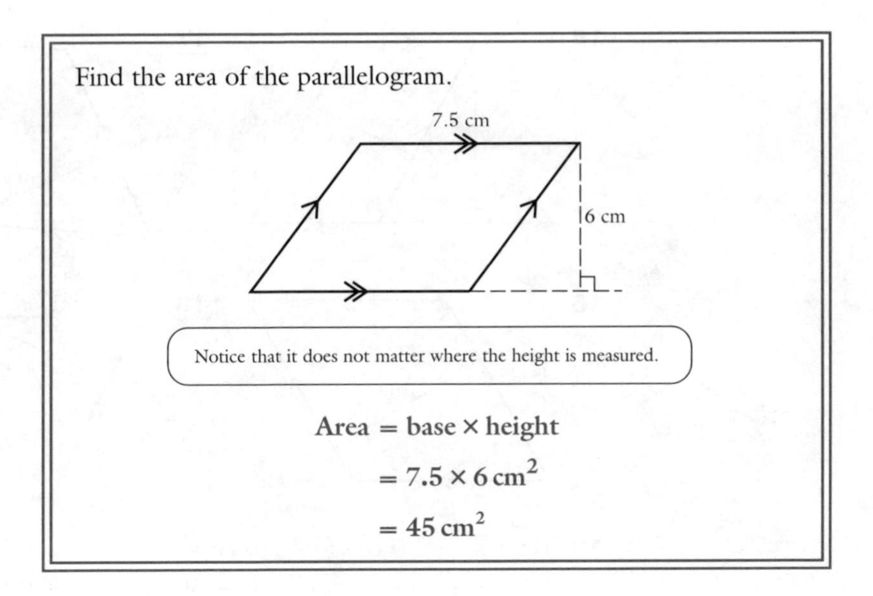

Notice that it does not matter where the height is measured.

$$\text{Area} = \text{base} \times \text{height}$$
$$= 7.5 \times 6\ \text{cm}^2$$
$$= 45\ \text{cm}^2$$

Find the areas of the parallelograms.

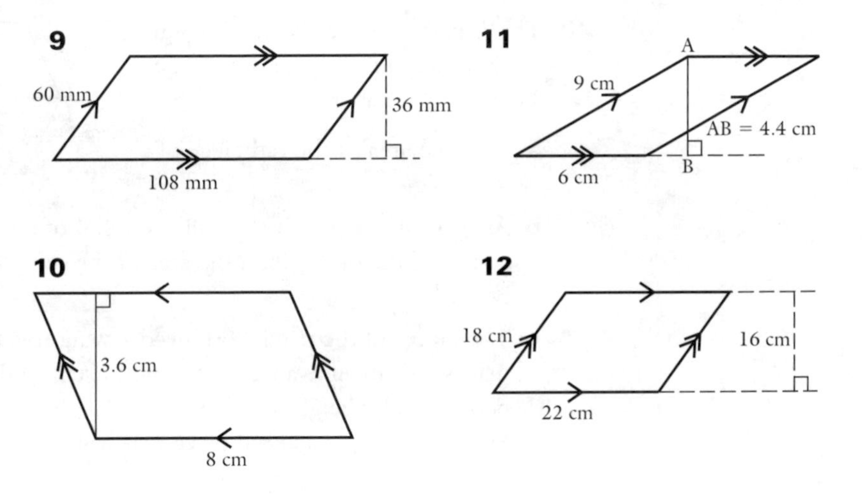

In questions **13** to **18** turn the page round if necessary so that you can see which is the base and which the height.

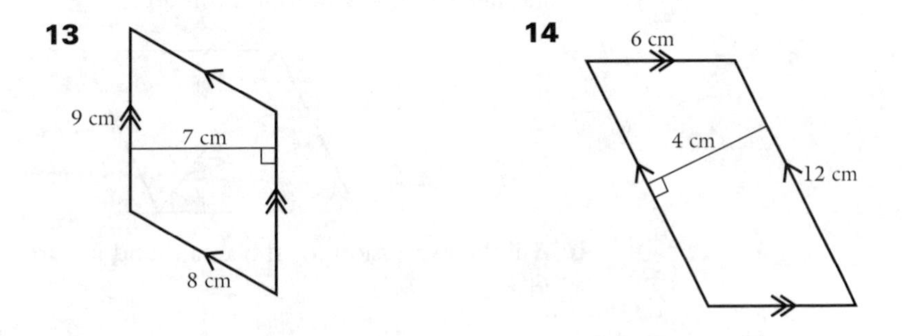

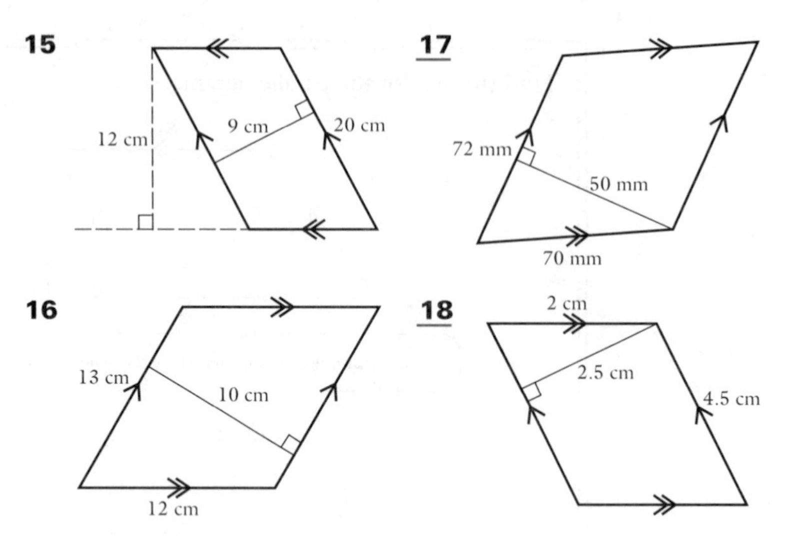

19 Draw x- and y-axes for values from -4 to 4. Use 1 square to 1 unit. Plot the points A(-2, 0), B(2, 0), C(3, 2) and D(-1, 2). Draw the parallelogram ABCD and find its area in square units.

20 This is part of Angela's initial design work for a quilt. Angela drew it on 1 cm squared paper.

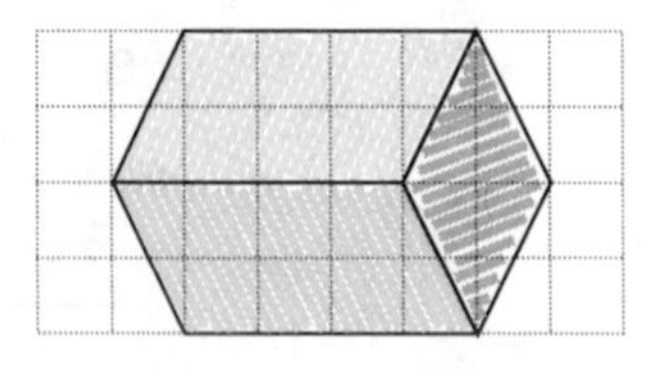

a Find the area of the red piece of the design.

b Angela calculates that she will need 250 of these red pieces to complete the quilt. Find the area of the completed quilt that will be red.

c The pieces of the patchwork need sewing together. Angela makes a seam allowance by adding 0.5 cm to the length and perpendicular height of each piece.
Find the area of each red piece that will be cut.

21 **a** Copy this diagram onto 1 cm squared paper. You know how to find the area of a parallelogram; use this knowledge to work out the area of the shaded triangle. Write down, in terms of its base and height, how you found this area.

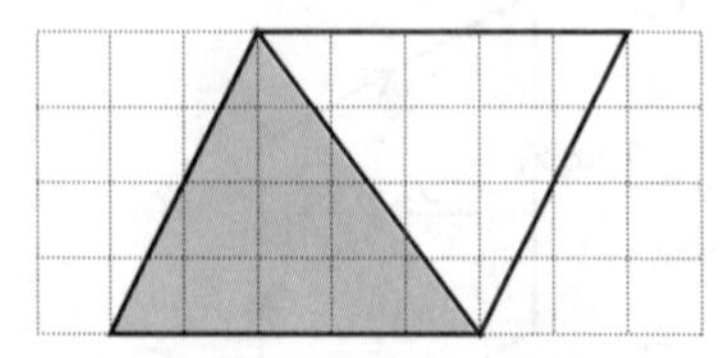

b Will the expression for the area found in part **a** work for any triangle?

22 **a** How many parallelograms can be drawn with these measurements?

b Do all parallelograms with base 10 cm and slant height 7 cm have the same area?

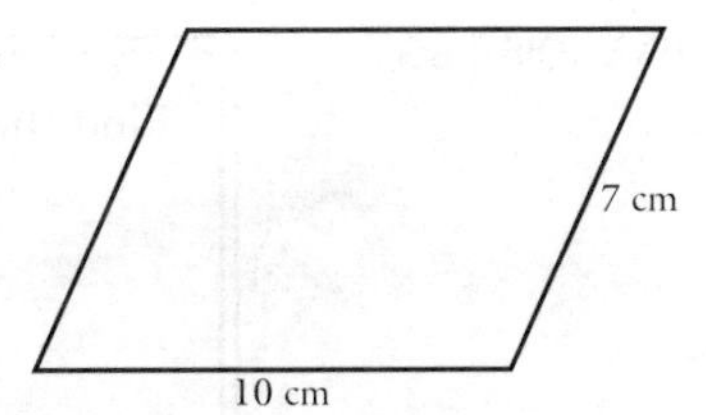

23 What can you say about the areas of the shapes shown in the diagram? Explain your answer.

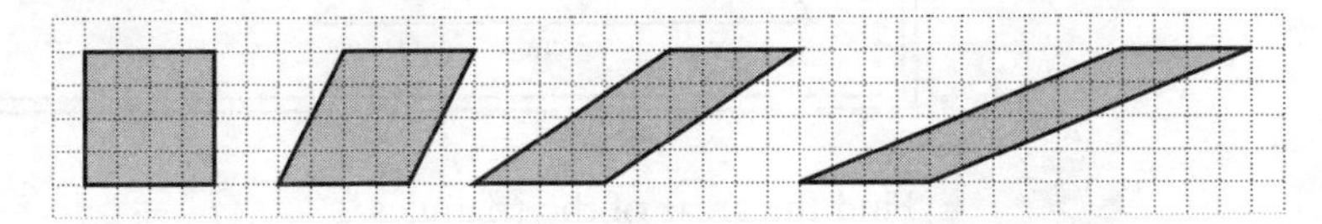

THE AREA OF A TRIANGLE

We can think of a triangle as half a parallelogram.

Area of triangle

$= \frac{1}{2} \times$ area of parallelogram

$= \frac{1}{2}$ (base $\times$ perpendicular height)

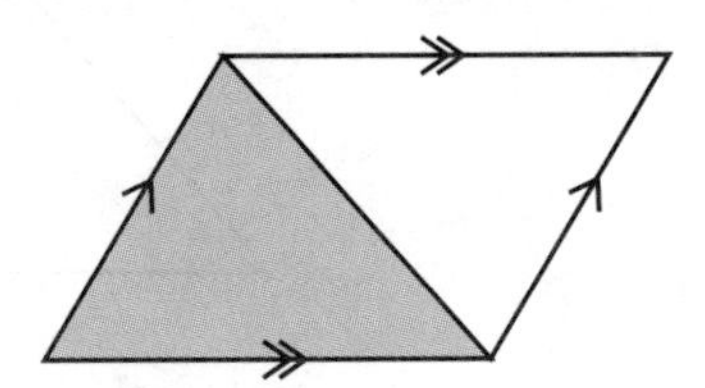

We can also see that if we enclose a triangle in a rectangle as shown below, the area of the triangle is half the area of the rectangle, i.e.

area of triangle

$= \frac{1}{2} \times$ area of enclosing rectangle

$= \frac{1}{2}$(base $\times$ height of triangle)

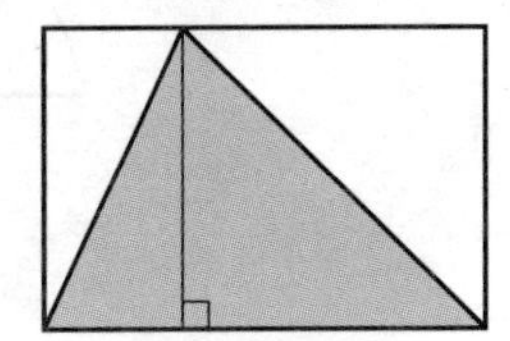

THE HEIGHT OF A TRIANGLE

When we talk about the height of a triangle (or a parallelogram) we mean its *perpendicular height* and *not* a slant height.

The three sides of a triangle are 12.5 cm, 10 cm and 7.5 cm long.

If the given triangle is drawn accurately on squared paper, we can see that the height of the triangle is neither 10 cm nor 7.5 cm but 6 cm.

Notice also that the foot of this perpendicular is *not* the midpoint of the base.

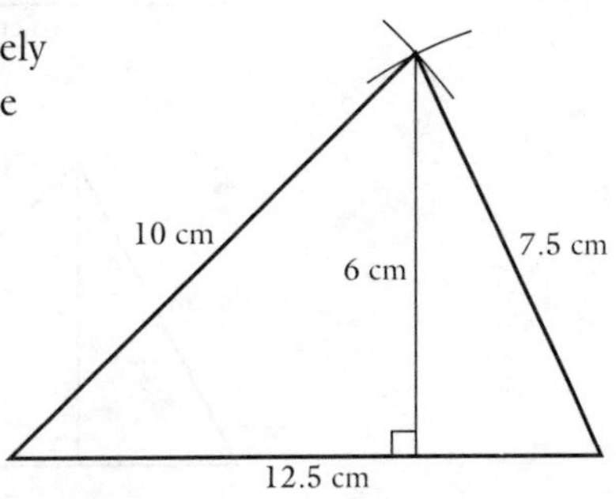

EXERCISE 8G

Find the area of a triangle with base 7 cm and height 6 cm.

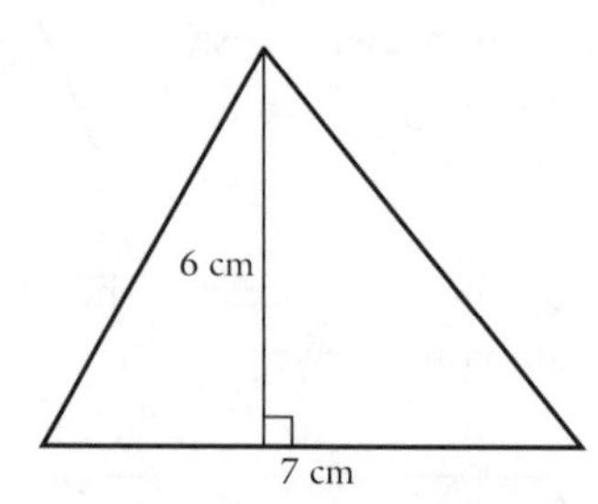

$$\text{Area} = \frac{1}{2}(\text{base} \times \text{height})$$

$$= \frac{1}{\not{2}_1} \times 7 \times \not{6}^3 \text{ cm}^2$$

$$= 21 \text{ cm}^2$$

Find the areas of the triangles.

1

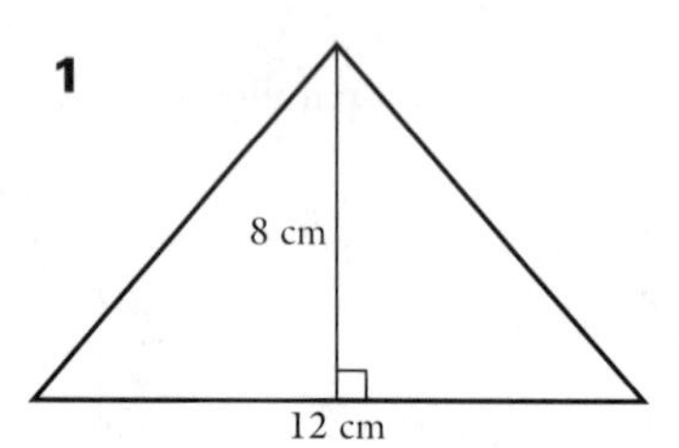

2

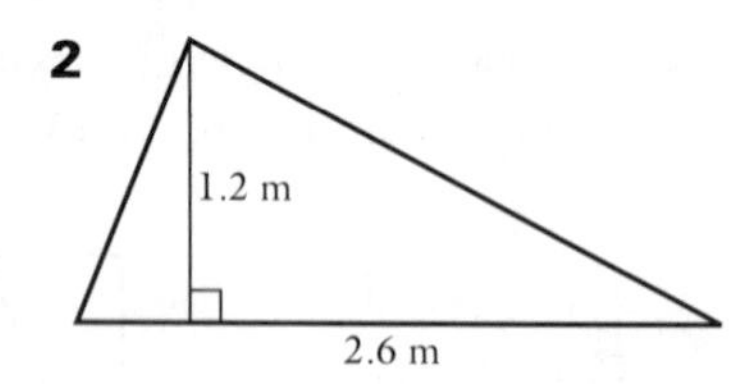

3

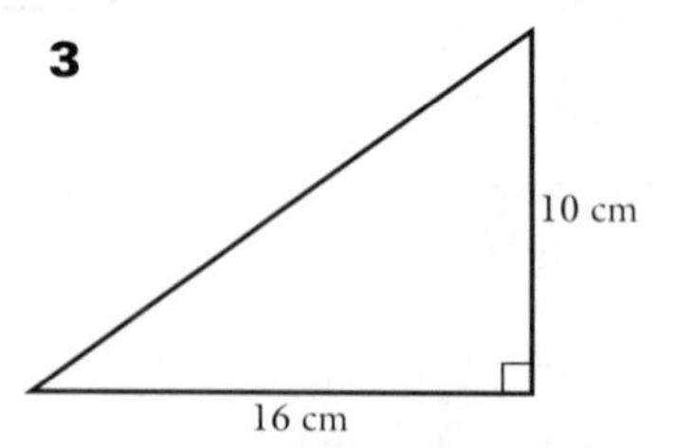

4

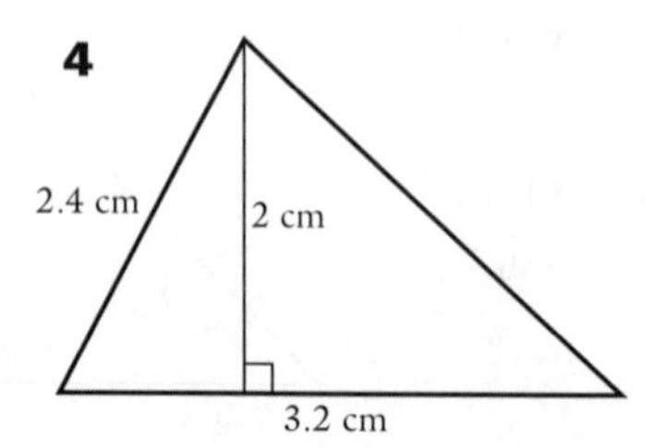

5

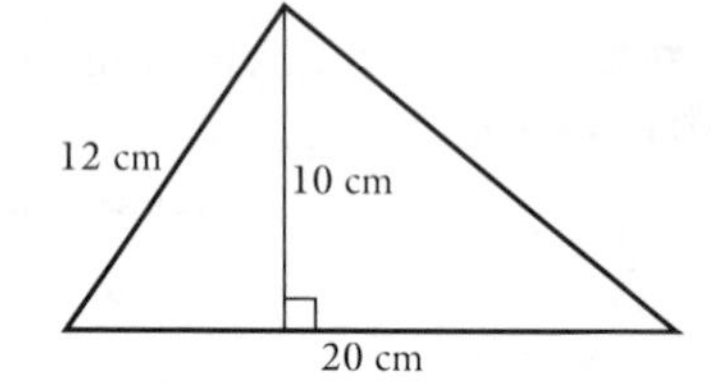

6

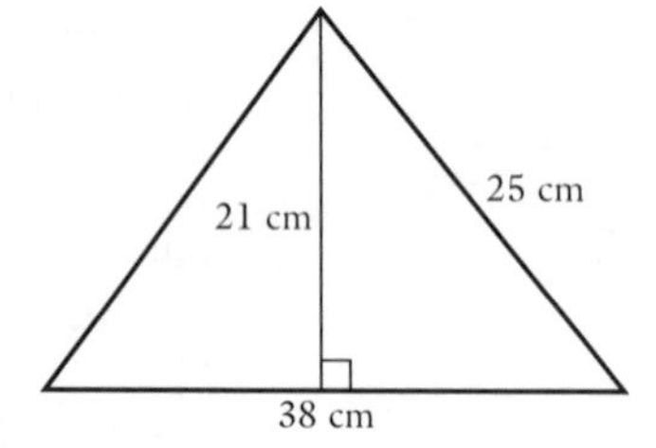

7

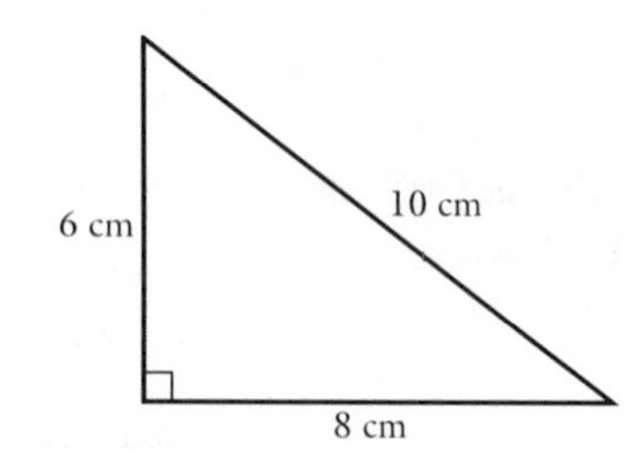

8

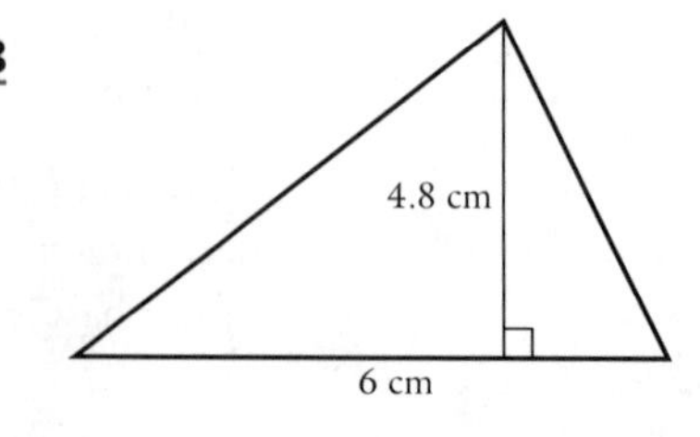

Find the area of the triangle.

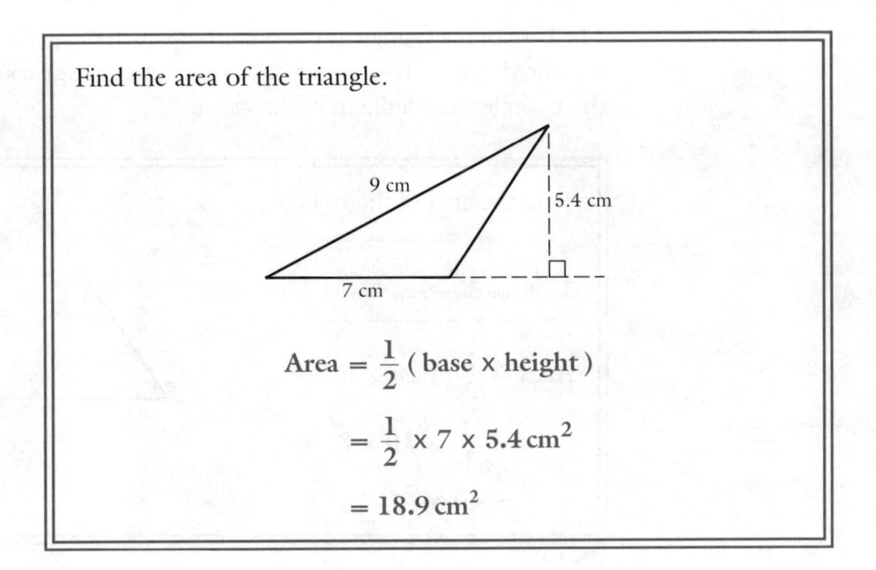

$$\text{Area} = \frac{1}{2}\,(\text{base} \times \text{height})$$

$$= \frac{1}{2} \times 7 \times 5.4\ \text{cm}^2$$

$$= 18.9\ \text{cm}^2$$

Find the areas of the triangles.

9 **12**

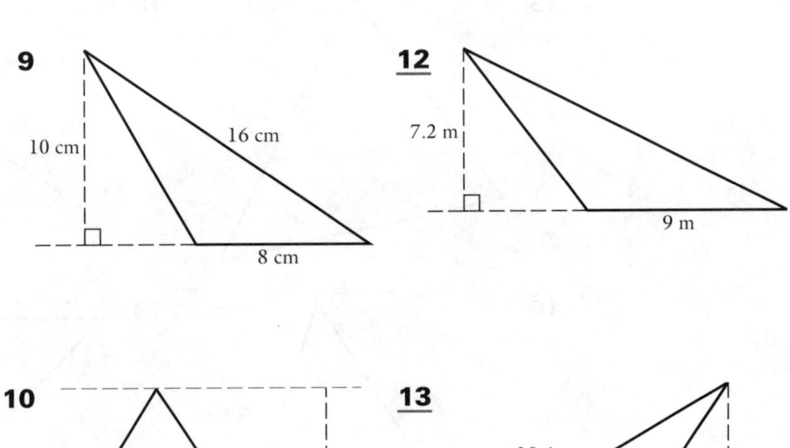

10 **13**

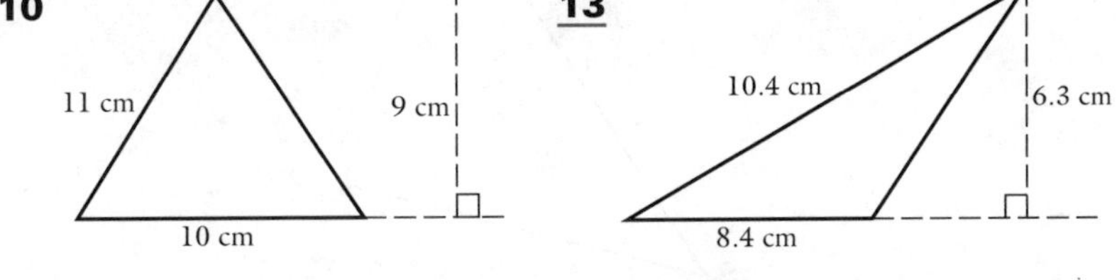

11 **14**

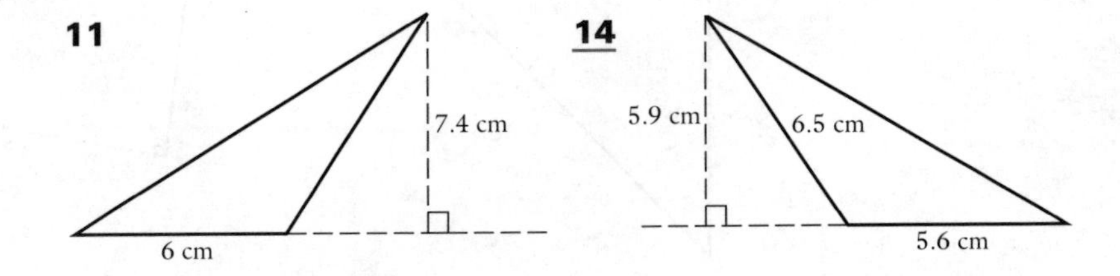

The base of the triangle is the side from which the perpendicular height is measured. If the base is not obvious, turn the page round and look at the triangle from a different direction.

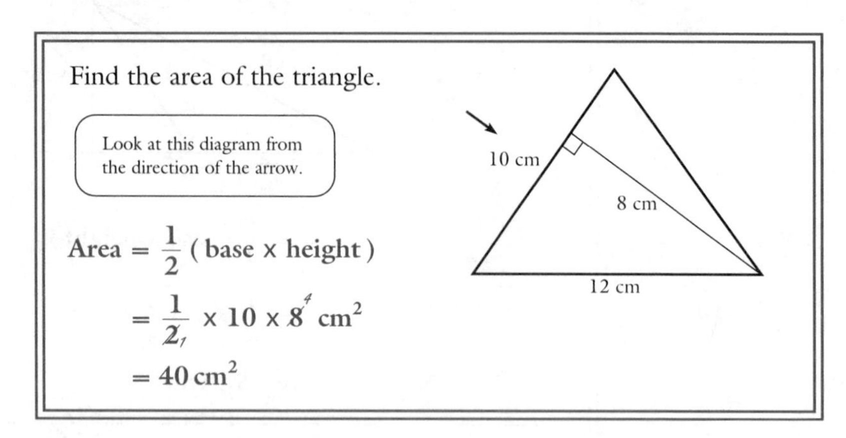

$$\text{Area} = \frac{1}{2}(\text{base} \times \text{height})$$

$$= \frac{1}{2} \times 10 \times 8 \text{ cm}^2$$

$$= 40 \text{ cm}^2$$

Find the areas of the triangles.

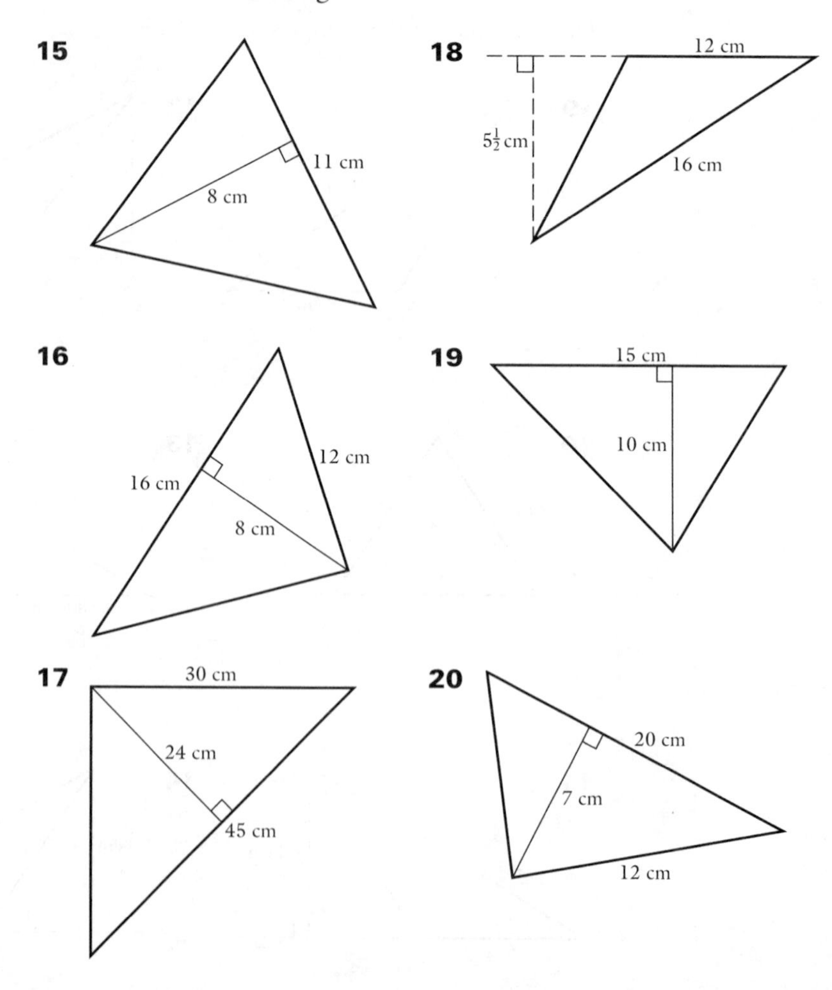

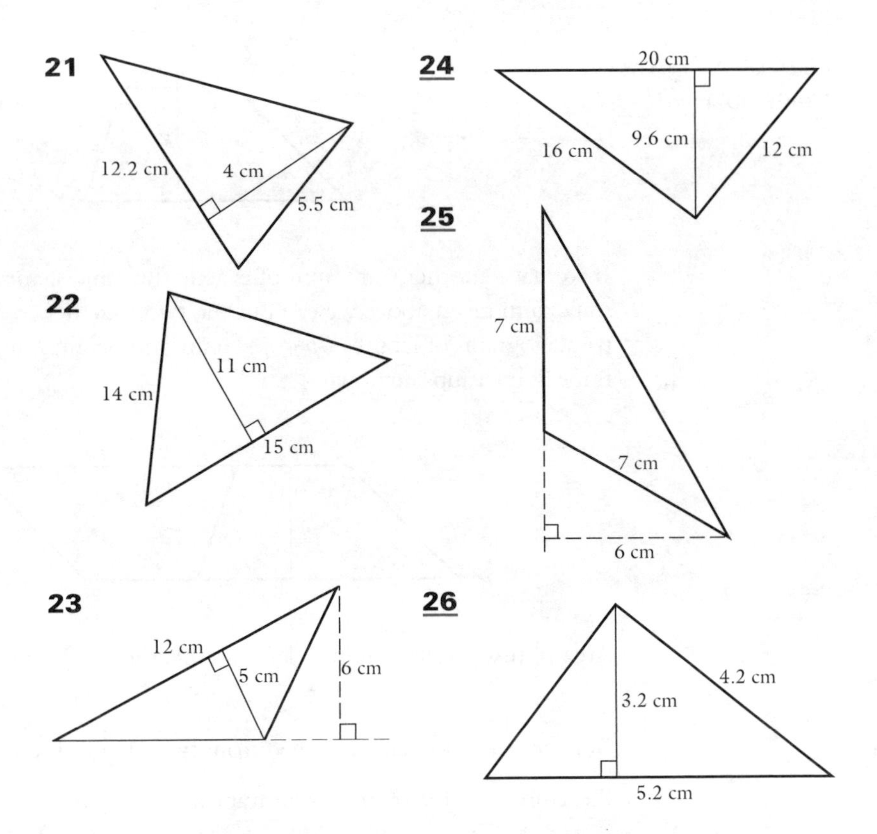

For questions **27** and **28**, use squared paper to draw axes for x and y from 0 to 6 using 1 square to 1 unit. Find the area of each triangle.

27 ΔABC with A(1, 0), B(6, 0) and C(4, 4)

28 ΔPQR with P(0, 2), Q(6, 0) and R(6, 4)

29 Find the area of each triangle in this diagram. The squares represent square centimetres. Explain your answers.

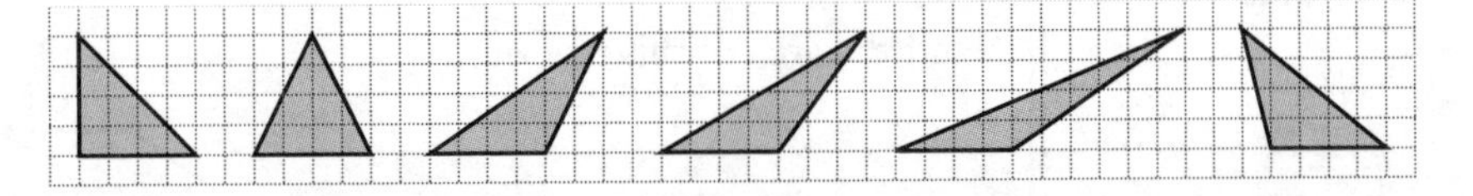

30 This company logo is made from a square and four congruent triangles. The logo is to be made from stainless steel and mounted on the front of a building. Find the area of steel needed if the inner square is made to measure 20 cm by 20 cm.

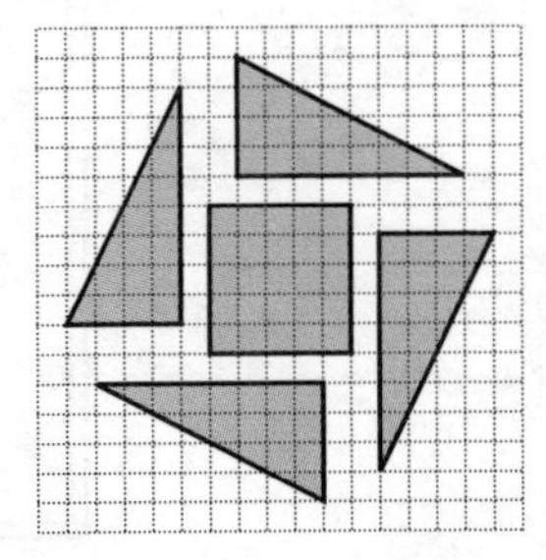

AREA OF A TRAPEZIUM

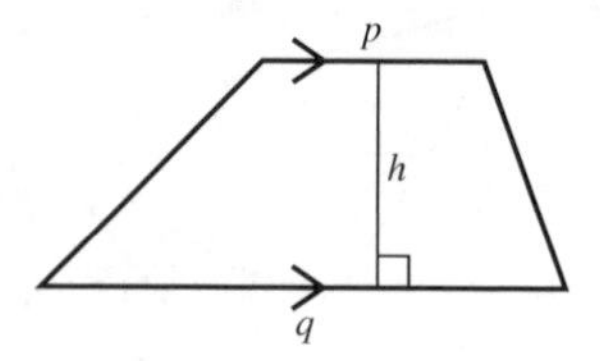

If we have another trapezium of exactly the same shape and size as the trapezium given above we can put the two together to form a parallelogram, of length $(p+q)$ units and height h units. (One of the trapeziums is upside down.)

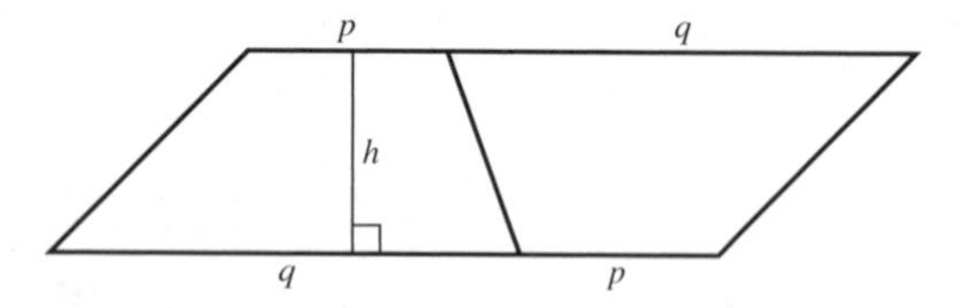

Area of this parallelogram = length × height

$= (p+q) \times h$

But the parallelogram is formed from two identical trapeziums,

therefore area of the given trapezium $= \frac{1}{2}(p+q) \times h$

This formula is easier to remember in words; $(p+q)$ is the sum of the parallel lengths, so

> the area of a trapezium is equal to
> $\frac{1}{2}$(sum of the parallel sides) × (distance between them)

EXERCISE 8H

Find the area of this tapezium.

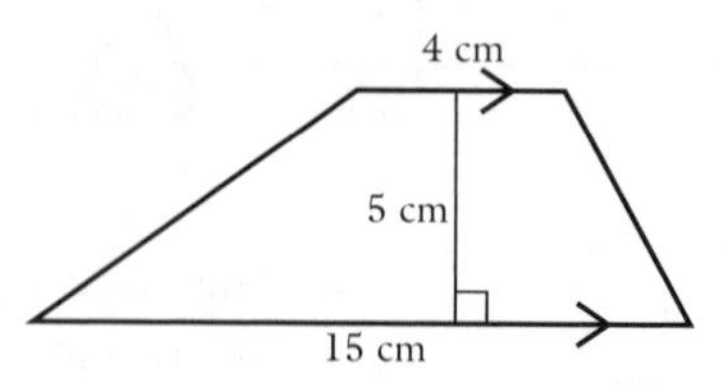

Area = $\frac{1}{2}$(sum of the parallel sides) × (distance between them)

$= \frac{1}{2}(15+4) \times 5\ \text{cm}^2$

$= 0.5 \times 19 \times 5\ \text{cm}^2 = 47.5\ \text{cm}^2$

Find the area of each of the following trapeziums.

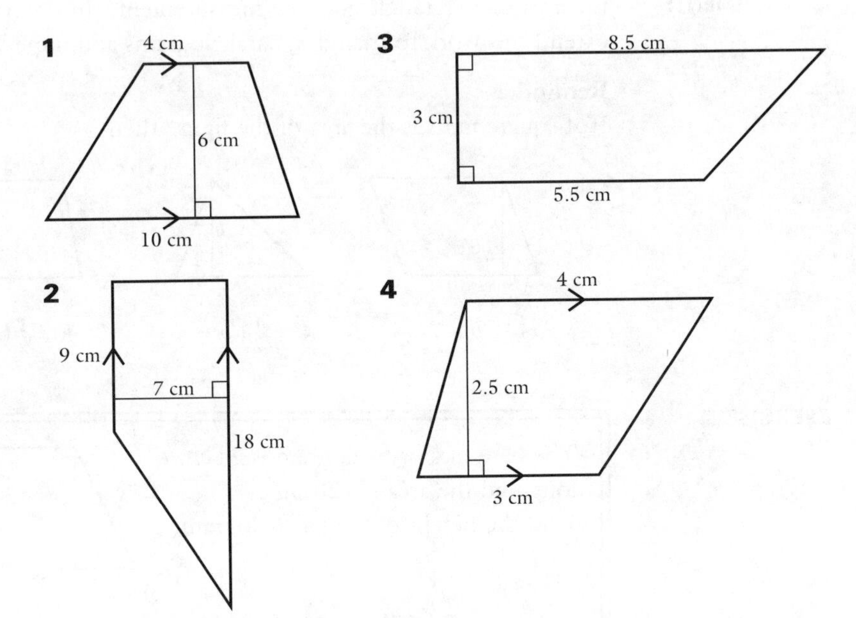

For questions **5** and **6** use squared paper and draw axes for x and y using the ranges $-6 \leqslant x \leqslant 6$ and $-6 \leqslant y \leqslant 6$ and a scale of one square to 1 unit. Plot the points and join them in alphabetical order to give a closed shape. Find, in square units, the area of the resulting shape.

5 A(6, 1), B(4, −3), C(−2, −3), D(−3, 1)

6 A(3, 5), B(−4, 4), C(−4, −2), D(3, −5)

7 This is the cross-section of a conduit which is used to carry computer cables. Find its area.

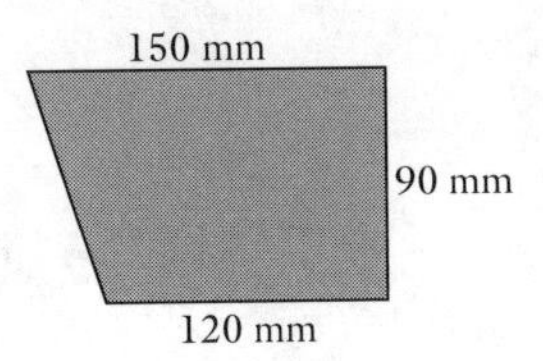

8

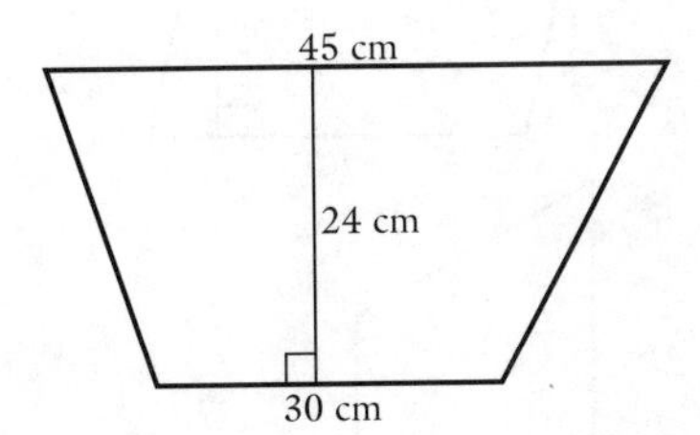

The diagram shows the cross-section of a drinking trough in the corner of a field.
Find the area of the cross-section.

FINDING MISSING MEASURMENTS

In **Exercise 8C** we found the missing measurement when we were given the area of a rectangle and one measurement. In the next exercise we extend this work to triangles, parallelograms and trapeziums.

Reminder

If A square units is the area of the figure then

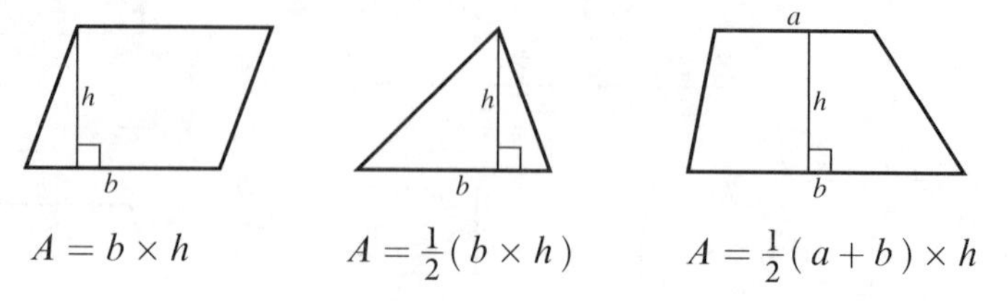

$A = b \times h$ $\quad A = \frac{1}{2}(b \times h)$ $\quad A = \frac{1}{2}(a + b) \times h$

EXERCISE 8I

The base of a parallelogram is 24 cm long and the area is 120 cm^2.
Find the height of the parallelogram.

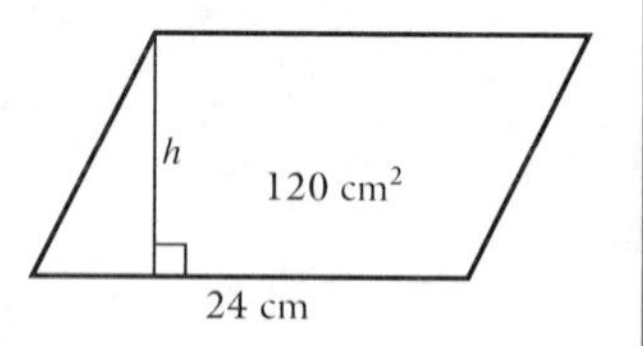

Using $A = b \times h$ with $A = 120$ and $b = 24$ gives

$120 = 24 \times h$ This is a simple equation that we can solve.

Therefore $h = 120 \div 24 = 5$

The height of the parallelogram is 5 cm.

Find the missing measurements for these parallelograms.

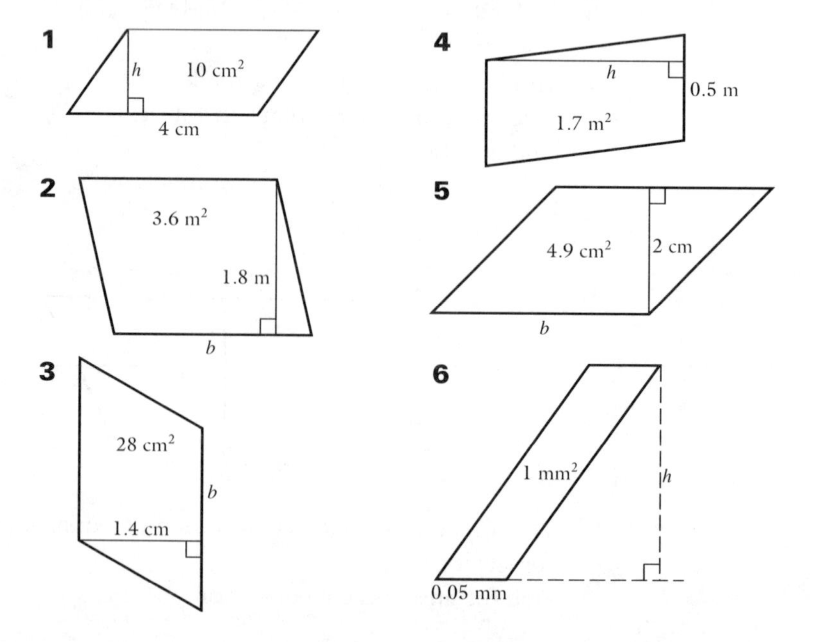

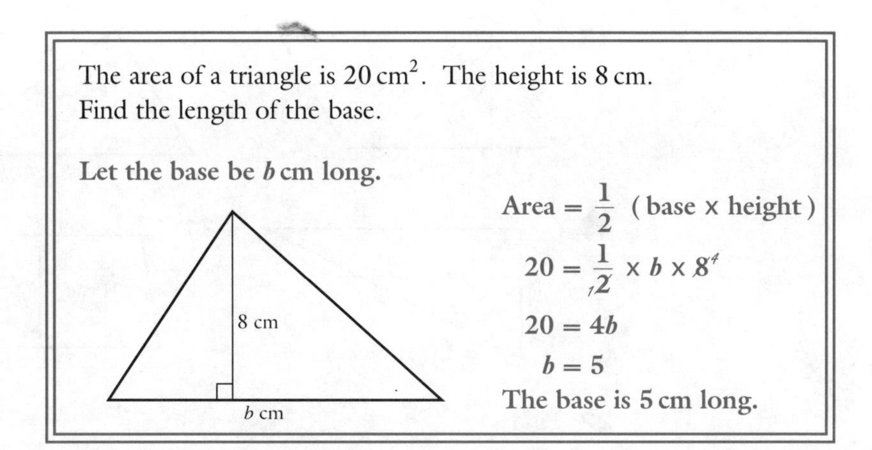

The table gives the area and one measurement for various triangles. Find the missing measurements.

	Area	Base	Height
7	24 cm^2	6 cm	
8	30 cm^2		10 cm
9	48 cm^2		16 cm
10	10 cm^2	10 cm	
11	36 cm^2	24 cm	

Find the missing measurement in each figure.

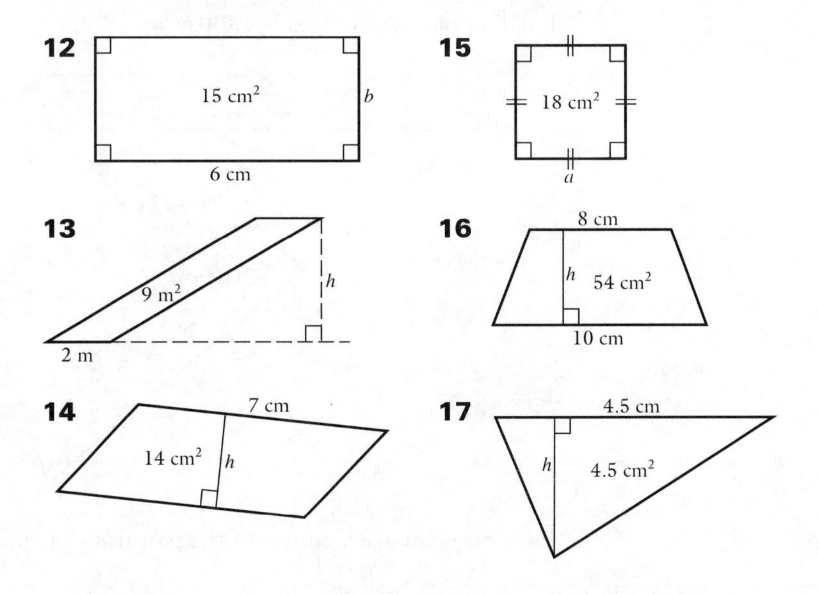

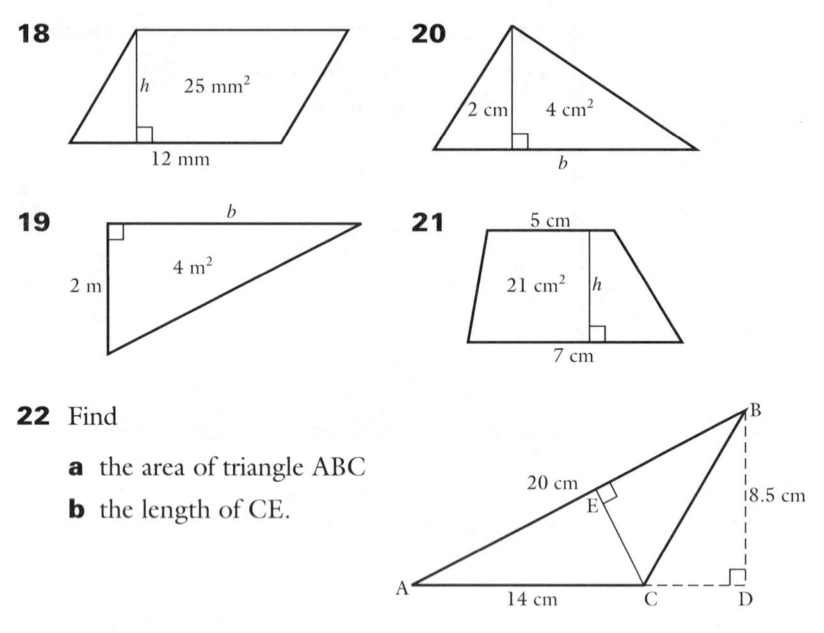

22 Find

a the area of triangle ABC

b the length of CE.

23 Jason wants to buy enough edging to go round a square flower bed whose area is $5\,\text{m}^2$.

a Find the distance round the edge of this flower bed.

b Is it sensible for Jason to buy exactly the length found in part **a**? Give reasons for your answer.

24 A rectangular building plot is advertised as having an area of $300\,\text{m}^2$ and a road frontage of $12\,\text{m}$. How deep is the plot?

25 This illustration is from a developer's scheme. It shows the plan of a building plot whose area is $4300\,\text{m}^2$.

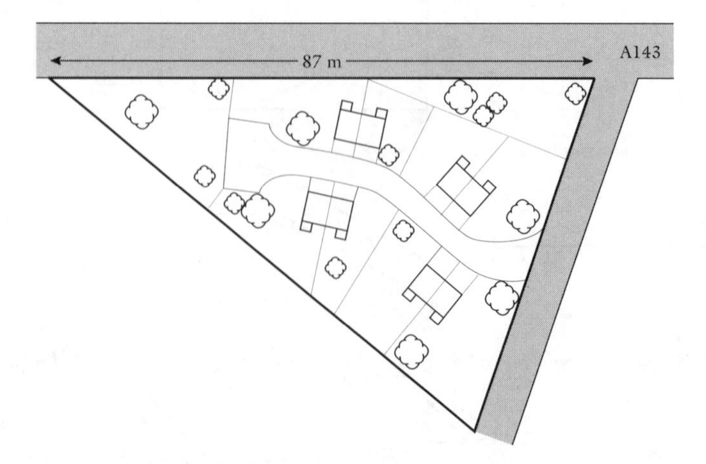

How far is the back corner of the plot from the main road?

FINDING THE AREA OF A COMPOUND SHAPE

A compound shape can often be divided into shapes whose areas we can find.

EXERCISE 8J

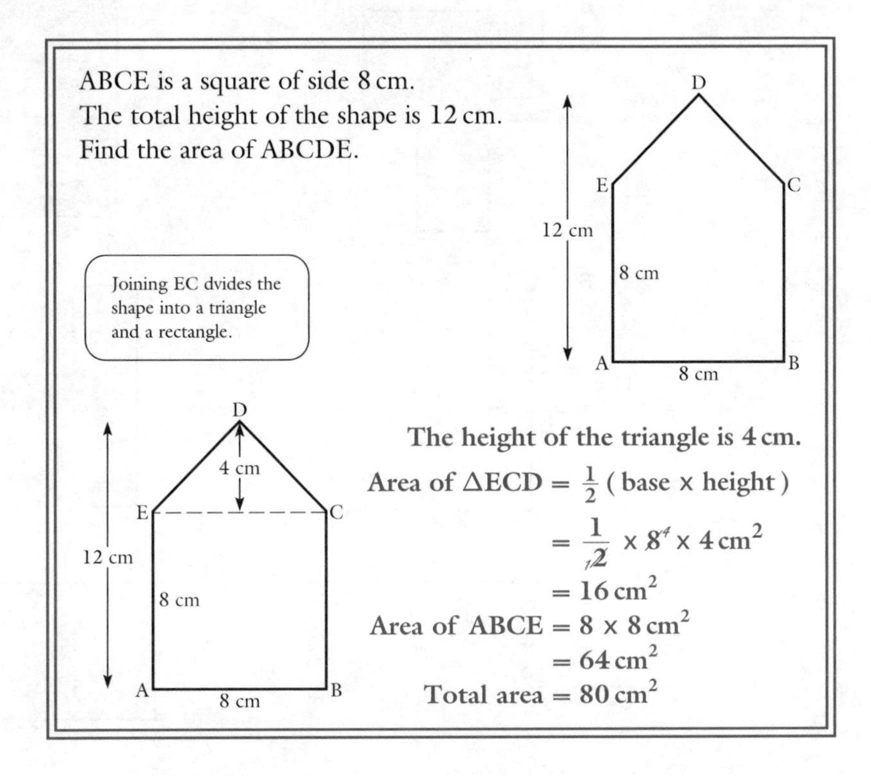

Find the areas of the following shapes. Remember to draw a diagram for each question and mark in all the measurements.

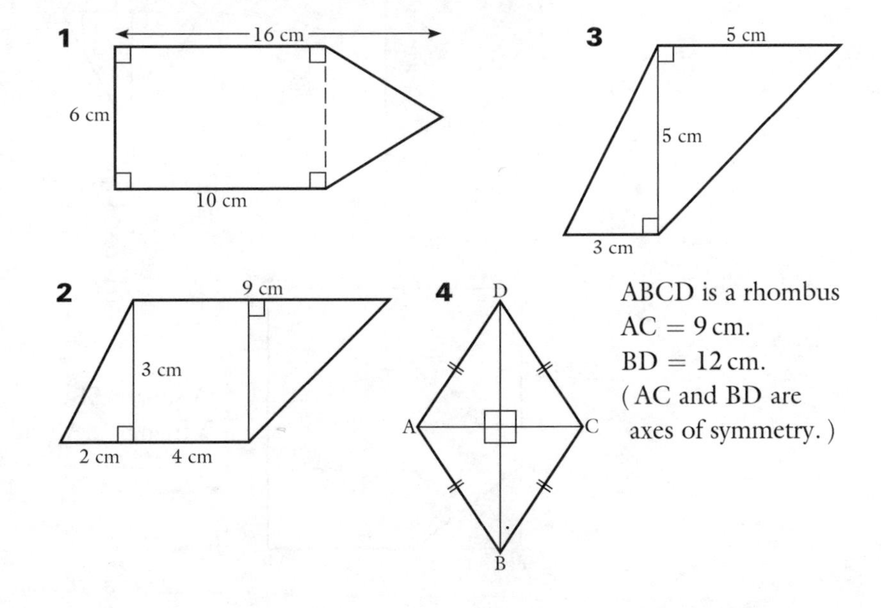

For questions **5** to **15** find the areas of the figures in square centimetres. The measurements are all in centimetres.

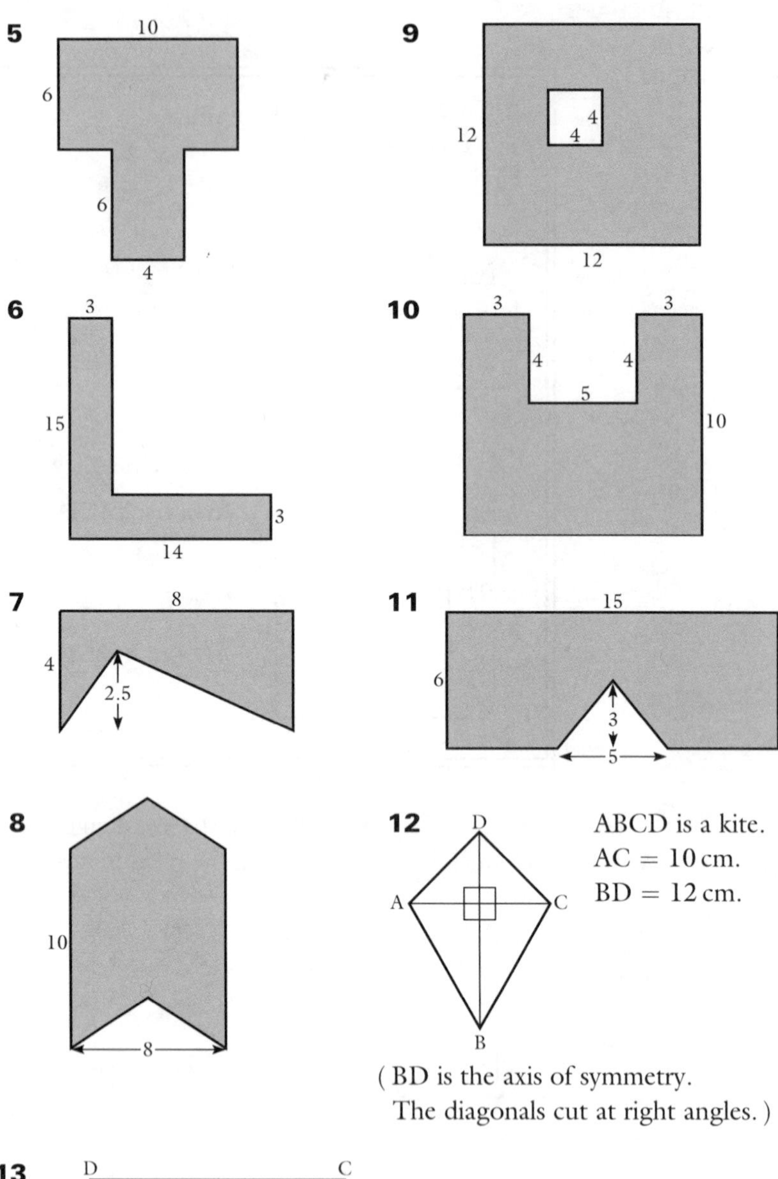

13

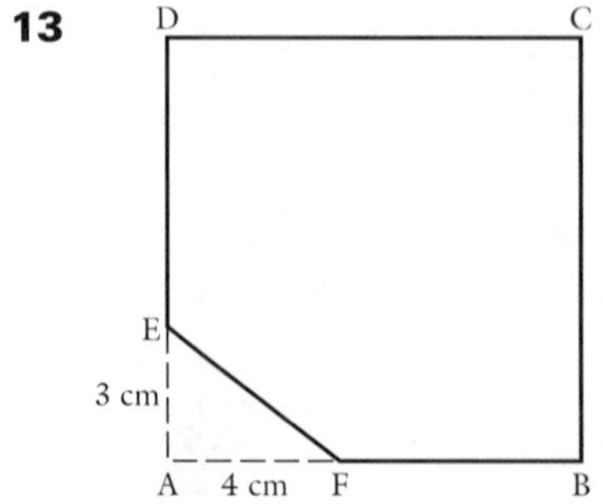

A square ABCD, of side 9 cm, has a triangle EAF cut off it.

14 **15**

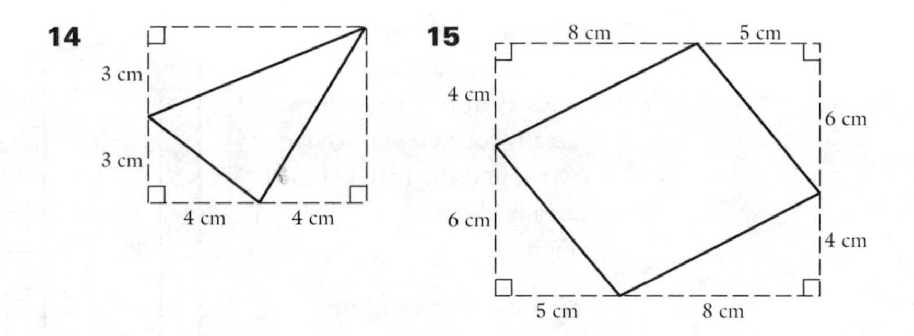

Find the area of these cork gaskets.

16

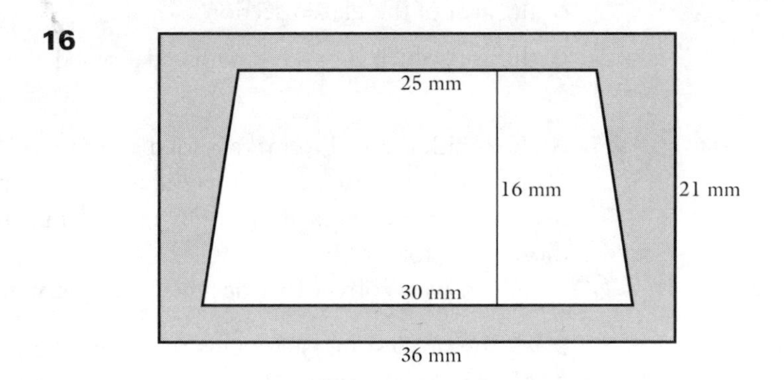

17

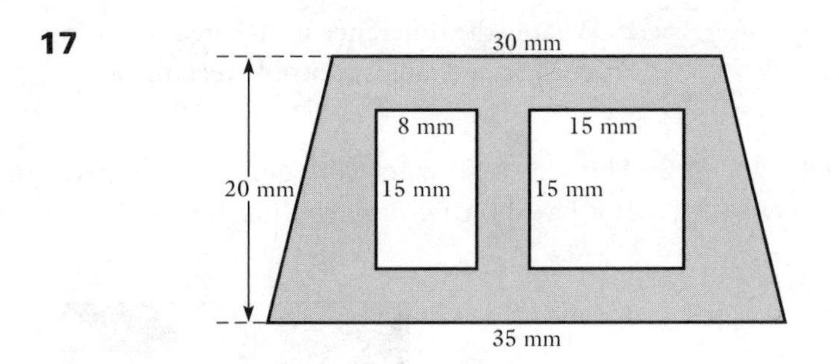

In questions **18** and **19** draw axes for x and y from -6 to $+6$, using 1 square to 1 unit.

Find the areas of the following shapes.

18 Quadrilateral ABCD with A$(-2, -3)$, B$(3, -3)$, C$(0, 4)$ and D$(-2, 4)$.

19 Quadrilateral EFGH with E$(-1, 1)$, F$(2, -3)$, G$(5, 1)$ and H$(2, 5)$.

20 The diagram shows the end wall of a lean-to conservatory. The shaded area is covered with cedar wood and the hatched area is glazed.
Find

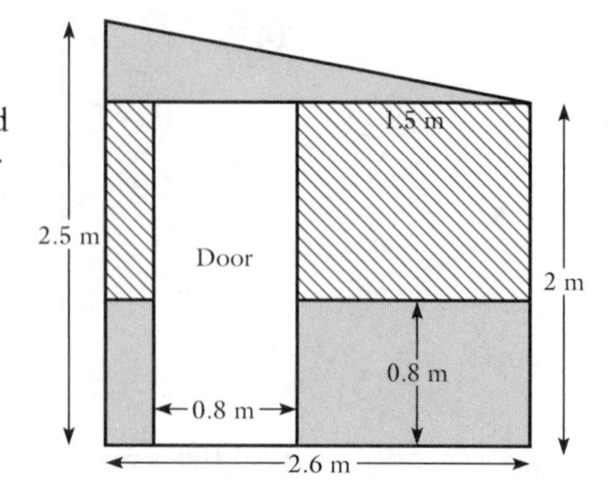

a the total area of the end wall

b the area of the door

c the area of the glazed section

d the area which is covered with cedar wood.

21 A silversmith is asked to make a solid silver rectangle measuring 10 mm by 9 mm, each correct to the nearest millimetre. He says that the measurements may vary by up to $\frac{1}{2}$ mm above or below those asked for.
Giving answers correct to 1 decimal place, what are

a **i** the smallest measurements that might be used
ii the largest measurements that might be used?

b What is the difference in the area of silver needed to make the smallest and largest possible rectangles?

22 This is a classic patchwork quilt pattern called 'the captain's wheel'. It is based on a 4 unit by 4 unit square.

a Find the area of the patterned part of the design if the length of one side of the large square is 12 cm.

b A quilt is made from 800 of these squares. What area of quilt is red?

23 Wood is used to make the top of this child's posting box.
It is drawn on a 1 cm grid and has been scaled down for this diagram.

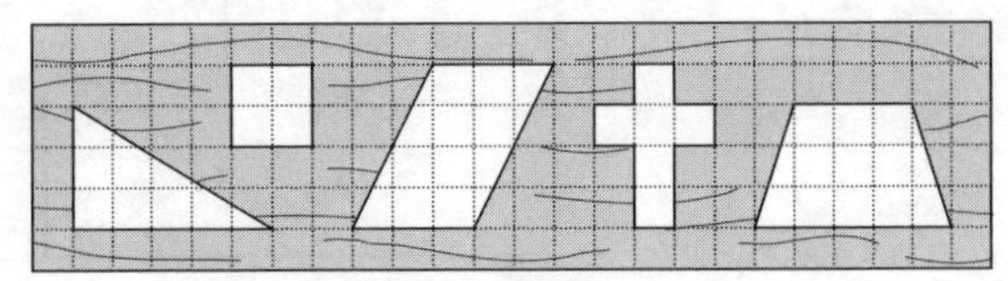

Find the area of the piece of wood.

24 This company logo is made by placing a rectangle on the shorter parallel side of a trapezium.
Find its area.

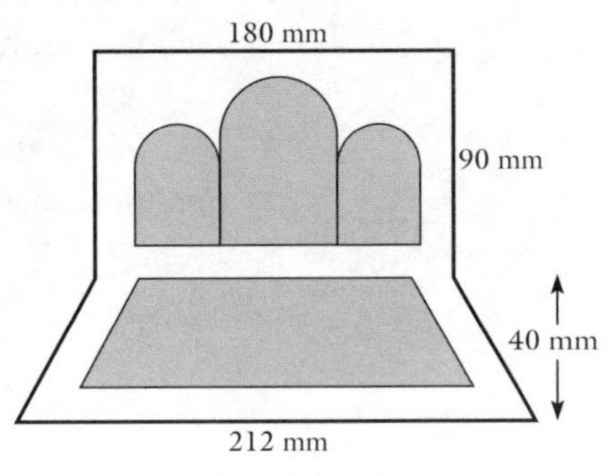

25 This silver necklace is made from sheet silver. Each pendant is either a whole rhombus whose diagonals are 2 cm and 4 cm or half one of these. Find the area of sheet silver used.

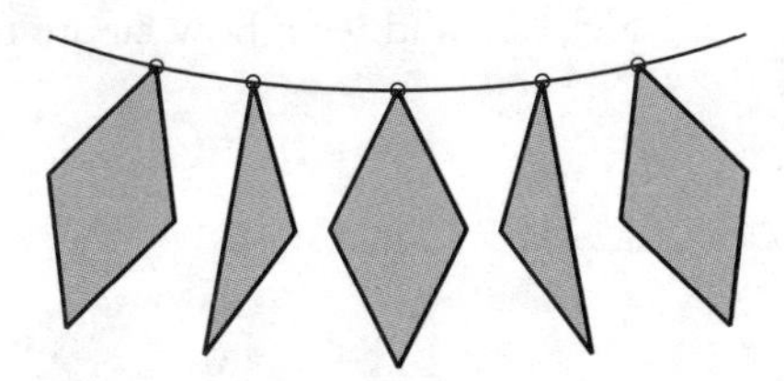

MIXED EXERCISE

EXERCISE 8K

Find the areas of the following figures.

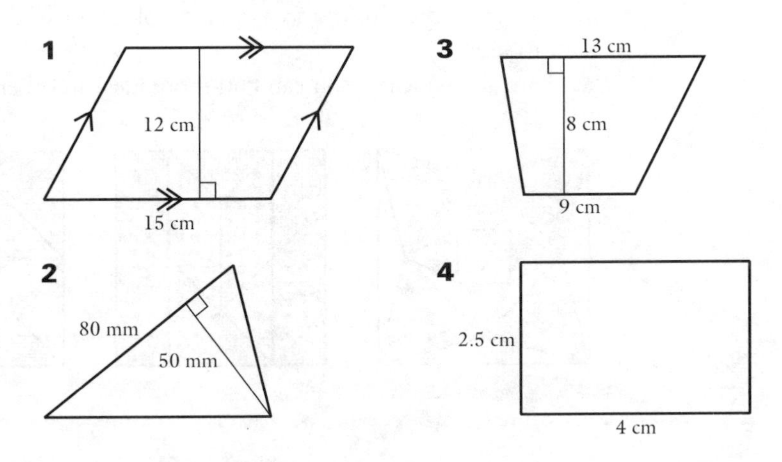

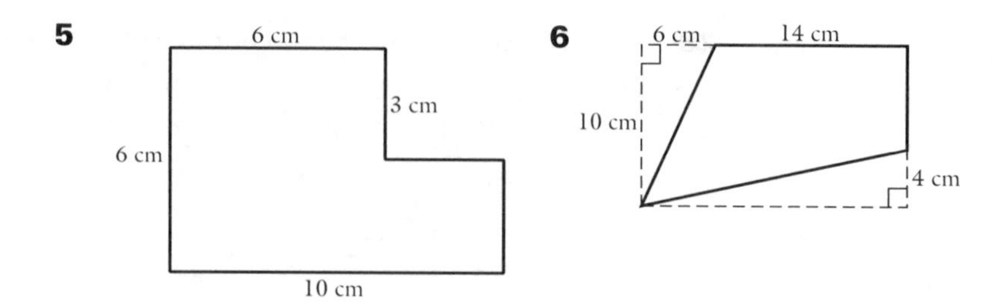

7 The area of a rectangle is 84 cm^2 and its width is 6 cm.
Find its length.

8 The area of this parallelogram is 52 cm^2.
Find the distance, d cm.

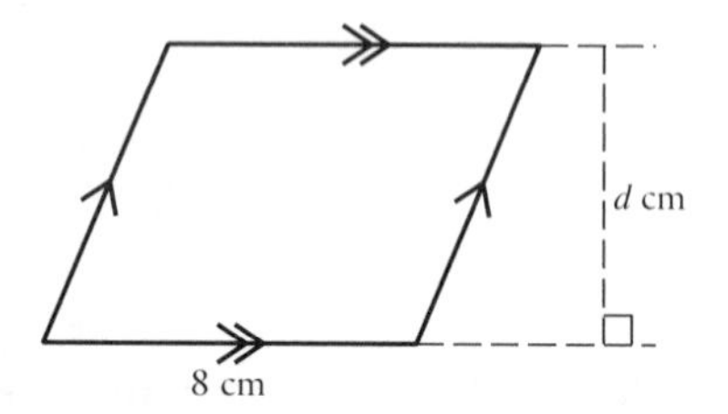

9 The area of a trapezium is 51 cm^2. If the lengths of the parallel sides are 8 cm and 9 cm how far are they apart?

PRACTICAL WORK

Design a patchwork mat measuring approximately 40 cm by 40 cm.
Base your design on a mixture of triangles, parallelograms, squares and rectangles.
Include an estimate of the area of each colour, or texture, that you want to use.
Here are a few ideas. You can find more ideas in other books.

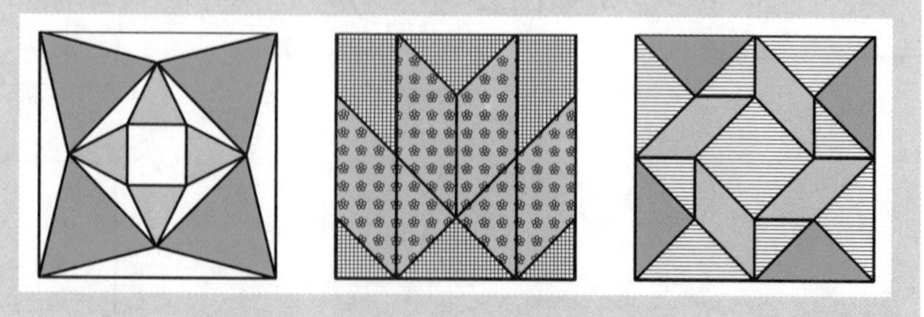

INVESTIGATION

These triangles are drawn on 1 cm grid dots.

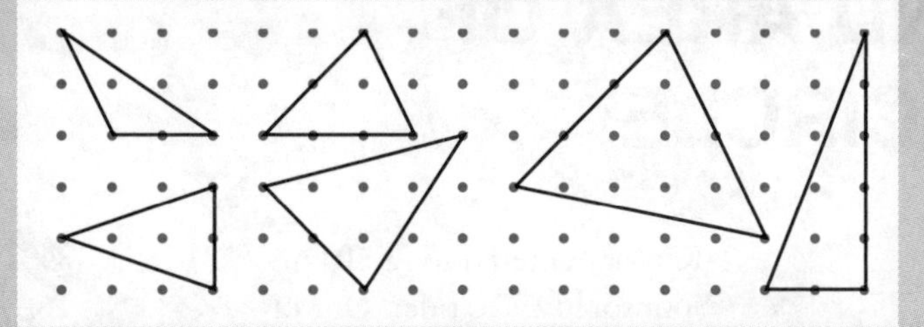

a Copy and complete this table for each triangle.

Number of dots on edge	Number of dots inside	Area (cm^2)

b Find a relationship between the number of dots on the edge, the number of dots inside and the area of each shape. Does this relationship hold for any triangle drawn on the grid?

c Investigate the relationship between number of dots on the edge, the number of dots inside and the areas of rectangles and parallelograms.

CIRCUMFERENCE AND AREA OF A CIRCLE

9

Ken has entered for a 50 km sponsored cycle ride. Out of idle curiosity he wonders how many pedal strokes this will involve. This problem can be solved by finding out how many times the wheels turn for each turn of the pedals and how far the bike moves forward for each turn of the wheels.

To find out how far the bike moves forward for each turn of the wheels we need to know the distance round the outside of each tyre. This can be found by measuring, but it is difficult to measure round a curved wheel accurately. It is much easier if we can calculate the distance round the wheel by first measuring the distance across the wheel. To solve this and many simple everyday problems we need to know the basic facts about a circle.

DIAMETER, RADIUS AND CIRCUMFERENCE

When you use a pair of compasses to draw a circle, the place where you put the point is the *centre* of the circle. The line that the pencil draws is the *circumference* of the circle. All the points on the circumference are the same distance from the centre.

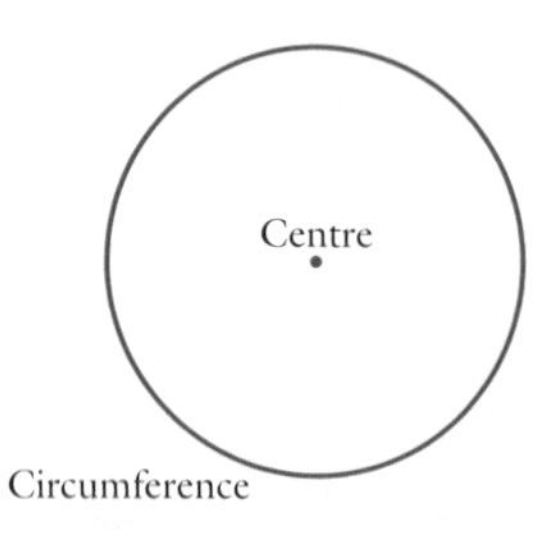

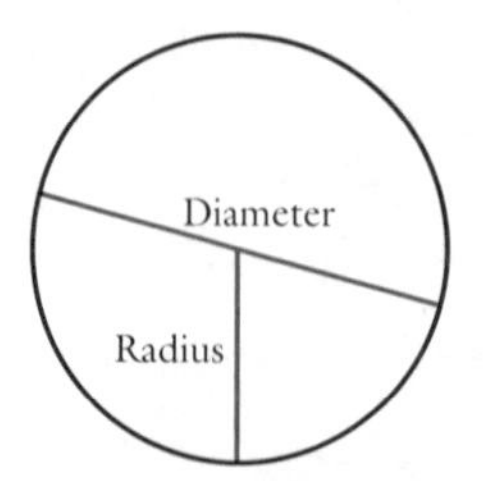

Any straight line joining the centre to a point on the circumference is a *radius*.

A straight line across the full width of a circle (going through the centre) is a *diameter*.

The diameter is twice as long as the radius. If d cm is the length of a diameter and r cm is the length of a radius, we can write this as a formula, i.e. $d = 2r$

EXERCISE 9A

In questions **1** to **6** write down the length of the diameter of the circle whose radius is given.

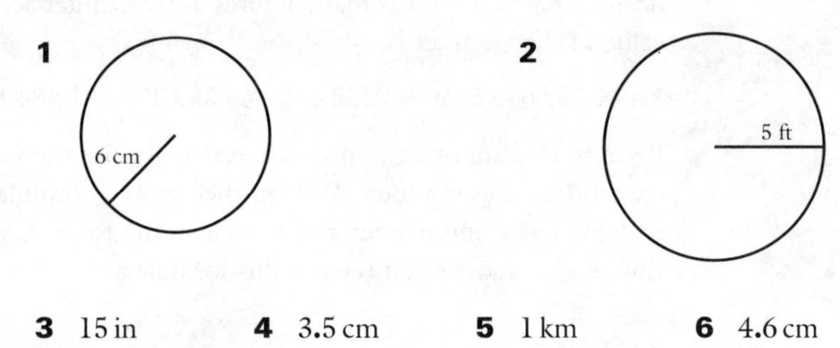

3 15 in **4** 3.5 cm **5** 1 km **6** 4.6 cm

7 For this question you will need some thread and a cylinder (e.g. a soft-drink can, the cardboard tube from a roll of kitchen paper).
Measure across the top of the cylinder to get a value for the diameter.
Wind the thread 10 times round the can. Measure the length of thread needed to do this and then divide your answer by 10 to get the value of the circumference.
If C mm is the length of the circumference and d mm is the length of the diameter find, approximately, the value of $C \div d$.

8 Compare the results from the whole class for the value of $C \div d$.

INTRODUCING π

From the last exercise you will see that, for any circle,

$$\text{circumference} \approx 3 \times \text{diameter}$$

The number that you have to multiply the diameter by to get the circumference is slightly larger than 3.

This number is unlike any number that you have met so far. It cannot be written down exactly, either as a fraction or as a decimal:

as a fraction it is approximately, but *not exactly*, $\frac{22}{7}$;

as a decimal it is approximately 3.142, which is correct to 3 decimal places.

Over the centuries mathematicians have spent a lot of time trying to find the true value of this number. The ancient Chinese used 3. Three is also the value given in the Old Testament (I Kings 7:23). The Egyptians (c. 1600 BC) used $4 \times (\frac{8}{9})^2$. Archimedes (c. 225 BC) was the first person to use a sound method for finding its value and a mathematician called Van Ceulen (1540–1610) spent most of his life finding it to 35 decimal places !

Now, with a computer to do the arithmetic we can find its value to as many decimal places as we choose: it is a never ending, never repeating, decimal fraction. To as many figures as we can get across the page, the value of this number is

3.141 592 653 589 793 238 462 643 383 279 502 884 197 169 399 375

Because we cannot write it down exactly we use the Greek letter π (pi) to stand for this number. We can then write a formula connecting the circumference and diameter of a circle in the form $C = \pi d$.
But $d = 2r$ so we can rewrite this formula as

$$C = 2\pi r$$

where C units is the circumference and r units is the radius.

Because π is close to 3, we can always use 3 as a value for π to work out estimated answers.

CALCULATING THE CIRCUMFERENCE

EXERCISE 9B

The radius of a circle is 3.8 m.

a Use $\pi \approx 3$ to estimate the circumference of this circle.

b Use the π button on your calculator to work out a more accurate value. Give your answer correct to 3 significant figures.

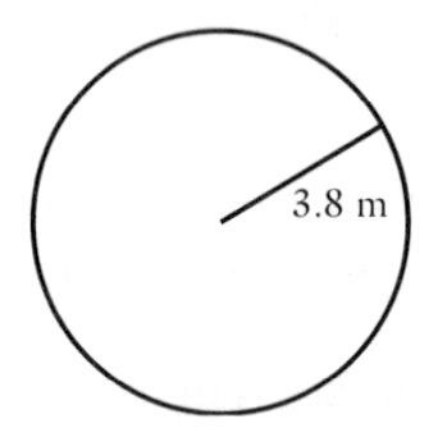

a Using $C = 2\pi r$ and $\pi \approx 3$ gives $C \approx 2 \times 3 \times 4 = 24$

b Using $C = 2\pi r$
gives $C = 2 \times \pi \times 3.8$

Press 2 x π x 3 . 8 =

$= 23.87\ldots$
$= 23.9$ (correct to 3 s.f.)

Circumference = 23.9 m (correct to 3 s.f.)

The approximate answer agrees closely with this, so the calculated answer is likely to be correct.

In questions **1** to **12**

a Use $\pi \approx 3$ to estimate the circumference of a circle with the given radius.

b Use the π button on your calculator, giving your answers correct to 3 significant figures, to find the circumference.

1 2.3 m	**4** 53 mm	**7** 4.8 m	**10** 28 mm
2 4.6 cm	**5** 250 mm	**8** 1.8 m	**11** 1.4 m
3 2.9 cm	**6** 36 ft	**9** 7 yd	**12** 35 in

Find the circumference of a circle of diameter 12.6 mm. Use the π button on your calculator. Check that your answer is sensible by finding an approximate answer using 3 for π.

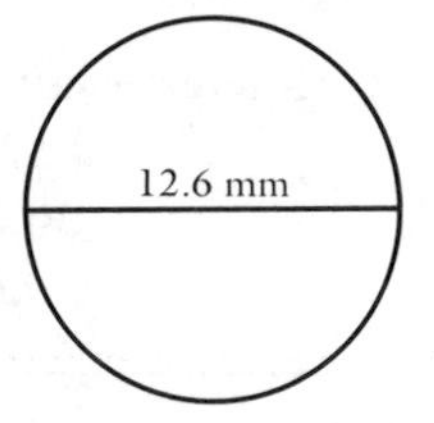

Using $C = 2\pi r$,

$$r = \tfrac{1}{2} \text{ of } 12.6 = 6.3$$

$$\therefore \quad C = 2 \times \pi \times 6.3$$
$$= 39.58\ldots$$
$$= 39.6 \text{ (correct to 3 s.f.)}$$

Circumference = 39.6 mm (correct to 3 s.f.)

Instead we could have used $C = \pi d$
Then $C = \pi \times 12.6$
$= 39.6$ (correct to 3 s.f.)

Check: If $\pi \approx 3$ and $d \approx 13$
then $C = \pi d \approx 3 \times 13 = 39$

Using the π button on your calculator, and giving your answers correct to 2 significant figures, find the circumference of a circle of

13 radius 154 mm	**16** radius 34.6 cm
14 diameter 28 in	**17** diameter 511 mm
15 radius 7.7 m	**18** diameter 630 ft

In the problems that follow use the π button on your calculator, and give your answers correct to 3 significant figures. Check that your answers are sensible by estimating them taking π as 3.

Find the perimeter of the given semicircle.
(The prefix 'semi' means half.)

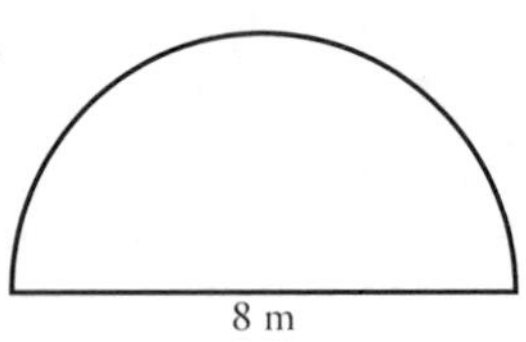

The complete circumference of the circle is $2\pi r$ m

The curved part of the semicircle is $\frac{1}{2} \times 2\pi r$ m

$$= \frac{1}{2} \times 2 \times \pi \times 4\,\text{m}$$

$$= 12.56\ldots\,\text{m}$$

***Check*: Curved part $\approx \frac{1}{2} \times 2 \times 3 \times 4\,\text{m} = 12\,\text{m}$**

The perimeter = curved part + straight edge
= (12.56... + 8) m
= 20.56... m
= 20.6 m (correct to 3 s.f.)

Find the perimeter of each of the following shapes.

19

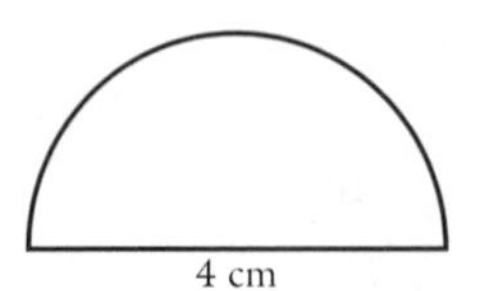

A semicircle

20

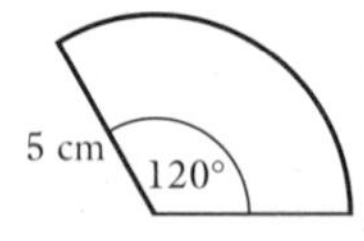

(This is one third of a circle because 120° is $\frac{1}{3}$ of 360°.)

21

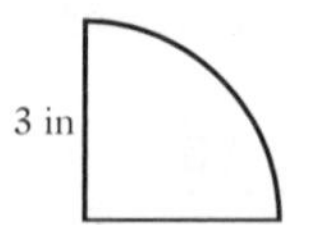

(This is called a quadrant: it is one quarter of a circle.)

22

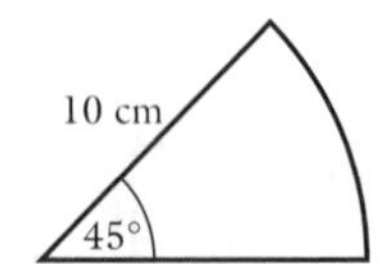

A 'slice' of a circle is called a sector. $\left(\frac{45°}{360°} = \frac{1}{8}\right.$, so this sector is $\frac{1}{8}$ of a circle.$\left.\right)$

23

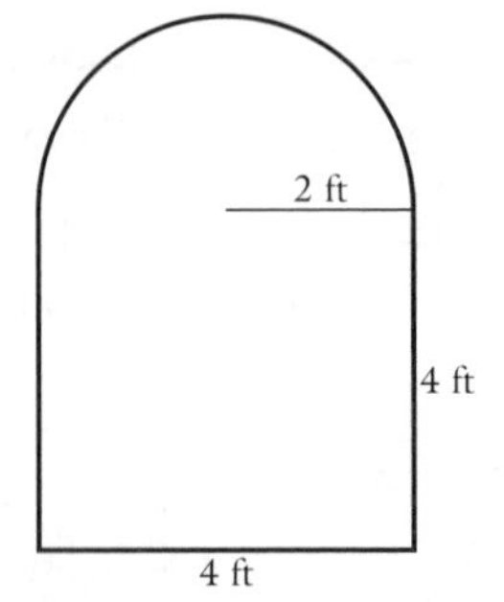

A window frame with a semicircular top

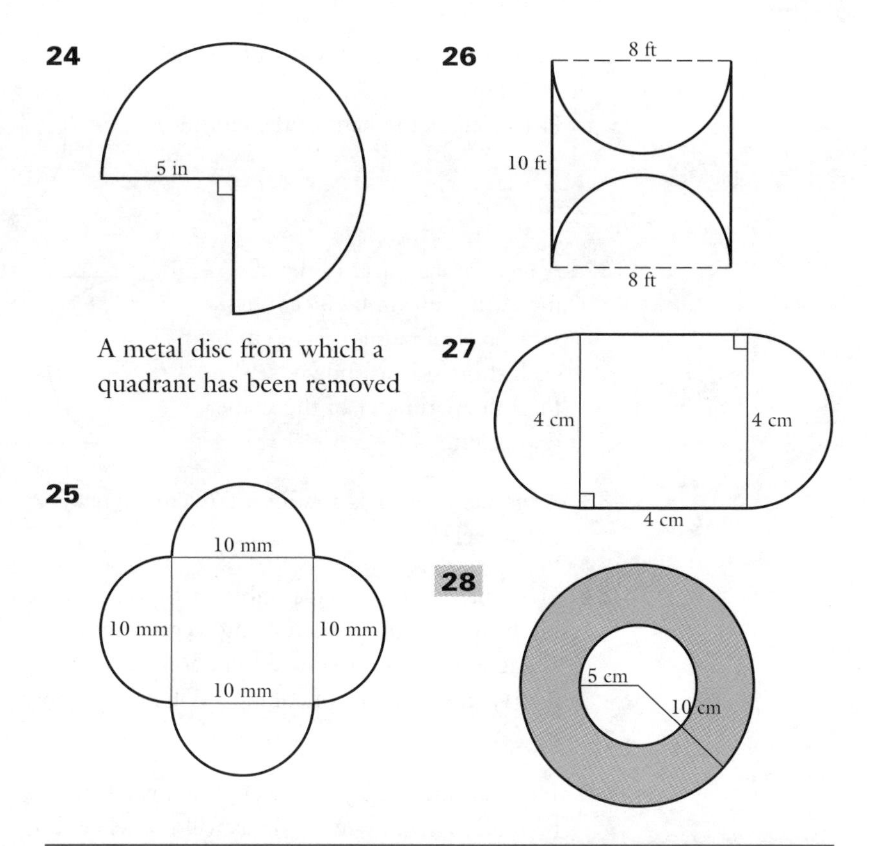

A circular flower-bed has a diameter of 1.5 m. A metal edging is to be placed round it. Find the length of edging needed and the cost of the edging if it is sold by the metre (i.e. you can only buy a whole number of metres) and costs 60 p a metre.

Using $C = \pi d$,

$$C = \pi \times 1.5$$
$$= 4.712\ldots$$

Length of edging needed = 4.71 m (correct to 3 s.f.)

Note that if you use $C = 2\pi r$, you must remember to halve the diameter.

As the length is 4.71 m we have to buy 5 m of edging.

Cost = 5 x 60 p
= 300 p or £3

29 Measure the diameter, in millimetres, of a 2 p coin. Use your measurement to find the circumference of a 2 p coin.

30 Repeat question **29** with a 10 p coin and a 1 p coin.

31 A circular table-cloth has a diameter of 1.4 m.
How long is the hem of the cloth?

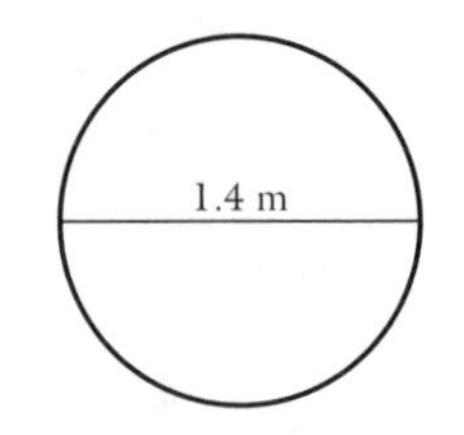

32 A rectangular sheet of metal measuring 50 cm by 30 cm has a semicircle of radius 15 cm cut from each short side as shown.
Find the perimeter of the shape that is left.

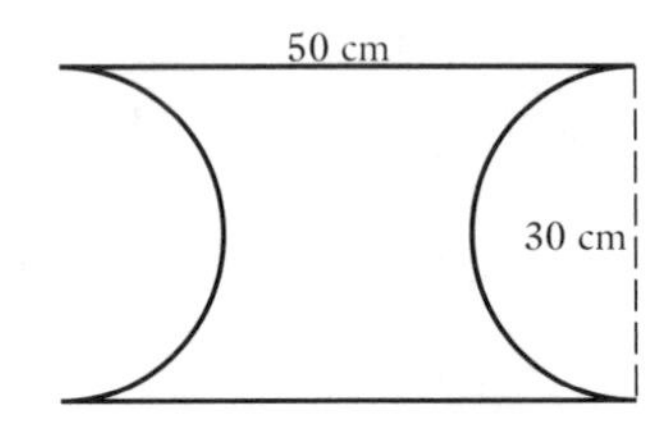

33 A bicycle wheel has a radius of 28 cm. What is the circumference of the wheel?

34 Hank has made a circular table that has a diameter of 1.2 m.
He wants to buy plastic edging to go round it.
Using 3 as an approximate value for π he calculates that he needs $3 \times 1.2\text{ m} = 3.6\text{ m}$ of edging. Will he have enough? Give reasons for your answer.

35 How far does a bicycle wheel of radius 28 cm travel in one complete revolution? How many times will the wheel turn when the bicycle travels a distance of 352 m?

36 A cylindrical tin has a radius of 2 cm.
What length of paper is needed to put a label on the tin if the edges just meet?

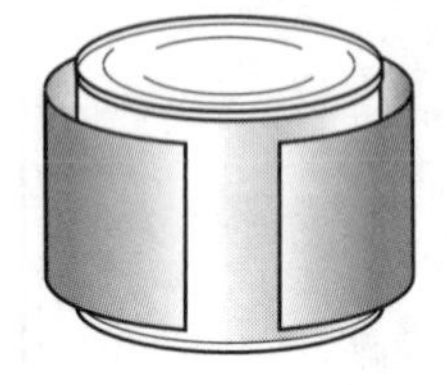

37 A square sheet of metal has sides of length 30 cm. A quadrant (one quarter of a circle) of radius 15 cm is cut from each of the four corners. Sketch the shape that is left and find its perimeter.

For the following problems, give your answers as accurately as you think is sensible.

38 A boy flies a model aeroplane on the end of a wire 10 m long. If he keeps the wire horizontal, how far does his aeroplane fly in one revolution?

39 If the aeroplane described in question **38** takes 1 second to fly 10 m, how long does it take to make one complete revolution? If the aeroplane has enough power to fly for 1 minute, how many turns can it make?

40 A cotton reel has a diameter of 2 cm. There are 500 turns of thread on the reel. How long is the thread?
Is your answer likely to be larger or smaller than the actual length on the reel? Give a reason.

41

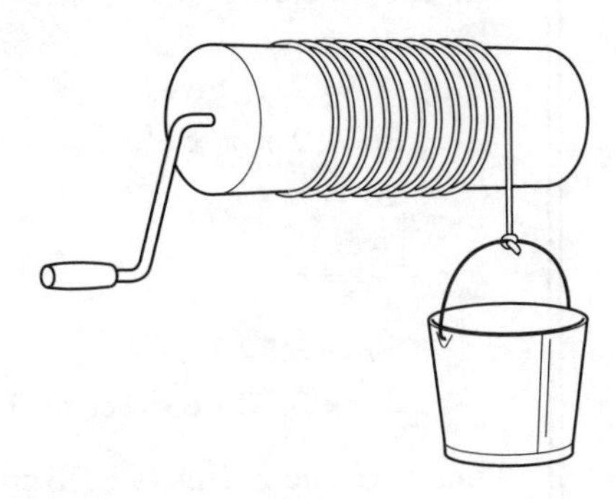

A bucket is lowered into a well by unwinding rope from a cylindrical drum. The drum has a radius of 20 cm and, with the bucket just out of the well, there are 10 complete turns of the rope on the drum. When the rope is fully unwound the bucket is at the bottom of the well. How deep is the well?

42 A garden hose is 100 m long. For storage it is wound onto a cylindrical hose reel of diameter 45 cm. How many turns of the reel are needed to wind up the hose?

43 The cage which takes miners up and down the shaft of a coal mine is raised and lowered by a steel cable wound round a circular drum of diameter 3 m. It takes 10 revolutions of the drum to lower the cage from ground level to the bottom of the shaft. How deep is the shaft?

FINDING THE RADIUS OF A CIRCLE FROM ITS CIRCUMFERENCE

If a circle has a circumference of 24 cm, we can find its radius by using the formula $C = 2\pi r$. This formula gives

$$24 = 2 \times \pi \times r$$

which is an equation that can be solved for r.

By taking π as 3, the formula $C = 2\pi r$ can be used to estimate r,

i.e. $C \approx 2 \times 3 \times r$ giving $C \approx 6r$

$\therefore$ when $C = 24$ we have $24 \approx 6r$ so $r \approx 4$.

i.e. the radius is approximately 4 cm.

EXERCISE 9C

1 By taking π as 3 estimate the radius of a circle whose circumference is

a 60 cm **b** 72 in **c** 40 m **d** 582 cm

> The circumference of a circle is 36 cm. Find its radius.
>
> Using $C = 2\pi r$ gives
>
> $$36 = 2 \times \pi \times r$$
>
> $$18 = \pi \times r \quad \text{Dividing both sides by 2.}$$
>
> $$\frac{18}{\pi} = r \quad \text{Dividing both sides by } \pi.$$
>
> $$r = 5.729\ldots$$
>
> $$r = 5.73 \text{ (correct to 3 s.f.)}$$
>
> Therefore the radius is 5.73 cm correct to 3 s.f.
>
> *Check*: Using $\pi \approx 3$, diameter $\approx 36 \div 3$ cm, so radius ≈ 6 cm

For the remaining questions in this exercise, use the π button on your calculator, and give your answers correct to 3 significant figures.

2 Find the radius of each circle given in question **1**.

3 Find the radius of a circle whose circumference is

a 275 cm **b** 462 mm **c** 831 in **d** 87.4 m

4 Find the diameter of a circle whose circumference is

a 550 mm **b** 52 cm **c** 391 yd **d** 76 ft

5 A roundabout at a major road junction is to be built. It has to have a circumference of 188 m. What is the diameter of the roundabout?

6 A bicycle wheel has a circumference of 200 cm. Find its radius.

7 A car has a turning circle whose circumference is 63 m. What is the narrowest road that the car can turn round in without going on the pavement?

8 When the label is taken off a tin of soup it is found to be 32 cm long.
If there was an overlap of 1 cm when the label was on the tin, what is the radius of the tin?

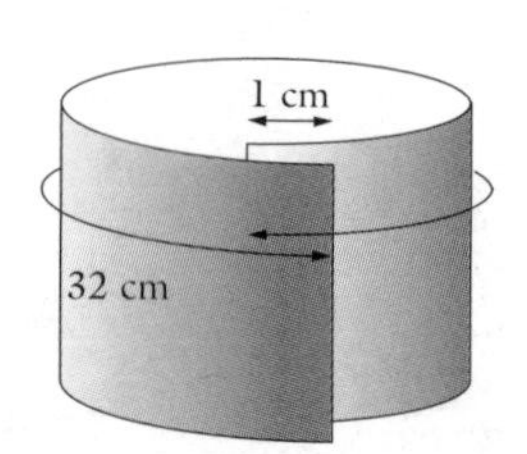

9 The diagram shows a quadrant of a circle.
If the curved edge is 15 cm long,
what is the length of a straight edge?

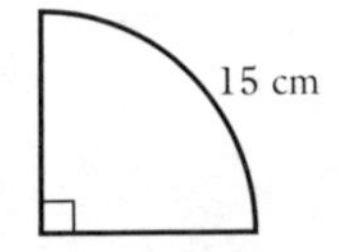

10 A tea cup has a circumference of 24 cm.

a What is the radius of the cup?

b Six of these cups are stored edge to edge in a straight line on a shelf. What length of shelf do they occupy?

11 The shape in the diagram is made up of a semicircle and a square.
Find the length of a side of this square.

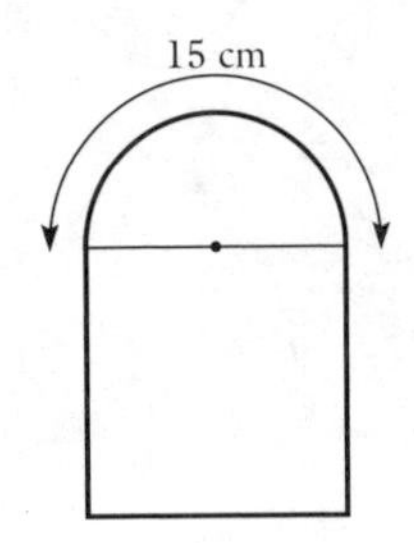

12 Make a cone from a sector of a circle as follows:
On a sheet of paper draw a circle of radius 8 cm. Draw two radii at an angle of 90°. Make a tab on one radius as shown. Cut out the larger sector and stick the straight edges together. What is the circumference of the circle at the bottom of the cone?

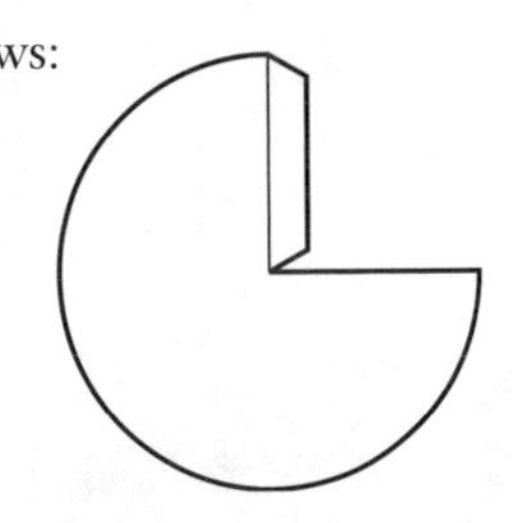

13 A cone is made by sticking together the straight edges of the sector of a circle, as shown in the diagram.

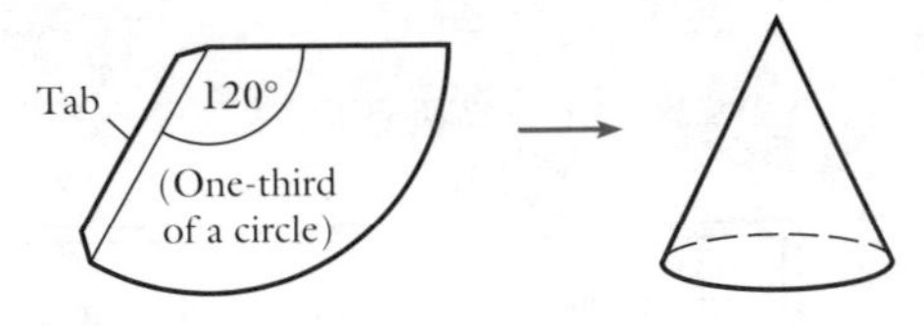

The circumference of the circle at the bottom of the finished cone is 10 cm. What is the radius of the circle from which the sector was cut?

14 A gardener wants to create a circular flower-bed with a circumference of 14 m. He marks out the edge by putting a stake in the centre and using a string with a peg tied at the other end. He works out the length of the string from the approximation
$14 \div 6\text{ m} \approx 2\text{ m}$.
Will this give a circumference of more or less than 14 m?
Justify your answer and comment on the method.

THE AREA OF A CIRCLE

A printer uses sheets of paper measuring 590 mm by 420 mm to print circular labels of radius 3.3 cm. He would like to know the largest number of these labels that can be printed on one sheet and the area of paper wasted in this case.

- To answer these questions the printer needs to know how to find the area of a circle.

The formula for finding the area of a circle is

$$A = \pi r^2$$

You can see this if you cut a circle up into sectors and place the pieces together as shown below to get a shape which is roughly rectangular.

Consider a circle of radius r cm whose circumference is $2\pi r$ cm.

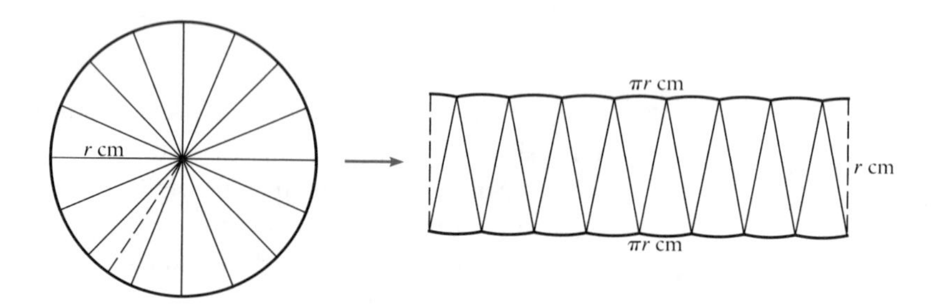

$$\begin{aligned}\text{Area of circle} &= \text{area of 'rectangle'}\\ &= \text{length} \times \text{width}\\ &= \pi r \times r\ \text{cm}^2 = \pi r^2\ \text{cm}^2\end{aligned}$$

EXERCISE 9D

Give your answers correct to 3 significant figures.

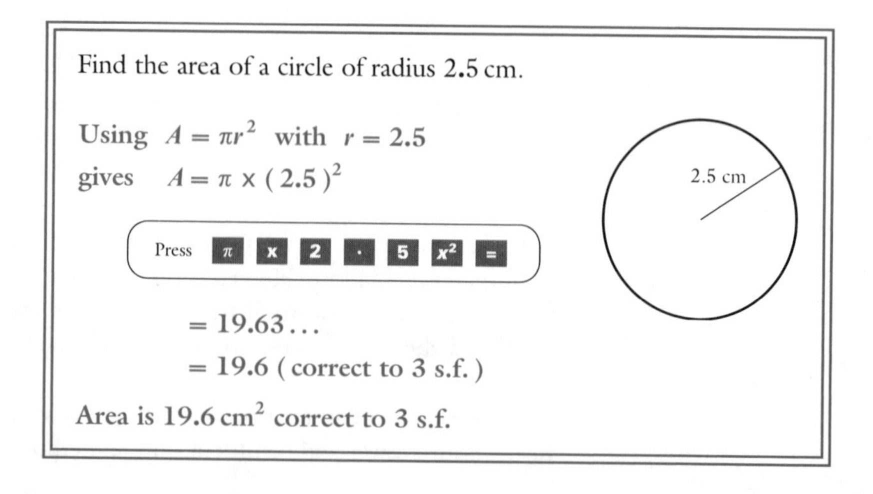

In questions **1** to **4** estimate the area and then find the area.

How do these values compare?

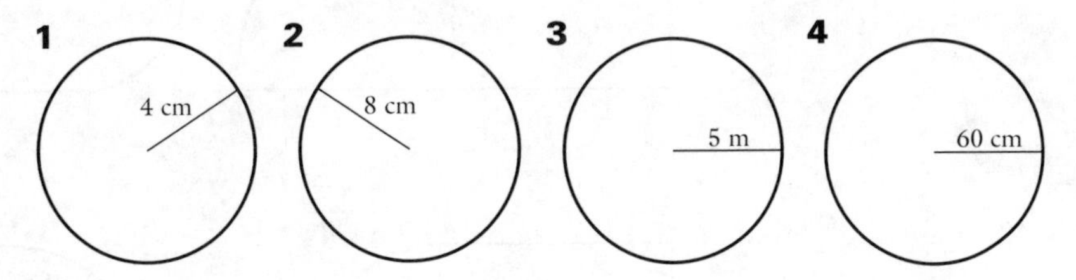

Find the areas of the following circles.

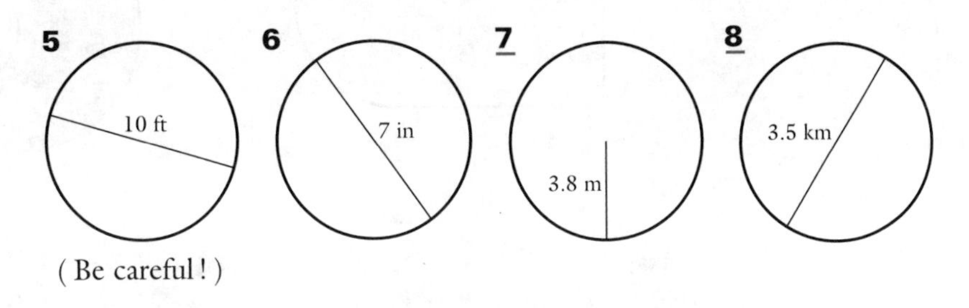

(Be careful !)

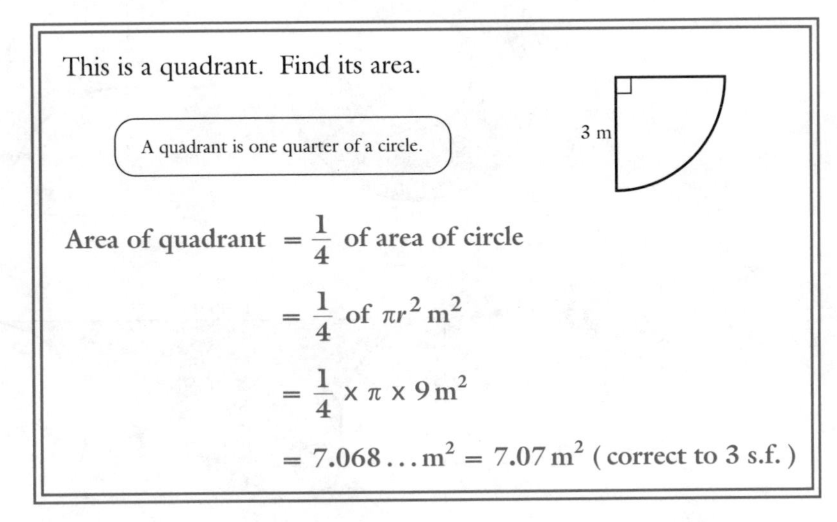

This is a quadrant. Find its area.

A quadrant is one quarter of a circle.

Area of quadrant $= \frac{1}{4}$ of area of circle

$= \frac{1}{4}$ of πr^2 m^2

$= \frac{1}{4} \times \pi \times 9$ m^2

$= 7.068\ldots$ m^2 $= 7.07$ m^2 (correct to 3 s.f.)

Find the areas of the following shapes.

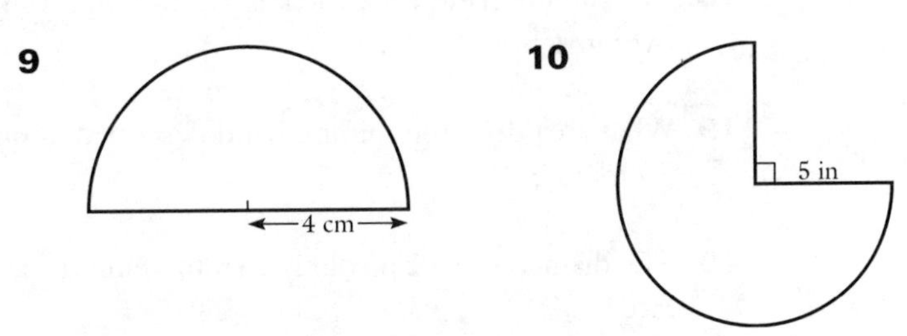

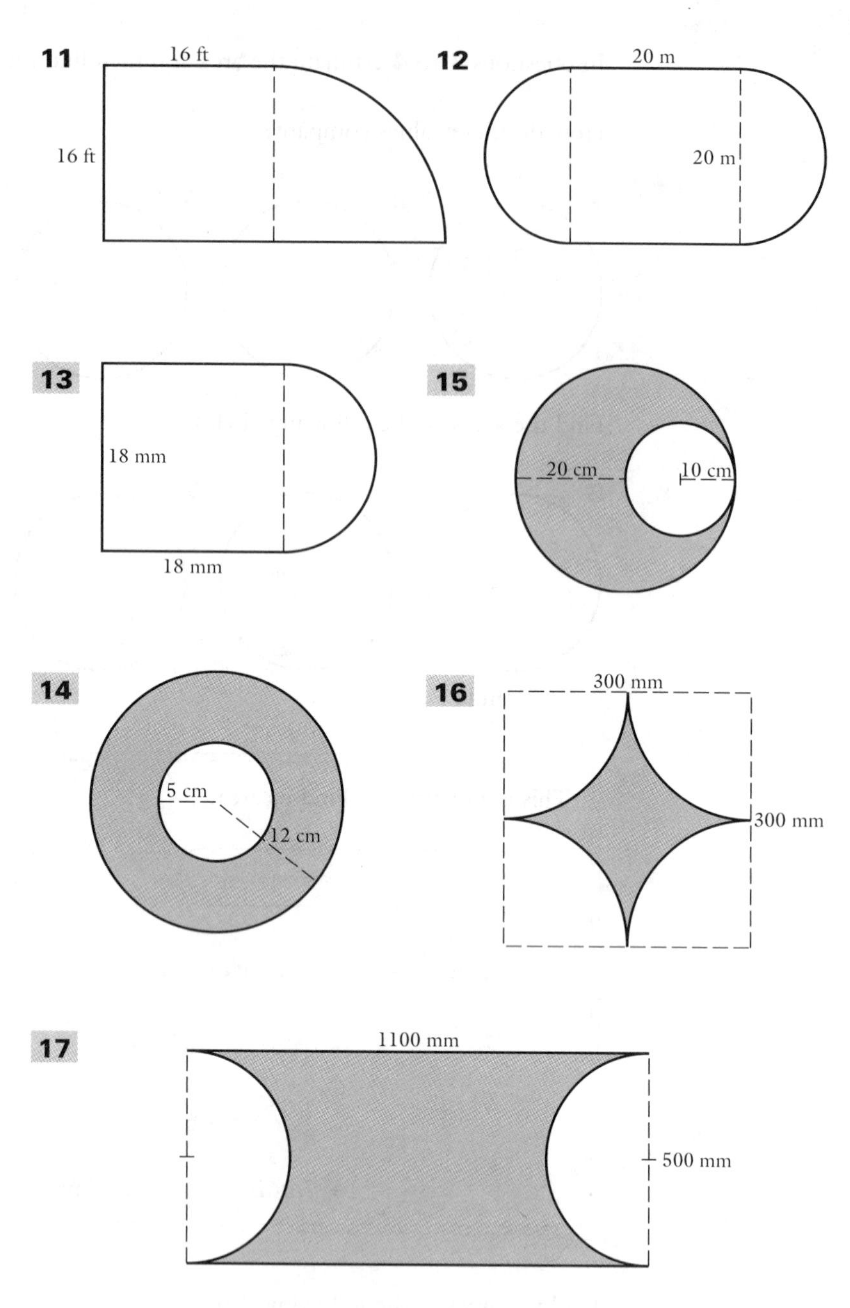

18 The minute hand on a clock is 15 cm long. What area does it pass over in 1 hour?

19 What area does the minute hand described in question **18** cover in 20 minutes?

20 The diameter of a 2 p coin is 26 mm. Find the area of one of its 'flat' faces.

21 The hour hand of a clock is 10 in long. What area does it pass over in 1 hour?

A circular table has a radius of 75 cm.

a Find the area of the table top.

b The top of the table is to be varnished. One tin of varnish covers 4 m^2. Will one tin be enough to give the table top three coats of varnish?

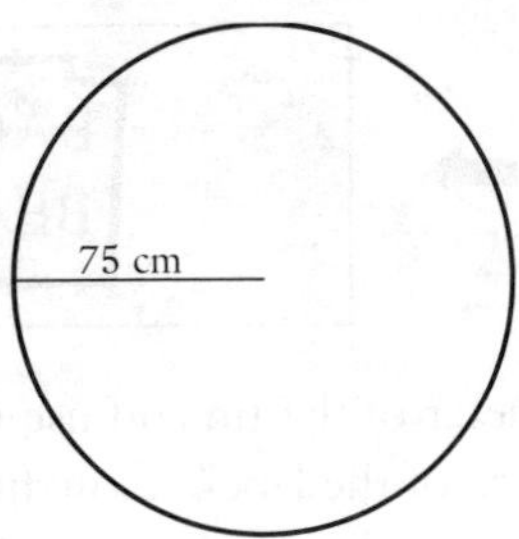

a **Area of table top is $\pi r^2\text{ cm}^2$**

$= \pi \times 75 \times 75\text{ cm}^2$

$= 17\,671.4\ldots\text{ cm}^2$

$= 17\,670\text{ cm}^2$ (correct to 4 s.f.)

To be able to compare the area of the table top with the area covered by 1 tin, we need both areas in the same unit. We will change the area in cm^2 to m^2.

b **Area** $= 17\,671.4 \div 100^2\text{ m}^2$

$= 1.767\text{ m}^2$ (correct to 4 s.f.)

For three coats, enough varnish is needed to cover

$$3 \times 1.767\text{ m}^2 = 5.301\ldots\text{ m}^2$$

So 1 tin of varnish is not enough.

22 A circular lawn has a radius of 5 m. The contents of a bottle of lawn weedkiller are sufficient to cover 50 m^2. Is one bottle enough to treat the whole lawn?

23 A circular flower bed has a radius of 120 cm. The contents of one bottle of fertiliser will treat 4 m^2. Is one bottle enough to treat the whole bed?

24 The largest possible circle is cut from a square of paper measuring 10 in by 10 in. What area of paper is left?

25 Circular place mats of diameter 8 cm are made by stamping as many circles as possible from a rectangular strip of card measuring 8 cm by 64 cm. How many mats can be made from the strip of card and what area of card is wasted?

26 A wooden counter top is a rectangle measuring 2800 mm by 450 mm. There are three circular holes in the counter, each of radius 100 mm. Find the area of the counter top.

27 The surface of the counter top described in question **26** is to be given four coats of varnish. If one tin of varnish covers $3.5\ \text{m}^2$, how many tins will be needed?

28 Take a cylindrical tin of food with a paper label:

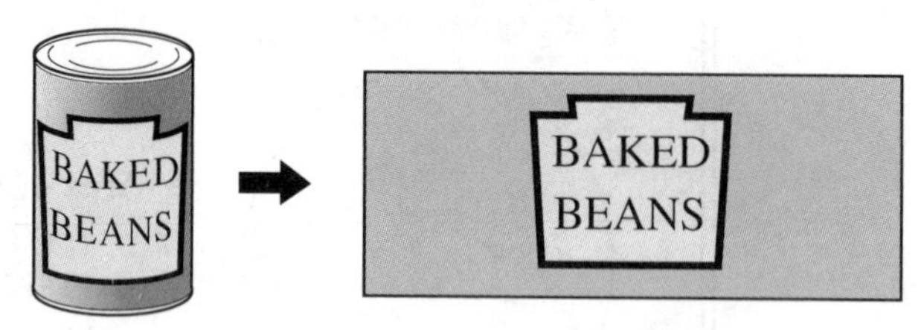

Measure the diameter of the tin and use it to find the length of the label. Find the area of the label. Now find the total surface area of the tin (two circular ends and the curved surface).

MIXED EXERCISE

EXERCISE 9E

Give your answer to 3 significant figures.
(Remember to give an estimate for each answer first.)

1 Find the circumference of a circle of radius 2.8 mm.

2 Find the radius of a circle of circumference 60 m.

3 Find the circumference of a circle of diameter 12 cm.

4 Find the area of a circle of radius 2.9 m.

5 Find the diameter of a circle of circumference 280 mm.

6 Find the area of a circle of diameter 25 cm.

7 Find the perimeter of the quadrant in the diagram.

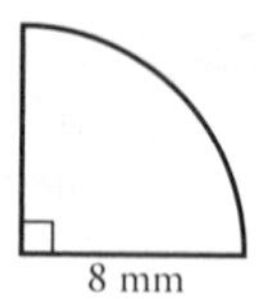

8 Find the area of the shaded part of the diagram.

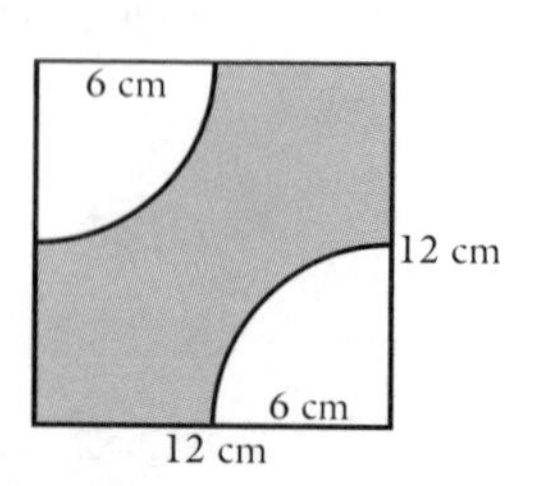

PRACTICAL WORK

Count Buffon's experiment

Count Buffon was an eighteenth-century scientist who carried out many probability experiments. The most famous of these is his 'Needle Problem'. He dropped needles onto a surface ruled with parallel lines and considered the drop successful when the needle fell across a line and unsuccessful when the needle fell between two lines. His amazing discovery was that the number of successful drops divided by the number of unsuccessful drops was an expression involving π.

You can repeat his experiment and get a good approximation for the value of π from it.

Take a matchstick or a similar small stick and measure its length. Now take a sheet of paper measuring about 50 cm each way and fill the sheet with a set of parallel lines whose distance apart is equal to the length of the stick. With the sheet on the floor drop the stick on to it from a height of about 1 m. Repeat this about a hundred times and keep a tally of the number of times the stick touches or crosses a line and of the number of times it is dropped. Do not count a drop if the stick misses the paper. Then find the value of

$$\frac{2 \times \text{number of times it is dropped}}{\text{number of times it crosses or touches a line}}$$

INVESTIGATION

a Can you provide Ken with the answer to the problem he posed at the beginning of the chapter? Justify your answer. (Assume that one pedal stroke gives one complete turn of the wheels.)

b What happens if Ken uses a gear that gives two turns of the wheels for each pedal stroke?

c Find out how the gears on a racing bike affect the ratio of the number of pedal strokes to the number of turns of the wheels. Discuss the assumptions made in order to answer parts **a** and **b**. Write a short report on how these assumptions affect the reasonableness of your answers.

SCATTER GRAPHS

10

Statements like these are commonplace.

- Young people buy more magazines than older people.
- People with large hands also have large feet.
- Not eating green vegetables makes people unhealthy.

Is there any truth in any of these? We can only find out by looking at some evidence.

Without evidence, or proof, any assertion is called a *hypothesis*.

In order to judge the truth of any one of the hypotheses given above, we need to start by gathering some evidence. For the first statement, information relating the age of a person to the number of magazines bought in, say, the last week, would be useful and we would need this for several people.

EXERCISE 10A

1 Discuss what information is needed before you can assess the truth or otherwise of each of these hypotheses.

a People with large hands also have large feet.

b Not eating green vegetables makes people unhealthy.

c Pupils spend more in the school canteen in the later part of a week than they do at the beginning of the week.

2 To find out if younger people do buy more magazines than older people, Mary asked several people their age and the number of magazines they had bought last week. She then arranged this information in two lists, each in order of size:

Age: 10, 12, 13, 14, 14, 15, 16, 18, 20, 35, 47, 60

Numbers of magazines: 0, 0, 1, 1, 1, 1, 2, 2, 2, 2, 3, 4.

Discuss why these lists will not help Mary with her investigation.

3 Pradesh wants to find out if there is a relationship between the ages of pupils and opinions about having to wear school uniform.
Discuss the advantages and disadvantages of each of the following methods for collecting the information shown opposite.

a In two separate observation sheets, i.e.

School Year					
7	8	9	10	11	12
///	/	//	//	/	///

School uniform is a good idea				
Strongly disagree	Disagree	No opinion	Agree	Strongly agree
///	////	//	/	//

b On one observation sheet, i.e.

		School uniform is a good idea				
Name	School year	Strongly disagree	Disagree	Neither agree nor disagree	Agree	Strongly agree
Jane	8				✓	
Austin	7		✓			

c Asking each individual to fill in a form, i.e.

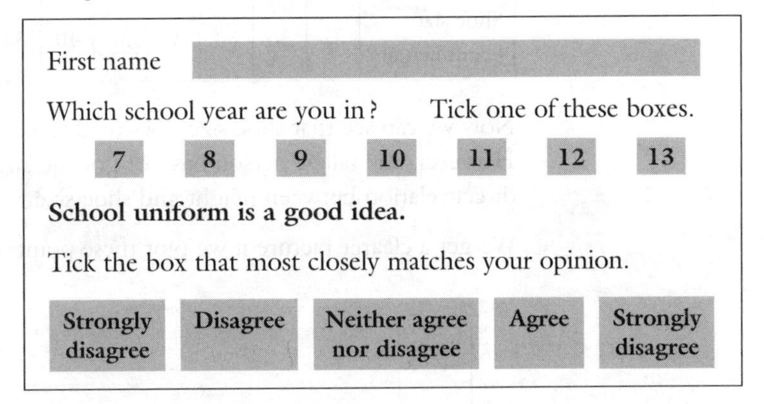
First name

Which school year are you in? Tick one of these boxes.

7 8 9 10 11 12 13

School uniform is a good idea.

Tick the box that most closely matches your opinion.

Strongly disagree	Disagree	Neither agree nor disagree	Agree	Strongly disagree

SCATTER GRAPHS

Each of the statements looked at in this chapter involves two pieces of information about one individual. (The technical name is *bivariate* data.) These pairs of data can be compared for several individuals.

Discussion of the examples in **Exercise 10A** shows that

- it is vital that corresponding items of information are kept together
- the simplest way of collecting two items of information about an individual is to use an observation sheet like the one in question 3, part b.

Consider this hypothesis: Tall people have larger feet than short people.
This is a commonplace belief, but how true is it?
Does it mean, for example, that if my friend and I are the same height, we take the same size in shoes?
Or is there not much truth in the statement, that is, there is not much relationship between a person's height and shoe size?

We can try to find out by gathering some evidence. This table gives the heights (in centimetres) and the shoe sizes of 12 females in the order in which they were asked.

Person	1	2	3	4	5	6	7	8	9	10	11	12
Height (cm)	160	166	174	158	167	161	170	171	166	163	164	168
Shoe size (continental)	36	38	40	37	37	38	42	41	40	39	37	39

There is no order in either the heights or the shoe sizes and, as it is difficult to see any pattern, we will rearrange the information so that the heights are in order of size (making sure that each shoe size is kept with its corresponding height).

Height (cm)	158	160	161	163	164	166	166	167	168	170	171	174
Shoe size (continental)	37	36	38	39	37	40	38	37	39	42	41	40

Now we can see that shoe size does tend to get larger as height increases. However, the tallest person has not got the largest feet so there is not a direct relation between height and shoe size.

We get a clearer picture if we plot these points on a graph.

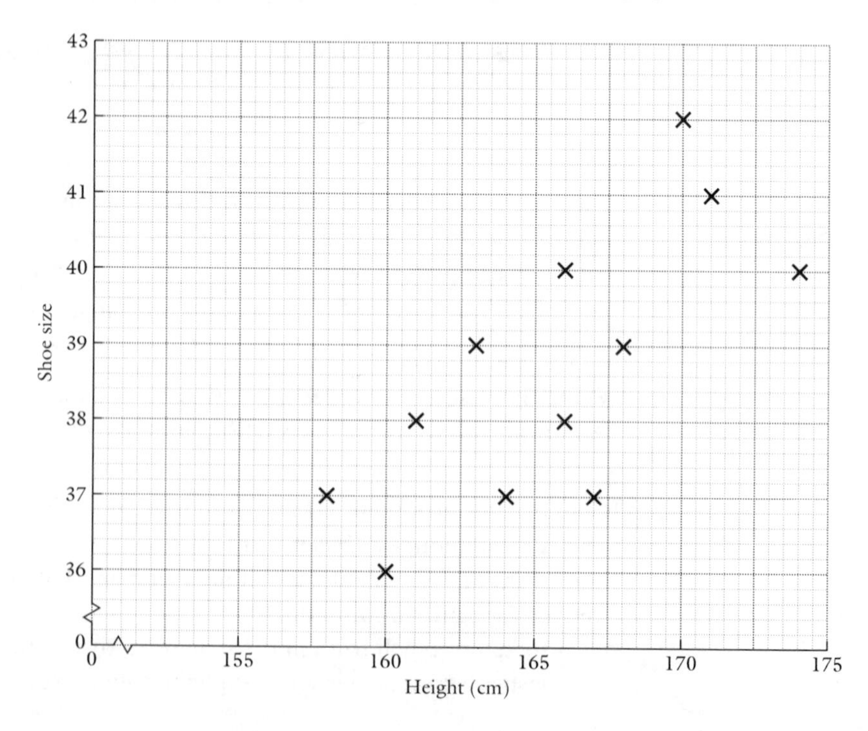

The points do not all fit on a straight line. A graph like this is called a *scatter graph*.

Now we can see that taller people tend to have larger feet but the relationship between height and shoe size is not strong enough to justify the original statement.

EXERCISE 10B

1 **a** In the example above this exercise, we state that information has been collected from 12 people, *all of whom were female*. Why is it important to say this?

b The axes for the scatter graph above have zig-zag lines near zero. Why?

2 This graph illustrates information relating the ages and prices of some second-hand cars. The cars are all the same model.

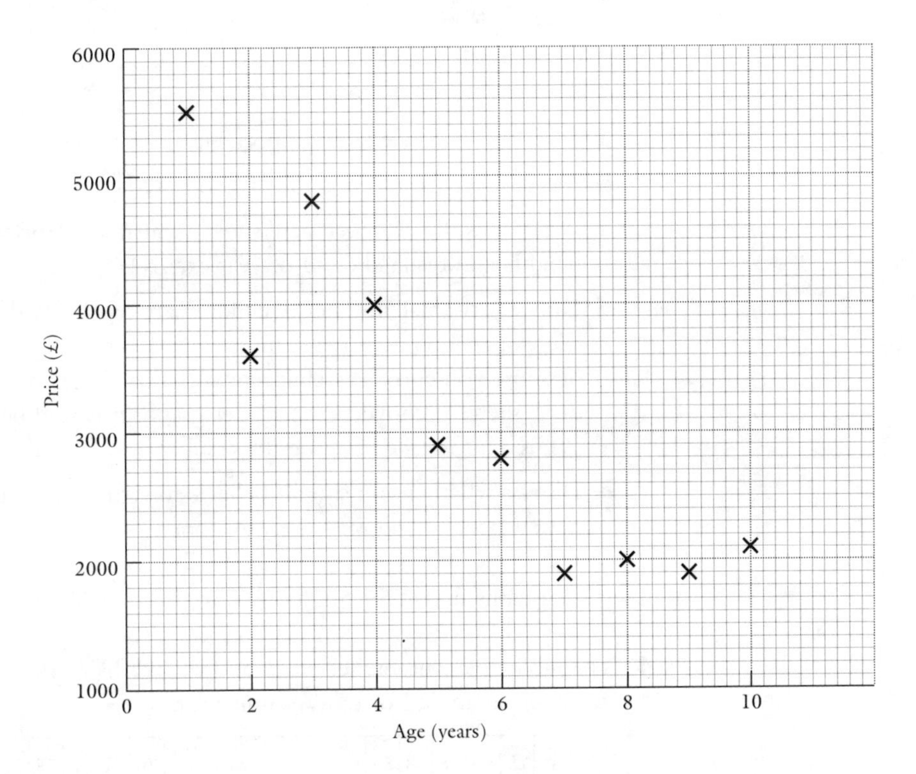

a Does this evidence support the statement 'The price of a second-hand car gets lower as the age increases'?

b Apart from age, what other factors do you think affect the price of a car?

c Is it true to say that a five-year-old car is always cheaper than a two-year-old car?

3 Lim saw this headline in a paper, 'TALL CHILDREN GET BETTER GRADES AT GCSE THAN SHORT CHILDREN.'
He did not read any further and, because he was short for his age, decided that his school career was doomed to failure.
This scatter graph shows the heights and grades obtained in end-of-year exams by a group of Year 9 pupils.

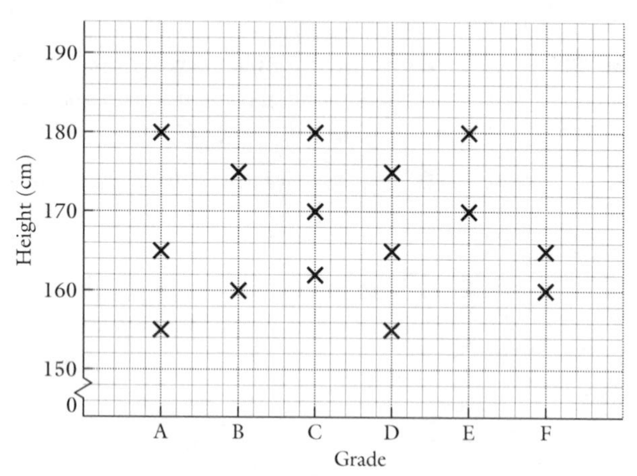

a Does the evidence here support the claim in the newspaper?

b Are end-of-year exam grades a good prediction of GCSE results.

c What does the evidence here show about the relationship between heights and results in end-of-year exams?

d Only a very small number of children are represented in this graph. We will assume that these children have been chosen randomly. Suppose you chose the children with a particular result in mind, draw sketches showing the scatter graphs it would be possible to get. (This is called *biasing* the results.)

e Discuss whether you should believe everything you read in newspapers (or books – even this one)?

Keep the graphs drawn for questions **4** to **7**: you will need them later.

4 The table gives the French mark and the maths mark of each of 20 pupils in an end-of-term examination.

French	45	56	58	58	59	60	64	64	65	65	66	70	71	73	73	75	76	76	78	80
Maths	50	38	45	48	56	65	60	58	70	75	60	79	64	80	85	69	82	77	69	75

a Show this information on a graph; use a scale of 1 cm for 5 marks on each axis. Mark the horizontal axis from 40 to 85 for the French mark and the vertical axis from 35 to 90 for the maths mark.

b John is good at French. Is he likely to be good at maths?

5 This table shows the heights and weights of 12 people.

Height (cm)	150	152	155	158	158	160	163	165	170	175	178	180
Weight (kg)	56	62	63	64	57	62	65	66	65	70	66	67

a Show this information on a graph; use a horizontal scale of 2 cm for each 5 cm of height and mark this axis from 145 to 185. Use a vertical scale of 2 cm for each 5 kg and mark this axis from 55 to 75.

b Carlos weighs 65 kg. Is he likely to be tall?

6 This table shows the number of rooms and the number of people living in each of 15 houses.

Number of rooms	3	4	4	5	5	5	6	6	6	6	7	7	7	8	8
Number of people	2	3	5	4	2	1	6	2	3	4	4	5	3	2	6

a Show this information by plotting the points on a graph; use a scale of 1 cm for one unit on each axis.

b Cheryl lives in a house with four other people. Is the house likely to have more than four rooms?

7 This table shows the number of pens and pencils and the number of books that each of 10 pupils has in a maths lesson.

Number of pens and pencils	2	3	3	5	6	6	12	15	20	25
Number of books	4	5	0	3	1	4	6	2	1	5

a Show this information by plotting the points on a graph; use a horizontal scale of 1 cm for two pens and pencils and a vertical scale of 1 cm for one book.

b Is the number of pens and pencils brought by a pupil a reliable indication of how many books that pupil has brought?

c Collect corresponding information for the pupils in your maths class and make a scatter graph from it.

8 Max worked for a recruitment agency.
He wanted to know if there was a relationship between the time it takes to travel to work and the hourly pay for jobs that applicants are willing to take. He looked at this scatter graph.

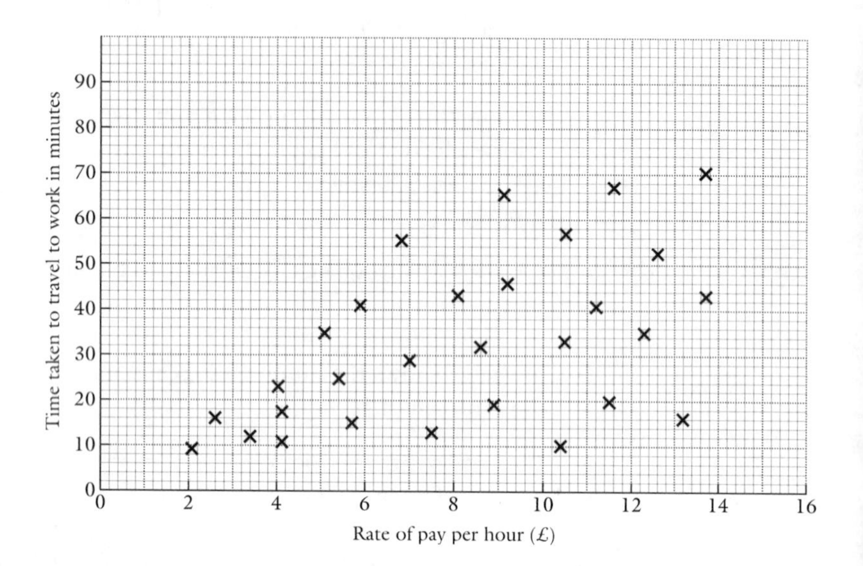

What does this graph show about the relationship between the time it takes people to travel to work and the hourly pay of the job they do?

9 Joyce owns a shoe shop.
She wants to find out if there is a relationship between the number of hours that the shop is open and the number of pairs of shoes sold.
She collected some information and drew this graph.

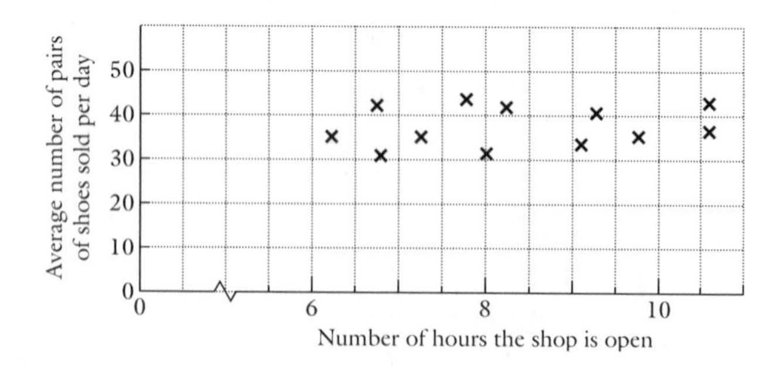

a What does this graph show Joyce about the relationship between the number of hours that the shop is open and the number of pairs of shoes sold?

b Draw a sketch to show what this scatter graph looks like if the vertical axis is scaled from 30 to 50.

LINE OF BEST FIT AND CORRELATION

If we look again at the scatter graph of height and shoe size, we see that the points are scattered about a straight line which we can draw by eye. This is called the *line of best fit*. When drawing this line, the aim is to get the points evenly distributed about the line, so that the sum of the distances from the line to points that are above it, is roughly equal to the sum of the distances from the line to points that are below it. This may mean that none of the points lies on the line.

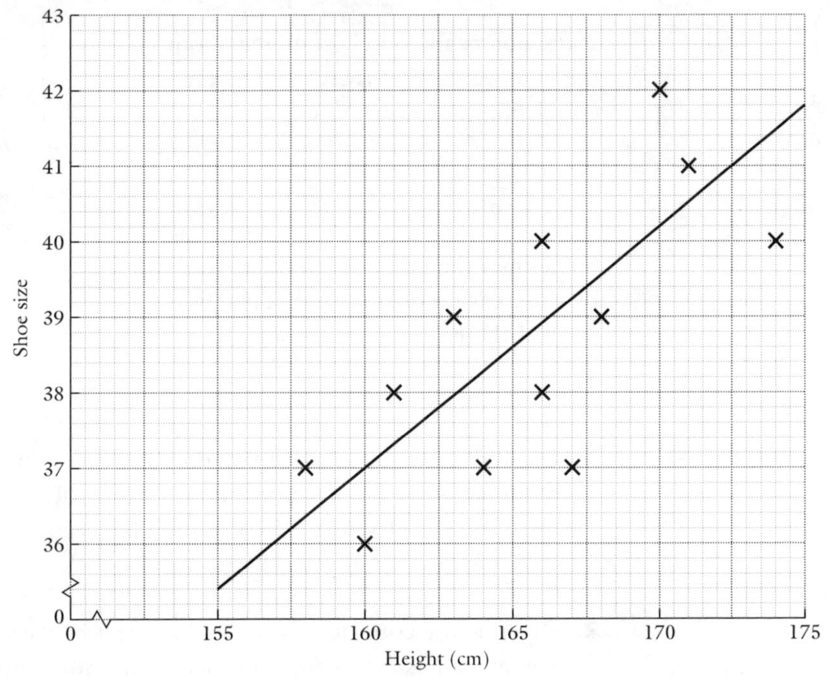

The less scatter there is about the line, the stronger is the relationship between the two quantities. We use the word *correlation* for the relationship between the two quantities.

In the diagram above, the line slopes upwards, that is, shoe size tends to increase with height. We call this *positive* correlation.

This scatter graph, from question 2 in Exercise 10B, shows that the price of cars tends to decrease as their age increases.

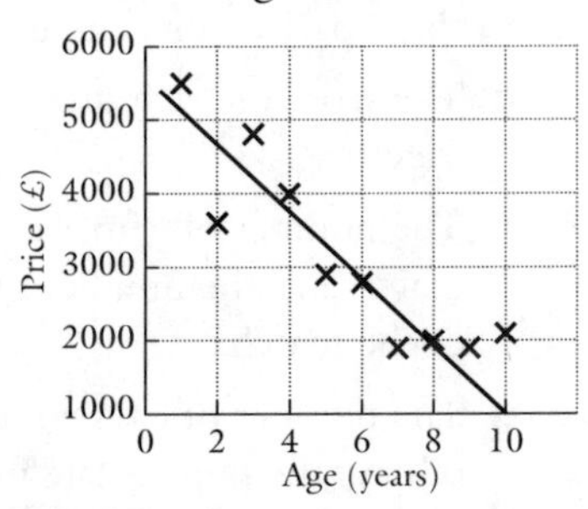

The line of best fit slopes downwards, and we say that there is *negative* correlation.

If the points are close to the line,
we say that there is a strong correlation.

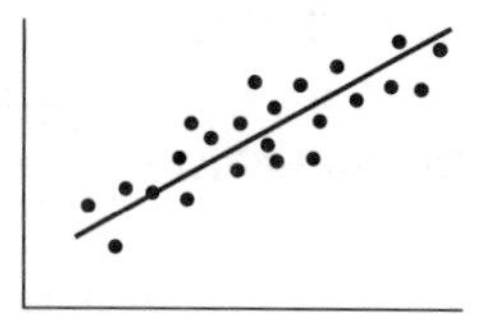
Strong positive correlation

If the points are loosely scattered about the line, we say that there is moderate correlation.

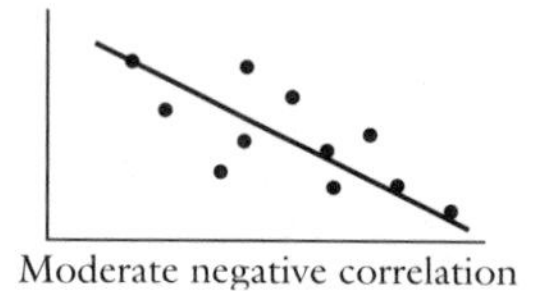
Moderate negative correlation

Sometimes the points are so scattered that there is no obvious line. Then we say that there is no correlation.

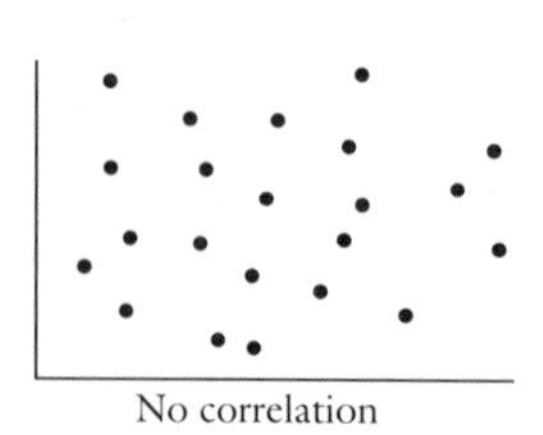
No correlation

EXERCISE 10C

1 Use the scatter graphs that you drew for questions **4** to **7** of **Exercise 10B**. For each one, draw the line of best fit, if you think there is one. Describe the correlation between the two quantities in each case.

2 Describe the correlation you would expect between these quantities. You are *not* asked to provide any evidence for your answers.

a The number of pages and the number of advertisements in a newspaper.

b The length and width of a cucumber.

c The weight of tomatoes produced by a tomato plant and its height.

d The number of miles a car will travel on one gallon of petrol and the capacity of its engine.

e The score on each dice when a red dice and a blue dice are thrown together.

f The number of games a player wins in the first set of a tennis match and the number of games the player wins in the second set of the match.

g The number of days a pupil is away from school and the number of days the pupil is late in handing in a technology project.

h The age of a pupil and that pupil's feeling about having to wear school uniform.

COLLECTING INFORMATION

Up to now the information that you have been asked to collect can be measured or counted, for example, heights, weights, times, numbers of heads when three coins are tossed, numbers of brothers and sisters.
In this chapter, we have introduced quantities that are not so easily measured or counted, such as shoe size. Some quantities cannot be measured, for example exam grades, eye colour, opinions and so on.
At some stage, you will have to collect such information yourself; you will need to plan in advance, anticipate some of the problems that might arise and decide how you are going to solve them.
The next exercise contains discussion topics.

EXERCISE 10D

1 Suppose that information is to be collected about the shoe sizes of pupils in your year.

a How many categories do you need? Should you stick to the whole number sizes?

b Will you ask for continental sizes or English sizes?

c If you decide on whole number sizes, what should you do about a pupil who insists that all her shoes are size $3\frac{1}{2}$?

d What should you do about someone whose left shoe is size 3 and whose right is size 4?

e Some people are shy about giving their shoe size. What can you do about this?

f If you ask people to write their shoes sizes on a piece of paper anonymously, what could go wrong?

2 Information is to be collected about the eye colour of pupils in your year.

a State the categories you would use. Why are categories needed?

b List the problems you might meet as you collect the information.

3 Information is to be collected about the time spent by pupils on maths homework last night.

a Pete decided to use these categories:

Less than 15 minutes   15 to 30 minutes   30 minutes to 1 hour.

What problems might he have with his choice of categories?

b Jacqui used these categories:

Less than 15 minutes   15 to 30 minutes
30 minutes to 45 minutes   More than 45 minutes.

i Why are these categories better than Pete's?

ii These categories are still not ideal. How can they be improved?

c What other problems might there be if you ask pupils how long they spent on their homework?

4 Evidence is needed about pupils' attitudes to starting the school day earlier and finishing earlier.
Discuss the problems with these attempts to get evidence.

a I like getting to school early.

Tick one of these boxes. | Yes | No |

b The school day should start earlier and finish earlier.
Tick the box that most closely matches your opinion.

Agree	Do not mind	Disagree

c The school day should start at 8 a.m. and end at 2 p.m.
Tick the box that most closely matches your opinion.

Strongly agree	Partly agree	No opinion	Partly disagree	Strongly disagree

d I would like to finish the school day at 2 p.m.

Tick one of these boxes. | Yes | No |

Discuss how you would tackle gathering the evidence.

5 Seema decided to collect information for question **4** by asking several pupils questions directly.

She asked James if he liked the idea of getting to school earlier and finishing earlier.

She then asked Cheryl if she thought that getting to school earlier and finishing earlier was a good idea.

She next approached Rafique and said, 'I don't want to have to get to school at 8 o'clock. Do you?'

Seema carried on like this, asking different questions of different pupils.

Discuss the problems caused by this approach.

QUESTIONNAIRES The information required sometimes concerns opinion on several different points. In questions **4** and **5** in the last exercise for example, you may have come to the conclusion that more than one question is needed to find out pupils' attitudes to a change in the timing of the school day. In cases like this a sheet of questions for each person might be more useful. A set of questions of this sort is called a *questionnaire*.

EXERCISE 10E

1 Copy and complete this questionnaire.
(Notice the different types of question and forms of answer.)

> **1.** How tall are you ? cm
>
> **2.** Do you consider yourself to be
> Tall Average Small ?
> (Underline your answer.)
>
> **3.** Do you like being the height you are ?
> Underline your answer.
> Love it Like it Don't mind Dislike it Hate it
>
> **4.** I want to grow taller 0 1 2 3
> (0 means 'not at all', 3 means 'very much')
> Ring the number that represents your answer.
>
> **5.** I am male/female. (Cross out the unwanted word.)

2 In the questionnaire above,

a why is item 5 needed ?

b item 3 could have had an answer in a different form, such as:

$$2 \quad 1 \quad 0 \quad -1 \quad -2$$

Ring the number which represents your liking.

What is the problem when the question is put in this form or in the form used for item 4 ?

3 There are several things wrong with the wording of the following questions and choice of responses. Discuss them.

a Do you like mathematics ? 0 1 2 3 4

b What colour is your hair ?

c How many people are there in your family ? ....

4 Two different groups conducted a survey on attitudes to turning the Town Centre into pedestrian access only.

Group 1 asked these questions:

Do cars cause pollution?
Is crossing the roads dangerous because of the traffic?
Should the Town Centre be made pedestrian only?

Group 2 asked these questions:

Would you find it difficult to get to the shops if the Town Centre was pedestrian only?
Can you manage to carry your shopping to outside the Town Centre?
Should the Town Centre be made pedestrian only?

The last question in each group is the same. Discuss what you think is the purpose of the first two questions in each group.

5 Write a questionnaire on a topic of your own choice, using different types of question. Sometimes the wording can be misunderstood: try the question out on a few people and adjust the wording where necessary.

PRACTICAL WORK

This chapter started with some assertions. One was that 'Not eating green vegetables makes people unhealthy.'
Find out how much truth you think there is in this statement.

You should include in your answer

- how you measured the quantity of green vegetables people eat
- how you decided what constitutes a person's state of health
- how you collected any evidence and who you collected it from
- any diagrams illustrating your evidence
- your conclusions
- how reliable you think your conclusions are.

SUMMARY 3

SQUARE ROOTS

$\sqrt{20}$ means the square root of 20, and is that number which, when multiplied by itself, gives 20.

For example, $\sqrt{4} = 2$ because $2 \times 2 = 4$.

POLYGONS

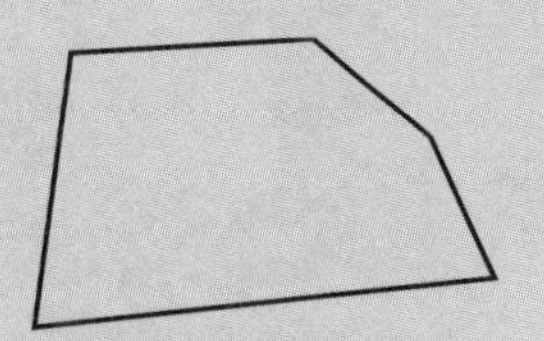

A polygon is a plane figure bounded by straight lines, e.g.

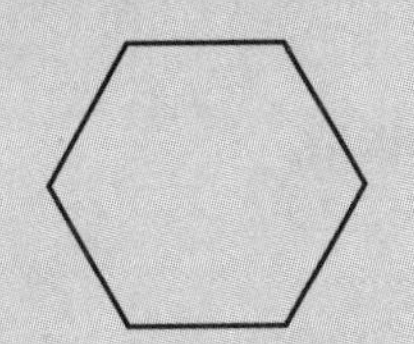

A *regular polygon* has all angles equal and all sides the same length.
This is a regular hexagon.

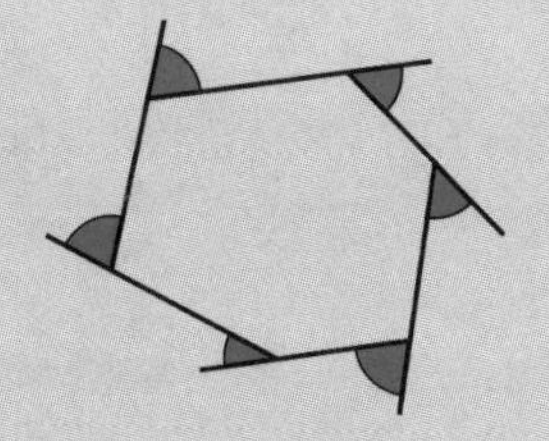

The *sum of the exterior angles* of any polygon is 360°.

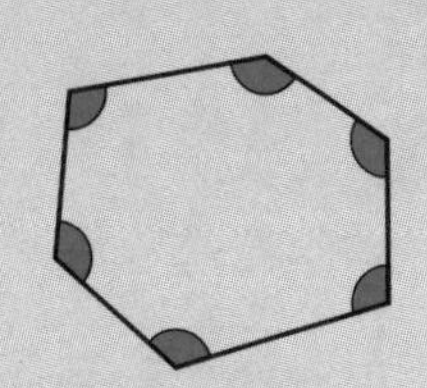

The *sum of the interior angles* of a polygon depends on the number of sides.
For a polygon with n sides, this sum is $(180n - 360)^\circ$ or $(2n - 4)$ right angles.

ENLARGEMENT

When an object is enlarged by a scale factor 2, each line on the image is twice the length of the corresponding line on the object.

The diagram shows an enlargement of a triangle, with centre of enlargement X and scale factor 2.
The dashed lines are guidelines.
$XA' = 2XA$

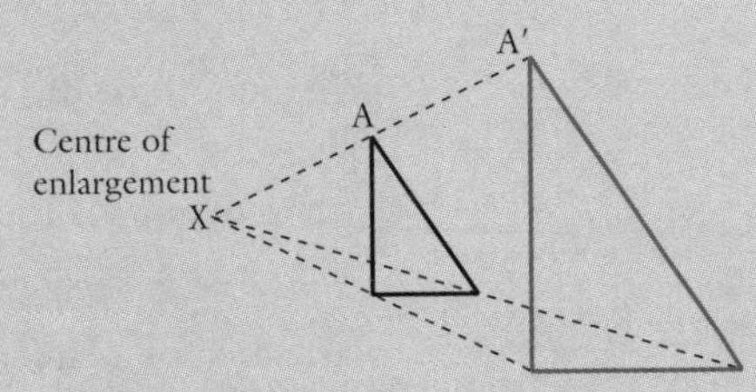

UNITS OF AREA

Area is measured by standard sized squares.

In metric units:

$$1\text{ cm}^2 = 10\text{ mm} \times 10\text{ mm} = 100\text{ mm}^2$$

and

$$1\text{ m}^2 = 100\text{ cm} \times 100\text{ cm} = 10\,000\text{ cm}^2$$

$$1\text{ km}^2 = 1000\text{ m} \times 1000\text{ m} = 1\,000\,000\text{ m}^2$$

$$1\text{ hectare (ha)} = 100\text{ m} \times 100\text{ m} = 10\,000\text{ m}^2$$

In Imperial units:

$$1\text{ sq ft} = 12\text{ in} \times 12\text{ in} = 144\text{ sq in}$$

and

$$1\text{ sq yd} = 3\text{ ft} \times 3\text{ ft} = 9\text{ sq ft}$$

$$1\text{ acre} = 4840\text{ sq yd}$$

To convert between hectares and acres, use $1\text{ ha} \approx 2.5$ acres

AREA

The area of a *parallelogram* is given by length × height,

i.e. $A = lh$

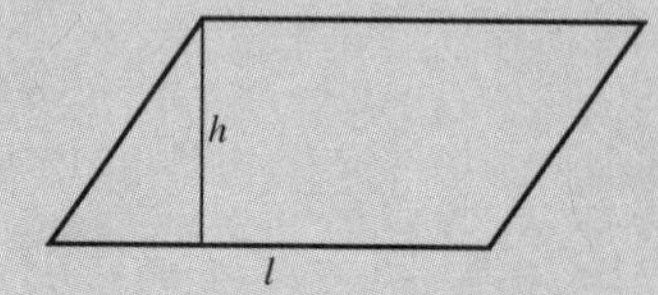

The area of a *triangle* is given by $\frac{1}{2}$base × height,

i.e. $A = \frac{1}{2}bh$

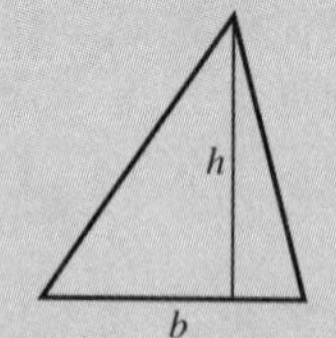

The area of a trapezium is given by

$\frac{1}{2}$(sum of parallel sides) × (distance between them),

i.e. $A = \frac{1}{2}(a + b) \times h$

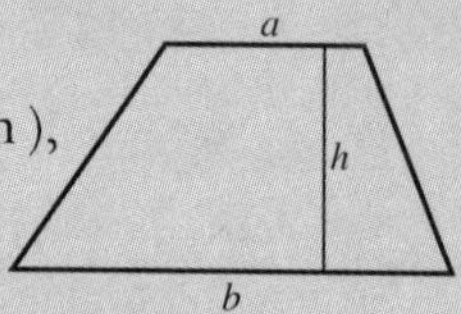

When we talk about the height of a triangle or of a parallelogram, we mean the perpendicular height.

CIRCLES

The names of the parts of a circle are shown in the diagram.
The diameter of a circle is twice the radius.

The length of the *circumference* is given by $C = 2\pi r$,
where r units is the radius of the circle and $\pi = 3.1415\ldots$

The area of a circle is given by $A = \pi r^2$

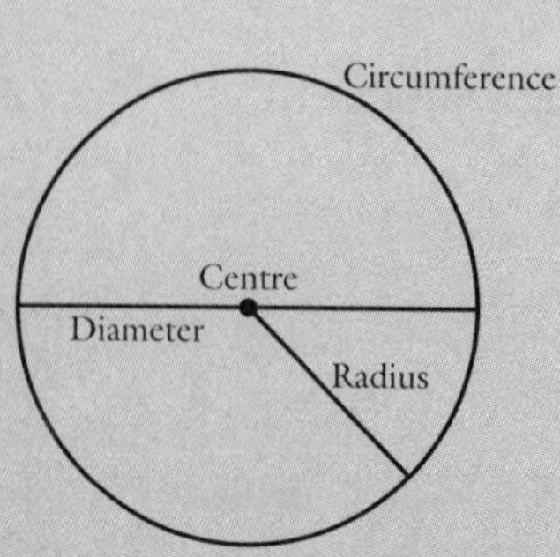

STATISTICS

A *hypothesis* is a statement that has not yet been shown to be true or untrue.

Scatter graphs

We get a scatter graph when we plot as points values of one quantity against corresponding values of another quantity.

When the points are scattered about a straight line, we can draw that line by eye; the line is called the *line of best fit*.

We use the word *correlation* when describing the amount of scatter about this line.

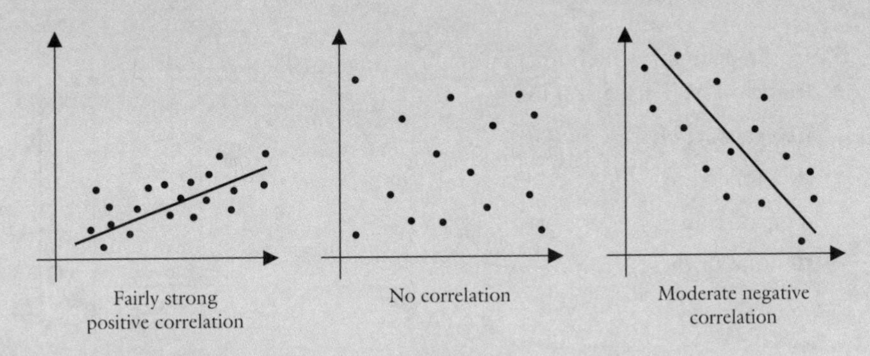

REVISION EXERCISE 3.1 (Chapters 6 to 8)

1 **a** How many sides has

i a hexagon **ii** an octagon **iii** a rhombus?

b How many interior angles are there in

i a pentagon **ii** a parallelogram **iii** a regular hexagon?

2 **a** Find the size of each exterior angle of a regular polygon with 15 sides. What is the size of each interior angle?

b How many sides has a regular polygon if each exterior angle is $12°$?

3 Find the size of each angle marked with a letter.

a

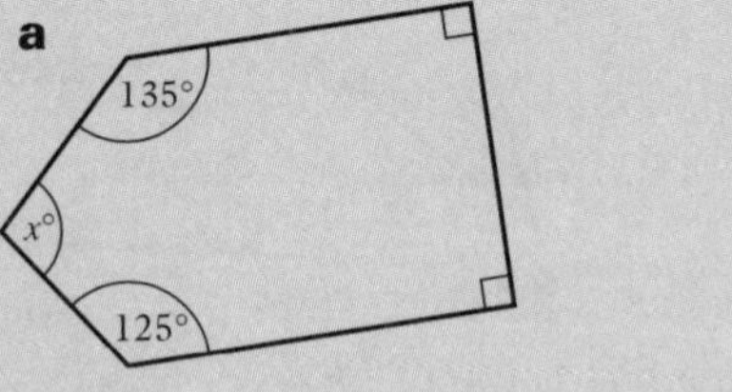

b

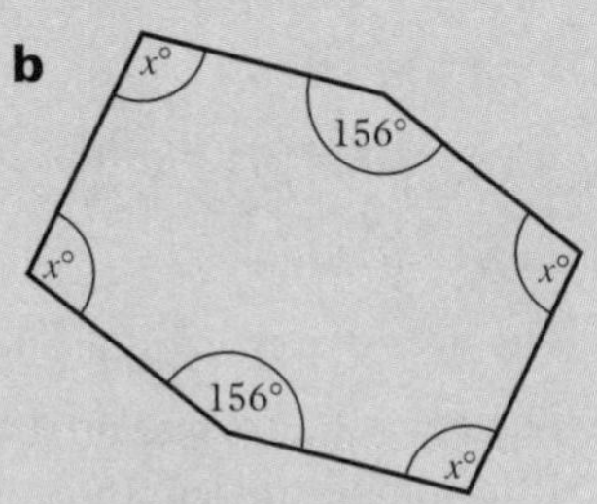

4

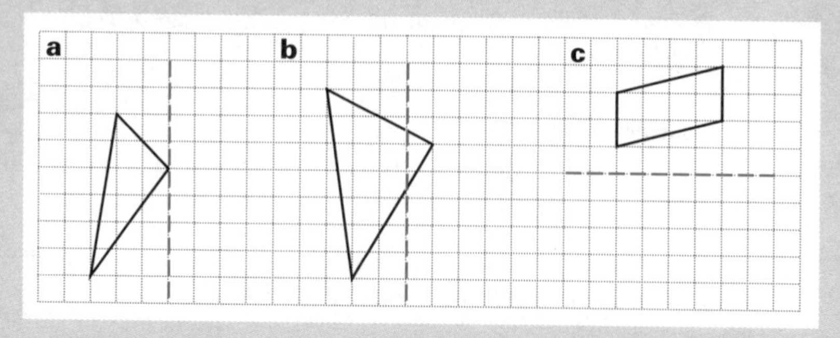

Copy the objects and mirror lines onto squared paper, and draw the image of each object, when it is reflected in the mirror line.

5 In the diagram, which images of triangle LMN are given by

a a translation

b a reflection

c a rotation

d none of these?

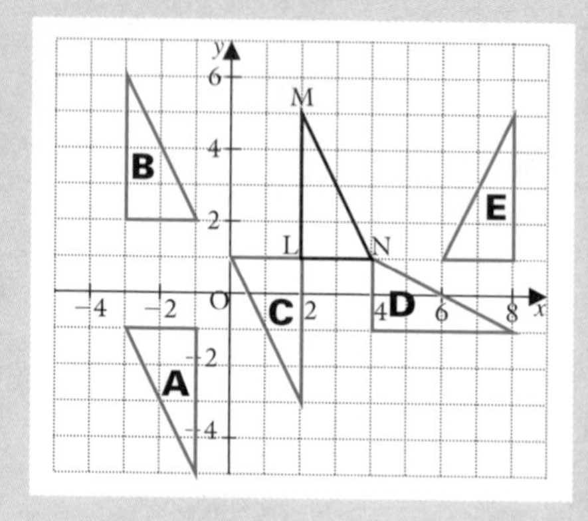

6 **a** Copy the diagram and draw the image $A'B'C'$ when ABC is rotated through 180° about the point (0, 1).

b Draw the image $A''B''C''$ when ABC is rotated 90° clockwise about the point (2, 0).

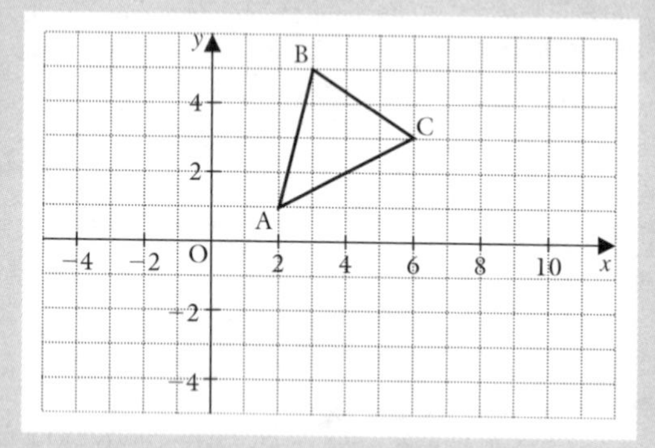

7 Find the area of each shape.

a

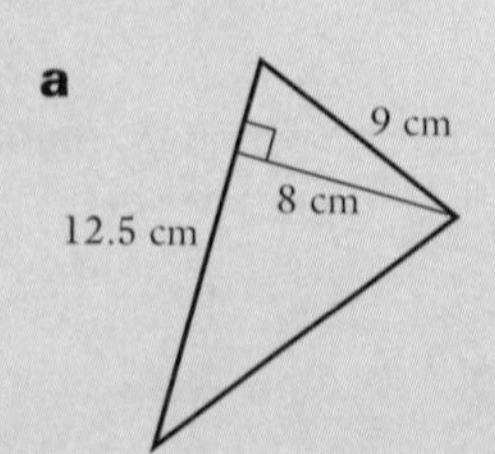

b

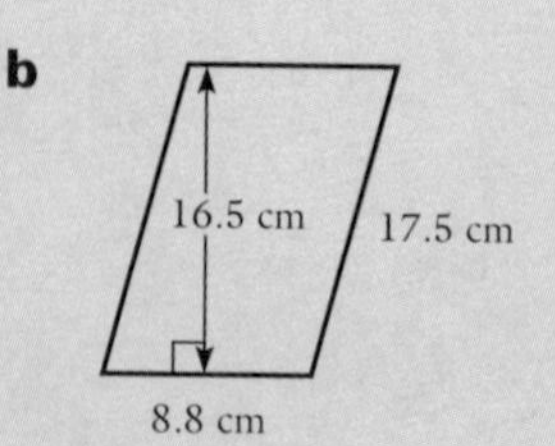

8 **a** The area of a rectangular washer is 8.5 cm^2. If it is 3.4 cm long, how wide is it?

b The area of a triangular-shaped gasket is 14.88 cm^2. If the height of the triangle is 4.8 cm, find the length of its base.

9 Use squared paper to draw axes for x and y from 0 to 8 using 1 square for 1 unit. Find the area of triangle ABC as a number of square units if the coordinates of the three corners are A(2, 4), B(6, 4) and C(2, 1).

10 Find the area of each shape in square centimetres. All measurements are given in centimetres.

a

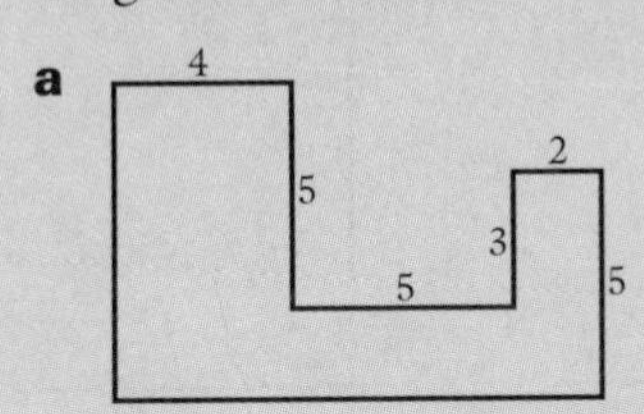

b

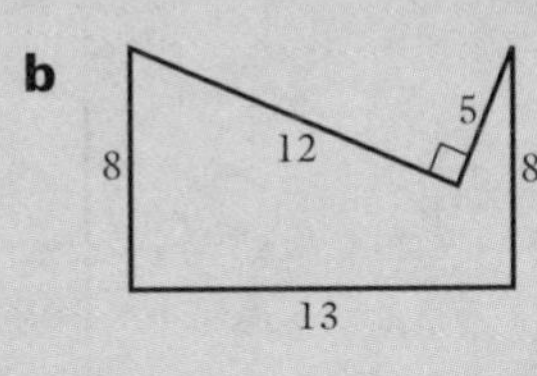

REVISION EXERCISE 3.2 (Chapters 9 and 10)

1 a Find the circumference of a circle of radius 3.4 cm.

b Find the area of a circle whose diameter is 1.2 m.

2 a Find the perimeter of the semicircle given in the diagram.

b What is the area of this semicircle?

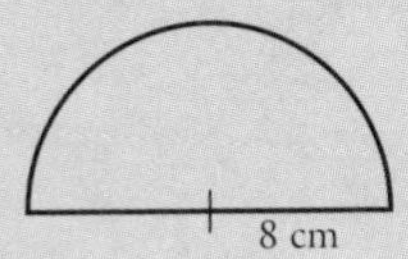

3 a Find the diameter of a circle whose circumference is 60 cm.

b Find the radius of a circle whose circumference is 30 inches.

4 The largest possible circle is cut from a square of paper of side 12 cm.

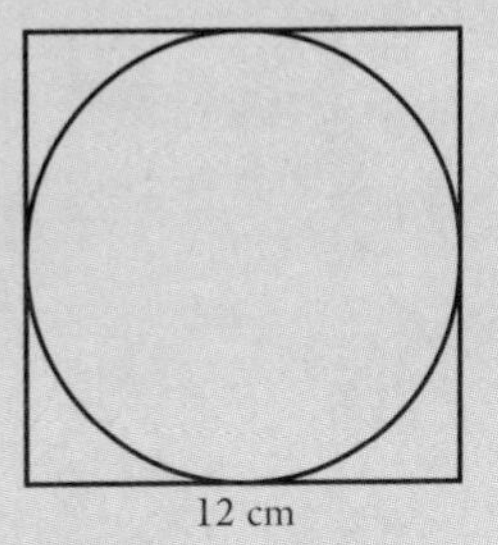

a Write down the diameter of the circle and find

i its circumference **ii** its area.

b What is the area of the original sheet?

c What area of paper is wasted?

d Express the amount of paper wasted as a percentage of the original sheet.

5 Find the area of the shaded region.

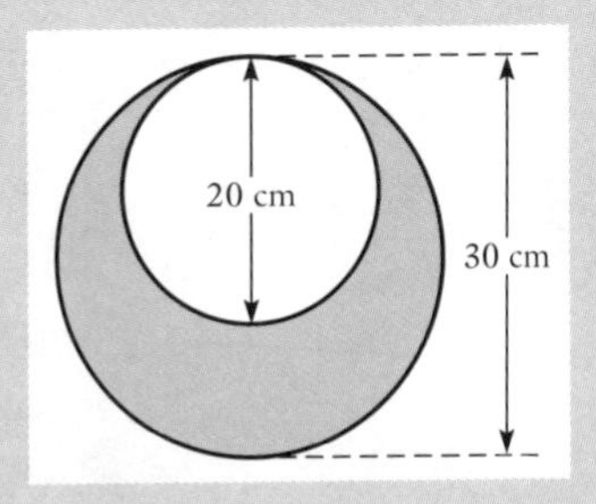

6 Find

a the perimeter of the quadrant

b the area of the quadrant

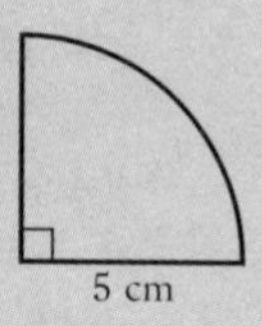

7

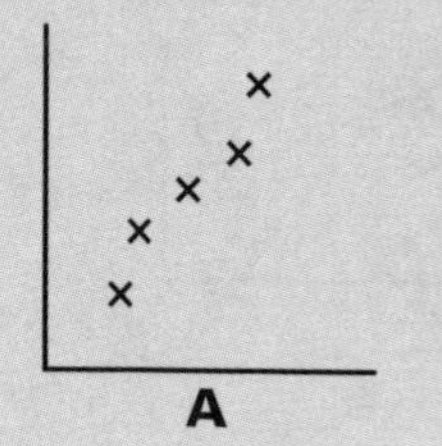

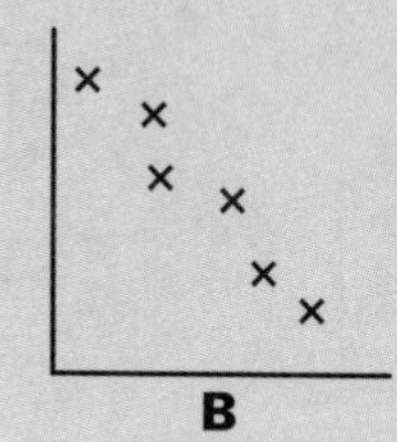

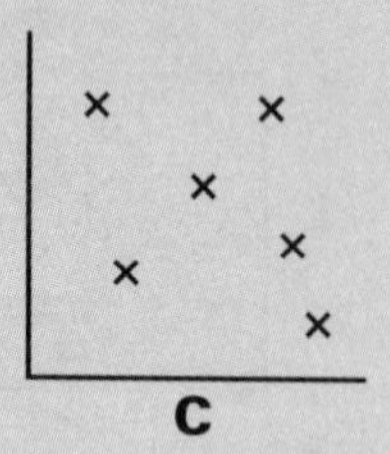

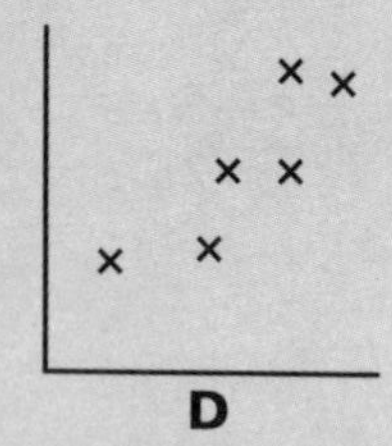

a Which of the above scatter graphs shows
  i strong negative correlation
  ii moderate positive correlation
  iii no correlation ?

b Describe the correlation illustrated in the remaining graph.

8 Six boys were selected as potentially good sprinters. The table shows the average number of hours each of them spent per week in training and the best times they recorded for 100 m during the last weeks of the season.

Sprinter	Ed	Brendan	Hank	Pete	Roger	Colin
Average number of of hours per week	9	3	8	15	4	10
Best time (seconds)	11.2	11.8	11.5	10.9	12.1	11.4

a Show this information on a scatter graph. Use a horizontal scale of 8 cm for 1 second, and mark this axis from 10.5 seconds to 12.5 seconds. Use 1 cm for 1 hour on the vertical axis and mark it from 0 to 16.

b Does this scatter graph suggest that increasing the number of hours spent in training will result in better times ? How would you describe the correlation between these two quantities ?

c George wants to join the group and is potentially as good as anyone already included. If he trains for 12 hours a week about what 'best time' can he expect ?

9 This table shows the number of bad grapefruit per box after different transit times.

Number of bad grapefruit	0	2	5	4	2
Number of hours in transit	4	10	18	14	6

a Plot this information on a scatter graph using 1 cm to represent 2 hours and 1 cm to represent 1 grapefruit.
Is there any correlation between the number of bad grapefruit per box and the time they are in transit?

b About how many bad grapefruit per box could be expected for a load for which the transit time is 12 hours?

10 The members of the organising committee were discussing previous village fêtes. They decided to find out if there were relationships between the number of people attending, the amount it rained on the day and the number of stalls at the fête. They plotted three scatter graphs.

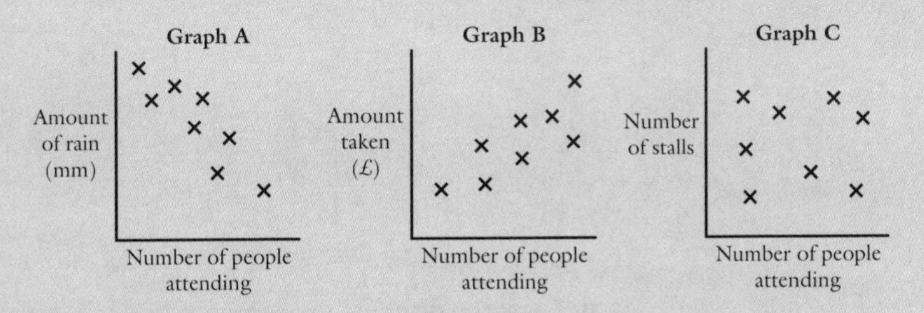

a What does graph A show about the relationship between the amount of rain falling on the day of the fête and the number of people attending?

b What does graph B show about the relationship between the amount of money taken and the number of people attending?

c What does graph C show about the relationship between the number of stalls and the number of people attending?

d Next year they intend having 8 more stalls. Should this increase their takings? Explain your answer.

REVISION EXERCISE 3.3 (Chapters 6 to 10)

1 Is it possible for each exterior angle of a regular polygon to be

a 30° **b** 35°?

If your answer is 'yes' state how many sides the polygon has.
If it is 'no', justify your answer.

2 Find the value of x.

a

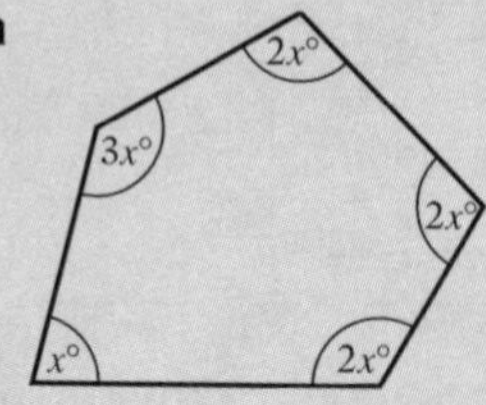

b

3

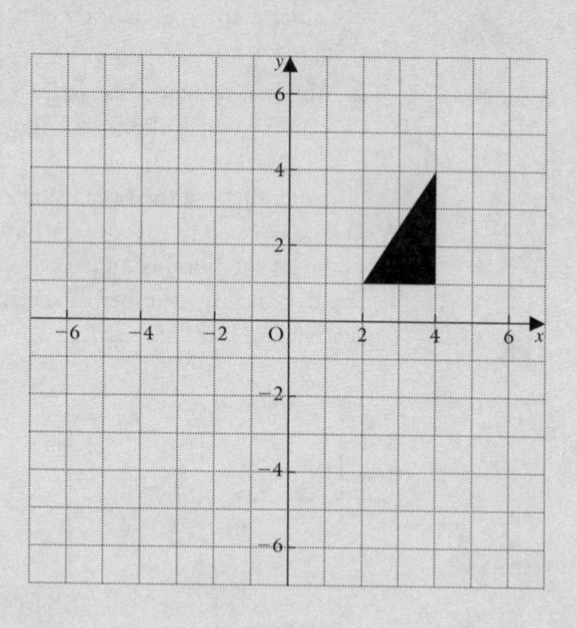

a Copy the diagram and carry out this compound transformation: reflection in the y-axis followed by reflection in the x-axis.

b What single transformation will map the original triangle onto the final triangle ?

4 **a** Draw axes for x and y. Scale the x-axis from -4 to 10 and the y-axis from -2 to 6.

Draw quadrilateral ABCD: A(5, 1), B(7, 1), C(7, 0), D(5, 0).

Draw quadrilateral A′B′C′D′: A′(-3, 5), B′(3, 5), C′(3, 2), D′(-3, 2).

Draw AA′, BB′, CC′ and DD′ and extend these lines until they meet.

b Give the coordinates of the centre of enlargement.

c Measure the sides and angles of the two quadrilaterals. What do you notice ?

5 For each of the following shapes the area is given, together with one dimension. Find the measurement marked with a letter.

a

c

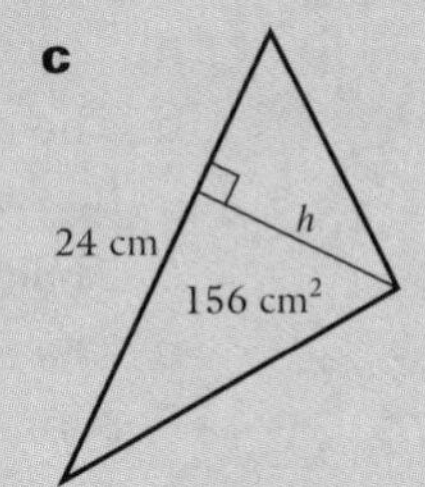

b

d

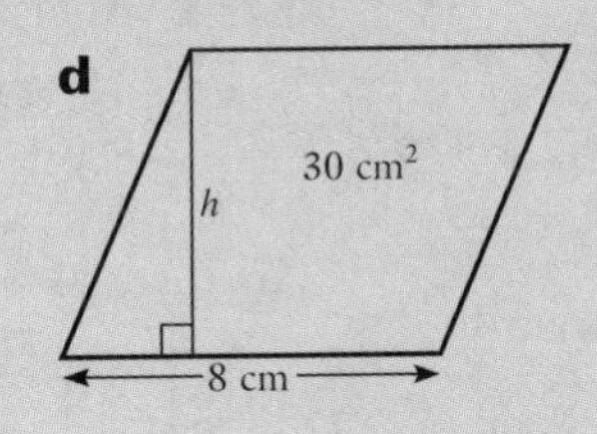

6 **a** Use your calculator to find
i the square of 0.77 **ii** the square root of 0.048.
Give each answer correct to 3 significant figures.

b Find
i the area of triangle ABC
ii the length of CD.

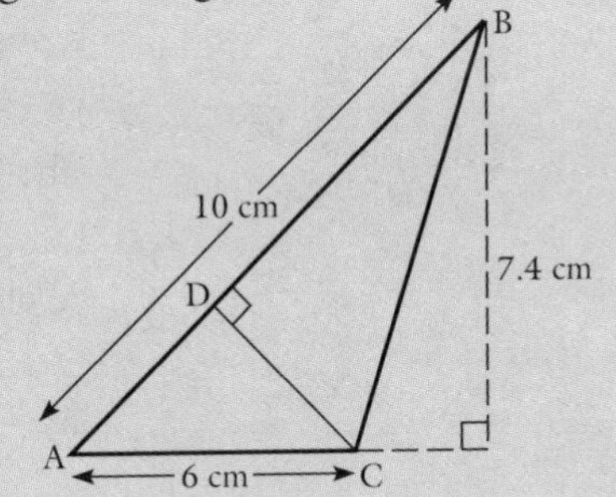

7 **a** Find the diameter of a circle which has a circumference of 76 cm. What is the area of this circle?

b For the given shape, find
i the perimeter
ii the area.

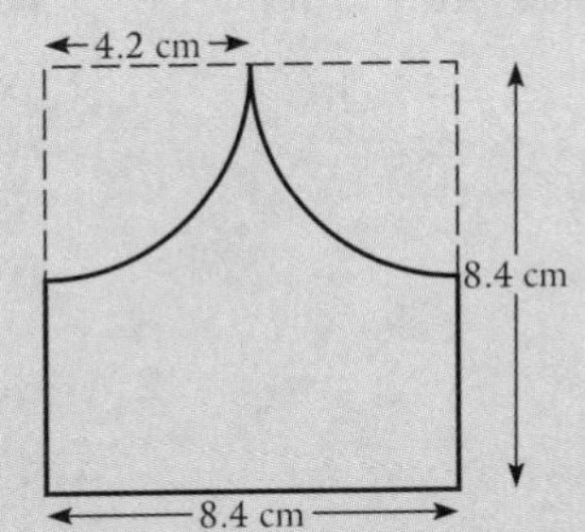

8 The minute hand of the City Hall clock is 1.6 m long while the hour hand is 1.1 m long. How far does the tip of each hand move in 1 hour?

9 In each case describe the correlation you think there may be between the two quantities. Explain your answer.

a The heights and weights of the girls in Year 9 of a school.

b The cost of a household electricity bill and the distance of the household north from the most southerly point in the country.

c Ability in foreign languages and ability in football.

d The monthly sale of umbrellas in London and its monthly rainfall.

e Ability in maths and ability in music.

f The sale of hot-water bottles during the winter months in Scotland and the outside temperature there.

10

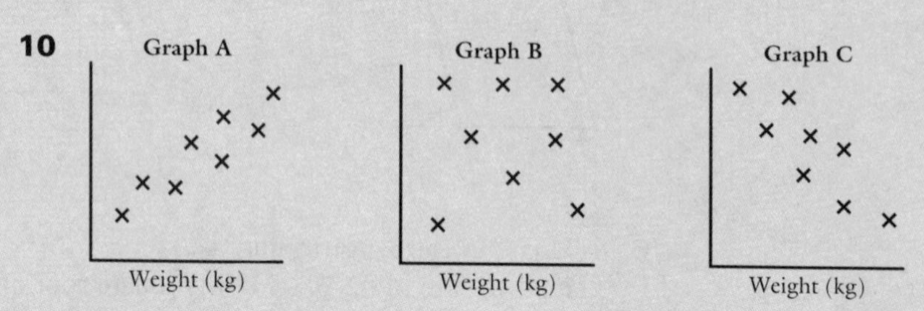

These scatter graphs were obtained by plotting information relating to 8 pupils against their weights.

a Describe the correlation shown in graph A. Suggest a possible label for the vertical axis.

b Describe the correlation shown in graph B. Suggest a possible label for the vertical axis.

c Describe the correlation shown in graph C. Suggest a possible label for the vertical axis.

REVISION EXERCISE 3.4 (Chapters 1 to 10)

1 **a** Round each number to the accuracy given in the brackets.

i 17.898 (3 s.f.) **iii** 67 546 (nearest 100)

ii 43.078 (2 d.p.) **iv** 0.008 097 (2 d.p.)

b Write down an *estimate* for each of the following calculations. Do all the working in your head.

i $17.89 + 2.08$ **iii** $(1.98)^2$

ii $5.97 \div 2.94$ **iv** 0.476×0.12

2 Write down the size of each marked angle

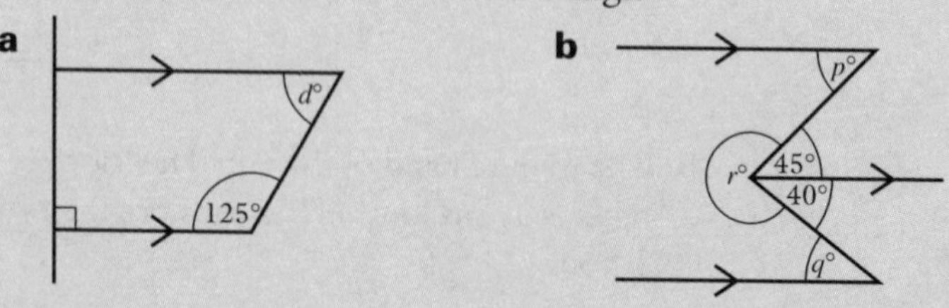

3 **a** Calculate

i $3\frac{5}{8} \div \frac{3}{16}$ **ii** $2\frac{5}{8} \div 12\frac{1}{4}$ **iii** $1\frac{3}{4} \div 2\frac{1}{3}$ **iv** $\frac{12}{25} \div \left(\frac{1}{2} + \frac{2}{5}\right)$

b Increase £280 by 45%.

c Decrease £480 by 25%.

d How many jars each holding $\frac{3}{8}$ lb can be filled from a tin containing 21 lb?

4 In the Christmas raffle for the local motor club 800 tickets are sold. If Gemma buys 10 tickets what is the probability that she will not win first prize?

5 **a** Calculate

i $(+5) \times (2)$ **ii** $7 \times (-4)$ **iii** $(-7) \times (-5)$ **iv** $2(-5)$

b If $P = 2x + 3y$ find P when

i $x = 3, y = 4$ **ii** $x = 6, y = -3$

6 The broken red line is a line of symmetry for this hexagon.

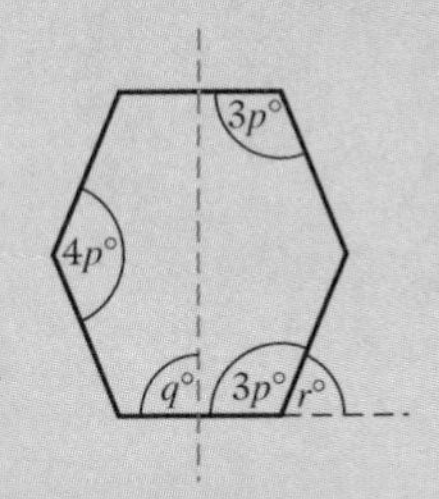

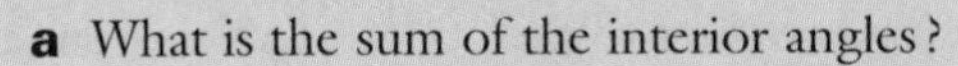

a What is the sum of the interior angles?

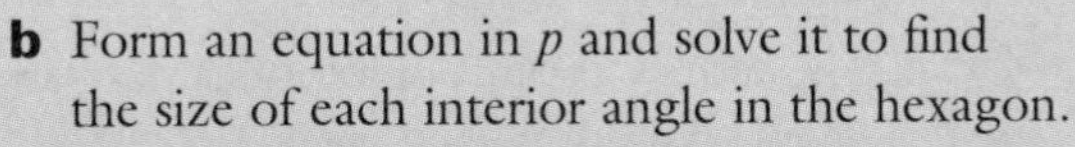

b Form an equation in p and solve it to find the size of each interior angle in the hexagon.

c Find the size of the angles marked $q°$ and $r°$.

7 Copy the diagram onto squared paper using 1 square as 1 unit. Draw AA′, BB′, CC′ and DD′ and extend the lines until they meet. Write down the coordinates of the centre of enlargement and the scale factor.

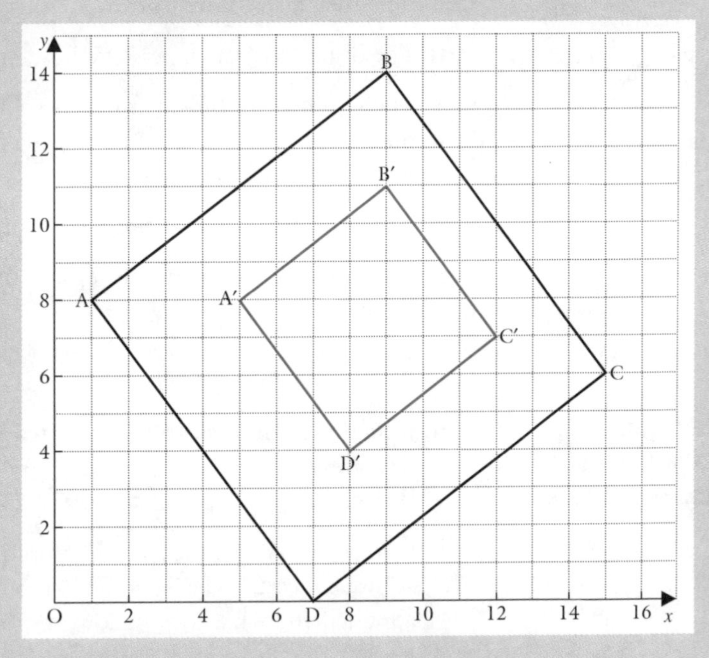

8 Find the area of each shape.

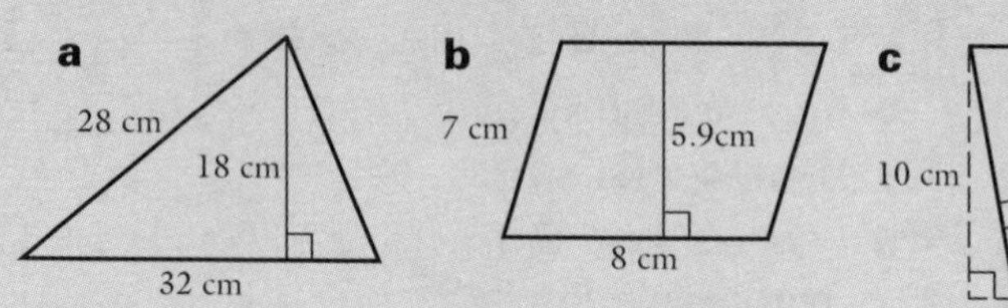

9 The diagram shows a window which is in the shape of a square surmounted by a semicircle. Find

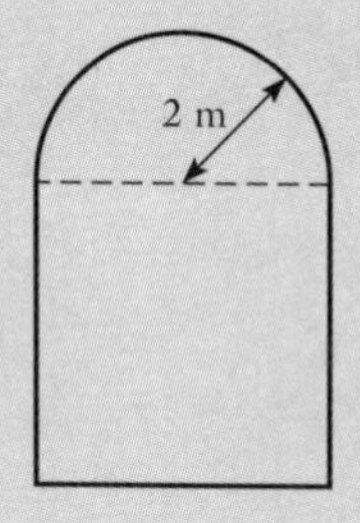

a the perimeter of the window

b the area of the window.

10 In each case describe the correlation you think there may be between the two quantities. Explain your answer.

a The weekly takings of a local supermarket and the number of people visiting it each week.

b The marks of the pupils of Class 9P in a maths test and their marks in a science test.

c The weights of all the 14-year-old pupils in the school and the time they take to run 100 m.

d The distance round a person's head and that person's shoe size.

e The number of deck-chair tickets sold at Bournemouth each day during the month of August and the number of millimetres of rain falling each day.

f The circumference of a circle and its radius.

g The average speed of a journey and the time taken to complete the journey.

REVISION EXERCISE 3.5 (Chapters 1 to 10)

1 **a** Round each number to the accuracy given in brackets

i 786.54 (3 s.f.) **iii** 457 298 (nearest 1000)

ii 153.6666 (2 d.p.) **iv** 7.556 (nearest 10)

b Correct to the nearest ten, 350 pupils and parents attended a school concert. What was the largest number that could have attended and what was the lowest?

2 Write down the size of each marked angle.

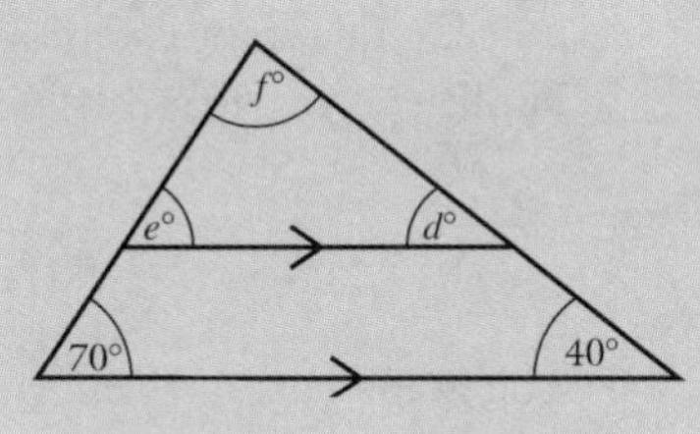

3 **a** Express 350 g as a fraction of 1.5 kg.

b Find 8.2% of 9.2 km.

c Which is the larger and by how much, $\frac{8}{9}$ of $2\frac{1}{4}$ or $\frac{7}{12} \div \frac{3}{10}$?

4 An ordinary dice is rolled 600 times. About how many times would you expect to get

a 1 **b** 6 **c** a score that is even?

5 **a** If $V = \frac{1}{f} + \frac{1}{p}$, find V when $f = 2$ and $p = 3$.

b If $A = 2a(b - 2c)$, find A when $a = 3$, $b = 4.5$, $c = 1.4$.

6 **a** Find the size of each exterior angle of a regular polygon with 20 sides.

b How many sides has a regular polygon if the interior angle is $157\frac{1}{2}°$?

7 Copy the diagram onto squared paper and draw the image when triangle ABC is rotated through 90° anticlockwise with centre of rotation at the point (4, 1).

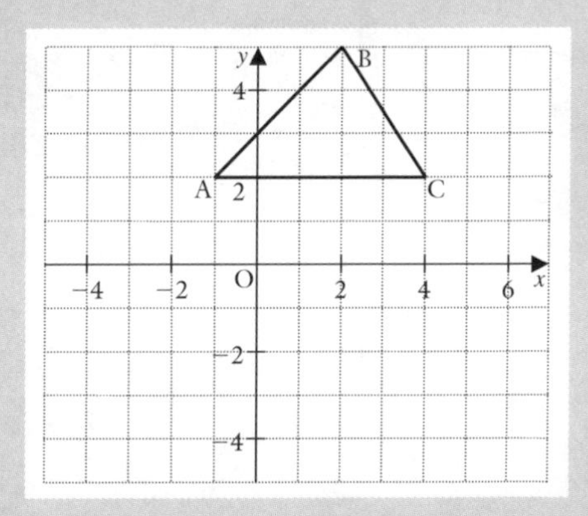

8 **a** The area of the top of a rectangular table is $2.34\ \text{m}^2$. If it is 1.2 m wide, how long is it?

b Find

i the area of the parallelogram

ii the length of the side marked a.

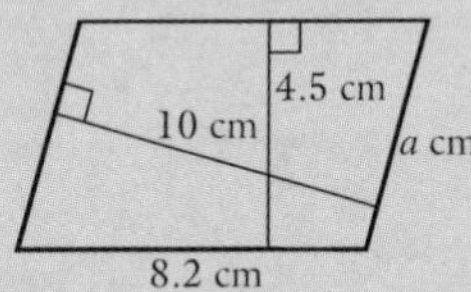

9 From a square sheet of card the largest possible quadrant is removed.
Find the area of card left.

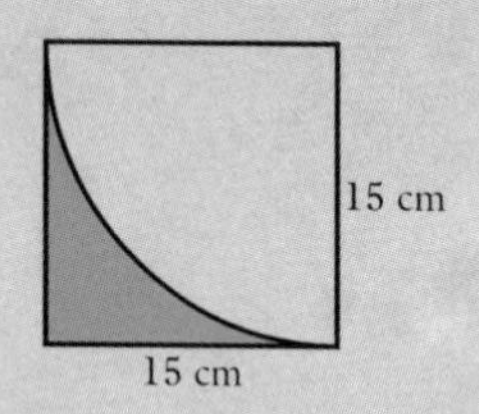

10 The graph illustrates information relating to the unit cost of the product a company manufactures and the number of units produced.

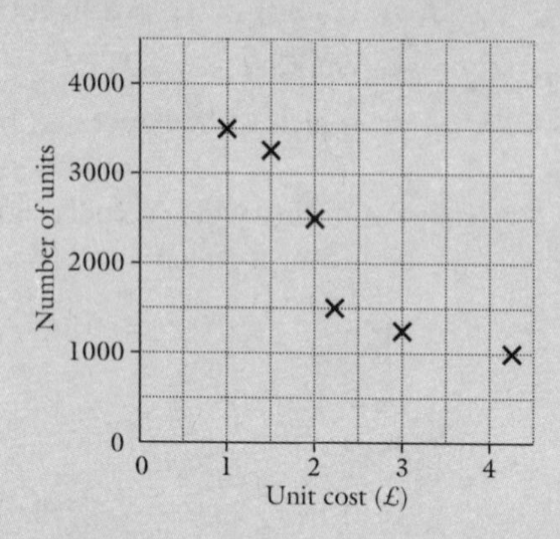

a Would you describe this correlation as
i positive or negative **ii** strong or moderate?

b Does the evidence support the statement, 'The more we produce the lower the unit cost'?

RATIO

PARTS OF A WHOLE

Orange squash is made by diluting a concentrate with water. The concentrate and water are parts of the diluted drink and we need to know how much of each to use. This information can be given in many ways, for example,
'Add 720 ml of water to 240 ml of concentrate.'
'Dilute so that one quarter of the drink is concentrate.'
'Add one part by volume of concentrate to three parts of water.'
These instructions all result in the same mixture but some are more easily understood than others.

- The first instruction is probably more detailed than necessary. Also some arithmetic is needed if a different quantity of drink is wanted, and it is not immediately possible to compare the proportions of concentrate and water in the diluted juice.
- The second instruction is not very clear and needs some thought to work out how much water should be added. It can be useful if a particular quantity of made-up juice is required.
- The third instruction is clear, allows for different quantities of drink to be made up and gives immediate information about the quantities of concentrate and water in the diluted drink.
  This diagram sums up that information very clearly.

EXERCISE 11A

1 'Compo' is made by mixing cement and sand. The weights of sand and cement required can be given as 'Five parts sand to two parts cement', or 'Five-sevenths of the mixture is sand', or 'Mix 500 kg of sand with 200 kg of cement.'
Discuss which of these instructions is most helpful if you want to

a make up some mix using the sand you have in stock

b end up with 350 kg of mix

c buy enough sand and cement to make about 7000 kg mix, but you are not sure exactly how much mix you will need.

2 School uniform shirts are usually made from material that contains a mixture of cotton and polyester. Discuss the ways in which the proportions of cotton and polyester can be described on the label.

3 'Green Fingers' potting compost is made by mixing one part of sand with two parts of peat.
Discuss these statements (they are not all necessarily true).

a To make 3 litres of compost you need 1 litre of sand and 2 litres of peat.

b Half this bag of compost is sand.

c To make 3 kg of compost you need 1 kg of sand and 2 kg of peat.

d The quantity of sand is half the quantity of peat.

RATIO

The last exercise shows that there are various ways of comparing the sizes of related quantities, and that giving the relative sizes rather than the actual sizes is often more useful. Question **3** shows that, unless the nature of the quantities being compared is given, comparisons of size are not much use.

When we say that orange squash is made by adding one part by volume of concentrate to three parts by volume of water, we are *not* giving the size of the quantities to be mixed; we *are* giving information about the relative sizes of the quantities; this is called the *ratio* of the sizes, that is, the volume of concentrate to the volume of water is in the ratio 1 to 3. Using the symbol ':' to mean 'to' we write this as

$$\text{volume of concentrate} : \text{volume of water} = 1:3$$

SIMPLIFYING RATIOS

The first instructions for making orange squash was

'Add 720 ml of water to 240 ml of concentrate.'

This can be simplified to give the ratio of the two quantities,

i.e. the ratio of concentrate to water is 240 ml : 720 ml,

which can be simplified, by dividing both numbers by 240, to

$$1\text{ ml} : 3\text{ ml}.$$

We can simplify this further by omitting the units, *provided that it is made clear that the ratio is of volumes,* for example, by writing

$$\text{volume of concentrate} : \text{volume of water} = 1:3$$

The advantage of not giving units in a ratio is that any convenient unit for measuring the quantities can be used, provided that it is the *same for both quantities.*

EXERCISE 11B

Simplify the ratio 1 m : 2 cm

Before we can leave out the units, they must both be the same, so we use 1 m = 100 cm

1 m : 2 cm = 100 cm : 2 cm

Ratio of the lengths = 100 : 2

= 50 : 1

Simplify the ratios.

1 2 cm : 8 cm

2 32 p : 96 p

3 45 g : 1 kg

4 £4 : 75 p

5 48 p : £2.88

6 10 m : 50 cm

7 5 ml : 20 ml

8 £1.50 : 75 p

9 2 kg : 500 g

10 2 kg : 75 g

11 75 mm : 6 cm

12 £3.80 : 95 p

Simplify the ratio 2 m : 0.5 m

Ratio of lengths = 2 : 0.5

= 4 : 1

Multiplying by 2 gives whole numbers, and these are easier to work with than fractions or decimals.

Simplify the ratios.

13 2 m : $1\frac{1}{2}$ m

14 £1 : £1.50

15 $2\frac{1}{2}$ km : 3 km

16 0.7 mm : 1.4 mm

17 $2\frac{1}{2}$ km : $1\frac{1}{2}$ km

18 5.1 m : 25.5 cm

19 $1\frac{1}{2}$ in : $1\frac{1}{2}$ in

20 2 kg : 1.4 kg

21 4.5 m : 36 cm

22 14.4 m : 3.6 m

23 2.6 kg : 13 kg

24 2 yd : 4 ft

We can use ratios to compare more than two quantities.

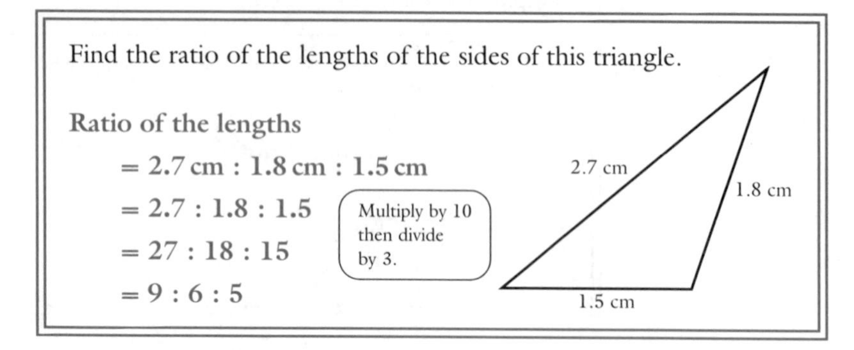

Find the ratio of the lengths of the sides of this triangle.

Ratio of the lengths

= 2.7 cm : 1.8 cm : 1.5 cm

= 2.7 : 1.8 : 1.5

= 27 : 18 : 15

= 9 : 6 : 5

Simplify the ratios.

25 2 cm : 4 cm : 6 cm

26 7 mg : 56 mg : 21 mg

27 2 kg : 3 kg : $1\frac{1}{2}$ kg

28 25 g : 100 g : 75 g

29 1 m : 20 cm : 50 mm

30 6 apples : 2 oranges : 2 bananas

A family has 12 pets of which 6 are cats or kittens, 2 are dogs and the rest are birds. Find the ratio of the numbers of

a birds to dogs **b** birds to pets.

There are 4 birds.

a Number of birds : number of dogs = 4 : 2
= 2 : 1

b Number of birds : number of pets = 4 : 12
= 1 : 3

In each question give your answer in its simplest form.

31 A couple have 6 grandsons and 4 granddaughters. Find

a the ratio of the number of grandsons to that of granddaughters

b the ratio of the number of granddaughters to that of grandchildren.

32 Square A has sides 6 cm long and square B has sides 8 cm long. Find the ratio of

a the length of the side of square A to the length of the side of square B

b the area of square A to the area of square B.

33 Tom walks 2 km to school in 40 minutes and John cycles 5 km to school in 15 minutes. Find the ratio of

a Tom's distance to John's distance

b Tom's time to John's time.

34 Mary has 18 sweets and Jane has 12. As Mary has 6 sweets more than Jane she tries to even things out by giving Jane 6 sweets. What is the ratio of the number of sweets Mary has to the number Jane has

a at the start **b** at the end?

35 Rectangle A has length 12 cm and width 6 cm while rectangle B has length 8 cm and width 5 cm. Find the ratio of

a the length of A to the length of B

b the area of A to the area of B

c the perimeter of A to the perimeter of B

d the size of an angle of A to the size of an angle of B.

36 A triangle has sides of lengths 3.2 cm, 4.8 cm and 3.6 cm. Find the ratio of the lengths of the sides to one another.

37 Two angles of a triangle are 54° and 72°. Find the ratio of the size of the third angle to the sum of the first two.

38 For a school fête, Mrs Jones and Mrs Brown make marmalade in 1 lb jars. Mrs Jones makes 5 jars of lemon marmalade and 3 jars of orange marmalade. Mrs Brown makes 7 jars of lemon marmalade and 5 of grapefruit marmalade. Find the ratio of the numbers of jars of

a lemon to orange to grapefruit marmalade

b Mrs Jones' to Mrs Brown's marmalade

c Mrs Jones' lemon to orange marmalade.

39 A recipe for the base of a cheesecake needs 25 g of butter and 150 g of crushed biscuits. Find the ratio of the weight of butter to the weight of biscuits.

40 Amir made a model plane from a kit. The model is 40 cm long and the actual plane is 35 m long.

a Find the ratio of the length of the model to the length of the actual plane.

b Explain whether the answer is the same for the ratio of the length of the actual plane to the length of the model.

41 David runs his own business.

a Last year his costs were £25 000 and his turnover was £40 000. Find the ratio of his costs to turnover last year.

b This year his costs have increased by 10% and his turnover has fallen by 5%.
Find the ratio of his costs to turnover this year.

42 An enlargement of a photograph is 6.5 cm wide. The original photograph is 3.5 cm wide.

a What is the ratio of the width of the enlarged photograph to the width of the original?

b The enlarging machine is set by entering this ratio on its control panel. Explain what you think would happen if the ratio was entered in the wrong order.

43 If $p : q = 2 : 3$, find the ratio $6p : 2q$

44 Find the ratios of the following areas

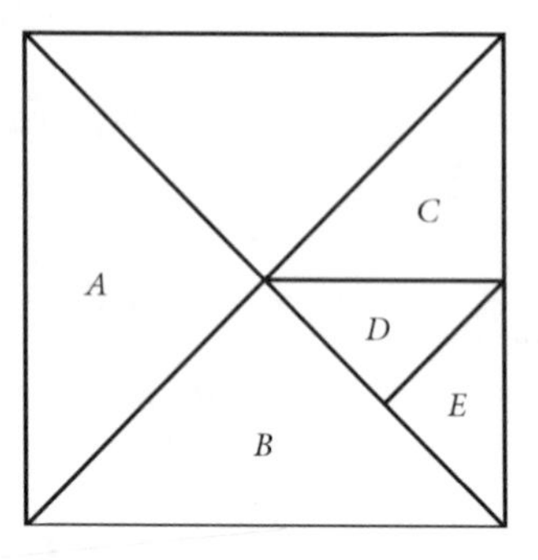

a $B : A$

b $C : B$

c $E : A + B$

d $E : D$

e $E : C + D$

f C : whole square

45

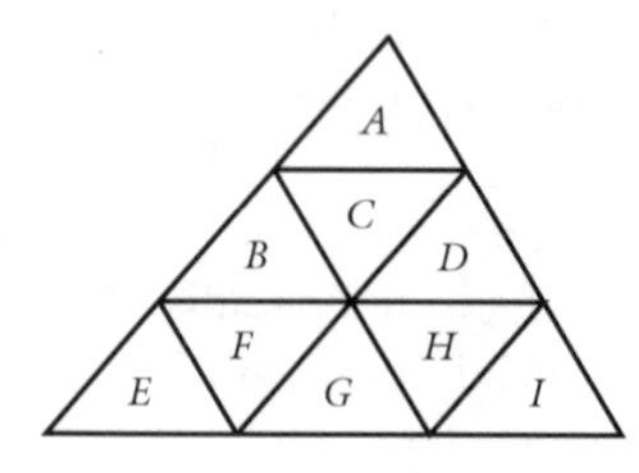

The areas of the small triangles are equal. Find the ratios of the following areas

a A : whole figure

b $A : A + B + C + D$

c $B + E + F + G$: whole figure

EXPRESSING A RATIO IN THE FORM 1 : n

Richard has a new scooter.

The instructions state that the tank must be filled with fuel mixed from oil and petrol in the ratio 1 : 50.

If Richard puts 20 ml of oil in the tank, the ratio 1 : 50 tells him he needs to add 50 times as much petrol, that is, 1000 ml which is 1 litre.

The ratio also tells him that 100 ml of oil has to be mixed with 100×50 ml of petrol, and so on.

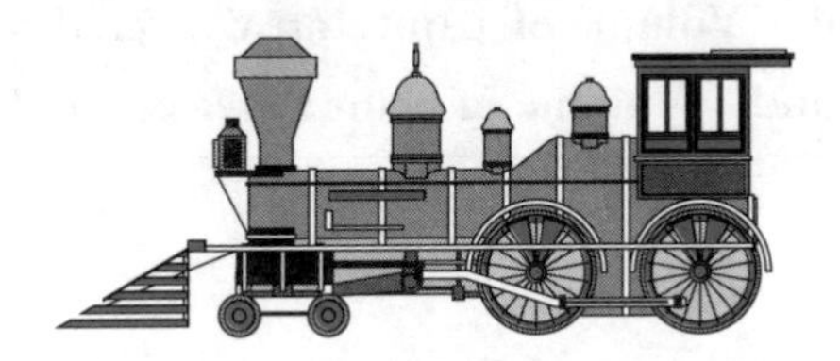

Richard's mother has a working model engine; it needs fuel that is a mixture of oil and paraffin in the ratio 2 : 25.

The amount of paraffin needed to mix with 50 ml of oil is not so obvious from the ratio in the form given.

If, however, we rewrite the ratio 2 : 25 as 1 : 12.5 (dividing both numbers by 2), we can immediately see that 50 ml of oil has to be mixed with 50×12.5 ml of paraffin.

These two examples show that a ratio expressed in the form 1 : n is often an easy form to work with.

EXERCISE 11C

> Express the ratio 5 : 7 in the form 1 : n.
>
> $5 : 7 = 1 : \frac{7}{5}$
>
> $= 1 : 1.4$
>
> Remember that a ratio is unaltered when each number is multiplied (or divided) by the same amount. In this case we divide both numbers by 5 to give 1 as the first number in the ratio.

Express the following ratios in the form 1 : n, giving n correct to 3 significant figures where necessary.

1 2 : 3	**4** 11 : 30	**7** 3 : 4	**10** $\frac{1}{3} : \frac{1}{4}$
2 5 : 12	**5** 5 : 3	**8** 4 : 3	**11** 0.75 : 0.25
3 7 : 6	**6** 8 : 21	**9** 7 : 10	**12** $1\frac{1}{2} : 2\frac{2}{3}$

For one brand of emulsion paint, the information given is that 5 litres covers 45 m². Another brand of emulsion paint has an average coverage of 20 m² for 2 litres.
Compare the ratios of the volume of paint to area covered for the two brands.

First brand. Volume of paint : area covered = 5 : 45

Second brand. Volume of paint : area covered = 2 : 20

The ratios are easier to compare if they are both expressed in the form 1 : n

First brand. Ratio = 1 : 9

Second brand. Ratio = 1 : 10

Hence the second brand of paint covers a greater area per litre than the first.

For questions **13** to **20**, compare the ratio of quantity to price and hence state which is cheaper.

13 Gravel at 4 p per kilogram or at £38 per tonne.

14 Eggs at 6 p each or 70 p per dozen.

15 Gold-coloured chain at £16.20 per metre or 15 p per centimetre.

16 Screws at 72 p for twenty or 4 p each.

17 Potatoes at £3 for a 25 kg bag or at 15 p per kg.

18 Light bulbs at 44 p each or at £2.49 per pack of 6.

19 Batteries at £2.20 per pack of 4 or at £5.60 per pack of 10.

20 A 500 ml bottle of liquid fertiliser that covers 90 m² and costs £2.56 or a 5 litre bag of granular fertiliser that covers 300 m² and costs £28.40.

RATIOS AS FRACTIONS

Vivian made a model of his father's car.
The model is 5 cm long and the car is 5 m long.
The ratio of the length of the model to the length of the car is 5 cm : 5 m, i.e.

$$\text{length of model} : \text{length of car} = 5 : 500$$
$$= 1 : 100$$

We can also compare these lengths using fractions,

$$\frac{\text{length of model}}{\text{length of car}} = \frac{5\text{ cm}}{5\text{ m}} = \frac{5}{500}$$
$$= \frac{1}{100},$$

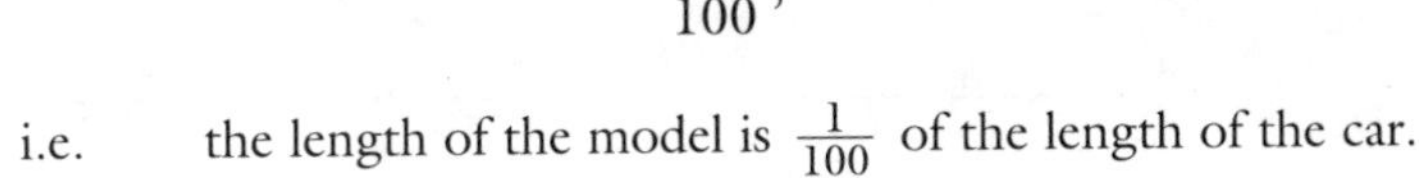

i.e. the length of the model is $\frac{1}{100}$ of the length of the car.

FINDING UNKNOWN QUANTITIES

Sometimes the unknown quantity is obvious.
For example, orange squash is made by mixing concentrate and water in the ratio 1 : 3. To find the volume of water needed for 36 ml of concentrate, we know that

$$36\text{ ml} : \text{volume of water} = 1 : 3$$

Now it is obvious that the volume of water needed is

$$3 \times 36\text{ ml} = 108\text{ ml}.$$

When the unknown quantity is not obvious, using ratios in fraction form is easier. We can then form an equation and solve it.
For example, the weights of icing sugar and butter are combined in the ratio 4 : 3 to make butter icing.
To find the weight of icing sugar needed to mix with 40 g of butter, we start by letting x g be the weight of icing sugar,

then $$x : 40 = 4 : 3$$

Writing these ratios as fractions gives the equation $\frac{x}{40} = \frac{4}{3}$

To find x, we have to make the left-hand side 40 times larger, that is, we need to multiply both sides by 40:

$$\frac{\overset{1}{\cancel{40}}}{1} \times \frac{x}{\cancel{40}_1} = \frac{40}{1} \times \frac{4}{3}$$

giving $$x = \frac{160}{3} = 53.3\ldots$$

so the weight of icing sugar needed is 53 grams (to the nearest gram).

EXERCISE 11D

Find the value of x when $2 : x = 3 : 5$

If we write the ratio as given, x will be on the bottom of the fraction, i.e. $\frac{2}{x} = \frac{3}{5}$.

It is easier to solve an equation when x is on top of a fraction; we can achieve this with ratios by changing their order. Make sure that the order of all ratios involved is changed in the same way.

If $2 : x = 3 : 5$, then $x : 2 = 5 : 3$

therefore $$\frac{x}{2} = \frac{5}{3}$$

$$\frac{\cancel{2}^1}{1} \times \frac{x}{\cancel{2}_1} = \frac{2}{1} \times \frac{5}{3}$$

$$x = \frac{10}{3} = 3\tfrac{1}{3}$$

If the value of x is obvious, write it down, otherwise form an equation to find the value of x.

1 $2 : 5 = 4 : x$

2 $x : 6 = 11 : 18$

3 $x : 9 = 3 : 5$

4 $x : 7 = 3 : 4$

5 $1 : 4 = 12 : x$

6 $x : 5 = 4 : 3$

7 $x : 4 = 1 : 3$

8 $4 : x = 1 : 3$

9 $4 : x = 3 : 5$

10 $3 : 5 = x : 6$

11 $7 : 3 = 3 : x$

12 $3 : x = 2 : 5$

13 $x : 1.2 = 2 : 3$

14 $1.5 : x = 2 : 3$

15 $4 : 5 = x : 1\frac{1}{2}$

16 $x : 4.2 = 4 : 3$

17 $2.5 : x = 5 : 2$

18 $3 : 4 = x : 2\frac{1}{2}$

19 Two lengths are in the ratio 3 : 7. The second length is 42 cm. Find the first length.

20 If the ratio in question **19** were 7 : 3, what would the first length be?

21 In a rectangle, the ratio of its length to its width is 9 : 4. The length is 24 cm. Find the width.

22 A length, originally 6 cm, is increased so that the ratio of the new length to the old length is 9 : 2. What is the new length?

23 Jane is making a model of the school building and the ratio of the lengths of the model to the lengths of the actual building is 1 : 20. The gym is 6 m high. How high, in centimetres, should the model of the gym be ?

24 The ratio of the measurements of a model boat to those of the actual boat is 3 : 50. Find the length of the actual boat if the model is 72 cm long.

25 A lemon drink is made by mixing freshly squeezed lemon juice, sugar and water in the ratio 2 : 2 : 5 by volume.

a How many tablespoons of sugar are needed for 6 tablespoons of lemon juice ?

b How many millilitres of water are needed for 25 ml of lemon juice ?

26 A mix for concrete is made from cement, sand and aggregate by weight in the ratio 2 : 3 : 6.

a How much aggregate should be mixed with 10 kg of sand ?

b How much cement is needed for 300 kg of aggregate ?

27 A photograph is enlarged so that the ratio of the lengths of the sides of the enlargement to the lengths of the sides of the original is 5 : 2.

a The original photo measures 6 cm by 10 cm. What does the enlargement measure ?

b Are the areas of the enlargement and original in the ratio 5 : 2 ? Explain your answer.

DIVISION IN A GIVEN RATIO

We sometimes know the size of the final quantity made from two or more quantities but not the size of the constituent quantities. However if we know the ratio of the contributing quantities, we can find their sizes.

Sarah made up 2 litres of orange squash. Owen asked how much concentrate she used. Sarah couldn't remember, but she did know that the ratio of concentrate to water was 1 : 3

From this Sarah worked out that the concentrate was $\frac{1}{4}$ of the made-up volume, so the volume of concentrate used was $\frac{1}{4}$ of 2 litres, that is, $\frac{1}{2}$ litre.

EXERCISE 11E

Gordon has 21 kg of carpet cleaning powder with which to clean these carpets.
How should he divide the powder so that each carpet gets the same quantity of powder per square metre?

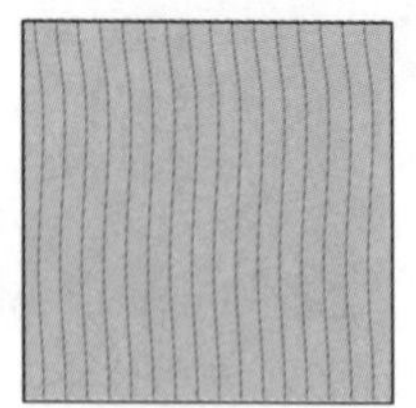
36 square metres

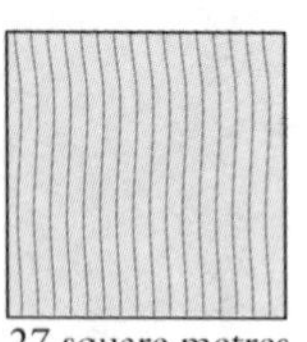
27 square metres

Gordon needs to divide the powder into two parts so that their weights are in the same ratio as the areas of the carpets.

The ratio of the areas is $36\,\text{m}^2 : 27\,\text{m}^2 = 4 : 3$

Therefore the area of the larger carpet is $\frac{4}{7}$ of the total area to be cleaned, and the area of the smaller carpet is $\frac{3}{7}$ of the total area to be cleaned. So we should divide 21 kg into two parts, one of which is $\frac{4}{7}$ of 21 kg and the other is $\frac{3}{7}$ of 21 kg.

The larger carpet needs $\frac{4}{7} \times 21\,\text{kg} = 12\,\text{kg}$

The smaller carpet needs $(21 - 12)\,\text{kg} = 9\,\text{kg}$

Check: $\frac{3}{7} \times 21 = 9$

1 Divide 80 p into two parts in the ratio 3 : 2.

2 Divide 32 cm into two parts in the ratio 3 : 5.

3 Divide £45 into two shares in the ratio 4 : 5.

4 Dick and Tom share the contents of a bag of peanuts between them in the ratio 3 : 5. If there are 40 peanuts, how many do they each get?

5 Mary is 10 years old and Eleanor is 15 years old. Divide 75 p between them in the ratio of their ages.

6 In a class of 30 pupils the ratio of the number of boys to the number of girls is 7 : 8. How many girls are there?

7 Divide £20 into two parts in the ratio 1 : 7.

8 In a garden the ratio of the area of lawn to the area of flower-bed is 12 : 5. If the total area is $357\,\text{m}^2$, find the area of

a the lawn **b** the flower-bed.

9 In a bowl containing oranges and apples, the ratio of the numbers of oranges to apples is 4 : 3. If there are 28 fruits altogether, how many apples are there?

10 A bowl of punch is made by mixing wine and fruit juice in the ratio 2 : 7.

a How much wine is there in 3 litres of this punch?

b How much fruit juice is needed to make 12 litres of punch?

11 The fibres used to make the material for some school uniform shirts are cotton and polyester in the ratio 3 : 2 by weight.

a How much polyester is there in a shirt that weighs 120 g?

b Explain whether your answer to part **a** is exact or an estimate.

12 The ratio of the length of a rectangular photograph to its width is 5 : 3.

a Find the length and width of the photograph if the perimeter is 72 cm.

b Find the length and width of the photograph if its area is 60 cm^2.

Divide 6 m of string into three lengths in the ratio 3 : 7 : 2

As the 6 m length of string is divided into three lengths in the ratio 3 : 7 : 2, one length is $\frac{3}{3+7+2}$, i.e. $\frac{3}{12}$, of 6 m.
The other lengths are also each a number of twelths of 6 m.

$$\text{First length} = \frac{3}{12} \times 6\text{ m} = \frac{3}{\cancel{12}_1} \times \cancel{600}^{50}\text{ cm} = 150\text{ cm}$$

$$\text{Second length} = \frac{7}{\cancel{12}_1} \times \cancel{600}^{50}\text{ cm} = 350\text{ cm}$$

$$\text{Third length} = \frac{2}{\cancel{12}_1} \times \cancel{600}^{50}\text{ cm} = 100\text{ cm}$$

Check: 150 cm + 350 cm + 100 cm = 600 cm = 6 m

13 Divide £26 among three people so that their shares are in the ratio 4 : 5 : 4.

14 The perimeter of a triangle is 24 cm and the lengths of the sides are in the ratio 3 : 4 : 5. Find the lengths of the three sides.

15 In a garden, the ratio of the areas of lawn to beds to paths is 3 : 1 : $\frac{1}{2}$. Find the three areas if the total area is 63 m^2.

16 A 25 litre bag of compost is made by mixing sand, peat and fertiliser by volume in the ratio 4 : 5 : 1. What volume of each ingredient is used?

17 The instructions for mixing paint to give a particular shade of green are: use colours 127, 139, 250 in the ratio 2 : 1 : 7.
How much of colour 127 is needed to give 20 litres of mixed paint?

The tank on Richard's scooter holds 20 litres of fuel which must be a mixture of oil and petrol in the ratio 1 : 50.
To fill the tank how much oil must Richard put in?

The fuel has to be 1 part oil to 50 parts petrol, therefore the 20 litres of fuel to fill the tank has to comprise 51 parts. Therefore the quantity of oil required is

$\frac{1}{51}$ **of 20 litres**

$= \frac{1}{51} \times 20\,000$ **ml**

$= 392$ **ml (correct to 3 s.f.)**

We have given 392 to the nearest millilitre. This is probably more accurate than necessary in this context for several reasons, one of which is that it is not easy or necessary to measure a quantity of oil as accutately as that.

Richard must put approximately 400 ml of oil in his tank.

Give your answer to each question as accurately as you consider to be appropriate in the context of the problem.

18 Concentrated orange juice has to be diluted with water in the ratio 2 : 5 by volume. How many millilitres of concentrated juice are needed to make up 2 litres of juice to drink?

19 The tank on a chemical sprayer holds 5 litres. For removing moss on hard surfaces, the instructions on a bottle of moss killer recommend dilution in the ratio of 3 : 50.

a If the tank is to be filled, how much moss killer should be put in?

b If only 3 litres of spray is to be made up, how much moss killer is required?

20 Bronze is a metal alloy which, for one purpose, contains copper and tin in the ratio 3 : 22 by mass. What mass of copper is needed to make 5 kg of this bronze?

21 Mr Brown, Mrs Smith and Mr Shah work for AB Engineering plc. Their salaries are £12 000, £15 000 and £14 000 respectively.
A bonus of £3000 is to be divided between these three employees in the ratio of their salaries.

a In what ratio are their salaries?

b What is the bonus that is paid to each employee?

22 Two students were presented with a telephone bill for £70.22 which they had to pay between them. They decided to share the cost in the ratio of the number of calls they had each made.

a James had made 42 calls and Sarah had made 75 calls. How much should they each pay?

b After they had paid the bill, Sarah remembered that she had in fact made 6 more calls. How much should she pay James?

MAP RATIO (OR REPRESENTATIVE FRACTION)

The Map Ratio of a map is the ratio of a length on the map to the length it represents on the ground. This ratio or fraction is given on most maps in addition to the scale. It is sometimes called the Representative Fraction of the map, or RF for short.

If two villages are 6 km apart and on the map this distance is represented by 6 cm, then the ratio is

$$6\text{ cm} : 6\text{ km} = 6\text{ cm} : 600\,000\text{ cm} = 1 : 100\,000$$

so the map ratio is $1 : 100\,000$

and the RF is $\frac{1}{100\,000}$

Any length on the ground is 100 000 times the corresponding length on the map.

EXERCISE 11F

Find the map ratio of a map if 12 km is represented by 1.2 cm on the map.

$$\begin{aligned}\text{Map ratio} &= 1.2\text{ cm} : 12\text{ km}\\ &= 1.2\text{ cm} : 1\,200\,000\text{ cm}\\ &= 12 : 12\,000\,000\\ &= 1 : 1\,000\,000\end{aligned}$$

Multiplying both numbers by 10, then dividing both numbers by 12.

Find the map ratio of the maps in the following questions.

1 2 cm on the map represents 1 km.

2 The scale of the map is 1 cm to 5 km.

3 10 km is represented by 10 cm on the map.

4 3.2 cm on the map represents 16 km.

5 $\frac{1}{2}$ cm on the map represents 500 m.

6 100 km is represented by 5 cm on the map.

> If the map ratio is 1 : 5000 and the distance between two points on the map is 12 cm, find the actual distance between the two points.
>
> **The map ratio is 1 : 5000,**
> **so 1 cm on the map represents 5000 cm on the ground,**
> **and 12 cm on the map represents 12 × 5000 cm on the ground,**
>
> **i.e. 12 cm represents 60 000 cm = 600 m**

7 The map ratio of a map is 1 : 50 000. The distance between A and B on the map is 6 cm. What is the true distance between A and B?

8 The map ratio of a map is 1 : 1000. A length on the map is 7 cm. What real length does this represent?

9 The map ratio of a map is 1 : 10 000. Find the actual length represented by 2 cm.

10 The map ratio of a map is 1 : 200 000. The distance between two towns is 20 km. What is this in centimetres? Find the distance on the map between the points representing the towns.

11 The map ratio of a map is 1 : 2 000 000. Find the distance on the map which represents an actual distance of 36 km.

MIXED EXERCISE

EXERCISE 11G

1 Express the ratio 96 : 216 in its simplest form.

2 Simplify the ratio $\frac{1}{4} : \frac{2}{5}$.

3 Divide £100 into three parts in the ratio 10 : 13 : 2

4 Two cubes have edges of lengths 8 cm and 12 cm. Find the ratio of

a the lengths of their edges **b** their volumes.

5 Find the missing number in the ratio $x : 18 = 11 : 24$

6 What distance does 1 cm represent on a map whose map ratio is 1 : 10 000?

7 A batch of lemonade was made by mixing 5 ml of lemon concentrate with 20 ml of sugar and 500 ml of water.
Find the ratio by volume of lemon concentrate to sugar to water.

INVESTIGATIONS

1 People come in all shapes and sizes but we expect the relative sizes of different parts of our bodies to be more or less the same.
For example, we do not expect a person's arms to be twice as long as their legs! We might expect the ratio of arm length to leg length to be about 2 : 3.

a Gather some evidence and use it to find out if the last statement is roughly correct.

b Does the age of a person make any difference?

c Investigate the ratio of shoe size to height.

2 The standard paper sizes used in the UK are called A1, A2, A3, A4, A5, and so on.
Ordinary file paper is usually A4.
You will need some sheets of A3, A4, A5 paper for this investigation.

a Investigate the ratio of length to width of A3, A4 and A5 paper. What do you notice?

b Investigate the ratio of the areas of A4 and A5 paper.

c Describe the relationship between the paper sizes.

EQUATIONS AND INEQUALITIES

Ben is making a model of a rectangular table. The table top must be 1 cm longer than it is wide. Ben also has 23 cm of edging material and he wants to use as much of this as he can.

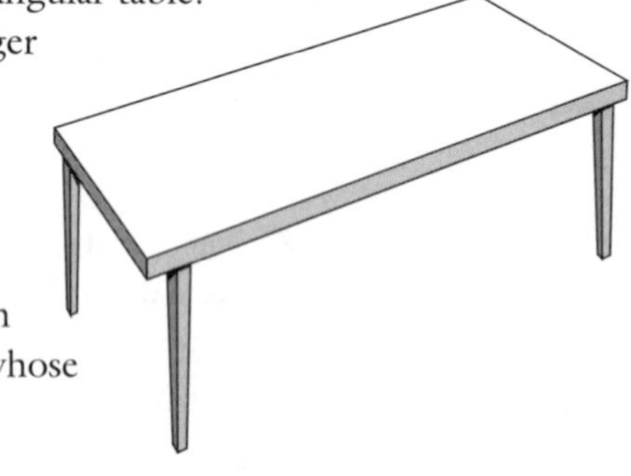

He needs to work out the length and width of a rectangular top whose perimeter is 23 cm.

- One way in which this can be done is to try different lengths and widths until values are found that give a perimeter of 23 cm.
- Alternatively Ben can form an equation using the information he has and then solve it.

EXERCISE 12A Work in a group for these questions.

1 Ranjit wants to make a square that has an area of 500 mm^2 from sheet silver. Discuss how Ranjit can find the length of a side of his square by trying different lengths. Include in your discussion

a what you think is the most efficient way to find this number

b how accurate the answer should be; for example, is an answer to the nearest 10 mm good enough for this problem

c whether your responses to parts **a** and **b** would be different if the area of the square was 100 mm^2.

2 Draw a diagram showing the square that Ranjit wants to make. Mark on it the area and, using a letter, the length of a side.

a Discuss the relationship between the area and the length of a side, and hence form an equation.

b Does this equation then help in organising the search for the length of the side?

FORMING EQUATIONS

By discussing the problems in the last exercise, you may have discovered a way through to a solution. One way is to start by identifying unknown quantities and then use known information to find a relationship between these quantities, that is, by forming an equation.

Consider Ben's problem again.
He needs to find a rectangle whose perimeter is 23 cm and which is 1 cm longer than it is wide.
He does not know the length or the width, but he does know that

$$\text{length} = \text{width} + 1\text{ cm}$$

If we use x cm as the width, this tells us that length $= (x + 1)$ cm
Now we can put this information on a diagram.

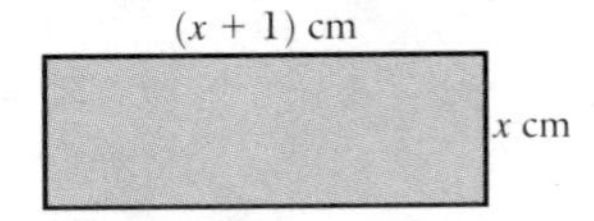

In this rectangle, the expression for length has two terms and we use brackets to keep them together.

The perimeter of the rectangle is twice the length added to twice the width. Since the perimeter is 23 cm we can form the equation

$$23 = 2 \times (x + 1) + 2 \times x$$

Now $2 \times x$ can be written as $2x$, and in the same way, we can leave out the multiplication sign in $2 \times (x + 1)$ and write $2(x + 1)$.

Therefore the equation can be written more simply as

$$23 = 2(x + 1) + 2x$$

Before we can solve this equation, we need to know how to deal with terms such as $2(x + 1)$.

MULTIPLYING OUT BRACKETS

As we have seen, $2(x + 1)$ means 'twice everything in the bracket',

i.e. $$2(x + 1) = 2 \times x + 2 \times 1$$
$$= 2x + 2$$

(This process is called 'multiplying out the bracket'.)

EXERCISE 12B

Multiply out **a** $3(4x+2)$ **b** $2(x-1)$

a $3(4x+2) = 12x + 6$

$3 \times 4x = 3 \times 4 \times x = 12 \times x = 12x$

b $2(x-1) = 2x - 2$

Multiply out the brackets.

1 $2(x+1)$

2 $3(3x-2)$

3 $5(x+6)$

4 $4(3x-3)$

5 $2(4+5x)$

6 $2(6+5a)$

7 $8(3-2x)$

8 $4(4x-3)$

9 $3(6-4x)$

10 $5(x-1)$

11 $7(2-x)$

12 $5(a+b)$

To simplify an expression containing brackets we first multiply out the brackets and then collect like terms.

Simplify **a** $6x + 3(x-2)$ **b** $2 + (3x-7)$

a $6x + 3(x-2) = 6x + 3x - 6$
$= 9x - 6$

First multiply out the bracket then collect like terms.

b $2 + (3x-7) = 2 + 3x - 7$
$= 3x + 2 - 7$
$= 3x - 5$

This means $2 + 1 \times (3x-7)$

Simplify the following expressions.

13 $2x + 4(x+1)$

14 $3 + 5(2x+3)$

15 $2(x+4) + 3(x+5)$

16 $6(2x-3) + 2x$

17 $4 + (3x-1)$

18 $3x + 3(x-5)$

19 $3(x+1) + 4$

20 $6(2x-3) + 5(x-1)$

21 $3x + (2x+5)$

22 $7 + 2(2x+5)$

Simplify **a** $4x - 2(x + 3)$ **b** $5 - (x + 4)$

a $4x - 2(x + 3)$ means $4x$ take away 2 xs *and* 2 threes

$$4x - 2(x + 3) = 4x - 2x - 6$$
$$= 2x - 6$$

b $5 - (x + 4) = 5 - x - 4$
$= 1 - x$

$5 - (x + 4)$ means 5 take away x and take away 4.

Simplify the following expressions.

23 $3x - 2(3x + 4)$ **26** $5x - 4(2 + x)$ **29** $10 - 4(3x + 2)$

24 $5 - 4(5 + x)$ **27** $9 - 2(4x + 1)$ **30** $40 - 2(1 + 5w)$

25 $7c - (c + 2)$ **28** $7a - (a + 6)$ **31** $6y - 3(3y + 4)$

32 The perimeter of this rectangle is $8x$ cm. Form an equation.

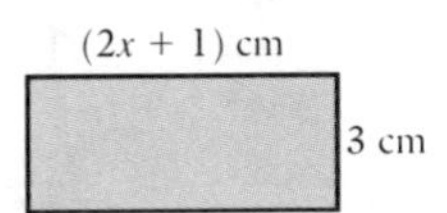

USING DIRECTED NUMBERS

The next exercise involves multiplying directed numbers. Remember that when the signs are the same (both + or both –), the product is positive, when the signs are different (one + and one –), the product is negative.

EXERCISE 12C

Multiply out **a** $-4(3x - 4)$ **b** $-(1 - x)$

a $-4(3x - 4) = -12x + 16$

$-4(3x - 4) = -4 \times +3x$ and -4×-4
$= -12x + 16$

b $-(1 - x) = -1 + x$

$-(1 - x)$ means 'take away 1 and take away $-x$', i.e. -1 and $-(-x)$

Multiply out the following brackets.

1 $-6(x - 5)$ **5** $-8(2 - 5x)$ **9** $-2(4 + 2x)$

2 $-5(3c + 3)$ **6** $-(2x - 3)$ **10** $-7(2 - 3x)$

3 $-2(5e - 3)$ **7** $-7(x + 4)$ **11** $-(4 - 5x)$

4 $-(3x - 4)$ **8** $-3(2d - 2)$ **12** $-(5x - 3)$

Simplify $4(x-3)-3(2-3x)$

$$4(x-3)-3(2-3x) = 4x - 12 - 6 + 9x$$

Multiply out the brackets first.

$$= 4x + 9x - 12 - 6$$

Collect like terms.

$$= 13x - 18$$

Simplify

13 $5x - 4(5x - 3)$

14 $42 - 3(2c - 5)$

15 $2m - 4(3m - 5)$

16 $7 - 2(3x - 2)$

17 $x - (5x - 4)$

18 $9 - 2(4g - 2)$

19 $4 - (6 - x)$

20 $10f - 3(4 - 2f)$

21 $7 - 2(5 - 2s)$

22 $7x - 3(4x - 1)$

23 $7(3x + 1) - 2(2x + 4)$

24 $5(2x - 3) - (x + 3)$

25 $2(4x + 3) + (x - 5)$

26 $7(3 - x) - (6 - 2x)$

27 $5 + 3(4x + 1)$

28 $6x + 2(3x - 7)$

29 $20x - 4(3 + 4x)$

30 $4(x + 1) + 5(x + 3)$

31 $3(2x - 3) - 5(x + 6)$

32 $5(6x - 3) + (x + 4)$

33 $3x + 2(4x + 2) + 3$

34 $4(x - 1) - 5(2x + 3)$

35 $7x + 8x - 2(5x + 1)$

36 $4(x - 1) - 5(2x - 3)$

37 $8(2x - 1) - (x + 1)$

38 $4(x - 1) + 5(2x + 3)$

39 $5 - 4(2x + 3) - 7x$

40 $3(x + 6) - (x - 3)$

41 $3(x + 6) - (x + 3)$

42 $4(x - 1) + 5(2x - 3)$

SOLVING EQUATIONS INVOLVING BRACKETS

Ben has to solve the equation $23 = 2(x + 1) + 2x$

Now that we can deal with a bracket, we start by multiplying it out.

$$23 = 2x + 2 + 2x$$

This is an equation like those that we met in Book 8B, so we know how to solve it. (If you need to practice solving equations, use Revision Exercise 1.9 at the front of this book.)

Collecting like terms gives $\quad 23 = 4x + 2$

Taking 2 from each side gives $\quad 21 = 4x$

Dividing both sides by 4 gives $\quad 5.25 = x$

EXERCISE 12D

Solve the equation $4 + 2(x + 1) = 22$

$$4 + 2(x + 1) = 22$$
$$4 + 2x + 2 = 22$$
$$6 + 2x = 22$$
$$2x = 16$$
$$x = 8$$

Check: When $x = 8$,

Left-hand side $= 4 + 2(8 + 1) = 4 + 2 \times 9 = 22$

Right-hand side $= 22$, so $x = 8$ is the solution.

Solve the following equations.

1 $6 + 3(x + 4) = 24$

2 $3x + 2 = 2(2x + 1)$

3 $5x + 3(x + 1) = 14$

4 $5(x + 1) = 20$

5 $2(x + 5) = 6(x + 1)$

6 $28 = 4(3x + 1)$

7 $4 + 2(x - 1) = 12$

8 $7x + (x - 2) = 22$

9 $1 - 4(x + 4) = x$

10 $8x - 3(2x + 1) = 7$

11 $16 - 4(x + 3) = 2x$

12 $5x - 2(3x + 1) = -6$

13 $4x - 2 = 1 - (2x + 3)$

14 $4 = 5x - 2(x + 4)$

15 $9x - 7(x - 1) = 0$

16 $16 - 2(2x - 3) = 7x$

17 $6x = 2x - (x - 4)$

18 $3(x + 2) + 4(2x + 1) = 6x + 20$

19 $9(2x - 1) + 2(3x + 4) = 20x + 3$

20 $3(x + 2) + 4(2x - 1) = 5(x - 2)$

21 $2(2x + 1) + 4 = 6(3x - 6)$

22 $6x + 4 + 5(x + 6) = 12$

23 $3 - 4(2x + 3) = -25$

24 $3x - 2 = 5 - (x - 1)$

25 $7x + x = 4x - (x - 1)$

26 $3 - 6(2x - 3) = 33$

27 $15 + 5(x - 7) = x$

28 $6x - 2 - 3(x - 4) = 13$

29 $6(x - 2) - (2x - 1) = 2$

30 $4(2x - 5) + 6 = 2$

The area of a trapezium is 36 cm^2. The length of one of the parallel sides is 8 cm and the distance between the parallel sides is 6 cm. Find the length of the other parallel side.

Let the length of the unknown side be a cm and the area be $A\text{ cm}^2$.

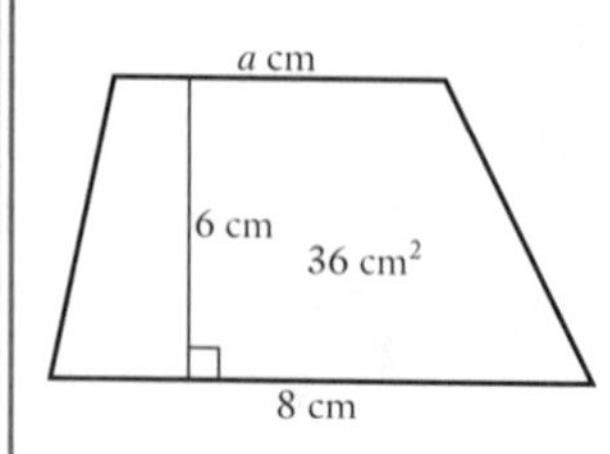

$$A = \tfrac{1}{2}(a + b) \times h$$

$$36 = \tfrac{1}{2}(a + 8) \times 6$$

$\tfrac{1}{2} \times (a + 8) \times 6 = \tfrac{1}{2} \times 6 \times (a + 8)$

$$36 = 3(a + 8)$$

$$36 = 3a + 24$$

$$12 = 3a$$

$$a = 4$$

The length of the other parallel side is 4 cm.

The table gives the area and two measurements for various trapeziums. Find the missing measurements. Start by drawing a diagram.

	Area	Lengths of the parallel sides		Distance between the parallel sides
		Long side	Short side	
31	42 cm^2	9 cm	5 cm	
32	35 cm^2	10 cm		5 cm
33	26 cm^2		5 cm	4 cm
34	22.5 cm^2	4.5 cm	3.6 cm	

35 The equation of a straight line is $y = 2(x - 5)$
The y-coordinate of a point on this line is 7.

a Write down the equation that can be used to find the x-coordinate of this point.

b Solve the equation.

36 The perimeter of this triangle is P cm.

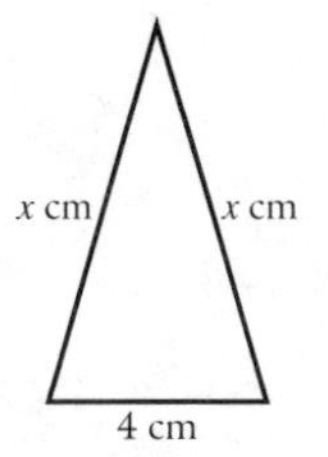

a Write down the formula connecting P and x.

b Use your formula to find x when $P = 24$.

c Check your answer by seeing that it fits the facts given in the question.

37 The perimeter of this rectangle is P cm.

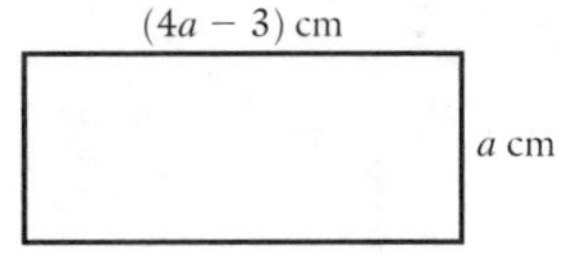

a Write down a formula connecting P and a.

b Write down the equation that you need to solve to find a when $P = 32$.

c Hence find the width of the rectangle when the perimeter is 32 cm.

d Check your answer to part **c** by seeing if it fits the information given about the rectangle.

38 **a** What is the name of this triangle?

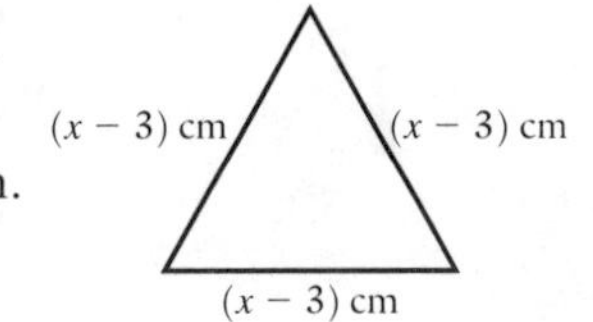

b The perimeter of this triangle is 36 cm. Write down the equation connecting 36 and the information on the diagram.

c Solve the equation to find x.

d Does your value of x fit the facts given?

39 A sequence of patterns is made with red and grey 1 cm square tiles.

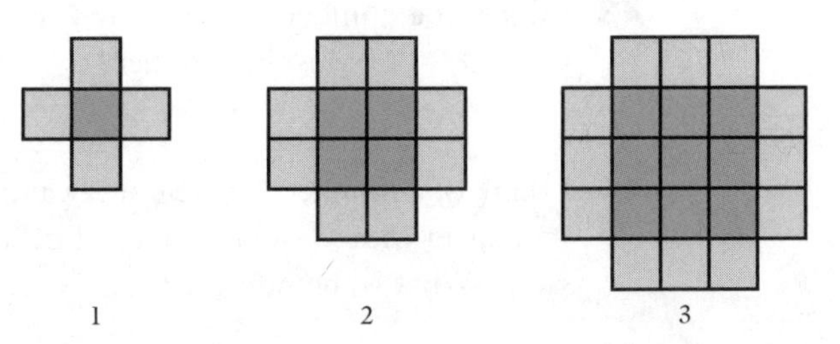

The formula for finding the perimeter, P cm, of the nth pattern is

$$P = 4(n + 2)$$

What pattern number gives a perimeter of 200 cm?

40 Working in my head, I think of a number, x, and then double it.

a Write down what I now have in my head in terms of x.

b I next add 14. What do I now have in my head in terms of x?

c I now have the number 36 in my head. Write down the equation connecting 36 to the answer to part **b**.

d Find the number I started with.

41 I think of a number, x, and add 6.

a What number do I now have in my head?

b I now double it. What number do I have now?

c I notice that the number I have in part **b** is three times the number I started with. Write down the equation connecting this fact with the answer to part **b**.

d Solve this equation to find x.

e Now work through the question again with your answer. Does it fit the information?

42 A bun costs x pence and a cake costs 5 pence more than a bun.

a Write down the cost of a cake in terms of x.

b Write down an expression for the cost of

i 4 cakes **ii** 3 buns.

c 4 cakes and 3 buns together cost £3.21.
Form an equation in x and solve it. How much does one bun cost?

43 I think of a number x, take away 7 and multiply the result by 3, giving 15. What is the number?

44 I think of a number x, take 4 away and double the result. Then I start again with x, treble it and subtract 12. The two results are the same. What is the number?

45 I think of a number x, add 3 and treble the result. Then I start again with x, subtract 3 and multiply the result by 4. The two results are the same. What is the number?

EQUATIONS INVOLVING DECIMALS

If a problem, or equation, is given in decimals, the answer should also be given in decimal form. Decide yourself whether or not you need to use a calculator.

EXERCISE 12E

Solve the equation $0.55x = 21$

$$0.55x = 21$$

Divide both sides by 0.55

$$\frac{0.55x}{0.55} = \frac{21}{0.55}$$

$$\frac{\cancel{0.55}^{1}}{1} \times \frac{x}{1} \times \frac{1}{\cancel{0.55}_{1}} = 38.18\ldots$$

$$x = 38.18\ldots$$

$$x = 38.2 \quad \text{(correct to 3 s.f.)}$$

Solve the following equations. Give answers that are not exact correct to 3 significant figures.

1 $0.75x = 6$

2 $0.3x = 9$

3 $3.5x = 1.4$

4 $2.8x = 5$

5 $3.7x = 7.2$

6 $0.5x = 12$

7 $0.4x = 19$

8 $5.4x = 4.32$

9 $7.8x = 4$

10 Melanie buys $3.8\,\text{m}^2$ of floor covering.

a If the cost of $1\,\text{m}^2$ is £x, write down the cost of $3.8\,\text{m}^2$ in terms of x.

b Melanie paid £22.23. Write down the connection between this information and your answer to part **b** to form an equation in x.

c Solve your equation. How much does the floor covering cost per square metre? Does your answer fit the information given?

11 The mass of $8.5\,\text{cm}^3$ of gold is 164.05 g.

a If the mass of $1\,\text{cm}^3$ is x grams what is the mass of $8.5\,\text{cm}^3$ in terms of x?

b Relate the answer to part **a** to the mass given at the start of this question to form an equation in x.

c Solve the equation. What is the mass of $1\,\text{cm}^3$ of gold?

12 In a French journal the area of a farm that is for sale is given as 88.4 hectares. An estate agent in the south of England advertises the same farm as having an area of 218.4 acres. If there are x acres in 1 hectare form an equation in x and solve it. How many acres are equivalent to 1 hectare?

Solve the equation $3.8x + 5 = 9.2$, giving your answer correct to 3 significant figures.

$$3.8x + 5 = 9.2$$

$$3.8x = 4.2$$ Subtracting 5 from each side.

$$x = \frac{4.2}{3.8}$$ Dividing both sides by 3.8.

$$= 1.105\ldots$$

$$x = 1.11 \text{ (correct to 3 s.f.)}$$

Solve the following equations, giving answers that are not exact correct to 3 significant figures.

13 $4.2x - 3 = 9.6$

14 $6.3x + 4.5 = 36$

15 $2.2x - 3 = 7.5$

16 $1.9x + 2.4 = 8.9$

17 $5.5x - 4 = 9.2$

18 $3.7x + 1.2 = 16$

19 $4.9x - 5.2 = 4.7$

20 $5.2x + 3.7 = 9.3$

INEQUALITIES

In Book 8B, Chapter 11, we used a number line to decide which of two positive or negative whole numbers is the larger.

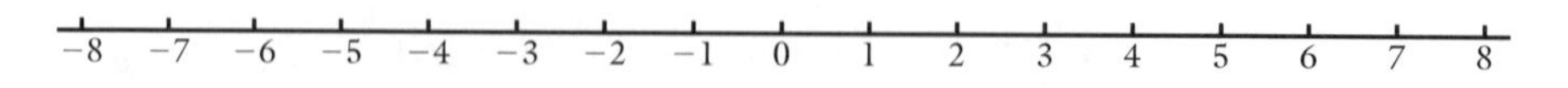

We used the inequality sign $>$ instead of writing 'is greater than' and the sign $<$ instead of writing 'is smaller than'.
Using the number line together with these symbols, we can see that

$$-1 > -4, \quad 3 > -1, \quad -5 < -2 \quad \text{and} \quad -3 < 1$$

Now suppose there are p metres of carpet left on a roll and this must be less than 30. Using symbols we can write this statement as

$$p < 30$$

This is an *inequality* as opposed to $p = 30$ which is an equality or an equation.
This inequality is true when p stands for any number less than 30; that is, there is a range of numbers that p can stand for and we can illustrate this range on a number line.

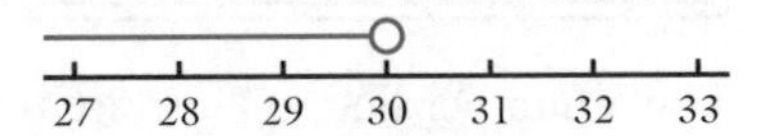

The circle at the right-hand end of the range is 'open', because 30 is not included in the range.

EXERCISE 12F

Use inequalities to give the following statements in symbols.

a The Cornflower Grill guarantee that the weight, w grams, of one of their steaks will be more than 150 g.

b When Anna is given letters to address, the number of letters, n, must be less than 250.

a $w > 150$ **b** $n < 250$

In questions **1** to **5** use inequalities to give each statement in symbols.

1 The government of Mostova passed a law that the number, n, of children per family should be less than 3.

2 In a freezer the temperature, x °C, should be lower than -6 °C.

3 Before Charleston School will run a course in motor mechanics the number, x, of pupils agreeing to follow the course must be more than 10.

4 Before Townlink will accept a parcel they check that its weight, w kg, is more than 5 kg.

5 A notice on the 'Big Wheel' at a theme park says that the height, x metres, of any passenger taking the ride must be more than 1 metre.

In questions **1** and **3**, the letter can only stand for a positive whole number; we cannot have $2\frac{1}{2}$ people! In questions **4** and **5**, the letter can stand for any positive number; a parcel can weigh 4.5 kg, whereas in question **2**, x could be any negative number less than -6.

Use a number line to illustrate the range of values of x for which $x < -1$.

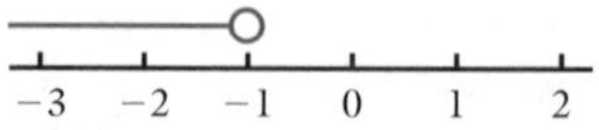

Use a number line to illustrate the range of values of x for which each of the following inequalities is true. Assume that x can stand for any number, whole or otherwise.

6 $x > 7$

7 $x < 4$

8 $x > -2$

9 $x > 0$

10 $x < -2$

11 $x > 1$

12 $x < 5$

13 $x < 0$

14 $x < 1.5$

15 State which of the inequalities given in questions **6** to **14** are satisfied when x is

a 2 **b** −3 **c** 0 **d** 1.5 **e** 0.0005

16 State which of the inequalities given in questions **1** to **5** are satisfied when x is

a 2 **b** −3 **c** 0 **d** 1.5 **e** 0.0005

Comment on your answers.

17 For each question from **6** to **14** give a possible value of x that is

a a whole number **b** not a whole number.

In questions **18** to **21** write each statement using symbols. Give two values that satisfy each inequality.

18 Before a wholesaler will deliver to a retailer, the value, £x, of the order must exceed £500.

19 Sid's lorry is licensed to carry any weight, w tons, provided it is less than 7.5 tons.

20 The Barland Bank does not make charges on a current account provided that the amount in the account, £x, is always greater than £500.

21 Before Spender & Co will open a store in an area the population, x, within 10 miles must be more than 250 000.

22 Consider the true inequality $3 > 1$

a Add 2 to each side.

b Add -2 to each side.

c Take 5 from each side.

d Take -4 from each side.

In each case state whether or not the inequality remains true.

23 Repeat question **22** with the inequality $-2 > -3$

24 Repeat question **22** with the inequality $-1 < 4$

25 Write down a true inequality of your own choice.

a Add the same number to each side. Does the inequality remain true?

b Subtract the same number from each side and see if the inequality remains true.

SOLVING INEQUALITIES

From the last exercise we can see that

> an inequality remains true when the *same* number is added to, or subtracted from, *each* side.

Consider the inequality $x - 2 < 3$
In this form, we cannot immediately see what range of values x can take.
Solving the inequality means finding the range of values of x for which it is true.
Adding 2 to each side gives $x < 5$

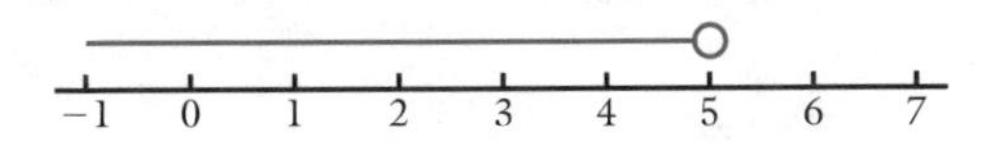

We have now solved the inequality.

EXERCISE 12G

Solve the following inequalities and illustrate your solutions on a number line.

1 $x - 4 < 8$

2 $x + 2 < 4$

3 $x - 2 > 3$

4 $x - 3 > -1$

5 $x + 4 < 2$

6 $x - 5 < -2$

7 $x - 3 < -6$

8 $x + 7 < 0$

9 $x + 2 < -3$

Solve the inequality $4 - x < 3$

$$4 - x < 3$$

We need the x term on the side where it will be positive: we can do this by adding x to each side.

Add x to each side $\quad 4 < 3 + x$

Take 3 from each side $\quad 1 < x \quad$ or $\quad x > 1$

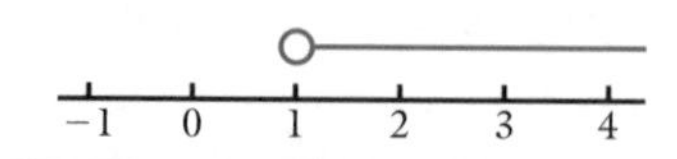

Solve the following inequalities and illustrate your solutions on a number line.

10 $4 - x > 6$

11 $2 < 3 + x$

12 $7 - x > 4$

13 $5 < x + 5$

14 $5 - x < 8$

15 $2 > 5 + x$

16 $3 - x > 2$

17 $2 + x < -3$

18 $2 > x - 3$

19 $4 < 5 - x$

20 $1 < -x$

21 $5 < x - 2$

22 $7 > 2 - x$

23 $3 > -x$

24 $4 - x > -9$

25 $5 - x < -7$

POLYNOMIAL EQUATIONS

So far, we have solved equations such as $3x - 8 = 25$.
In equations like these the letter does not have an index; they are called *linear equations*.
We now look at equations containing letter terms involving indices, e.g. $x^2 = 500$, $x^3 + x = 12$, and so on. These are called *polynomial equations*. Before we find how to solve this type of equation, we look at indices again.

INDICES

Using index notation, we know that $2 \times 2 \times 2$ can be written as 2^3.
The small 3 is called the *index* or *power*.
We can also use index notation with letters that stand for unknown numbers,

e.g. we can write $a \times a$ as a^2,
and $b \times b \times b$ can be written as b^3.

In the same way, d^5 means $d \times d \times d \times d \times d$
and $3b^4$ means $3 \times b \times b \times b \times b$

Notice that the index applies only to the number it is attached to: $2x^2$ means that x is squared, 2 is not.

If we want also to square 2, we write $(2x)^2$ or 2^2x^2.

EXERCISE 12H

Simplify $3a \times 2a$

$$3a \times 2a = 3 \times a \times 2 \times a$$
$$= 6 \times a \times a$$
$$= 6a^2$$

Remember that numbers can be multiplied in any order,
i.e. $3 \times a \times 2 \times a = 3 \times 2 \times a \times a$
$= 6 \times a^2$

Write in index notation

1 $x \times x$

2 $p \times p \times p$

3 $s \times s \times s$

4 $t \times t \times t \times t$

5 $2a \times 4a$

6 $5d \times 3d$

7 $4x \times 3x$

8 $3y \times y$

9 $a \times 2a \times 3a$

10 $4n \times n \times 2n$

11 $2p \times 2p \times 3p$

12 $5s \times 3s \times 4$

FINDING SQUARE ROOTS

In question **1** of **Exercise 12A**, Ranjit wants to make a square that has an area of 500 mm^2 from sheet silver.

By placing the information on a diagram and using the fact that the area of a square is found by multiplying the length of a side by itself, he can form the equation

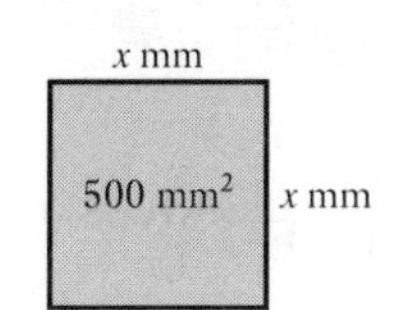

$$x^2 = 500$$

Now x^2 means $x \times x$, so to solve this equation Ranjit needs to find a number which, when multiplied by itself, gives 500.

We start by considering the simpler equation $x^2 = 16$
To solve this equation we need to find a number which, when multiplied by itself, gives 16.
This number, as we know from Chapter 8, is called the *square root* of 16.

Now $4 \times 4 = 16$, so 4 is a square root of 16,
But $(-4) \times (-4) = 16$, therefore -4 is also a square root of 16.

So when $x^2 = 16$, we have $x = 4$ or -4.
This is shortened to $x = \pm 4$

This is true for the square root of any number.

Any number has two square roots, one positive and one negative.

We use the symbol $\sqrt{\ }$ to mean the *positive square root*, so when $x^2 = 16$ we can write $x = \pm\sqrt{16}$
Therefore the equation $x^2 = 16$ has *two* solutions, $x = 4$ and $x = -4$.

Now we can solve Ranjit's equation, $x^2 = 500$
Using a calculator, $x = \pm 22.36\ldots$
Clearly the length of a side of a square cannot be negative, so the side is 22.36... mm long.

If we correct 22.36... to 3 significant figures, we are rounding the number up to 22.4. When we square 22.4 mm we will get an area slightly larger than 500 mm^2; as sheet silver is expensive, it is safer not to round up and for Ranjit to cut his square with sides 22.3 mm long; this will give a square whose area is a bit less than 500 mm^2.

EXERCISE 12I

Use your calculator to solve the equation $x^2 = 725$, giving solutions correct to 3 significant figures.

$x^2 = 725$ (Press √ 7 2 5 = The display shows 26.9258...)

$\therefore \quad x = \pm\sqrt{725} = \pm 26.92\ldots$

$= \pm 26.9$ (correct to 3 s.f.)

Check: $26.9^2 = 723.6\ldots$ (Using a calculator; press 2 6 · 9 x² =)

Use your calculator to solve the equations, giving solutions correct to 3 significant figures.

1 $x^2 = 38.4$	**6** $x^2 = 650$	**11** $x^2 = 10\,300$
2 $x^2 = 19.8$	**7** $x^2 = 65$	**12** $x^2 = 61$
3 $x^2 = 428$	**8** $x^2 = 0.22$	**13** $x^2 = 115$
4 $x^2 = 42.8$	**9** $x^2 = 58$	**14** $x^2 = 24$
5 $x^2 = 4.28$	**10** $x^2 = 19$	**15** $x^2 = 0.57$

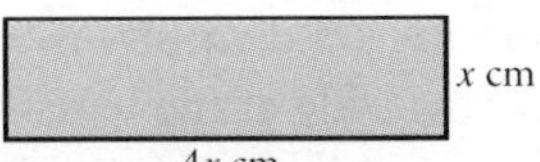

The rectangle in the diagram has an area of 31 cm^2.
Form an equation in x and solve it to find the width of the rectangle.

The area of the rectangle = $4x \times x\text{ cm}^2$

therefore $4x^2 = 31$

To find x, we need to solve this equation.

$x^2 = 7.75$

Dividing both sides by 4.

$\therefore$ $x = \pm\sqrt{7.75}$

$= \pm 2.783\ldots$

The width of a rectangle cannot be a negative number, so only the positive square root gives a solution to the problem.

The width of the rectangle is 2.78 cm correct to 3 s.f.

16 The area of the square in the diagram is 50 cm^2.

a Form an equation in x.

b Solve the equation to find the length of a side.

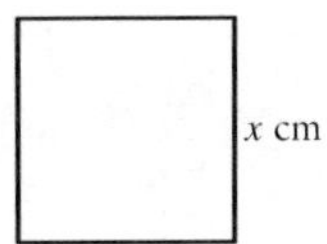

17 The area of the rectangle in the diagram is 120 cm^2.

a Form an equation in x.

b Solve the equation to find the width of the rectangle.

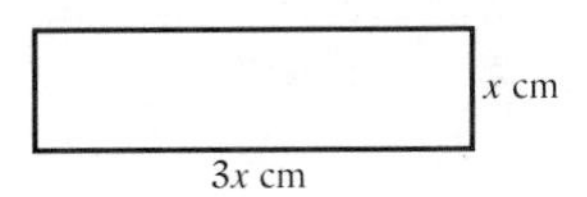

18 The area of this triangle is 290 cm^2.
Form an equation and solve it to find the height of the triangle.

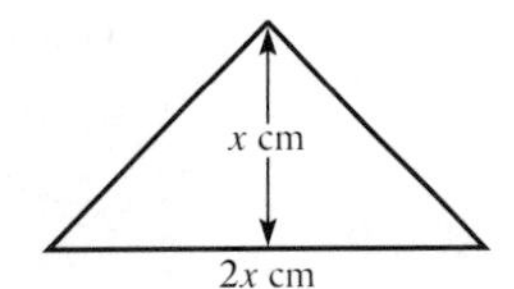

19 The area of this parallelogram is 250 cm^2.
Form an equation in x and solve it to find the height of the parallelogram.

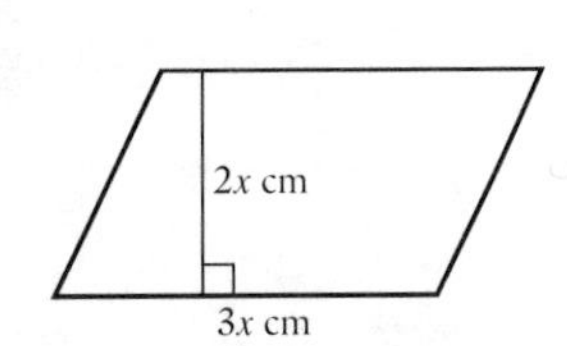

SOLVING EQUATIONS BY TRIAL AND IMPROVEMENT

Moira has $1200\,\text{mm}^2$ of silver to make a triangular pendant that is 5 mm higher than it is wide at the base.

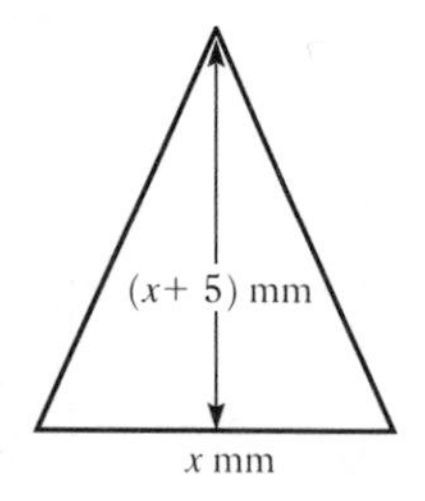

Using x mm as the width of the base, she can form the equation

$$\tfrac{1}{2} \times x \times (x + 5) = 1200$$

which simplifies to $x^2 + 5x = 2400$

Having formed the equation, Moira now needs to solve it.

As this equation is not in the form 'x^2 = a number' we cannot use square roots to find x, so we will try some values for x and see if we can find one that fits.
If we try numbers for x at random, we could spend hours before finding one that fits, so an organised approach is needed.

Firstly we give x a value that looks reasonable and try it in the equation.

Try $x = 50$: $50^2 + 5 \times 50 = 2750$; so 50 is too big.

The obvious next step is try a number smaller than 50;

Try $x = 40$: $40^2 + 5 \times 40 = 1800$; so 40 is too small.

Now it is clear that the value of x is between 40 and 50, so we try a number between 40 and 50 to get an improvement.

Try $x = 45$: $45^2 + 5 \times 45 = 2250$; so 45 is too small.

If we use a number line to illustrate where the results of our tries are in relation to the result we want, we get a picture of how close we are and where to go next.

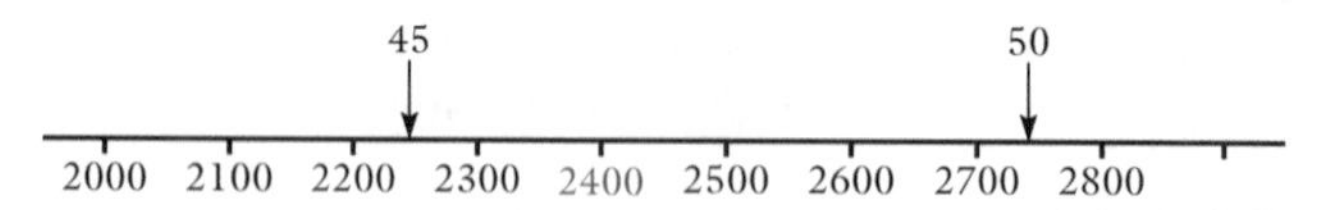

This shows that 45 is nearer than 50 to the result we want. It is sensible to try next a number between 45 and 50, but nearer to 45.

Try $x = 47$: $47^2 + 5 \times 47 = 2444$; so 47 is too big, but only just.

We can continue placing the trials on the number line and use the information to judge what number to try next.

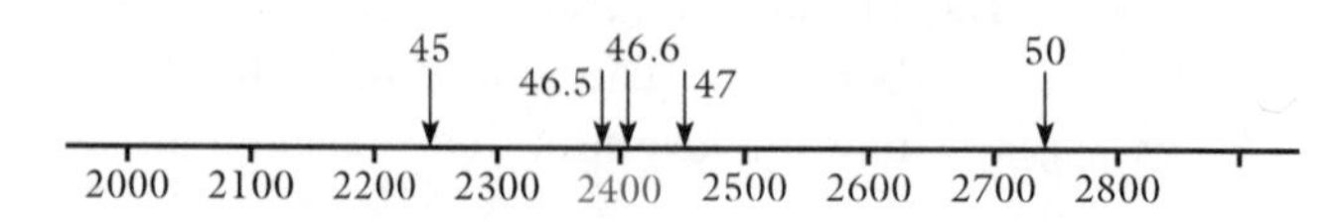

Try $x = 46.5$: $46.5^2 + 5 \times 46.5 = 2394.75$; so 46.5 is just too small.

Try $x = 46.6$: $46.6^2 + 5 \times 46.6 = 2404.56$; so 46.6 is just too big.

Now we can see that x lies between 46.5 and 46.6.

Now x cm is the width of the base of a triangle that can be made from 1200 mm^2 of silver. In this context, a measurement that gives slightly under 1200 mm^2 for the area is sensible. Also it is probably impossible to cut sheet silver more accurately than to the nearest tenth of a millimetre. Therefore we do not need to look any further for an acceptable solution to the problem, that is taking x as 46.5 gives a triangle whose measurements fit the requirements.

If the context from which the equation arose needed a more accurate solution, we could draw another number line for the range 2392 to 2408,

i.e.

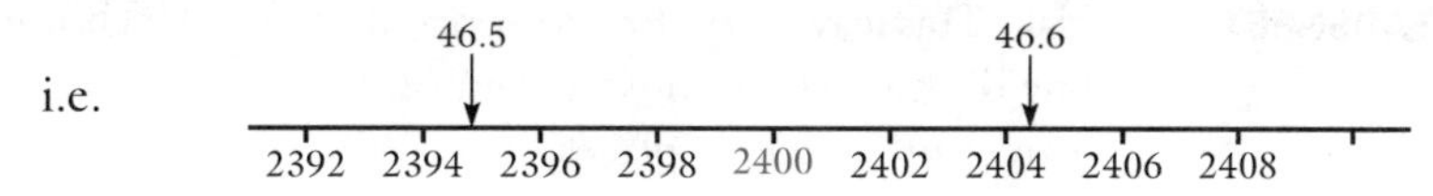

The next try could then be 46.55.

EXERCISE 12J

Find, by trial and improvement, a positive solution of the equation $x^3 - 4x = 7$, giving the answer correct to 1 decimal place.

If we try 1 as a trial solution, we get a negative result, so we will start with 2.

Try 2:	$2^3 - 4 \times 2 = 0$;	too small
Try 3:	$3^3 - 4 \times 3 = 15$;	too big
Try 2.5:	$2.5^3 - 4 \times 2.5 = 5.625$	too small
Try 2.6:	$2.6^3 - 4 \times 2.6 = 7.176$	too big

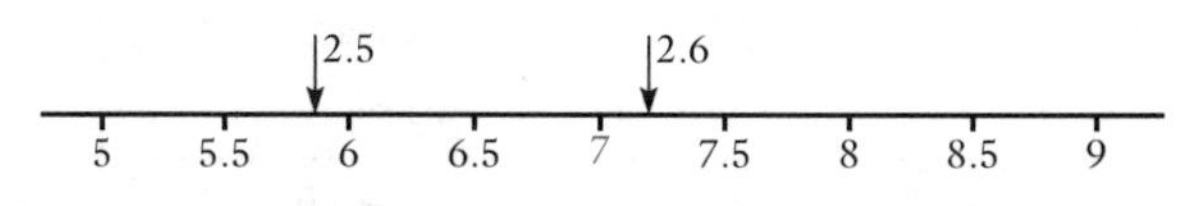

Now we can see that the solution is nearer 2.6 than 2.5.

$x = 2.6$ (correct to 1 d.p.)

Find a positive solution of each equation by trial and improvement, giving answers correct to 1 decimal place. (Start by trying the value of x given in the bracket.)

1 $x^3 + 7x = 12$ $(x = 1)$ **2** $x^2 + x = 4$ $(x = 1)$ **3** $x^3 - 2x = 10$ $(x = 2)$

4 $x^2 + 3x = 7 \ (x = 1)$

5 $2x^2 - 3x = 10 \ (x = 2)$

6 $x^3 + 2x = 500 \ (x = 10)$

7 $x^3 + x^2 + x = 50 \ (x = 3)$

8 $x^3 - x = 12$

9 $2x^2 + 5x = 20$

10 $5x^2 - 7x = 4$

11 $3x^3 + x = 8$

12 $8x^2 - x^3 = 12$

13 $x^4 - 3x^3 = 10$

14 $3x^3 + 2x^2 = 7$

15 $x^2 + 3 = 5x$

USING A SPREADSHEET

A spreadsheet takes the work out of the calculations needed for each trial. This leaves you free to concentrate on the choice of numbers to try. The diagram shows how a solution to $x^3 - 4x = 7$ can be found correct to 2 decimal places.

	A	B	C	
1	x^3 – 4x = 7			
2				
3		Try x =	x^3 – 4x	
4		1	–3	
5		2	0	
6		3	15	
7		2.5	5.625	
8		2.6	7.176	
9		2.55	6.381375	
10		2.57	6.694593	
11		2.59	7.013979	
12		2.58	6.853512	
13			0	
14			0	

Enter formula B4^3 – 4*B4 in this cell.

Use the fill command for these cells.

From the entries in cells B11, C11 and B12, C12 we can see that $x = 2.59$ gives a result nearer to 7 than does $x = 2.58$, so we deduce that $x = 2.59$ (correct to 2 d.p.)

EXERCISE 12K

Use a spreadsheet to find solutions to the equations in **Exercise 12J**, giving answers correct to 2 decimal places.

MIXED EXERCISE

EXERCISE 12L

1 Multiply out

a $6(2x+4)$ **b** $3(2a-b)$ **c** $-4(2a-3)$

2 Simplify **a** $4+3(2x+5)$ **c** $-4(2a-3)$

b $3b-(a+b)$ **d** $2p-3(2p-5)$

3 Solve the equations

a $5-2(3-x)=1$ **b** $x=2+3(x-2)$

4 Solve the equations, giving your answers correct to 1 decimal place if necessary.

a $2.5x=15$ **b** $2.4x-6=1.3$

5 Illustrate the inequalities on a number line.

a $x<-1$ **b** $x>3$

6 The number of people allowed in a lift must be not more than 5.

a If N is the number of people allowed in the lift, copy and complete the statement $N<\ldots$

b State whether N can have the value

i 4 **ii** 2.5 **iii** 6 **iv** -2

7 Solve the inequalities **a** $x-2<1$ **b** $4<3-x$

8 Write in index notation **a** $b\times b$ **b** $2a\times a$ **c** $3x\times 2x$

9 Solve the equation $x^2=45$ giving the solutions correct to 3 signficant figures.

10 a Use the information in the diagram to form an equation.

b Find the width of the rectangle.

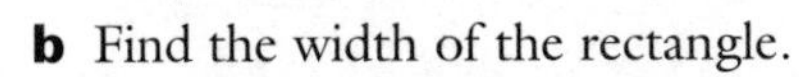

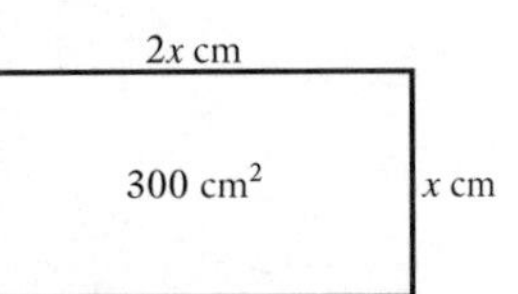

11 Use trial and improvement to find a positive solution of the equation $x^2+9x=5$
Start by trying $x=0$ and give the solution correct to 1 decimal place.

INVESTIGATIONS

1 Elson thought of a simple way of finding out his grandfather's age without asking him. Elson asked his grandfather to do the following calculations. 'Think of your age, add 5, and double your answer. Now take away your age and tell me what answer you have.'
Elson's grandfather replied that his answer was 78.
'That means you must be 68 years old', said Elson.
How did Elson work out his grandfather's age from the number he was given?
Form an algebraic equation which proves that the method will always work with anyone's age.

2 **a** Use your calculator to find
$\sqrt{0.04}$ $\sqrt{0.4}$ $\sqrt{4}$ $\sqrt{40}$ $\sqrt{400}$ $\sqrt{4000}$
What do you notice?

b Use your calculator to find
$\sqrt{0.06}$ $\sqrt{0.6}$ $\sqrt{6}$ $\sqrt{60}$ $\sqrt{600}$ $\sqrt{6000}$

c Repeat part **a** for the sequence
$\sqrt{0.012}$ $\sqrt{0.12}$ $\sqrt{1.2}$ $\sqrt{12}$ $\sqrt{120}$ $\sqrt{1200}$
Try some different numbers.

d Using the results from part **a** and, *without* using your calculator, write down the first significant figure of $\sqrt{400\,000}$.

e *Without* using your calculator, find the first significant figure of
$\sqrt{50}$, $\sqrt{5000}$, $\sqrt{0.5}$.
Is this the same as the first significant figure of $\sqrt{5}$?

f Try to explain how to find the first significant figure of the square root of a number without using a calculator. Test your explanation on some other numbers.

STRAIGHT LINE GRAPHS

13

In Book 8B, we found that the formula that gives the relationship between the y-coordinate and the x-coordinate of a point on a line is called the *equation of that line*.

If we know that the equation of a line is $y = 3x$, this tells us that the y-coordinate of any point on this line is 3 times the x-coordinate of that point.

We also found that *an equation of the form* $y = mx$ gives a graph that is a *straight line* and that this line

- *passes through the origin*
- *makes an acute angle with the positive x-axis if m is positive*, i.e. slopes up when moving from left to right, e.g.

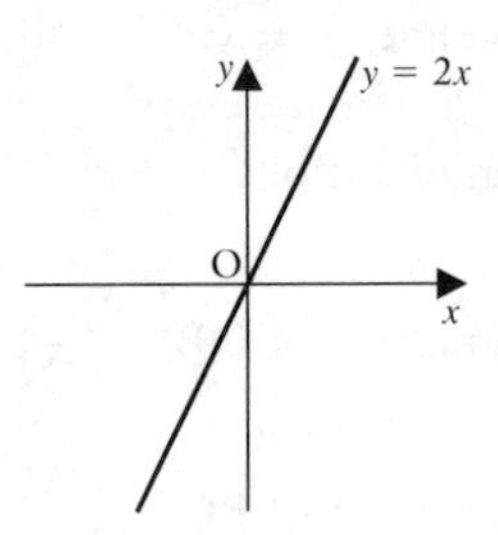

- *makes an obtuse angle with the positive x-axis if m is negative*, i.e. slopes down when moving from left to right, e.g.

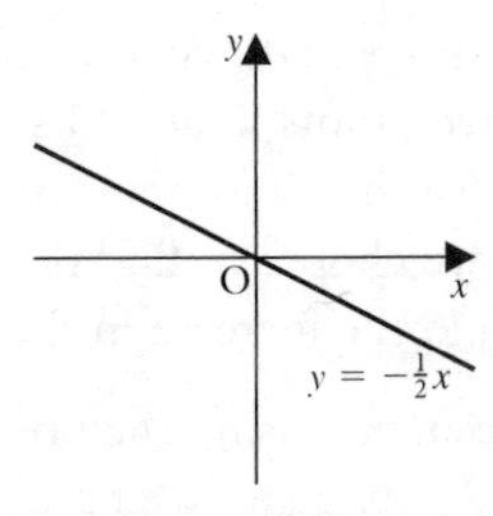

We also saw that the bigger the value of m, the steeper is the slope of the line. We now explain exactly what is meant by the slope of a line.

GRADIENT OF A STRAIGHT LINE

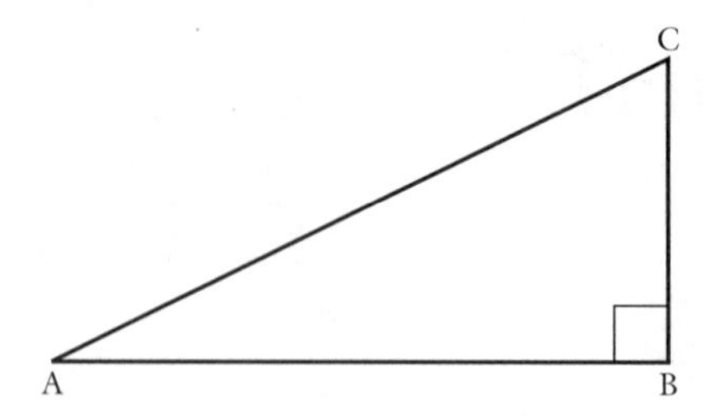

The *gradient* or slope of a line is defined as the amount the line rises vertically divided by the distance moved horizontally,

i.e. the gradient, or slope, of AC $= \dfrac{\text{BC}}{\text{AB}}$

If a line is drawn on a set of axes, we can find the gradient by taking any two points on the line. Then the gradient of the line is given by

$$\frac{\text{the increase in } y\text{-value}}{\text{the increase in } x\text{-value}}$$

when we move from one point to the other.

The points O, B and C are three points on the line $y = x$.

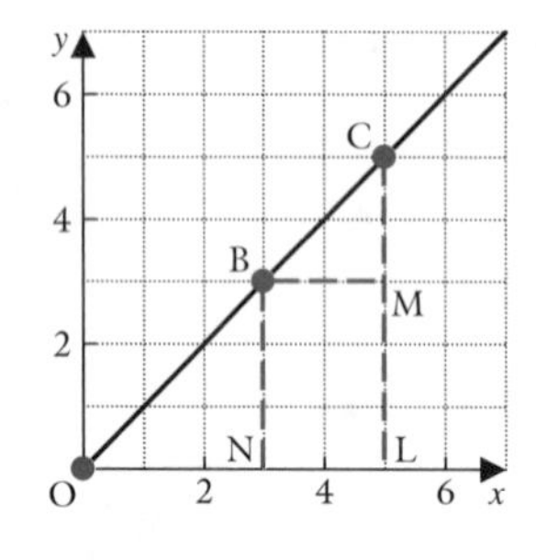

The gradient of OC $= \dfrac{\text{CL}}{\text{OL}} = \dfrac{5}{5} = 1$

The gradient of OB $= \dfrac{\text{BN}}{\text{ON}} = \dfrac{3}{3} = 1$

The gradient of BC $= \dfrac{\text{CM}}{\text{BM}} = \dfrac{5-3}{5-3} = \dfrac{2}{2} = 1$

These show that, whichever two points are taken, the gradient of the line $y = x$ is 1.

This means that, when working out the gradient of a line, we can choose *any* two points, P and Q say, on a line.
However it is important that we use the points in the same order, i.e. if we choose to find the increase in the y-value from P to Q, we must also find the increase in the x-value from P to Q.

For example, using the points P and Q to find the gradient of the line in the next diagram, we have

$$\text{gradient} = \frac{\text{the increase in } y\text{-value from P to Q}}{\text{the increase in } x\text{-value from P to Q}}$$

As we move from P to Q,

the y-value goes *down* from 6 to -8,

i.e. y *decreases* by 14, so

y *increases* by -14,

the x-value increases from -3 to 4,

i.e. x increases by 7.

Therefore the gradient $= \dfrac{-14}{7}$

$= -2$

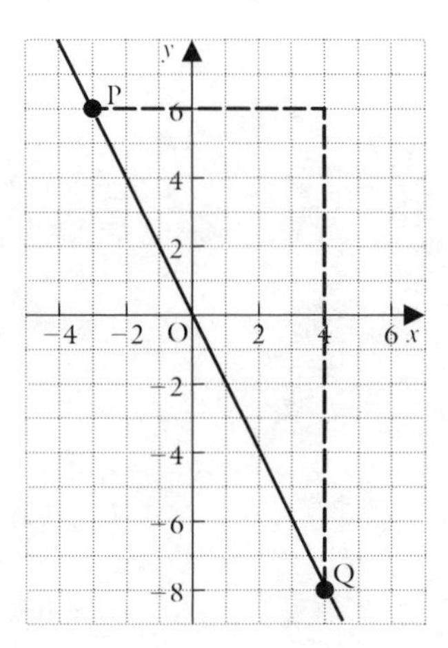

EXERCISE 13A

1 For each graph, choose two points on the line and calculate the gradient of the line.

a

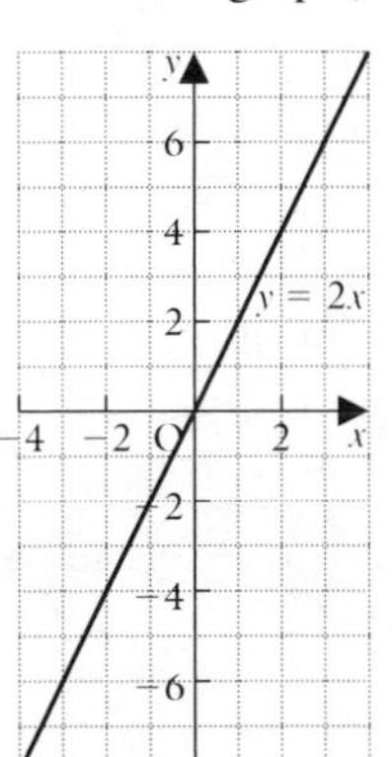

b

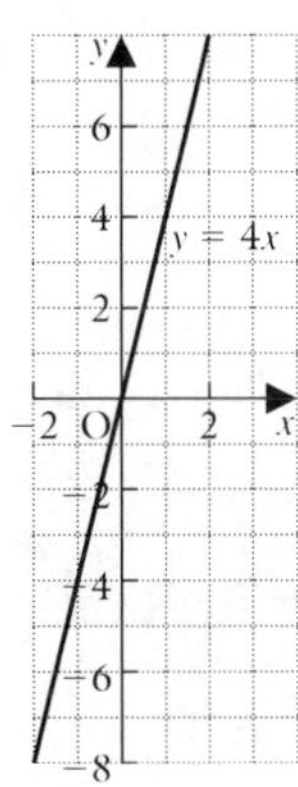

c

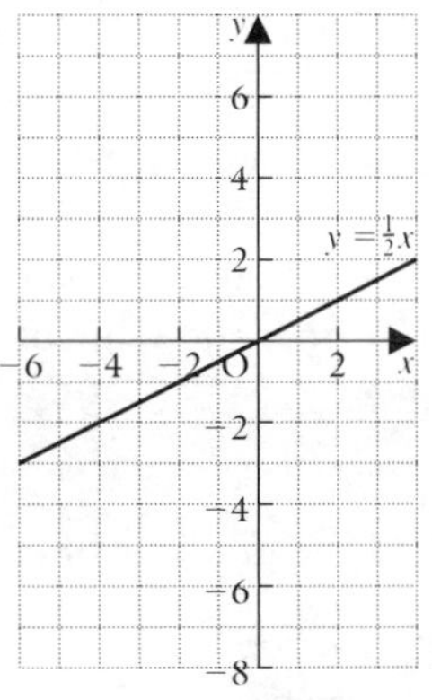

d

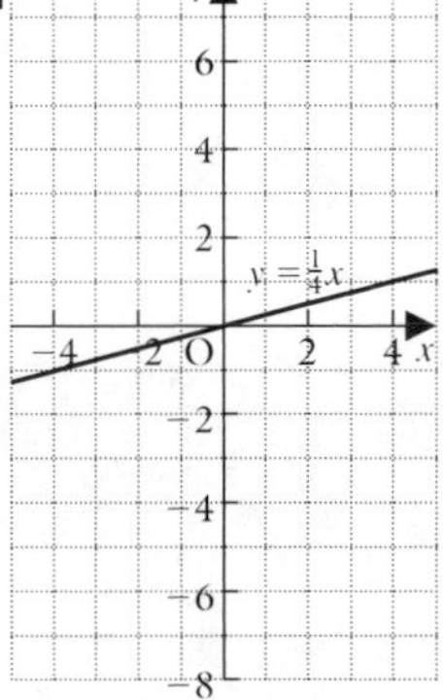

2 Repeat question **1** for these graphs.

a

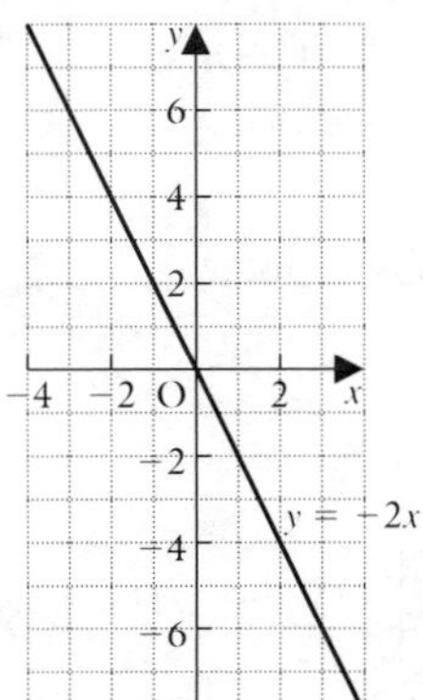

b

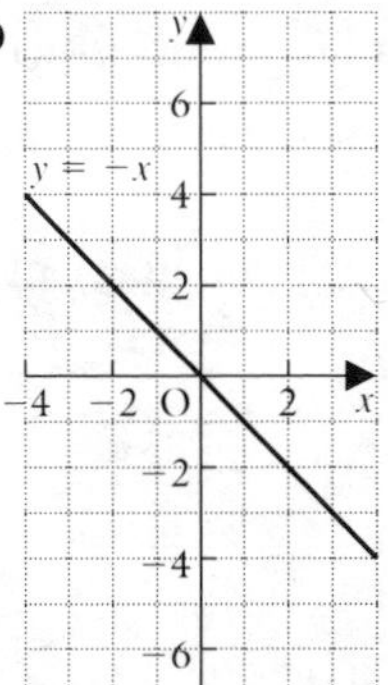

c

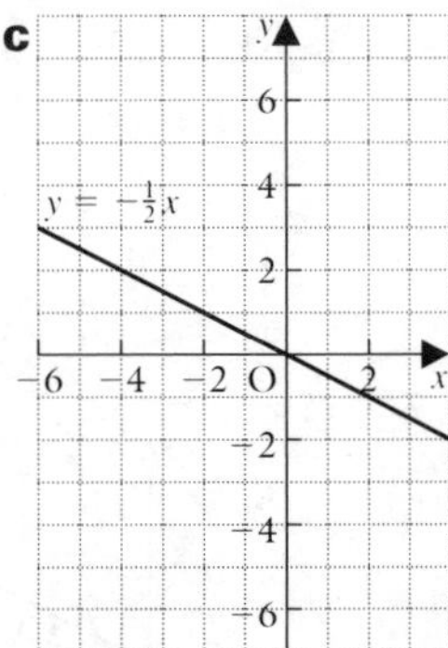

d

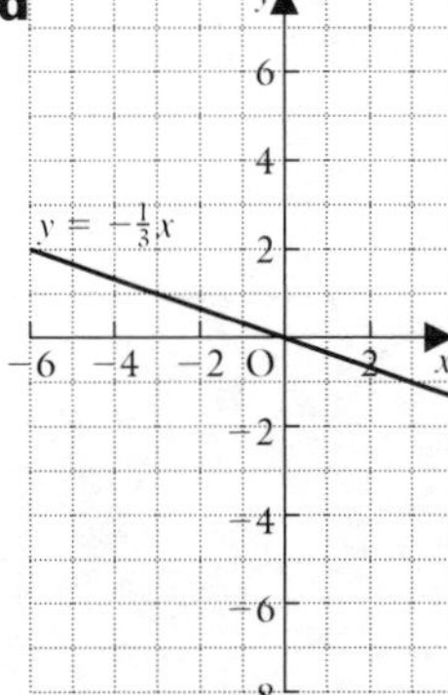

3 In questions **1** and **2**, what relationship is there between the gradient of each line and its equation?

For questions **4** and **5**, use a copy of the grid for questions **1** part **c**.

4 Copy and complete the following table and use it to draw the graph of $y = 2.5x$.

x	-3	0	3
y			

Choose your own pair of points to find the gradient of this line. How does the value of the gradient compare with the equation of the line?

5 Copy and complete the following table and use it to draw the graph of $y = 0.5x$.

x	-6	-2	4
y			

Choose your own pair of points to find the gradient of this line. How does the value of the gradient compare with the equation of the line?

6 Find the gradient of each line.

a $y = 5x$

b $y = -7x$

c $y = 12x$

d $y = -\frac{1}{4}x$

This exercise shows that, for a line whose equation is $y = mx$,

the value of m gives the gradient of the line.

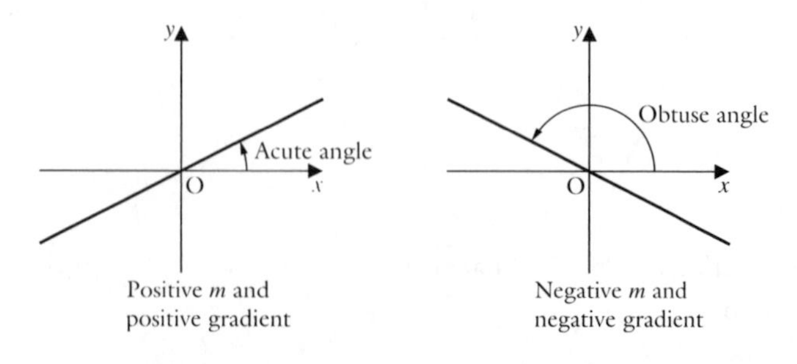

EXERCISE 13B

For each of the following pairs of lines, state which line is the steeper. Sketch both lines on the same diagram. A sketch does not need scaled axes but should give an indication of the slope of the line and at least one special point that it passes through.

1 $y = 5x,\ y = \frac{1}{5}x$

2 $y = 2x,\ y = 5x$

3 $y = \frac{1}{2}x,\ y = \frac{1}{3}x$

4 $y = -2x,\ y = -3x$

5 $y = 10x,\ y = 7x$

6 $y = -\frac{1}{2}x,\ y = -\frac{1}{4}x$

7 $y = -6x,\ y = -3x$

8 $y = 0.5x,\ y = 0.75x$

Determine whether each of the following straight lines makes an acute angle or an obtuse angle with the positive x-axis.

9 $y = 4x$

10 $y = -3x$

11 $y = 3.6x$

12 $y = \frac{1}{3}x$

13 $y = 10x$

14 $y = 0.5x$

15 $y = -6x$

16 $y = -\frac{2}{3}x$

17 $y = \frac{4}{3}x$

18 Estimate the gradient of each of the lines shown in the sketch.
(The same scale is used on each axis.)

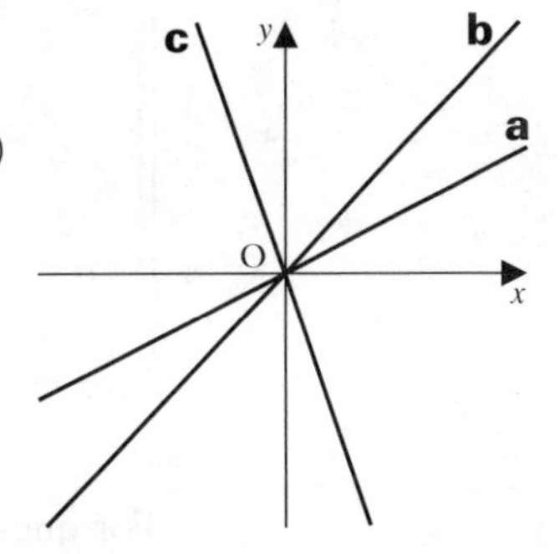

LINES THAT DO NOT PASS THROUGH THE ORIGIN

When we are given a line drawn on a graph, we can find its gradient and where it crosses the y-axis. We can also make a table showing the coordinates of some points on the line. From this table we may be able to see the formula which gives y when we know x, so we may be able to find the equation of the line. This process is shown in the following worked example. We can then see if there is a connection between the equation of the line and its gradient and where it crosses the y-axis.

EXERCISE 13C

a Find the gradient of this line.

b Where does the line cross the y-axis?

c Copy and complete the table for the given points on the line.

x	-1	0	1	2
y	-4			2

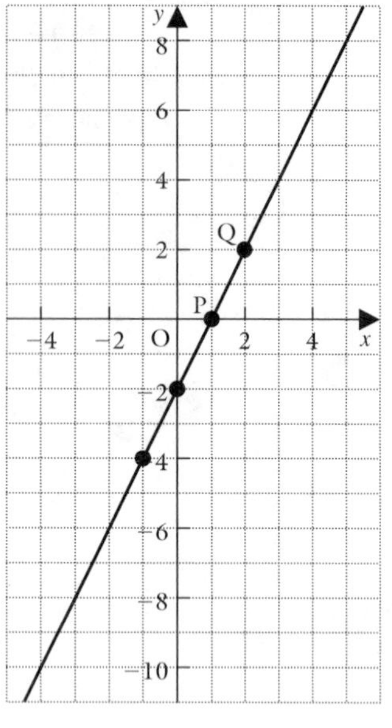

d Find the equation of the line.

e Is there a relationship between the equation of the line and the answers to parts **a** and **b**?

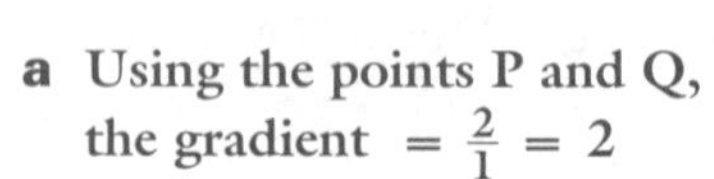

a Using the points P and Q, the gradient $= \frac{2}{1} = 2$

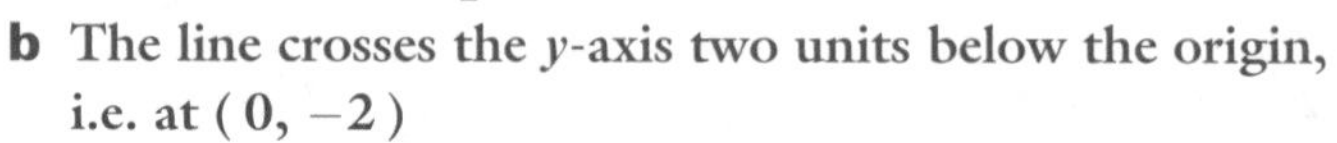

b The line crosses the y-axis two units below the origin, i.e. at $(0, -2)$

c Using the points marked on the graph,

x	-1	0	1	2
y	-4	-2	0	2

d From the table we can see that when x goes up by 1 unit, y goes up by 2 units. This means that the equation is $y = 2x + \ldots$ Also from the table we see that when we double the x-coordinate we have to subtract 2 to give the y-coordinate, i.e. $y = 2x - 2$.

The equation of the line is $y = 2x - 2$.

e The gradient is the same as the number of x s in the equation and -2 describes where the line cuts the y-axis.

For questions **1** to **4**

a Find the gradient of the line.

b Write down the value of y where the line crosses the y-axis.

c Make a table showing the x- and y-coordinates of the points on the line where x is -1, 0, 1, 2.

d Find the equation of the line.

e Compare your answers to parts **a** and **b** with the numbers on the right-hand side of the equation.

1

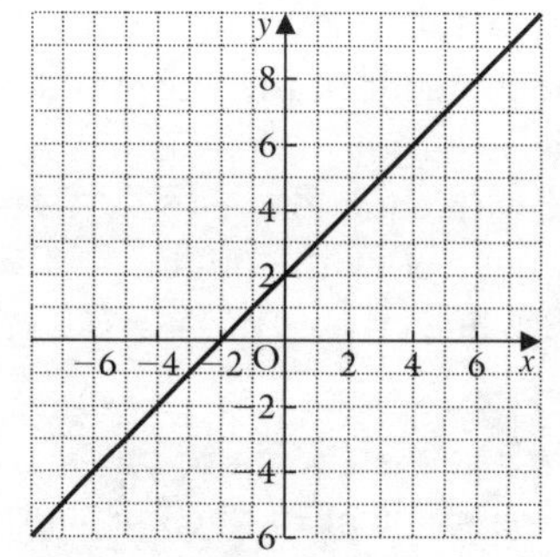

3

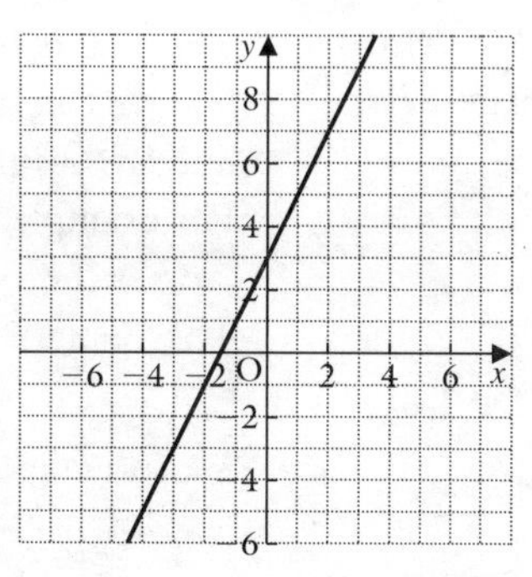

2

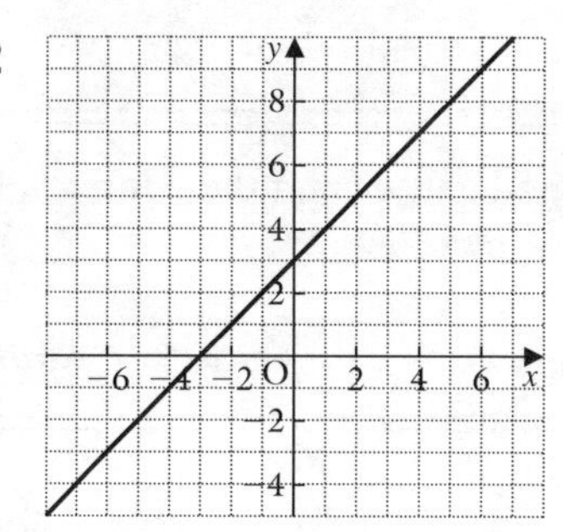

4

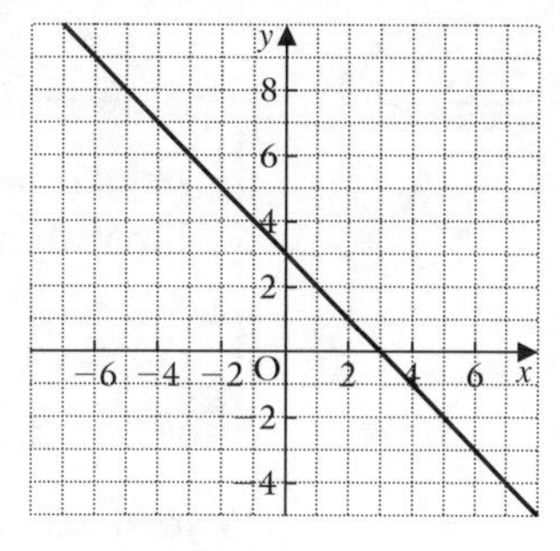

For questions **5** to **8**

a Make a copy of the grid used for questions **1** to **4** and draw the graph of the line whose equation is given. Use the stated values of x to find the points on the line.

b Hence find the gradient of the line and the value of y where it crosses the y-axis.

c Compare these values with the numbers on the right-hand side of the equation of the line.

5 $y = 3x + 1$; x-values $-3, 1, 3$

Use your graph to find y when x is **i** -2 **ii** 2

6 $y = -3x + 4$; x-values $-2, 2, 4$

Use your graph to find y when x is **i** -1 **ii** 3

7 $y = \frac{1}{2}x + 4$; x-values $-8, 0, 6$

Use your graph to find **i** y when x is -2 **ii** x when y is 6

8 $y = -2x - 7$; x-values $-6, -2, 1$

Use your graph to find **i** y when x is -1 **ii** x when y is 6

THE EQUATION $y = mx + c$

The results of **Exercise 13C** show that, from the equation of a straight line we can 'read' the gradient of the line and the value of y where the line crosses the y-axis.
For example, the line with equation $y = 3x - 4$ has a gradient of 3 and crosses the y-axis 4 units below the origin.
The value of y where a line crosses the y-axis is called the *y-intercept*.

In general we see that the equation $y = mx + c$ gives a straight line where m is the gradient of the line and c is the y-intercept.

EXERCISE 13D

Write down the gradient, m, and the y-intercept, c, for the straight line with equation $y = 5x - 2$

For the line $y = 5x - 2$ $m = 5$ and $c = -2$

Write down the gradient, m, and y-intercept, c, for the straight line with the given equation.

1 $y = 4x + 7$

2 $y = \frac{1}{2}x - 4$

3 $y = 3x - 2$

4 $y = -4x + 5$

5 $y = 7x + 6$

6 $y = \frac{2}{5}x - 3$

7 $y = \frac{3}{4}x + 7$

8 $y = -3x + 4$

9 $y = 4 - 3x$

Sketch the straight line with equation $y = 5x - 7$

A sketch does not need scaled axes, but the important features of the graph must be marked, i.e. where it crosses the y-axis and its gradient; we can read these from the equation of the line.

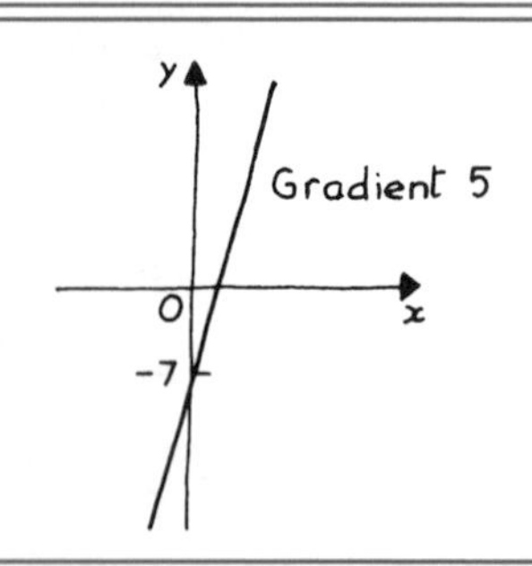

Sketch the straight lines with the given equations.

10 $y = 2x + 5$

11 $y = 7x - 2$

12 $y = \frac{1}{2}x + 6$

13 $y = -2x - 3$

14 $y = -\frac{2}{3}x + 8$

15 $y = 4x + 2$

<u>16</u> $y = -5x - 3$

<u>17</u> $y = 3x + 7$

<u>18</u> $y = \frac{3}{4}x - 2$

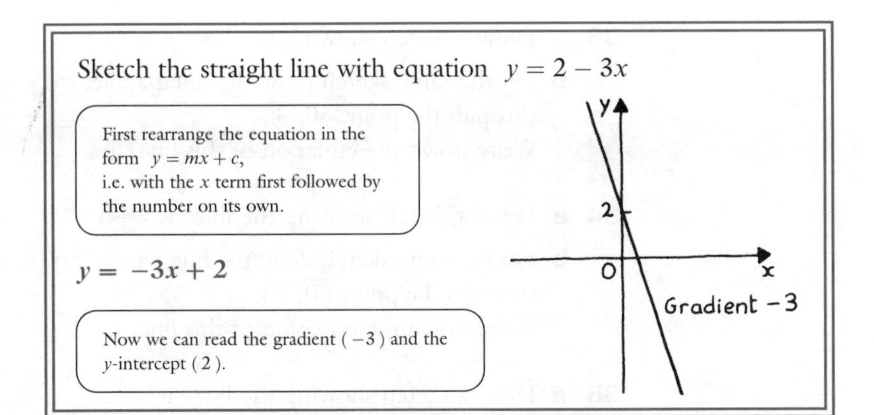

Sketch the straight lines with the given equations.

19 $y = 4 - x$

20 $y = 3 - 2x$

21 $y = 8 - 4x$

22 $y = -3 - x$

23 $y = 1 + x$

24 $y = 3(x - 2)$

25 $y = -5(x - 1)$

26 $y = 3(4 - x)$

27 $3y = (x - 4)$

If you know the gradient of a line and where it cuts the y-axis, you can write down its equation.
For example, the line that cuts the y-axis where $y = -4$ and whose gradient is 2, has equation $y = mx + c$ where $m = 2$ and $c = -4$,
i.e. $y = 2x + (-4)$
$\Rightarrow y = 2x - 4$

28 Draw a sketch showing the line that has a gradient 3 and cuts the y-axis at the point (0, 3). Write down the equation of the line.

29 Draw a sketch showing the line whose gradient is -2 and that cuts the y-axis 2 units above the origin. Write down the equation of the line.

In questions **30** to **32**

a find the gradient of the line

b write down the y intercept

c write down the equation of the line.

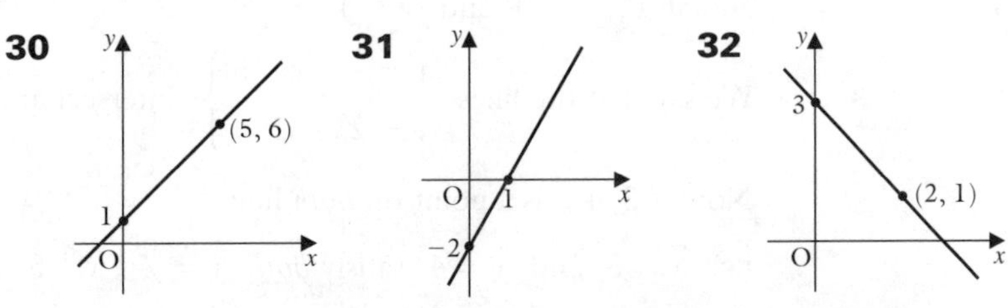

When two lines are parallel they have the same gradient

33 **a** Draw a sketch showing the line $y = 4x$.

b On the same sketch draw the line parallel to $y = 4x$ that goes through the point $(0, 3)$.
Write down the equation of this line.

34 **a** Draw a sketch showing the line $y = -x$.

b On the same sketch draw the line parallel to $y = -x$ that goes through the point $(0, 1)$.
Write down the equation of this line.

35 **a** Draw a sketch showing the line $y = \frac{1}{2}x$.

b On the same sketch draw the line parallel to $y = \frac{1}{2}x$ that cuts the y-axis 2 units below the origin.
Write down the equation of this line.

36 Write down the equation of the line that is parallel to the line $y = 2x$ and that goes through the point $(0, 4)$.

INTERSECTING LINES

The point where two lines cross is called the *point of intersection* of the lines.

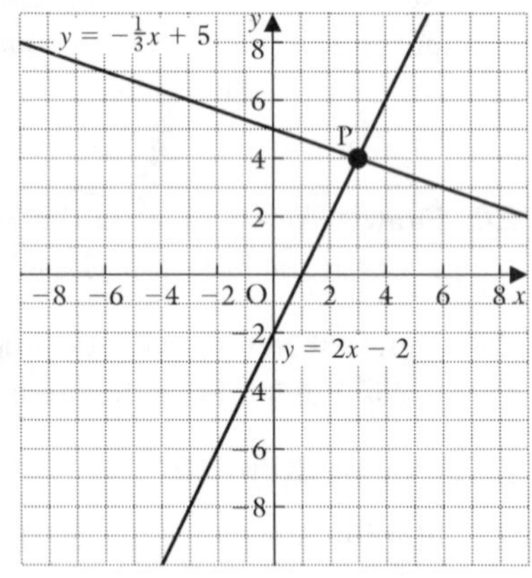

The point of intersection of the two lines in the diagram is P, and at P, $x = 3$ and $y = 4$.

We say that the lines $\left.\begin{array}{l} y = -\frac{1}{3}x + 5 \\ y = 2x - 2 \end{array}\right\}$ intersect at the point $(3, 4)$.

Now $(3, 4)$ is a point on *both* lines,

i.e. $x = 3$ and $y = 4$ satisfy *both* $y = -\frac{1}{3}x + 5$ *and* $y = 2x - 2$.

We say that $\left.\begin{array}{l} x = 3 \\ y = 4 \end{array}\right\}$ satisfy $\left.\begin{array}{l} y = -\frac{1}{3}x + 5 \\ y = 2x - 2 \end{array}\right\}$ *simultaneously*.

EXERCISE 13E

For questions **1** to **3** you will need a copy of the set of axes used above this exercise drawn on squared paper.

Draw the graphs of the lines whose equations are given. Hence find the coordinates of the point of intersection of the two lines.

1 $y = 2x - 1$
$y = x + 2$

2 $y = \frac{1}{2}x + 1$
$y = -x - 2$

3 $y = 4x + 5$
$y = x - 4$

For questions **4** to **6**, you will need a copy of the set of axes used for questions **1** to **3**, drawn on *graph* paper using 1 cm for 1 unit on each axis.
Draw the graphs of the lines whose equations are given.
Find the value of x and the value of y that satisfies the two equations simultaneously, giving answers correct to 1 decimal place where necessary.

4 $y = -x + 6$
$y = x + 3$

5 $y = \frac{2}{3}x + 4$
$y = -\frac{1}{2}x - 1$

6 $y = -2x + 3$
$y = -x + 2.5$

USING A GRAPHICS CALCULATOR

Plotting graphs to find their points of intersection is time consuming; using a graphics calculator takes out the hard work.
Calculators vary, but the general principles are similar. First the range has to be set; this specifies the scales on the axes. Then a function button is used to display 'Y = '; then the rest of the equation is entered.

The diagram shows the display on a graphics calculator when the graphs $y = -\frac{1}{3}x + 5$ *and* $y = 2x - 2$ are plotted.

The range was set to
x min: -2.5
x max: 5
scale: 1
y min: -1
y max: 7
scale: 1

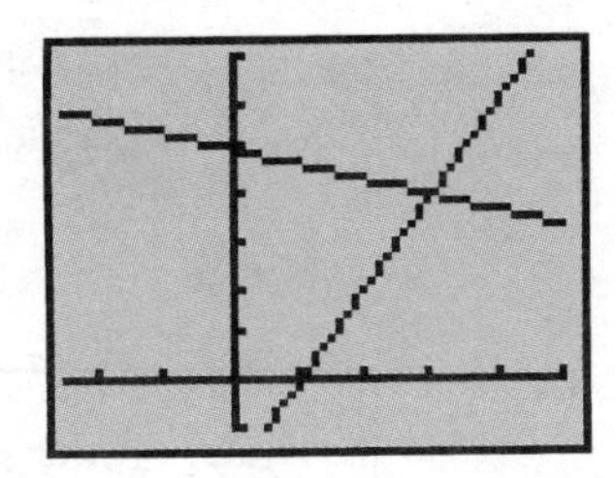

The 'TRACE' button can then be used to give the coordinates of the point of intersection. A cursor appears on the display which can be moved until it is over the point where the graphs cross. The coordinates of the position of the cursor are displayed at the bottom of the screen.

The display will look something like this:

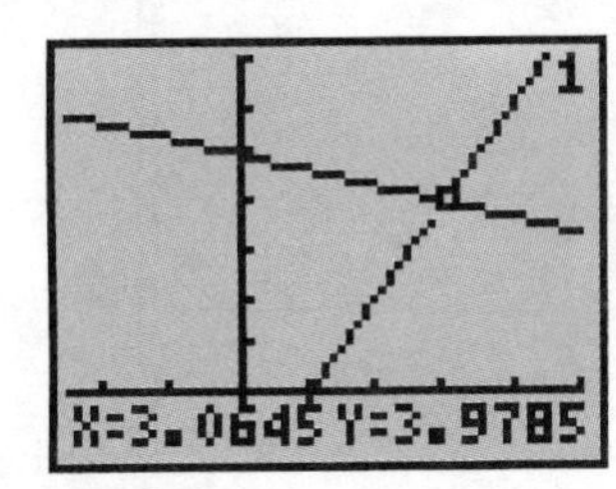

Use the lines given in **Exercise 13H** to practice using a graphics calculator.

LINES PARALLEL TO THE AXES

The line in the diagram is parallel to the x-axis and, at every point on it, the y-coordinate is 5.
Therefore an instruction for finding the y-coordinate of any point on this line in terms of its x-coordinate could be 'whatever the x-coordinate is, the y-coordinate is 5',

i.e. $y = 5$ for all values of x
or, even more briefly, $y = 5$.

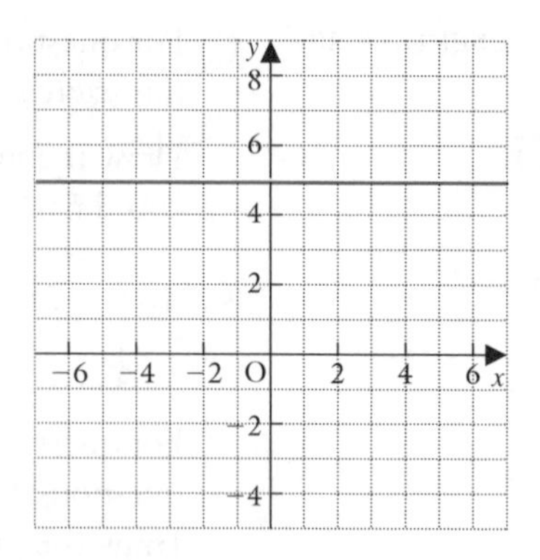

Any line parallel to the x-axis can be described in a similar way,

> therefore an equation of the form $y = c$ gives a line that is parallel to the x-axis and distant c units from it.

The line in this diagram is parallel to the y-axis, and the x-coordinate of every point on it is 3.
Hence $x = 3$ is all that is needed to give the relationship between the x- and y-coordinates of all the points on this line.

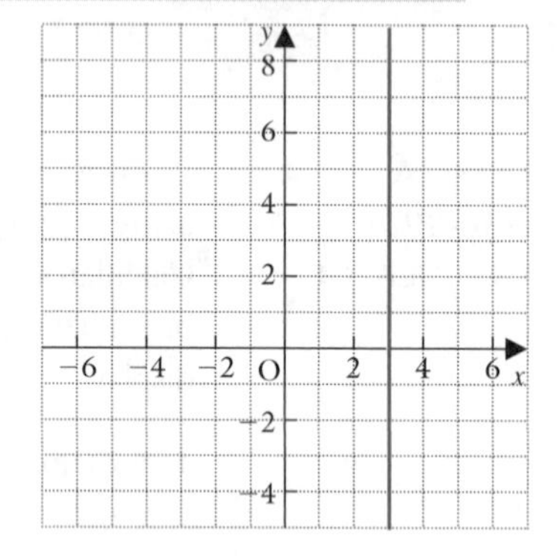

> Therefore $x = b$ is the equation of a straight line parallel to the y-axis at a distance b units from it.

EXERCISE 13F

Draw, on the same diagram, the graphs of

$$x = -3, \quad x = 5, y = -2 \quad \text{and} \quad y = 4.$$

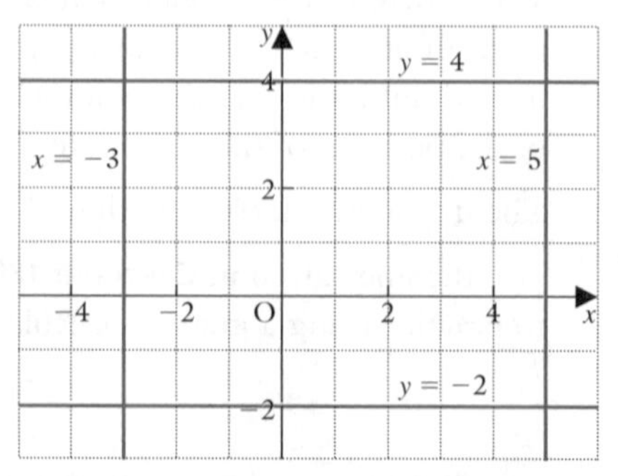

In the following questions take both x and y in the range -8 to $+10$. Use squared paper and 2 squares for 1 unit on each axis.

1 Draw the straight line graphs of the following equations in a single diagram: $x = 2$, $x = -5$, $y = \frac{1}{2}$, $y = -3\frac{1}{2}$

2 Draw the straight line graphs of the following equations on a single diagram: $y = -5$, $x = -3$, $x = 6$, $y = 5.5$
Name the shape of the area enclosed by these lines.

3 On one diagram, draw graphs to show the following equations:

$$x = 5, \quad y = -5, \quad y = 2x$$

Write down the coordinates of the three points where these lines intersect. What kind of triangle do they form

4 On one diagram, draw the graphs of the straight lines with equations

$$x = 4, \quad y = -\tfrac{1}{2}x, \quad y = 3$$

Write down the coordinates of the three points where these lines intersect. What kind of triangle is formed by these lines?

5 On one diagram, draw the graphs of the straight lines with equations

$$y = 2x + 4, \quad y = -5, \quad y = 4 - 2x$$

Write down the coordinates of the three points where these lines intersect. What kind of triangle is enclosed by the lines?

MIXED EXERCISE

EXERCISE 13G

1 Write down the gradient of the line whose equation is $y = 3x - 2$.

2 **a** Draw a sketch of the line whose equation is $y = -3x$.

b Write down the equation of the line parallel to $y = -3x$ that goes through the point $(0, 5)$.

3 What is the value of y where the line $y = 3x - 2$ cuts the y-axis?

4 The table gives the coordinates of three points on a line.
What is the equation of the line?

x	-2	0	2
y	-1	1	3

5 For the line shown find

a the gradient

b the y-intercept

c the equation.

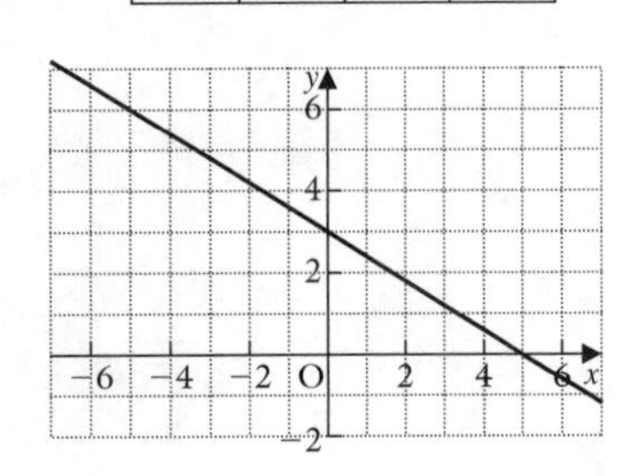

INVESTIGATION

a Give the coordinates of the points A, B, C and D.

b What name do we give to the shape ABCD?

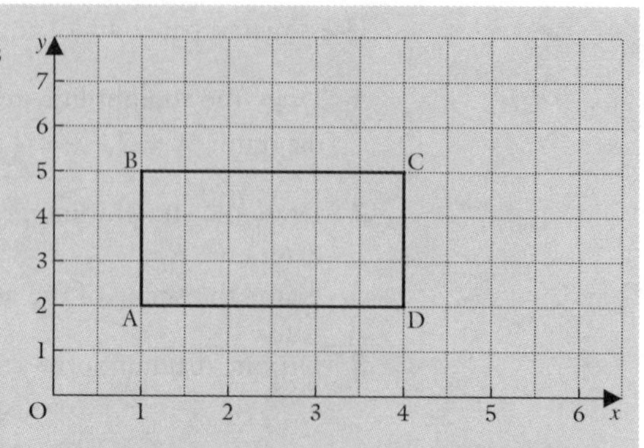

c Copy this grid. Using the coordinates found in part **a** plot the points A, B, C and D on the grid.
Join the points to give a quadrilateral. What name do we give to this shape?
Is this the same shape as you found in part **a**?

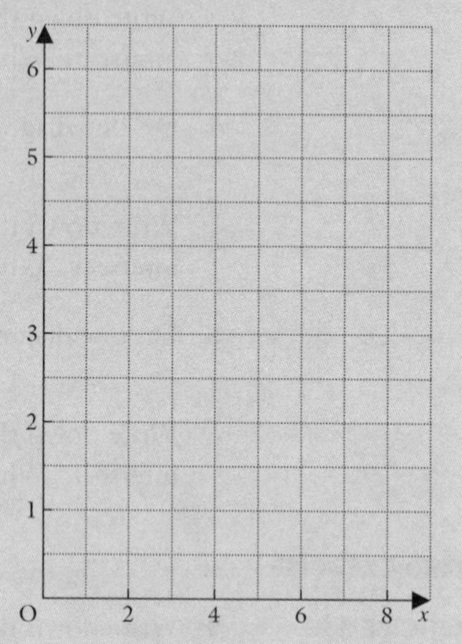

d Repeat part **c** using this grid.

e In view of your answers to parts **c** and **d** do you still think that your answer to part **b** is correct?
Explain your conclusion.

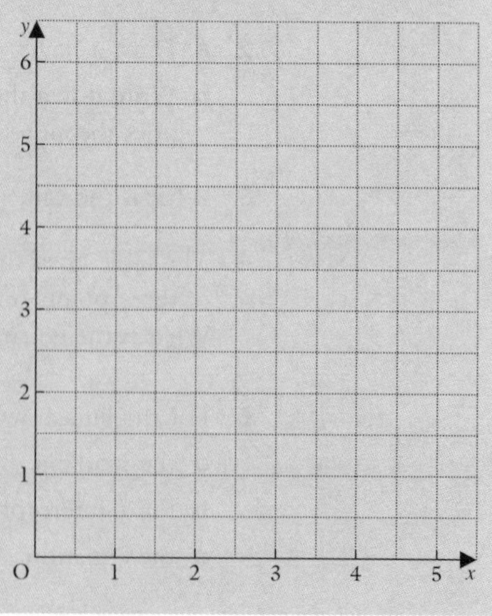

CURVED GRAPHS

Peter is designing floor tiles. He has decided to make rectangular tiles that are twice as long as they are wide.

He must now consider what size to make the tiles and whether to make them in more than one size. One factor in the decision must be the floor area that each tile covers as this is clearly related to the lengths of the sides of the tile.

To get some idea of how the area varies with different lengths of the sides, Peter can

- find the area for some particular lengths; for example, for a tile measuring 5 cm by 10 cm, the area is $5 \times 10\,\text{cm}^2 = 50\,\text{cm}^2$.
  This is likely to lead to values being found in a haphazard order where it is difficult to see any pattern in the relationship between the areas and the dimensions of the tiles.
- find a formula for the area, $A\,\text{cm}^2$, in terms of the width, x cm, of a tile and use this to tabulate values of A that correspond to some values of x. If Peter does this systematically, he may be able to get some sense of how the area varies with the length of the sides.
- try and get a 'picture' of how area varies with the dimensions.

EXERCISE 14A

1 Peter looks first at a tile 5 cm wide, and then at a tile 12 cm wide.

a Find the area of each tile.

b Peter decides he needs to look at a tile between 5 cm and 12 cm wide. Discuss what width would be a sensible choice.

c Discuss what information these values give about the relationship between the area and width of the tiles.

2 Peter decided to use a formula to work out some values for the areas of tiles of different widths.

The area of a rectangle is length × width.

2*x* cm

A cm²

x cm

Therefore $A = 2x \times x$

i.e. $A = 2x^2$

Peter used this formula to find the values in the table.

x	1	2	4	6	8	10	12
A	2	8	32	72	128	200	288

a Discuss what the results show about the relationship between the area covered by a tile and its width.

b Discuss whether it is possible to find easily the width of a tile that covers an area of 150 cm².

3 Discuss how the results in the table could be illustrated and if any of your suggestions help with the problems in question **2**, parts **a** and **b**.

GRAPHS INVOLVING CURVES

You may have discovered, from question **3** above, that plotting values of A against values of x on a graph gives a useful picture of how A varies when x varies.

When these values are plotted, we find that the points do not lie on a straight line, but they do lie on a smooth curve.

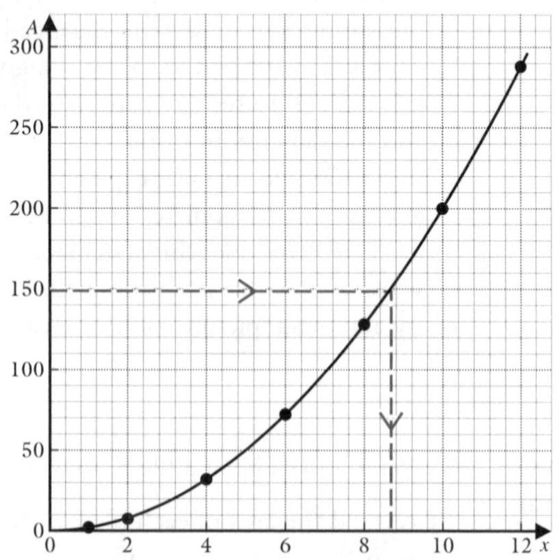

Even though the scales on the axes are far from equal, the graph shows that A increases at a much faster rate than x.

This graph can be used to 'read' the width of a tile whose area is 150 cm², or any other area.

When the area is $150\,\text{cm}^2$, i.e. when $A = 150$,
from the graph we see that x is about 8.7.
So a tile whose width is about 8.7 cm will cover an area of $150\,\text{cm}^2$.

When two quantities that are related are plotted one against the other we often find that the points lie on a smooth curve. If they do, useful information can be found easily from the graph.

EXERCISE 14B

1 In the text before this exercise, we read the value of x when $A = 150$ and found it to be 'about 8.7'. Discuss why we cannot give an exact value for x.

2 This graph shows the relationship between Jason's height and his age (the points shown give his heights on his birthdays).

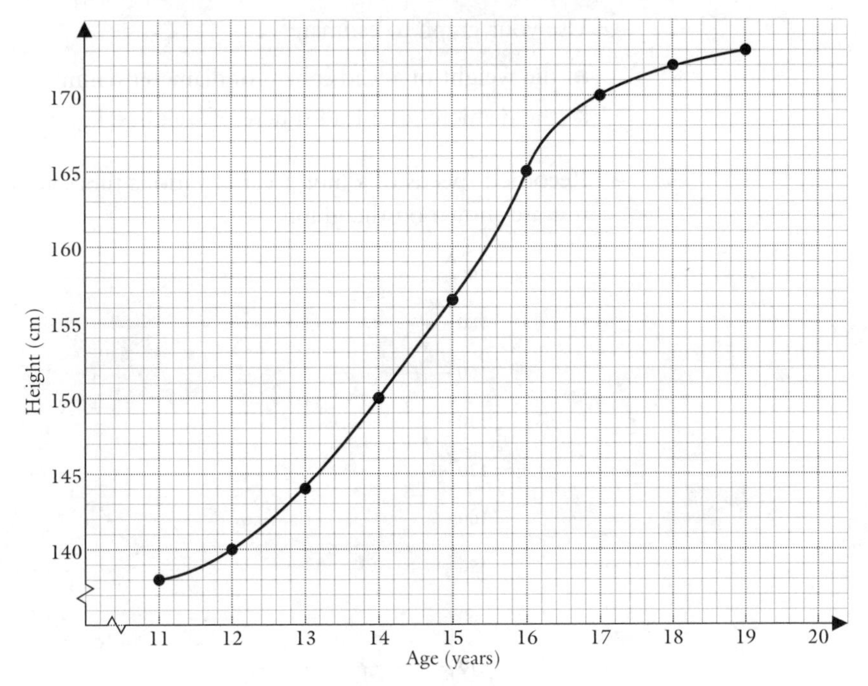

a Use the graph to estimate Jason's height when he was

i $15\frac{1}{2}$ years old **ii** $13\frac{1}{2}$ years old.

b Estimate how old Jason was when he was 171 cm tall.

c The flattest part of the curve is between 18 and 19 on the horizontal axis. How would you describe Jason's growth rate for this part of the curve ?

d Between which two consecutive birthdays did Jason grow most ? How would you describe the part of the curve you used to find this ?

e Would you be able to get as much information from the graph if the vertical scale started at zero ? Explain your answer.

3 The weights of lead spheres of various diameters are shown in the table.

Diameter, D, in mm	4	5.2	6.4	7.2	7.9	8.8
Weight, W, in grams	380	840	1560	2230	2940	4070

Use 2 cm for 1 unit on the D-axis and 2 cm for 500 units on the W-axis to plot this information on a graph.
Draw a smooth curve through the points.
Use a pencil to draw a smooth curve – you may find that you need several attempts to get a smooth curve. Most people find the best way to draw a curve is to keep their hand on the inside of the curve, like this:

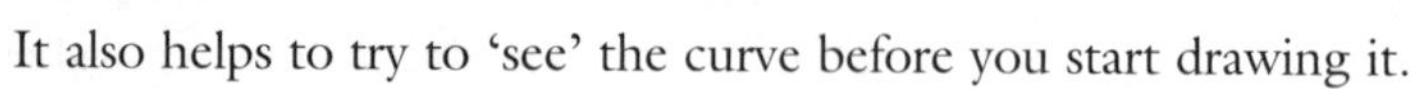

It also helps to try to 'see' the curve before you start drawing it.

Use your graph to estimate

a the weight of a lead sphere of diameter 6 mm
b the diameter of a lead sphere of weight 2 kg.

4 Recorded speeds of a motor car at various times after starting from rest are shown on the graph.

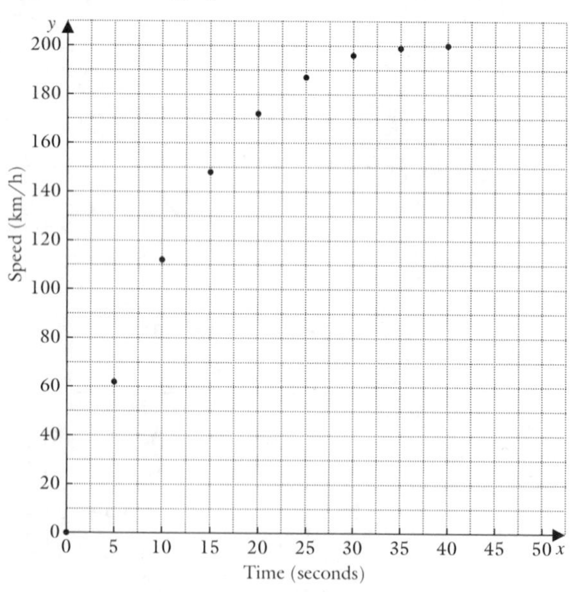

Copy the graph and complete it by drawing a smooth curve to pass through these points.

Use your graph to estimate

a the time which passes before the car reaches
i 100 km/h **ii** 150 km/h
b its speed after **i** 13 seconds **ii** 27 seconds.

5 The graph shows the weight of a puppy at different ages.

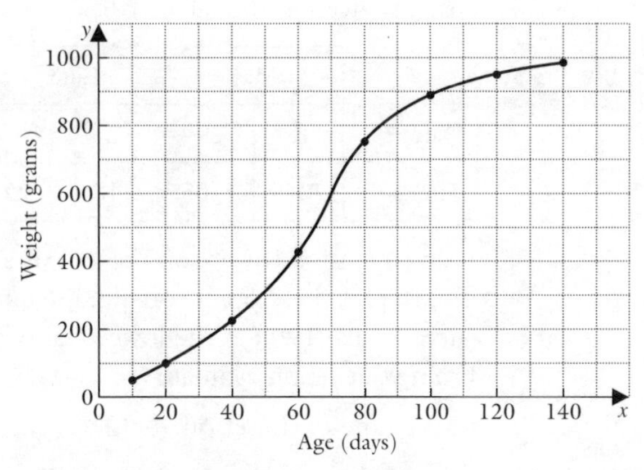

Use the graph to estimate

a the weight of the puppy after

i 50 days **ii** 114 days

b the age of the puppy when it weighs

i 500 g **ii** 1000 g

c the weight it puts on between day 25 and day 55

d its birth weight

e the period of 10 days within which its weight increased most.

6 The cost of fuel, £C, per nautical mile for a ship travelling at various speeds, v knots, is given in the table.

(1 knot means 1 nautical mile per hour).

v	12	14	16	18	20	22	24	26	28
C	18.15	17.16	16.67	16.5	16.5	16.67	16.94	17.36	17.82

Draw a graph to show how the cost of fuel changes with speed.
Use 1 cm = 1 knot and 10 cm = £1.

(Take 16 as the lowest value for C and 10 as the lowest value for v.)

Use your graph to estimate

a the most economical speed for the ship and the corresponding cost per nautical mile

b the speeds when the cost per nautical mile is £17

c the cost when the speed is

i 13 knots **ii** 24.4 knots.

7 The time of sunset at Greenwich on different dates, each two weeks apart, is given in the table.

	May		June		July		Aug	
Date, D	15	29	12	26	10	24	7	21
Time, T	2045	2105	2118	2122	2116	2101	2039	2012

Using 1 cm for 1 week on the D-axis and 8 cm for 1 hour on the T-axis, plot these points on a graph and join them with a smooth curve. Take 1900 as the lowest value of T and start D at 15 May. From your graph estimate

a the time of sunset on 17 July

b the date on which the sun sets at 2027.

8 In the United Kingdom the petrol consumption for a vehicle is measured in miles per gallon (mpg) whereas in mainland Europe it is measured in litres per 100 kilometres (litres/100 km). The table gives several rates of petrol consumption in mpg and their correspondng values in litres/100 km.

Miles per gallon	15	20	28	34	45	60	70
Litres/100 km	18.8	14.1	10.1	8.3	6.3	4.7	4.0

Draw a graph for this data using 1 cm to represent 5 mpg on the horizontal axis and 1 cm to represent 1 litre/100 km on the vertical axis.
Use your graph to express

a 55 mpg in litres/100 km

b 6 litres/100 km in miles per gallon.

9 A rectangle measuring l cm by b cm has an area of 24 cm^2. The table gives different values of l with the corresponding values of b.

l	1	2	3	4	6	8	12	16
b	24		8		4		2	1.5

Copy and complete the table and draw a graph to show this information. Join the points with a smooth curve.
Take 1 cm for 1 unit on the l-axis and 1 cm for 2 units on the b-axis.
Use your graph to estimate the value of

a l when b is **i** 14 **ii** 2.4

b b when l is **i** 10 **ii** 2.8

CONSTRUCTING A TABLE FROM A FORMULA

In the last exercise, the data was given in tables. In many problems we start with a formula and have to construct our own table.

On page 294, when Peter wanted to find how the width of his tiles affected the area they cover, he started with tiles twice as long as they were wide and this gave the formula

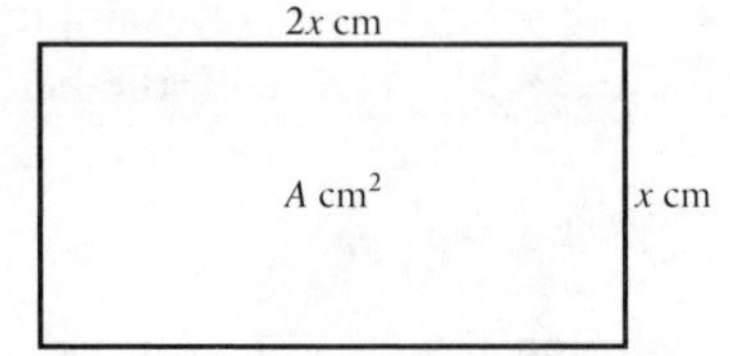

$$A = 2x^2$$

To draw a graph showing the relationship $A = 2x^2$, we need some corresponding values of A and x.
We will take values of x from 0 to 4 at half-unit intervals.
(Remember that $2x^2$ means $2 \times x^2$, i.e. $2 \times x \times x$.)

When $x = 0$, $A = 2 \times 0^2 = 2 \times 0 = 0$,

when $x = 0.5$, $A = 2 \times 0.5^2 = 2 \times 0.25 = 0.5$, and so on.

We could continue with this list and then enter the corresponding values of A and x in a table, but it is more efficient to use a table from the start, i.e.

x	0	0.5	1	1.5	2	2.5	3	3.5	4
x^2	0	0.25	1	2.25	4	6.25	9	12.25	16
$A(=2x^2)$	0	0.5	2	4.5	8	12.5	18	24.5	32

Using values of x on the horizontal axis and values of A up the vertical axis, we plot these points. Then we can draw a smooth curve through the points.

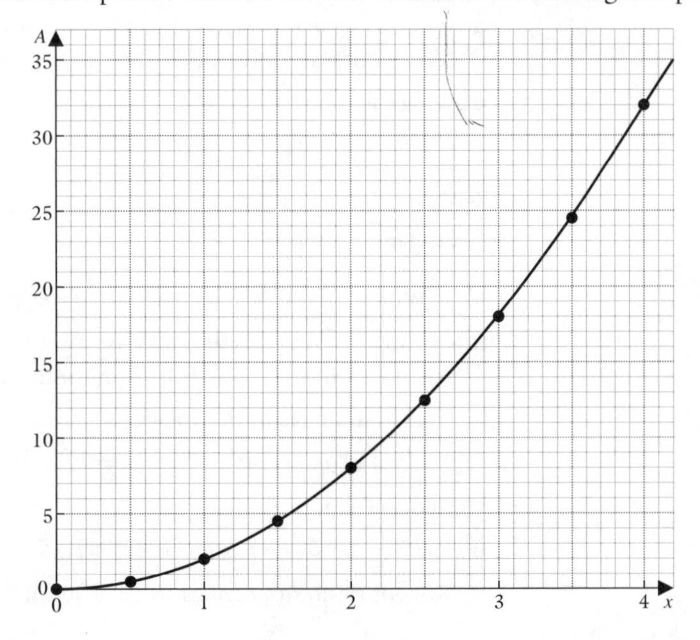

Sometimes a situation leads to a formula where the letters can stand for negative as well as positive numbers.
For example at various times after a stone is thrown up from the top of a cliff, the height of the stone relative to the cliff top may be positive or negative, i.e. the stone may be above or below the cliff top.

EXERCISE 14C

1 A wave generator in a pool causes the water level to rise and fall. There is a mark on the side wall of the pool showing the normal water level.

When the wave generator is switched on, the level, h cm, of the water above normal can be estimated using $h = 1 - t^2$ for values of t from -1.5 to 1.5, where t seconds is the time from where the water level is at its highest point.

a Copy and complete this table.

t	-1.5	-1	-0.5	0	0.5	1	1.5
t^2	2.25	1	0.25		0.25		2.25
$h = 1 - t^2$	-1.25	0	0.75		0.75		-1.25

b Plot these points on a graph using 2 cm for one unit on both axes. Draw a smooth curve through the points.

c Where is the water level

i half a second before it reaches its highest point

ii half a second after it reaches its highest point?

d What is the value of t when $h = -1$? Interpret this value in the context of the problem.

e Where is the water level 1.2 seconds after it reaches its highest point?

2 A stone is dropped down a vertical mine shaft. After t seconds it has fallen s metres where $s = 5t^2$.

(In this question the downward measurement is positive.)

a Construct a table to show the relationship between s and t for values of t from 0 to 6 at half-unit intervals.

b Use these values to draw a graph, using a scale of 1 cm to $\frac{1}{2}$ second on the horizontal axis and 1 cm to 25 metres on the vertical axis.

Use your graph to find

c how far the stone has fallen 3.4 seconds after it was dropped

d how long the stone takes to fall 100 metres.

THE EQUATION OF A CURVE

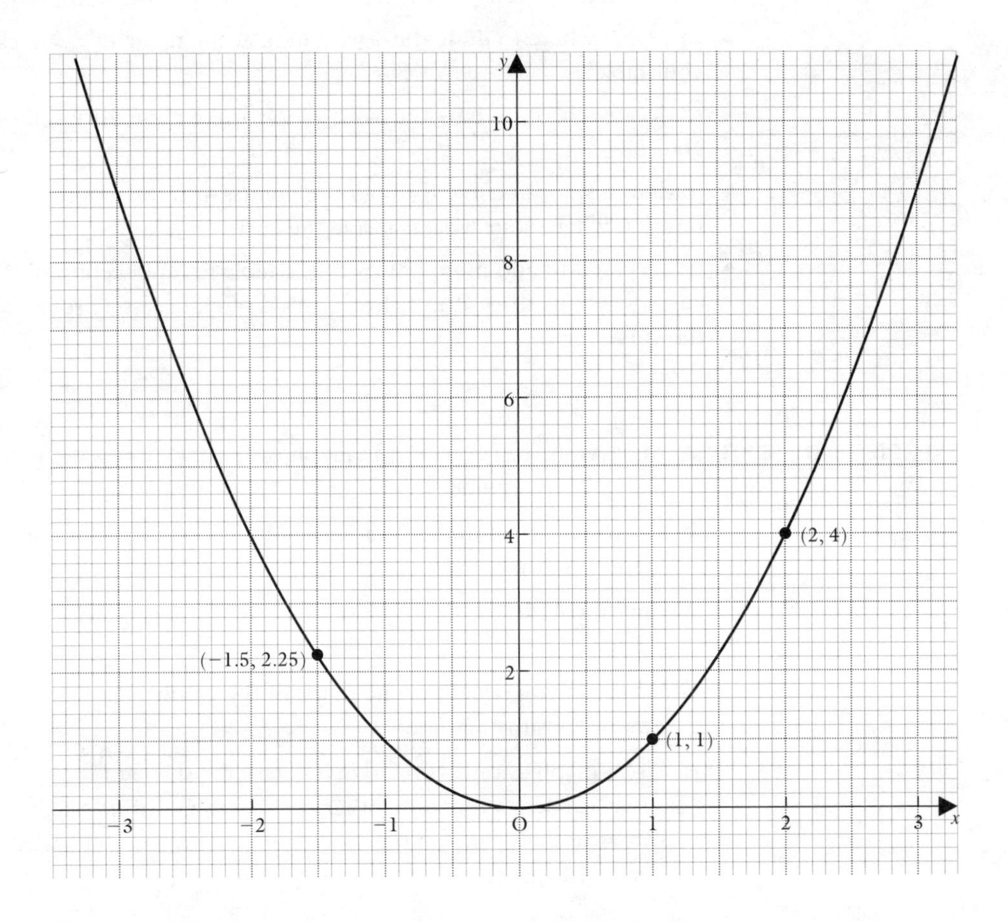

If we look at the relationship between the x- and y-coordinates of particular points on this curve, we find that the y-coordinate is always equal to the square of the x-coordinate.

This relationship between the coordinates is true for all the points on this curve, that is, for every point on the curve, $y = x^2$.

This formula giving the y-coordinate of a point on the curve in terms of its x-coordinate is called the *equation of the curve*.

We refer briefly to *the curve* $y = x^2$.

To draw the graph of a curve we start by using the equation of the curve to make a table of corresponding values of x and y (in the same way as we used a formula earlier in this chapter).

When drawing a curve

- do not take too few points – about ten are usually needed
- to decide where to draw the y-axis, look at the range of x-values in your table
- to decide where to draw the x-axis, look at the range of y-values in your table
- to draw a smooth curve through the points, turn the graph paper to a position where your wrist is inside the curve
- be prepared to add more points to the table for any section of the curve where its shape is not clear. This is often necessary round where the curve turns.

EXERCISE 14D

1 **a** Make your own copy of the graph of $y = x^2$ using the graph on page 301 as a guide.

b On your copy, draw the graph of $y = 3x^2$ using values of x from -2 to 2 to make your table.

c Repeat part **b** for the graph of $y = \frac{1}{2}x^2$ using values of x from -3 to 3.

d What can you say about the shape of the graph of $y = ax^2$ when a is any positive number?

e Use a graphics calculator to investigate the shape of the curve $y = ax^2$ for some other positive values of a. Sketch the shapes of the graphs. How does the evidence you find affect your answer to part **d**?

2 **a** Make another copy of the graph on page 301 but this time extend the y-axis down to give values of y from -4 to 8.

b On your copy draw the graphs of $y = x^2 + 4$ and $y = x^2 - 4$ using values of x from -3 to 3 to make the tables for both graphs.

c What can you say about the shape of the graph of $y = x^2 + a$ when a is any number, positive or negative?

d Use a graphics calculator to investigate the shape of the curve $y = x^2 + a$ for some other values of a. Sketch the shapes of the graphs. How does the evidence you find affect your answer to part **c**?

3 Use a graphics calculator to investigate the shape of the graphs of $y = -x^2$, $y = -2x^2$, $y = -3x^2$. How do the shapes of these curves compare with the shapes of the curves in question **1**?

Draw the graph of $y = x^2 + x - 6$ for whole number values of x from -4 to $+4$. Take 1 cm as 1 unit on the x-axis and 1 cm as 2 units on the y-axis. Use your graph to find

a the lowest value of $x^2 + x - 6$ and the corresponding value of x

b the values of x when $x^2 + x - 6$ is 4.

x	-4	-3	-2	-1	0	1	2	3	4	$-\frac{1}{2}$
x^2	16	9	4	1	0	1	4	9	16	$\frac{1}{4}$
x	-4	-3	-2	-1	0	1	2	3	4	$-\frac{1}{2}$
-6	-6	-6	-6	-6	-6	-6	-6	-6	-6	-6
$x^2 + x - 6$	6	0	-4	-6	-6	-4	0	6	14	$-6\frac{1}{4}$

It is clear that the middle of the curve is where $x = -\frac{1}{2}$.
To find this point accurately, we can add another column to the table.

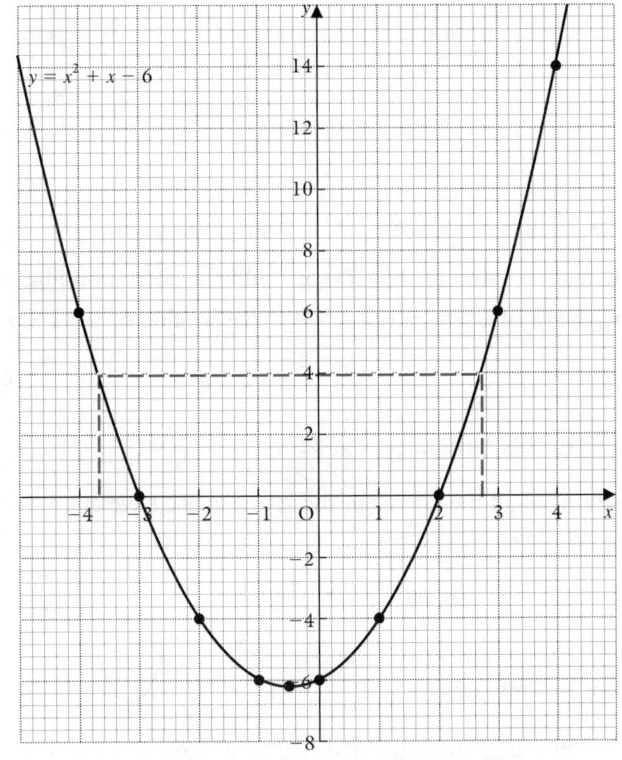

a $x^2 + x - 6 = y$, so we want the lowest value of y.

From the graph, the lowest value of $x^2 + x - 6$ is $-6\frac{1}{4}$.
This occurs when $x = -\frac{1}{2}$

b $x^2 + x - 6 = y$, so when $x^2 + x - 6$ is 4, y is 4.

The values of x when $x^2 + x - 6$ is 4 are -3.7 and 2.7.

4 Use the graph of $y = x^2 - 2x - 3$ to find

a the lowest value of $x^2 - 2x - 3$ and the corresponding value of x

b the values of x when $x^2 - 2x - 3$ has a value of
i 1 **ii** 8

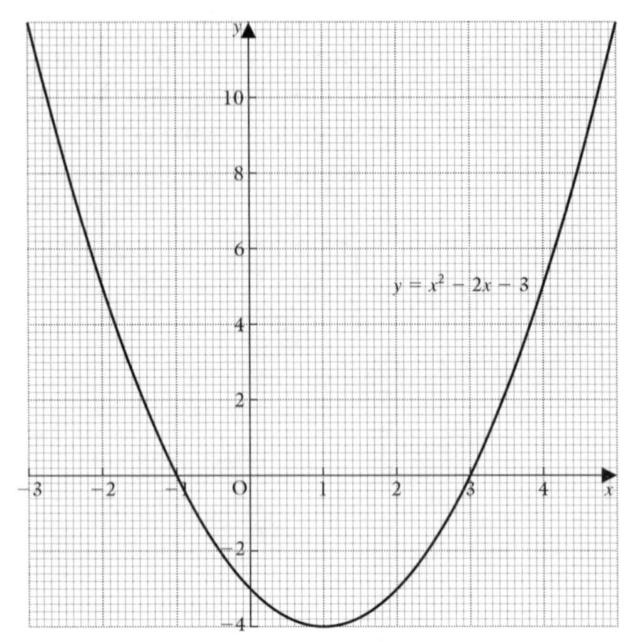

5 Draw the graph of $y = 6 + x - x^2$ for whole number values of x from -3 to 4. Take 2 cm as 1 unit on both axes. Use your graph to find

a the highest value of $6 + x - x^2$ and the corresponding value of x

b the values of x when $6 + x - x^2$ has a value of **i** -2 **ii** 4

THE SHAPE OF THE CURVE $y = ax^2 + bx + c$

The equations of all the curves in the last exercise have an x^2 term and/or an x term and/or a number.

All these curves have the same basic shape.

When the x^2 term is positive, e.g. $y = x^2$, the curve is this way up.

If the x^2 term is negative, e.g. $y = -x^2 + x - 6$, the shape is upside down.

All curves with this shape are called *parabolas*.

The equation of a parabola has the form $y = ax^2 + bx + c$, where a, b and c are numbers; a cannot be zero but b and/or c can be zero.

For example, $y = x^2$, $y = 3x^2$, $y = x^2 - 4$, and $y = -x^2 + x - 6$ all give parabolas.

EXERCISE 14E

1 The equation of a curve is $y = 6x^2$. Which of these sketches shows the curve?

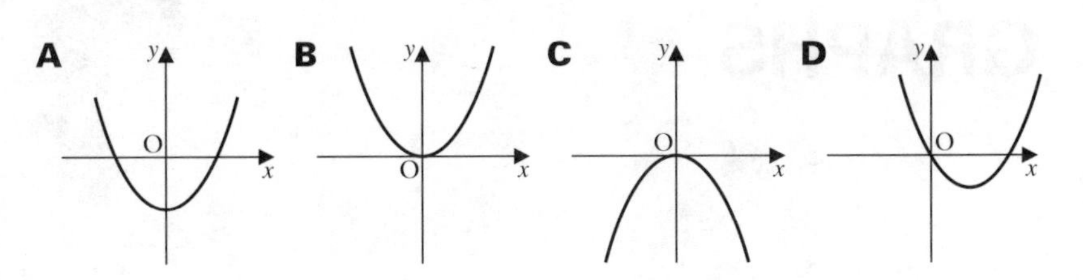

2 Explain why you rejected some of the curves in question **1**.

3 Draw a sketch of the curve $y = -5x^2$.

4 Write down an equation that could be the equation of each curve shown.

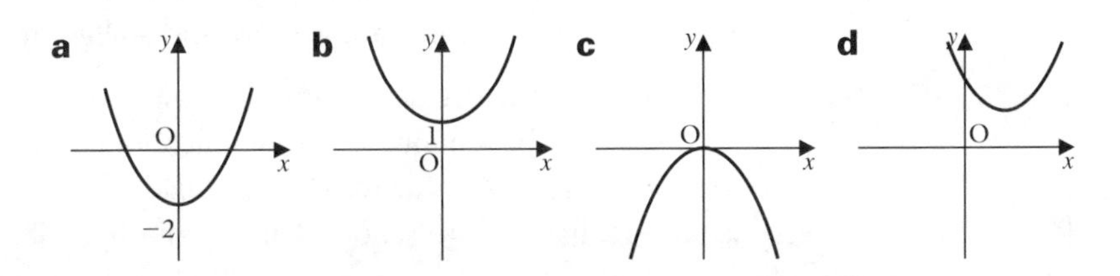

INVESTIGATION

The readings in the table were taken from the computer in a car that showed the petrol consumption for different speeds.

Speed, v mph	5	10	20	30	40	50	60	70
Petrol consumption, n miles per gallon	9	15	29	37	42	38	27	15

a Plot these points on a graph using 1 cm for 5 mph on the horizontal axis and 1 cm for 2 miles per gallon on the vertical axis.

b Now draw the curve whose equation is $n = 2v - \dfrac{v^2}{40}$.

c How well does the curve fit the points?

d Try adjusting the equation of the curve to get a better fit.

e Does your curve fit the points better for some values than others. Why do you think this is?

f Can you use your curve to predict the petrol consumption when the car is travelling at 100 mph? Explain your answer.

TRAVEL GRAPHS

When Isobel gets to the bus stop she has to travel 1 mile along the bus route to get to school, and she must be in school by 8.50. She can walk at 4 mph and if she catches the bus, it will travel at an average speed of 20 mph. The times that a bus arrives at the bus stop are unpredictable so Isobel is often undecided whether to wait for a bus or to walk.

- What is the latest time that Isobel can leave the bus stop on foot to be certain of arriving in school on time?
- If she is sure of catching a bus as soon as she gets to the bus stop, what is the latest time she can arrive there and still get to school in time?
- One morning she decides to walk but sees a bus pass her after she has been walking for 5 minutes. How much longer would she have had to wait before the bus arrived? If she had waited, how much earlier would she have got to school than she did by walking?

These questions can be answered by drawing suitable travel graphs. A travel graph is drawn by plotting distance covered against time taken.

FINDING DISTANCE FROM A GRAPH

When we went on holiday in the car we travelled to our holiday resort at a steady speed of 50 kilometres per hour (km/h), that is in each hour we covered a distance of 50 km.

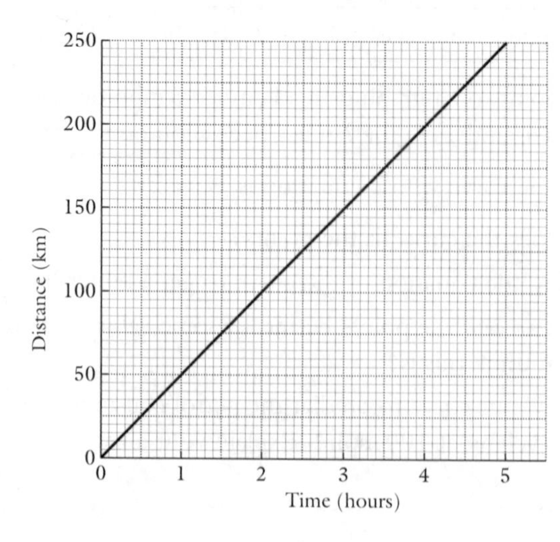

This graph plots distance covered against time taken and shows that

in 1 hour we travelled 50 km
in 2 hours we travelled 100 km
in 3 hours we travelled 150 km
in 4 hours we travelled 200 km
in 5 hours we travelled 250 km.

EXERCISE 15A The graphs that follow show five different journeys. For each journey find

a the distance travelled

b the time taken

c the distance travelled: in 1 hour (questions **1**, **2** and **3**)
or in 1 second (questions **4** and **5**).

1

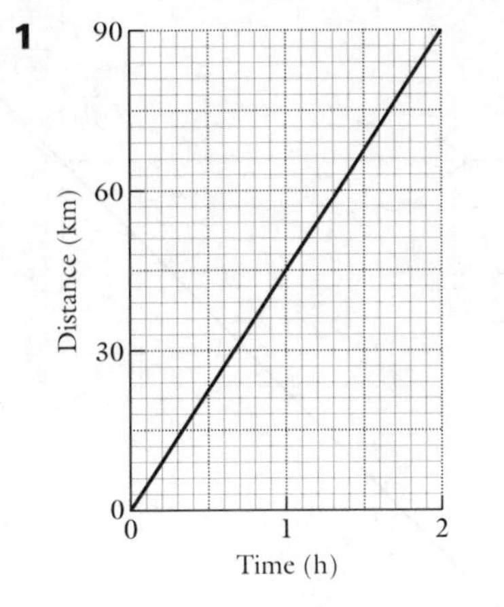

2

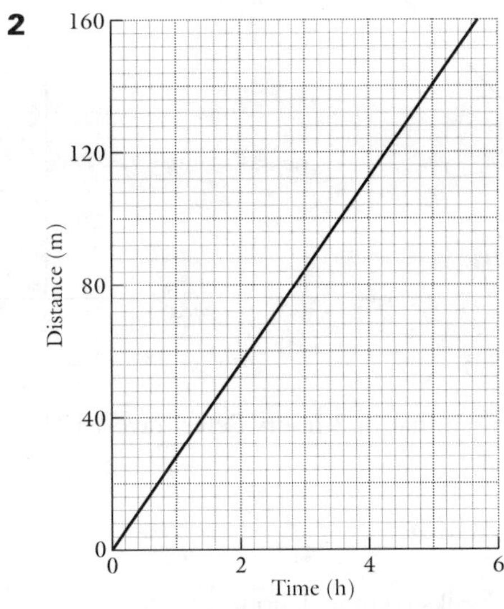

3

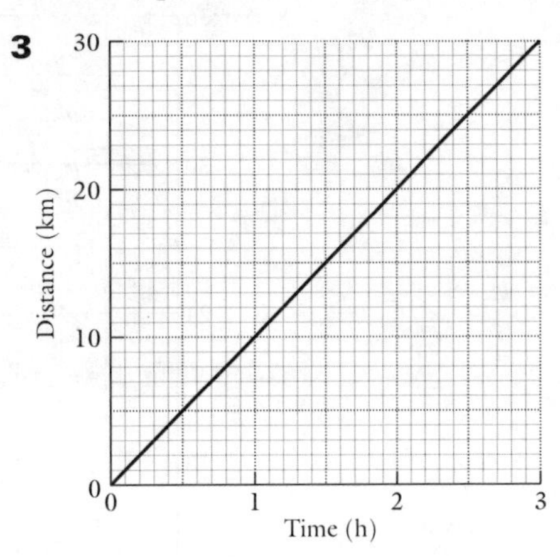

4

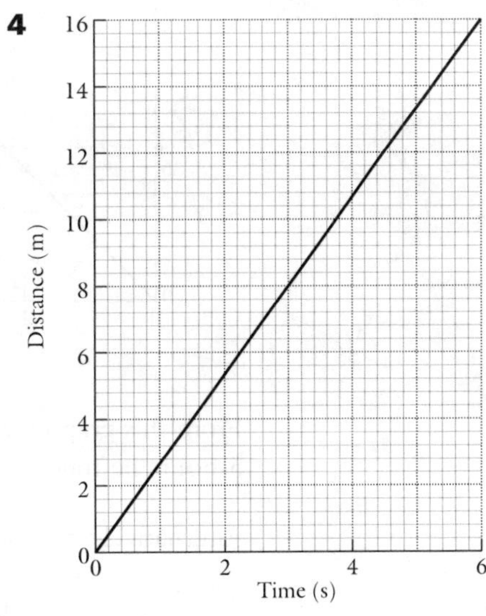

5

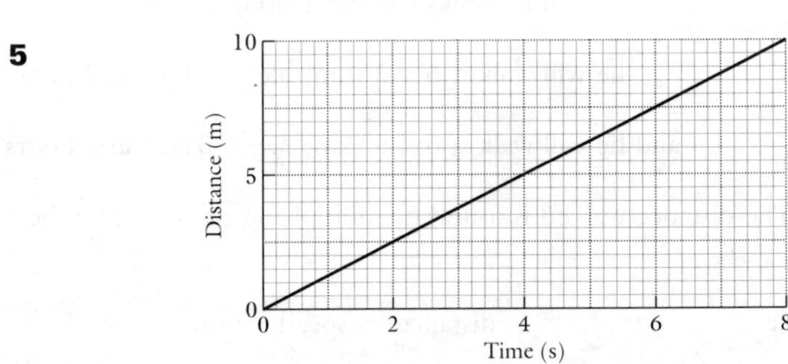

DRAWING TRAVEL GRAPHS

If Peter walks at 6 km/h, we can draw a graph to show this, using 2 cm to represent 12 km on the distance axis and 2 cm to represent 1 hour on the time axis.

Plot the point which shows that in 1 hour he has travelled 6 km. Join the origin to this point and extend the straight line to give the graph shown.

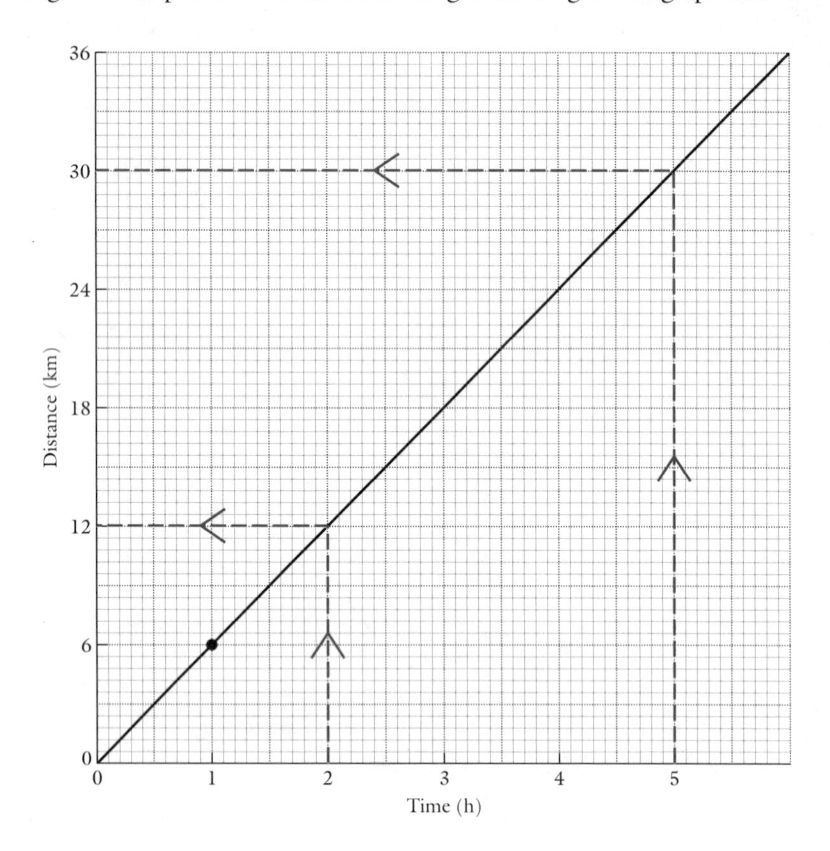

From this graph we can see that in 2 hours Peter travels 12 km and in 5 hours he travels 30 km.

Alternatively we could say that

if he walks 6 km in 1 hour

he will walk (6×2) km, i.e. 12 km in 2 hours

and he will walk (6×5) km, i.e. 30 km in 5 hours

The distance walked is found by multiplying the speed by the time,

i.e. **distance = speed × time**

EXERCISE 15B

Draw a travel graph to show Sally's journey of 150 km in 3 hours. Plot distance along the vertical axis and time along the horizontal axis. Let 4 cm represent 1 hour and 2 cm represent 50 km.

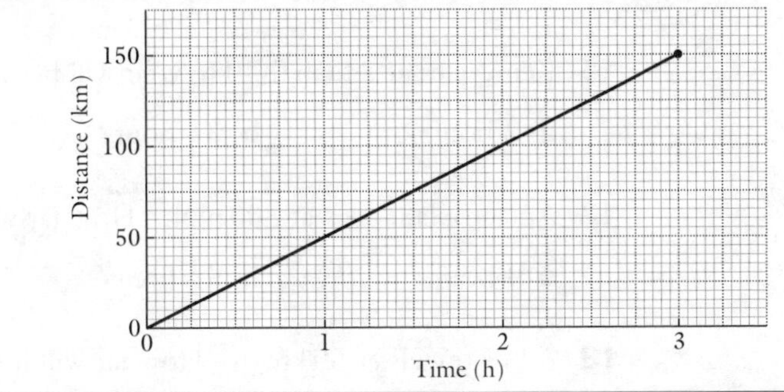

Draw travel graphs to show the following journeys. Plot distance along the vertical axis and time along the horizontal axis. Use the scales given in brackets.

1 60 km in 2 hours ($4\text{ cm} \equiv 1$ hour, $1\text{ cm} \equiv 10$ km)

2 180 km in 3 hours ($4\text{ cm} \equiv 1$ hour, $2\text{ cm} \equiv 50$ km)

3 100 km in $2\frac{1}{2}$ hours ($2\text{ cm} \equiv 1$ hour, $2\text{ cm} \equiv 25$ km)

4 75 miles in $1\frac{1}{4}$ hours ($8\text{ cm} \equiv 1$ hour, $2\text{ cm} \equiv 25$ miles)

5 240 m in 12 sec ($1\text{ cm} \equiv 1$ sec, $2\text{ cm} \equiv 50$ m)

6 Alan walks at 5 km/h. Draw a graph to show him walking for 3 hours. Take 4 cm to represent 5 km and 4 cm to represent 1 hour. Use your graph to find how far he walks in

a $1\frac{1}{2}$ hours **b** $2\frac{1}{4}$ hours.

7 Julie can jog at 10 km/h. Draw a graph to show her jogging for 2 hours. Take 1 cm to represent 2 km and 8 cm to represent 1 hour. Use your graph to find how far she jogs in

a $\frac{3}{4}$ hour **b** $1\frac{1}{4}$ hours.

8 Jo drives at 35 mph. Draw a graph to show her driving for 4 hours. Take 1 cm to represent 10 miles and 4 cm to represent 1 hour. Use your graph to find how far she drives in

a 3 hours **b** $1\frac{1}{4}$ hours.

9 John walks at 4 mph. Draw a graph to show him walking for 3 hours. Take 1 cm to represent 1 mph and 4 cm to represent 1 hour. Use your graph to find how far he walks in

a $\frac{1}{2}$ hour **b** $3\frac{1}{2}$ hours.

The remaining questions should be solved by calculation.

10 An express train travels at 200 km/h. How far will it travel in

a 4 hours **b** $5\frac{1}{2}$ hours?

11 Ken cycles at 24 km/h. How far will he travel in

a 2 hours **b** $3\frac{1}{2}$ hours **c** $2\frac{1}{4}$ hours?

12 An aeroplane flies at 300 mph. How far will it travel in

a 4 hours **b** $5\frac{1}{2}$ hours?

13 A bus travels at 60 km/h. How far will it travel in

a $1\frac{1}{2}$ hours **b** $2\frac{1}{4}$ hours?

14 Susan can cycle at 12 mph. How far will she ride in

a $\frac{3}{4}$ hour **b** $1\frac{1}{4}$ hours?

15 An athlete can run at 10.5 metres per second.
How far will he travel in **a** 5 sec **b** 8.5 sec?

16 A boy cycles at 12 mph. How far will he travel in

a 2 hours 40 min **b** 3 hours 10 min?

17 A Boeing 747 travels at 540 mph. How far does it travel in

a 3 hours 15 min **b** 7 hours 45 min?

18 A racing car travels around a 2 km circuit at 120 km/h. How many laps will it complete in

a 30 min **b** 1 hour 12 min?

CALCULATING THE TIME TAKEN

Georgina walks at 6 km/h so we can find out how long it will take her to walk 24 km; as she walks 6 km in 1 hour, it will take her $\frac{24}{6}$ hours to walk 24 km, i.e. 4 hours.

In the same way if Georgina walks 15 km, it will take her $\frac{15}{6}$ hours, i.e. $2\frac{1}{2}$ hours.

This demonstrates that

$$\text{time} = \frac{\text{distance}}{\text{speed}}$$

EXERCISE 15C

1 How long will Zena, walking at 5 km/h, take to walk

a 10 km **b** 15 km?

2 How long will a car, travelling at 80 km/h, take to travel

a 400 km **b** 260 km?

3 How long will it take David, running at 10 mph, to run

a 5 miles **b** $12\frac{1}{2}$ miles?

4 How long will it take an aeroplane flying at 450 mph to fly

a 1125 miles **b** 2400 miles?

5 A cowboy rides at 14 km/h. How long will it take him to ride

a 21 km **b** 70 km?

6 A rally driver drives at 50 mph. How long does it take him to travel

a 75 miles **b** 225 miles?

7 An athlete runs at 8 m/s. How long does it take him to cover

a 200 m **b** 1600 m?

8 A dog runs at 20 km/h. How long does the dog take to travel

a 8 km **b** 18 km?

9 A liner cruises at 28 nautical miles per hour. How long will it take to travel

a 6048 nautical miles **b** 3528 nautical miles

10 A car travels at 56 mph. How long does it take to travel

a 70 miles **b** 154 miles?

11 A cyclist cycles at 12 mph. How long will it take him to cycle

a 30 miles **b** 64 miles?

12 How long will it take a car travelling at 64 km/h to travel

a 48 km **b** 208 km?

AVERAGE SPEED

Russell Compton left home at 8 a.m. to travel the 50 km to his place of work. He arrived at 9 a.m. Although he had travelled at many different speeds during his journey he covered the 50 km in exactly 1 hour.
We say that his *average speed* for the journey was 50 kilometres per hour, or 50 km/h. If he had travelled at the same speed all the time, he would have travelled at 50 km/h.

$$\text{Average speed} = \frac{\text{distance travelled}}{\text{time taken}}$$

This formula can also be written:

$$\text{distance travelled} = \text{average speed} \times \text{time taken}$$

and $$\text{time taken} = \frac{\text{distance travelled}}{\text{average speed}}$$

A useful way to remember these relationships is from the triangle:
(Cover up the one you want to find.)

Suppose that a car travels 35 km in 30 min, and we want to find its speed in kilometres per hour. To do this we must express the time taken in hours instead of minutes,

i.e. $$\text{time taken} = 30\text{ min} = \tfrac{1}{2}\text{ hour}$$

Then $$\text{average speed} = \frac{35}{\frac{1}{2}}\text{ km/h} = 35 \times \frac{2}{1}\text{ km/h}$$

$$= 70\text{ km/h}$$

Be careful with units. If we want a speed in kilometres per hour, we need the distance in kilometres and the time in hours. If we want a speed in metres per second, we need the distance in metres and the time in seconds.

EXERCISE 15D

Find the average speed for each of the following journeys.

1 80 km in 1 hour

2 120 km in 2 hours

3 60 miles in 1 hour

4 480 miles in 4 hours

5 80 m in 4 sec

6 135 m in 3 sec

7 150 km in 3 hours

8 520 km in 8 hours

9 245 miles in 7 hours

10 104 miles in 13 hours

11 252 m in 7 sec

12 255 m in 15 sec

Tony drives 39 km in 45 minutes. Find his average speed.

First, convert the time taken to hours.

$$45 \text{ min} = \frac{45}{60} \text{ hour} = \frac{3}{4} \text{ hour}$$

$$\text{average speed} = \frac{\text{distance travelled}}{\text{time taken}}$$

$$= \frac{39 \text{ km}}{\frac{3}{4} \text{ hour}}$$

$$= \frac{39}{1} \div \frac{3}{4} \text{ km/h}$$

$$= \frac{\overset{13}{\cancel{39}}}{1} \times \frac{4}{\underset{1}{\cancel{3}}} \text{ km/h} = 52 \text{ km/h}$$

Find the average speed in km/h for a journey of

13 40 km in 30 min

14 60 km in 40 min

<u>15</u> 48 km in 45 min

<u>16</u> 66 km in 33 min

Find the average speed in km/h for a journey of 5000 m in $\frac{1}{2}$ hour.

We need distance in kilometres.

$$5000 \text{ m} = \frac{5000}{1000} \text{ km} = 5 \text{ km}$$

$$\text{average speed} = \frac{\text{distance travelled}}{\text{time taken}}$$

$$= \frac{5 \text{ km}}{\frac{1}{2} \text{ hour}}$$

$$= \frac{5}{1} \div \frac{1}{2} \text{ km/h}$$

$$= \frac{5}{1} \times \frac{2}{1} \text{ km/h} = 10 \text{ km/h}$$

Find the average speed in km/h for a journey of

17 4000 m in 20 min

18 6000 m in 45 min

<u>19</u> 40 m in 8 sec

<u>20</u> 175 m in 35 sec

Find the average speed in mph for a journey of

21 27 miles in 30 min

22 18 miles in 20 min

23 25 miles in 25 min

24 28 miles in 16 min

The following table shows the distances in kilometres between various places in the United Kingdom.

	London	Bradford	Cardiff	Leicester	Manchester	Oxford	Reading
Bradford	320						
Cardiff	250	332					
Leicester	160	160	224				
Manchester	310	55	277	138			
Oxford	90	280	172	120	230		
Reading	64	320	192	164	264	45	
York	315	53	390	174	103	290	210

Use this table to find the average speeds for journeys between

25 London, leaving at 1025, and Manchester, arriving at 1625

26 Oxford, leaving at 0330, and Cardiff, arriving at 0730

27 Leicester, leaving at 1914, and Oxford, arriving at 2044

28 Reading, leaving at 0620, and London, arriving at 0750

29 Bradford, leaving at 1537, and Oxford, arriving at 1907

30 Cardiff, leaving at 1204, and York, arriving at 1624

31 Bradford, leaving at 1014, and Reading, arriving at 1638.

JOURNEYS WITH SEVERAL PARTS

More usually, different parts of a journey are travelled at different speeds in different times and we need to find the average speed for the whole journey.

Consider for example Roger May, who travels the first 50 miles of a journey at an average speed of 25 mph and the next 90 miles at an average speed of 30 mph.

Using $\text{time in hours} = \dfrac{\text{distance in miles}}{\text{speed in mph}}$

gives $\text{time to travel 50 miles at 25 mph} = \dfrac{\text{distance}}{\text{speed}}$

$$= \frac{50 \text{ miles}}{25 \text{ mph}} = 2 \text{ hours}$$

$$\text{time to travel 90 miles at 30 mph} = \frac{\text{distance}}{\text{speed}}$$

$$= \frac{90 \text{ miles}}{30 \text{ mph}} = 3 \text{ hours}$$

$\therefore$ the total distance of 140 miles is travelled in 5 hours

i.e. $\text{average speed for whole journey} = \dfrac{\text{total distance}}{\text{total time}}$

$$= \frac{140 \text{ miles}}{5 \text{ hours}} = 28 \text{ mph}$$

Note: never add or subtract average speeds.

You can keep track of what you are doing by entering this information in a table like the one given below. You may need to do some calculations like those shown above, before you can complete the table.

	Speed in mph	Distance in miles	Time in hours
First part of journey	25	50	2
Second part of journey	30	90	3
Whole journey		140	5

We can add the distances to give the total length of the journey, and add the times to give the total time taken for the journey.

$$\text{Average speed for whole journey} = \frac{\text{total distance}}{\text{total time}}$$

$$= \frac{140 \text{ miles}}{5 \text{ hours}} = 28 \text{ mph}$$

EXERCISE 15E

1 I walk for 24 km at 8 km/h, and then jog for 12 km at 12 km/h.
Find my average speed for the whole journey.

2 A cyclist rides for 23 miles at an average speed of $11\frac{1}{2}$ mph before his cycle breaks down, forcing him to push it the remaining distance of 2 miles at an average speed of 4 mph.
Find his average speed for the whole journey.

3 An athlete runs 6 miles at 8 mph, then walks 1 mile at 4 mph.
Find his average speed for the whole journey.

4 A woman walks 3 miles at an average speed of $4\frac{1}{2}$ mph and then runs 4 miles at 12 mph.
Find her average speed for the whole journey.

5 A motorist travels the first 30 km of a journey at an average speed of 120 km/h, the next 60 km at 60 km/h, and the final 60 km at 80 km/h.
Find the average speed for the whole journey.

6 Phil Sharp walks the 2 km from his home to the bus stop in 15 min, and catches a bus immediately which takes him the 9 km to the railway station at an average speed of 36 km/h.
He arrives at the station just in time to catch the London train which takes him the 240 km to London at an average speed of 160 km/h.
Calculate his average speed for the whole journey from home to London.

7 A liner steaming at 24 knots takes 18 days to travel between two ports.
By how much must it increase its speed to reduce the length of the voyage by 2 days?
(A knot is a speed of 1 nautical mile per hour.)

GETTING INFORMATION FROM TRAVEL GRAPHS

If we are given a graph representing a journey, which shows the distance travelled plotted against the time taken, we can get a lot of information from it. The worked example in the next exercise shows how we can extract such information.

EXERCISE 15F

The graph below shows the journey of a coach which passes three service stations A, B and C on a motorway. B is 60 km north of A and C is 20 km north of B. Use the graph to answer the following questions.

a At what time does the coach leave A?

b At what time does the coach arrive at C?

c At what time does the coach pass B?

d What is the average speed of the coach for the whole journey?

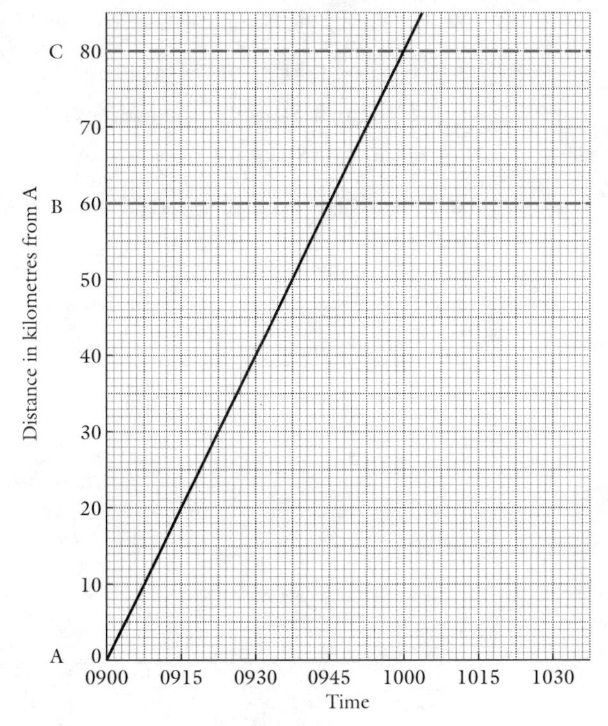

a The coach leaves A at 0900.

b Find the point on the graph level with C, then use a ruler as a guide to find the point on the time axis that is immediately below this point.

It arrives at C at 1000.

c It passes through B at 0945.

d Distance from A to C = 80 km.

Time taken to travel from A to C is 1000 – 0900, i.e. 1 hour.

$$\text{Average speed} = \frac{\text{distance travelled}}{\text{time taken}}$$

$$= \frac{80\text{ km}}{1\text{ hour}} = 80\text{ km/h}$$

1 The graph shows the journey of a car through three towns, Axeter, Bexley and Canton. Axeter is 100 km south of Bexley and Canton is 60 km north of it. Use the graph to answer the following questions.

a At what time does the car

i leave Axeter

ii pass through Bexley

iii arrive at Canton?

b How long does the car take to travel from Axeter to Canton?

c How long does the car take to travel

i the first 80 km of the journey?

ii the last 80 km of the journey?

d What is the average speed of the car for the whole journey?

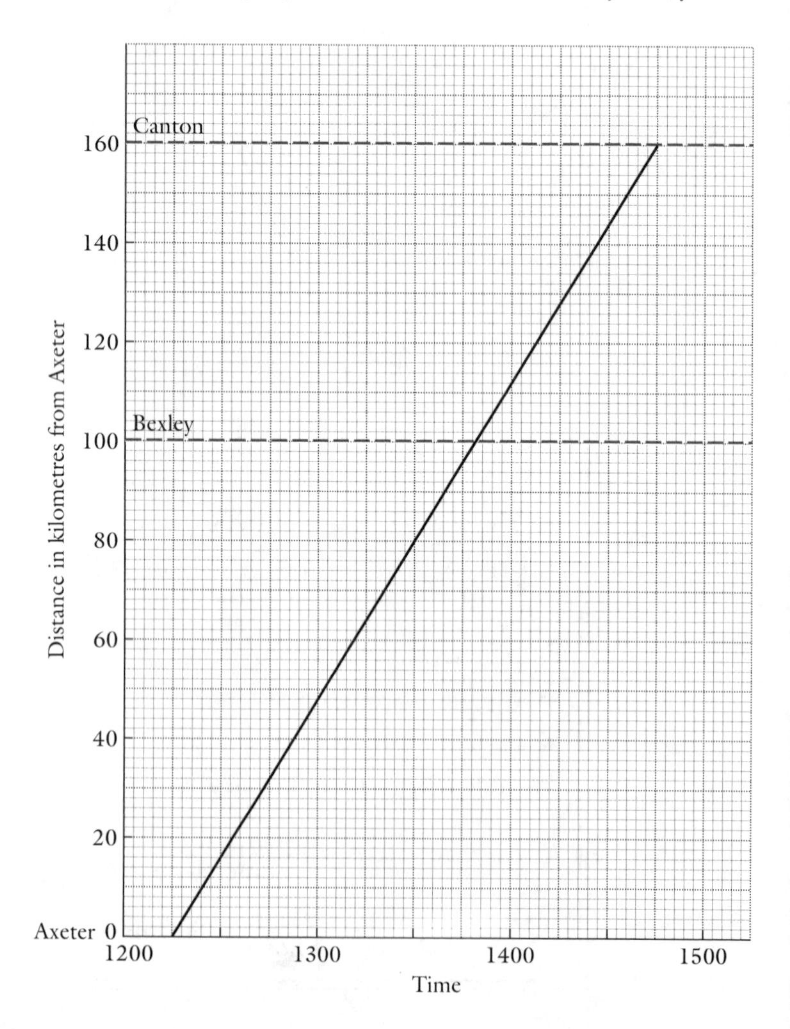

2 The graph shows the journey of an express train which starts from A and passes through stations at B and C on the way to its destination at D.

a How far is it

i from A to B

ii from B to C

iii from C to D?

b How long does the journey take

i from A to D

ii from B to C?

c Find the average speed for the whole journey.

d Where is the train at 1100?

e What time is it when the train is 20 miles short of C?

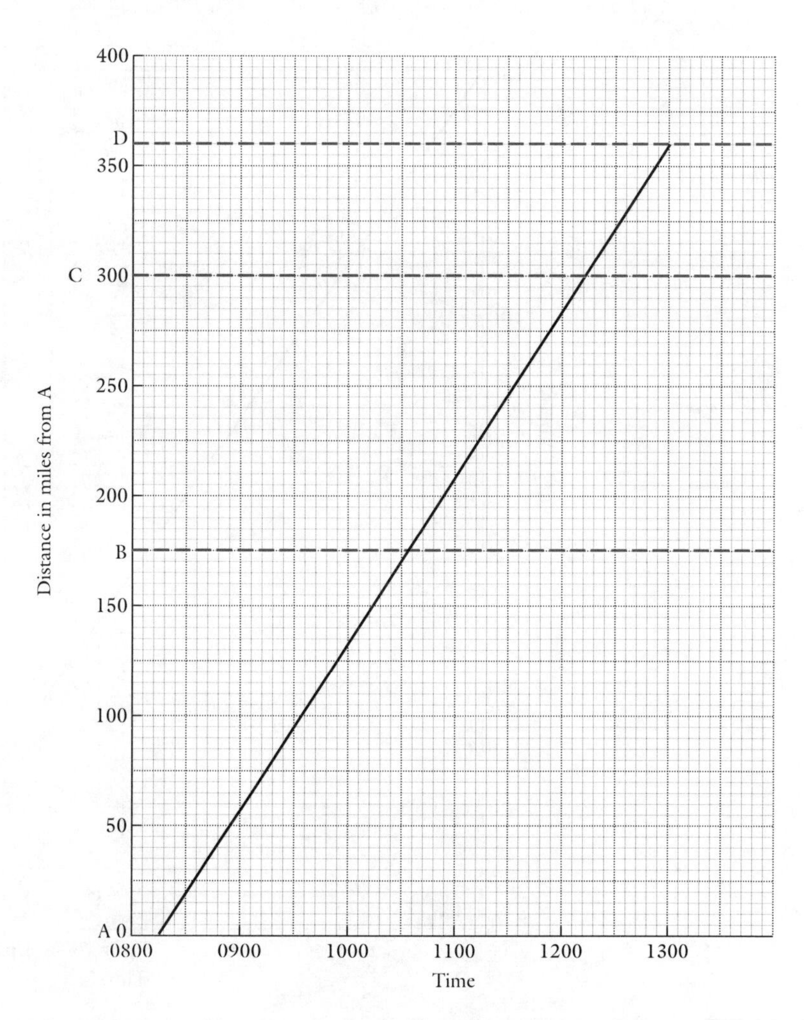

3 A coach leaves Newcombe at noon on its journey to Lee via Manley. The graph shows its journey.

a How far is it

i from Newcombe to Manley

ii from Manley to Lee?

b How long does the coach take to travel from Newcombe to Lee?

c What is the coach's average speed for the whole journey?

d How far does the coach travel between 1.30 p.m. and 2.30 p.m.?

e After travelling for $1\frac{1}{2}$ hours, how far is the coach from

i Newcombe

ii Manley?

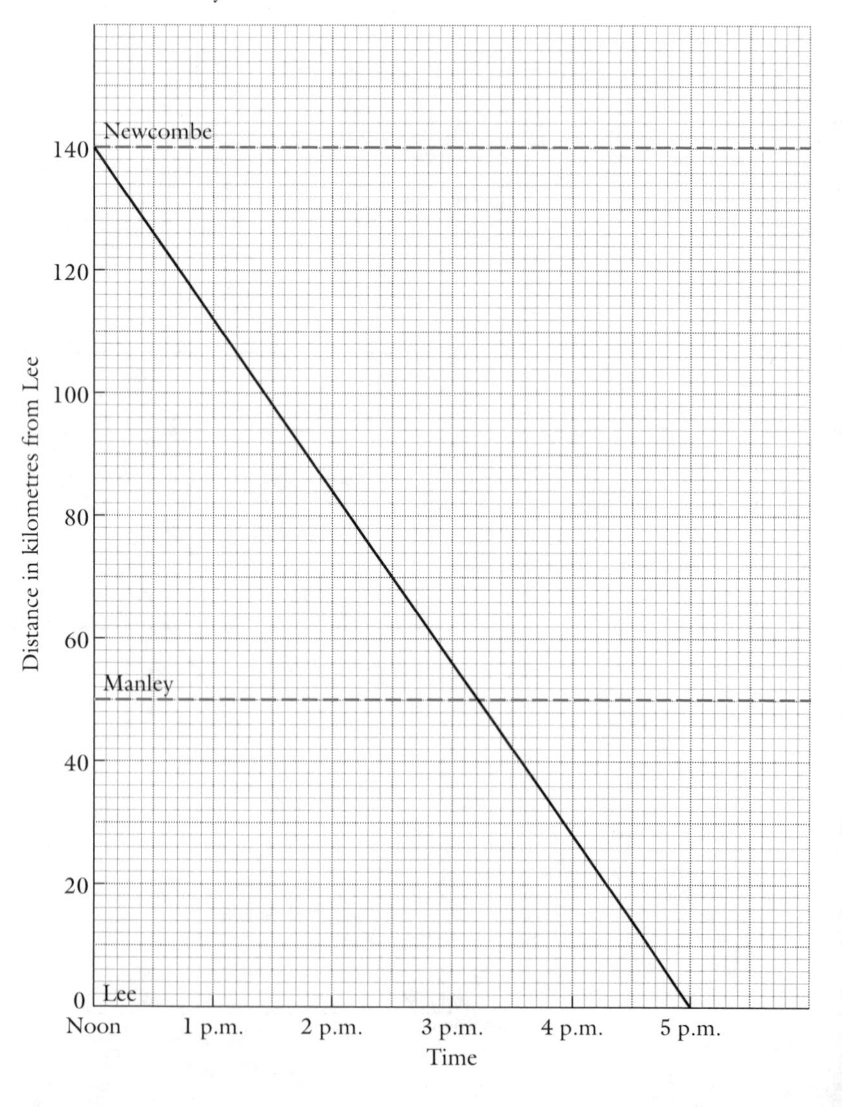

4 Mr Brown used the family car to transport his children from their home to the nearest mainline railway station and then returned home. The graph shows his journey.

a How far is it from home to the station?

b How long did it take the family to get to the station?

c What was the average speed of the car on the journey to the station?

d How long did the car take for the return journey?

e What was the average speed for the return journey?

f What was the car's average speed for the round trip?

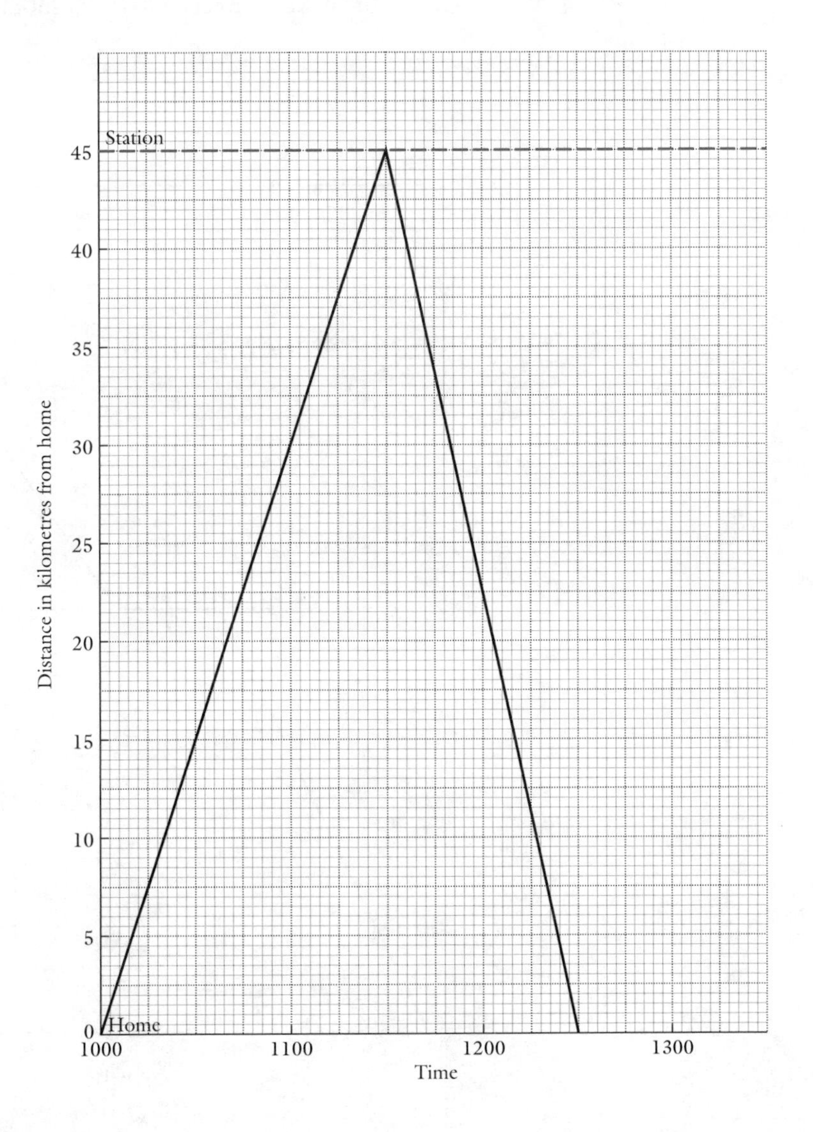

5 The graph shows the journey of a car through three service stations A, B and C, on a motorway.

a Where was the car at

i 0900

ii 0930?

b What was the average speed of the car between

i A and B **ii** B and C?

c For how long does the car stop at B?

d How long did the journey take?

e What was the average speed of the car for the journey from A to C? Give your answer correct to 1 significant figure.

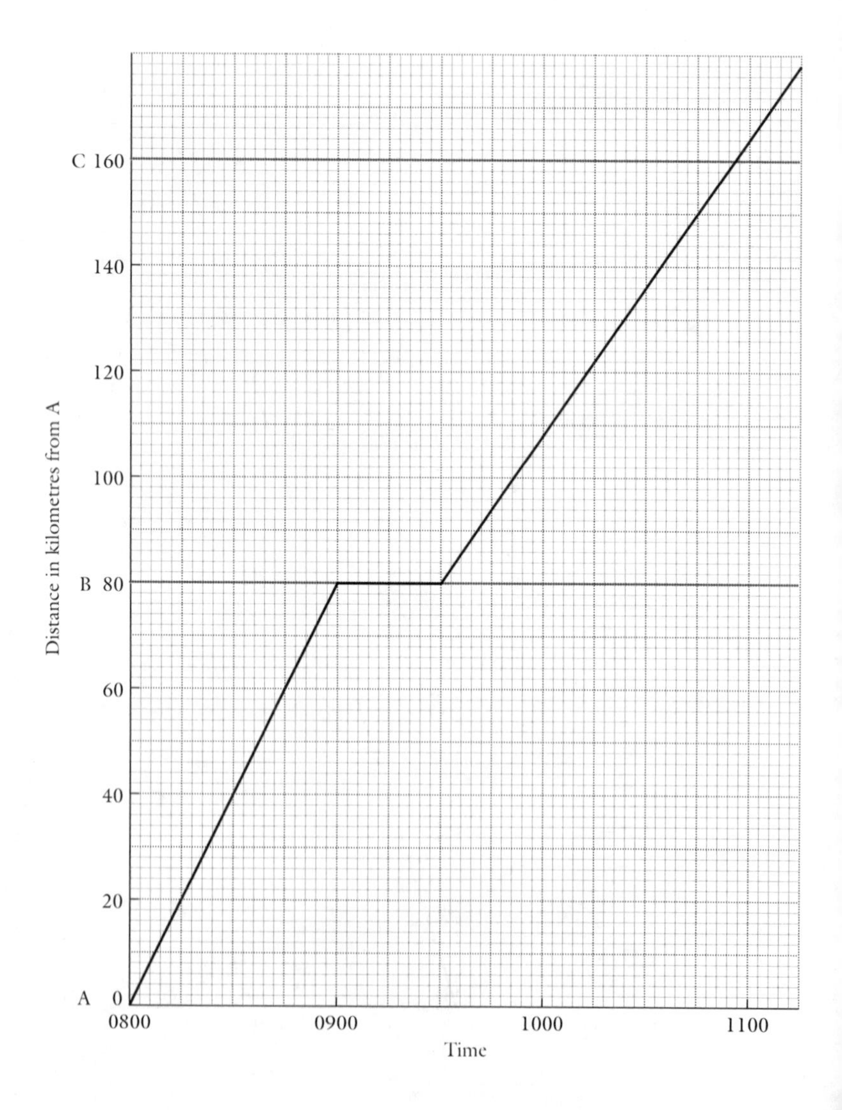

6 The graph shows Bill's journey on a sponsored walk.

a How far did he walk?

b How many times did he stop?

c What was the total time he spent resting?

d How long did he actually spend walking?

e How long did the walk take him?

f What was his average speed for the whole journey?

g Over which of the four stages did he walk fastest?

h Over which two stages did he walk at the same speed?

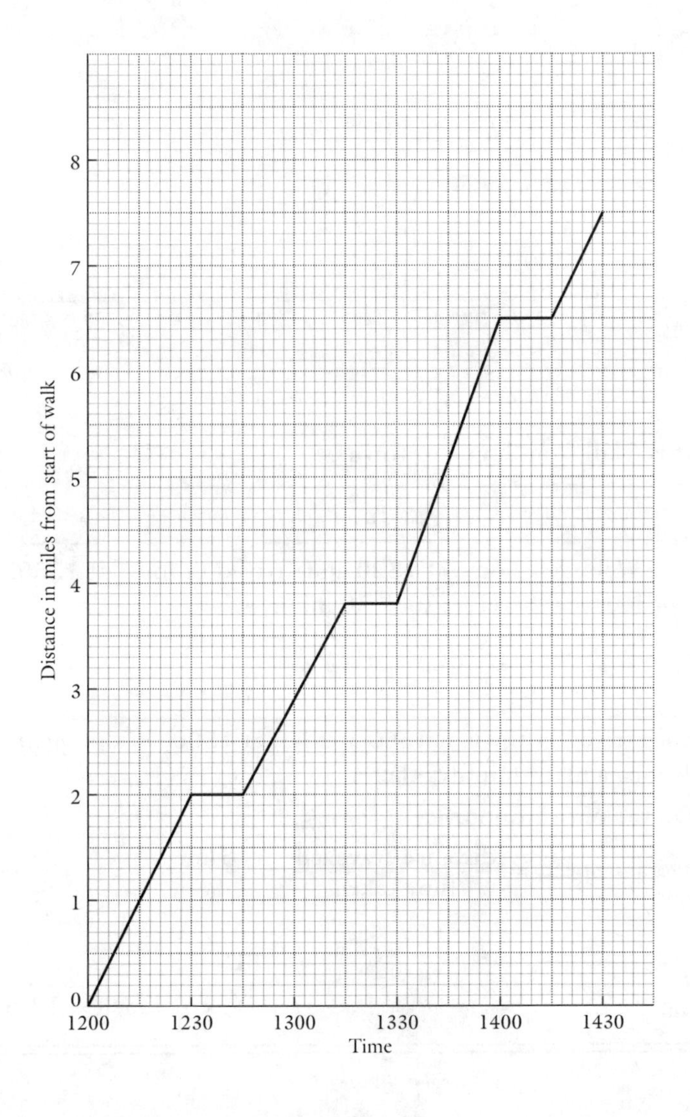

The graph shows Mrs Webb's shopping trip to the nearest town on a bicycle.

a How far is town from home? **b** How long did she take to get to town?

c How long did she spend in town?

d What was her average speed on the outward journey?

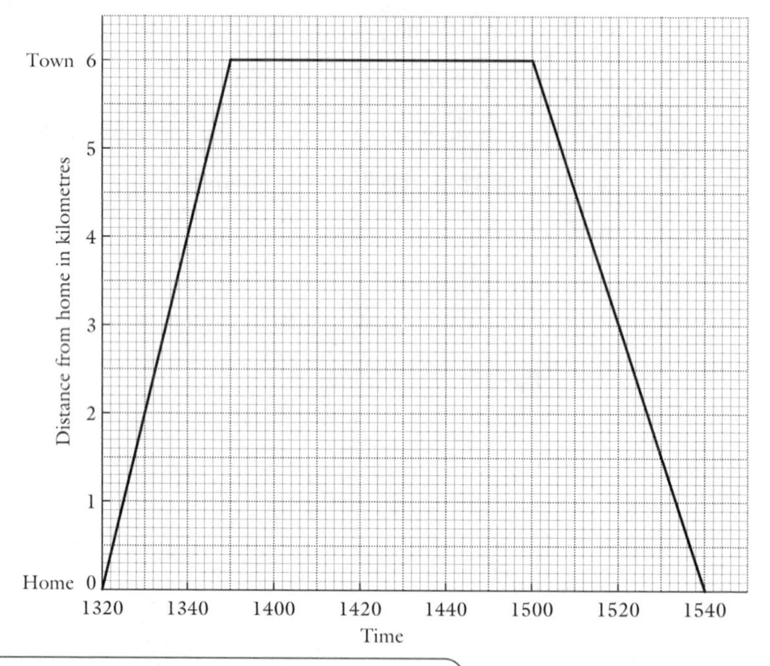

a The greatest distance the graph rises from 0 (home) is 6 km.

It is 6 km from home to town.

b She arrived in town when she stopped going further away from home. This is where the graph stops going up.

Mrs Webb left home at 1320 and arrived in town at 1350.
The journey therefore took 30 minutes.

c She left for home when the graph starts to go down,
i.e. she stayed in town for the time that the graph is parallel to the time axis.

She arrived in town at 1350 and left at 1500, so she spent 1 hour and 10 minutes there.

d On the outward journey:

$$\text{average speed} = \frac{\text{distance travelled}}{\text{time taken}} = \frac{6\text{ km}}{\frac{1}{2}\text{ hour}}$$

$$= \frac{6}{1} \div \frac{1}{2}\text{ km/h}$$

$$= \frac{6}{1} \times \frac{2}{1}\text{ km/h} = 12\text{ km/h}$$

7 The graph shows the journey of a train from Newpool to London and back again. Use the graph to answer the questions that follow.

a How far is Newpool from London?

b How long did the outward journey take?

c What was the average speed for the outward journey?

d How long did the train remain in London?

e At what time did the train leave London, and how long did the return journey take?

f What was the average speed on the return journey?

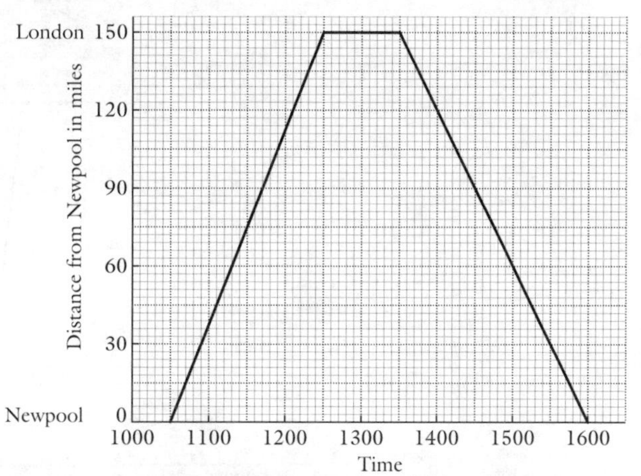

8 The graph represents the journey of a motorist from Leeds to Manchester and back again. Use this graph to find

a the distance between the two cities

b the time the motorist spent in Manchester

c his average speed on the outward journey

d the average speed on the homeward journey (including the stop).

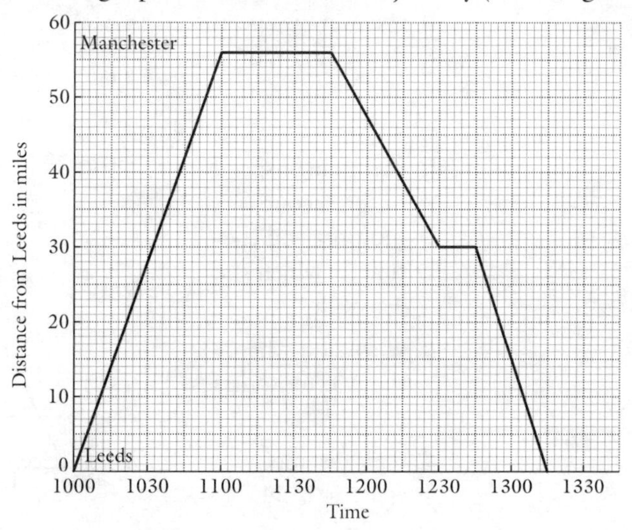

9 The graph below shows Judith's journeys between home and school.

a At what time did she leave home in
i the morning **ii** the afternoon?

b How long was she in school during the day?

c How long was she away from school for her midday break?

d What was the average speed for each of these journeys?

e Find the total time for which she was away from home.

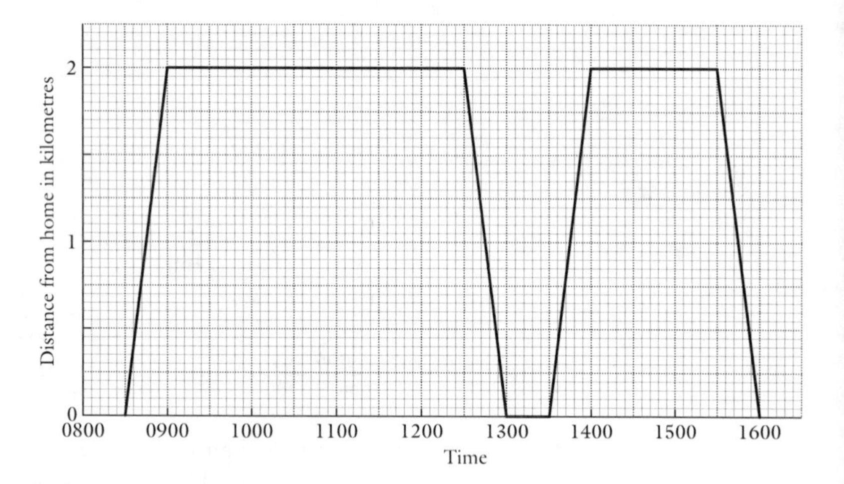

10 The graph below shows the journeys of two cars between two service stations, A and B, which are 180 km apart.
Use the graph to find

a the average speed of the first motorist and his time of arrival at B

b the average speed of the second motorist and the time at which she leaves B

c when and where the two motorists pass

d their distance apart at 1424.

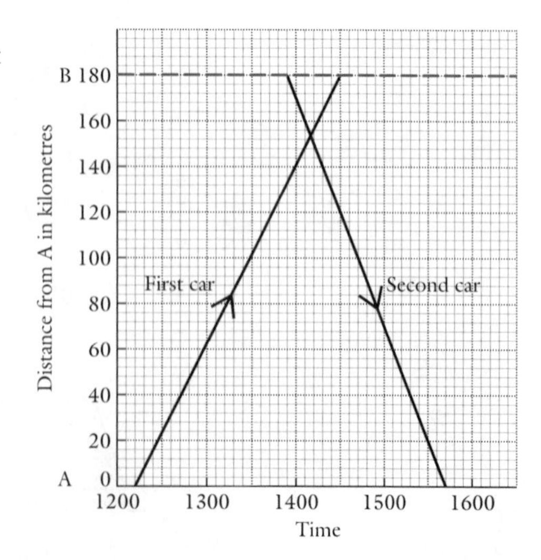

11 The school fête is always held on the first Saturday in July. The graphs show the journeys to school of three pupils on the day of the fête last year.

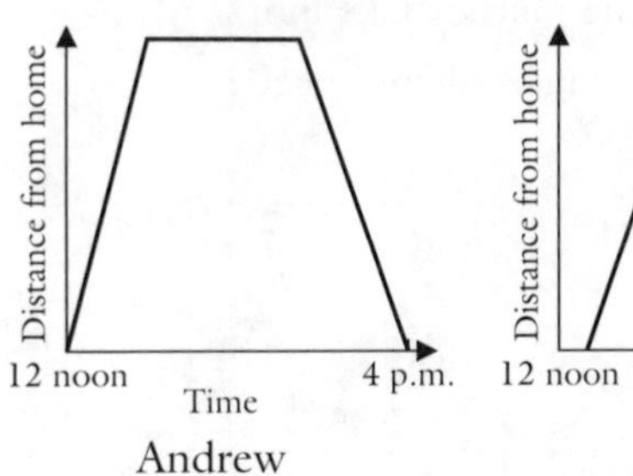

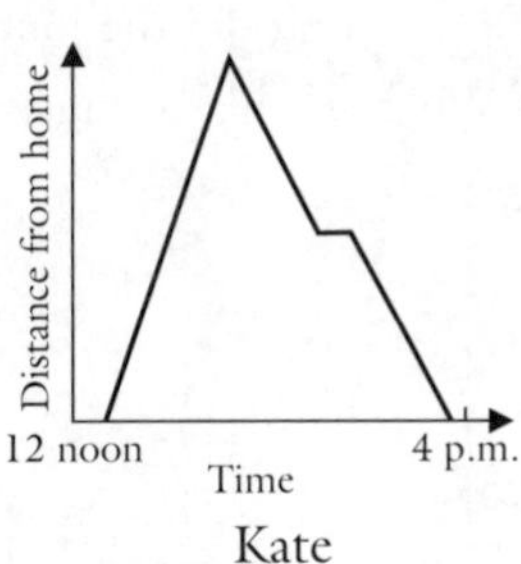

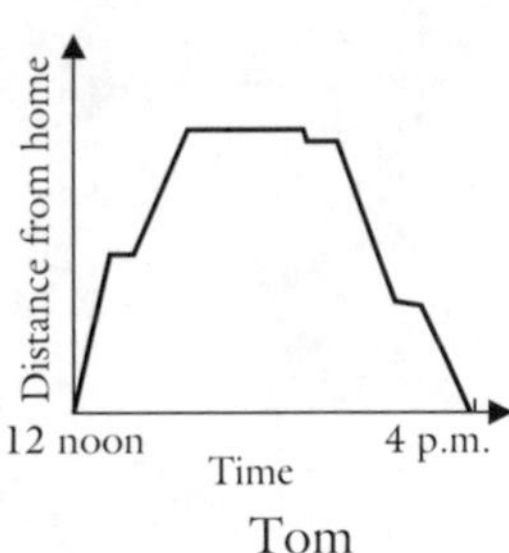

Use these graphs to answer the following questions.

a Who got to the fête first?

b Who stayed there longest?

c Who left for home first?

d Who took the longest time to get home?

e Who had the slowest journey to the fête?

f What did Kate do when she got to school?

g What did Tom do?

12 Jane leaves home at 1 p.m. to walk at a steady 4 mph towards Cornforth, which is 6 miles away, to meet her boyfriend Tim. Tim leaves Cornforth at 2.00 p.m. and jogs at a steady 6 mph to meet her. Draw a graph for each of these journeys taking $4\text{ cm} \equiv 1$ hour on the time axis and $1\text{ cm} \equiv 1$ mile on the distance axis. From your graph find

a when and where they meet,

b their distance apart at 2.10 p.m.

13 Solve the problems set at the beginning of the chapter.

MIXED EXERCISE

EXERCISE 15G

1 Jenny runs at $12\frac{1}{2}$ km/h. Draw a graph to show her running for $2\frac{1}{2}$ hours. Use your graph to find

a how far she has travelled in $1\frac{3}{4}$ hours

b how long she takes to run the first 20 km.

2 A ship travels at 18 nautical miles per hour. How long will it take to travel **a** 252 nautical miles **b** 1026 nautical miles?

3 Find the average speed in km/h of a journey of 48 km in 36 min.

4 The graph shows John's walk from home to his grandparents' home.

a How far away do they live?

b How long did the journey take him?

c What was his average walking speed?

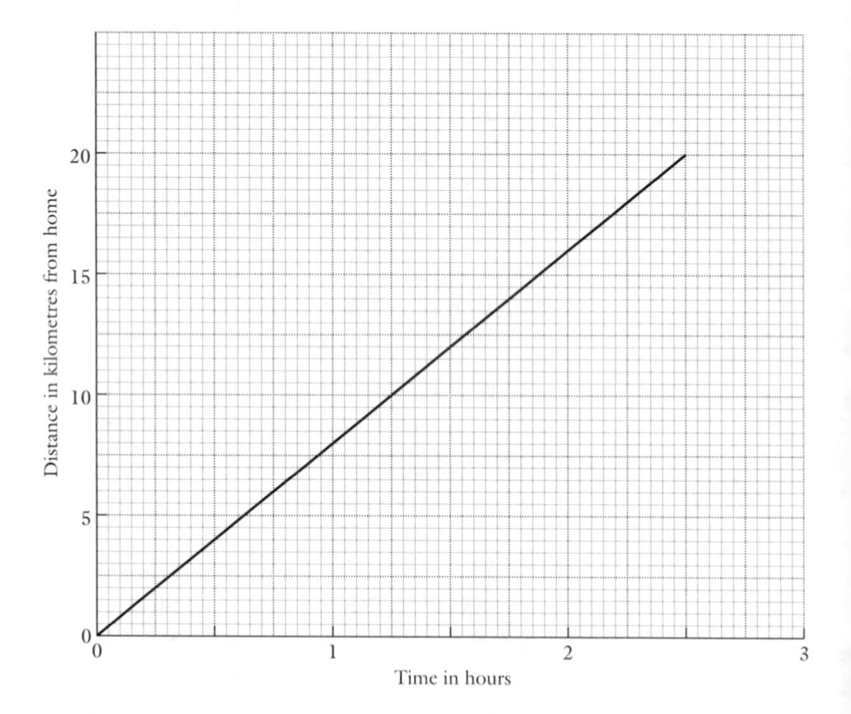

5 I left London at 1147 to travel the 315 miles to York. If I arrived at 1717, what was my average speed?

6 I walk $\frac{2}{3}$ mile in 10 minutes and then run $\frac{1}{3}$ mile in 2 minutes. What is my average speed for the whole journey?

7 The graph opposite shows Paul's journey in a sponsored jog from A to B. On the way his sister, who is travelling by car in the opposite direction from B to A, passes him.

a How far does Paul jog?

b How long does he take?

c How much of this time does he spend resting?

d What is his average speed for the whole journey?

e What is his sister's average speed?

f How far from A did Paul and his sister pass each other?

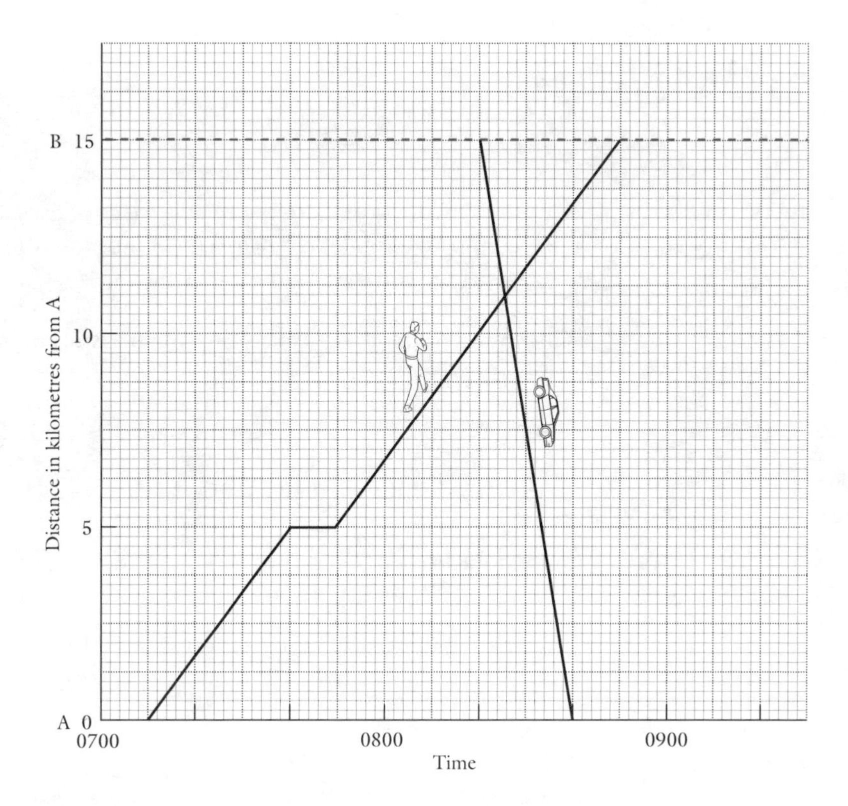

PRACTICAL WORK

a Describe in words your journey to or from school. For example, walk, wait at the bus stop, bus ride, walk.

b Time the different parts of the journey.

c Use a map to work out the distance travelled for each part of the journey.

d Draw a graph of your journey. You will have to assume that any bus, car or train you use travels at a steady speed from where you start to where you get off.

e Work out the average speed for the various parts of the journey and for the whole journey.

f Think of ways of making the graph more realistic. For instance, how does the varying speed of the bus affect the graph?

g Draw a travel graph to show alternative ways of making the journey.

h What extra information can you get from your graph?

SUMMARY 4

RATIO

Ratios are used to compare the relative sizes of quantities.
For example, if a model of a car is 2 cm long and the real car is 200 cm long, we say that their lengths are in the ratio 2 : 200.

Ratios can be simplified by dividing the parts of the ratio by the same number,

e.g. $2 : 200 = 1 : 100$ (dividing 2 and 200 by 2).

To divide a quantity in a given ratio $a : b$,

find the fractions $\frac{a}{a+b}$ and $\frac{b}{a+b}$ of the quantity,

e.g. to divide £20 in the ratio 2 : 3, find $\frac{2}{5}$ of £20 and $\frac{3}{5}$ of £20.

MAP RATIO

A map ratio is the ratio of a length on the map to the length it represents on the ground.
When expressed as a fraction, it is called the *Representative Fraction.*

EQUATIONS

Solution of equations
When an equation contains brackets, first multiply out the brackets,

e.g. $3x - 2(3 - x) = 6$

gives $3x - 6 + 2x = 6$ which can be solved easily.

Polynomial equations in one unknown contain terms involving powers of x, e.g. $x^3 - 2x = 4$ and $2x^2 = 5$ are polynomial equations.

Equations containing an x^2 term and a number only can be solved by *finding square roots.* Now the square root of 9 can be 3, since $3 \times 3 = 9$; it can also be -3 since $(-3) \times (-3) = 9$, that is a positive number has two square roots, one positive and one negative.

For example, if $x^2 = 9$ then $x = \pm\sqrt{9}$, so $x = +3$ and $x = -3$ are solutions.

More complex equations can be solved by *trial and improvement,* that is by trying possible values for x until we find a value that fits the equation.

Inequalities

An inequality remains true when the same number is added to, or subtracted from, both sides,

e.g. if $x > 5$ then $x + 2 > 5 + 2$

and $x - 2 > 5 - 2$

GRAPHS

The equation of a line or curve gives the y-coordinate of a point in terms of its x-coordinate. This relationship between the coordinates is true only for points on the line or curve.

Straight lines

The *gradient* of a straight line can be found from two points, P and Q, on the line, by calculating

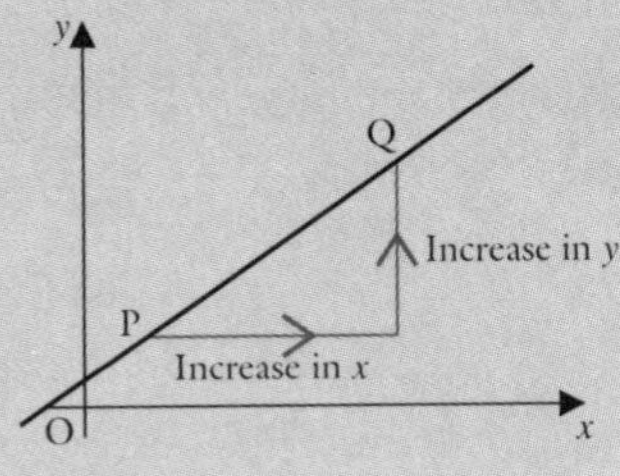

$$\frac{\text{increase in } y \text{ in moving from P to Q}}{\text{increase in } x \text{ in moving from P to Q}}$$

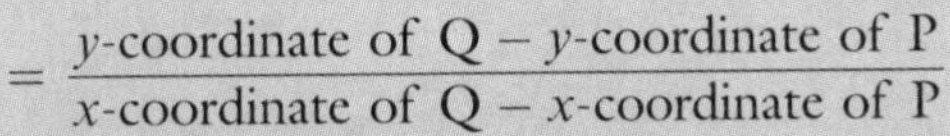

$$= \frac{y\text{-coordinate of Q} - y\text{-coordinate of P}}{x\text{-coordinate of Q} - x\text{-coordinate of P}}$$

When the gradient is positive, the line slopes uphill when moving from left to right.

When the gradient is negative, the line slopes downhill when moving from left to right.

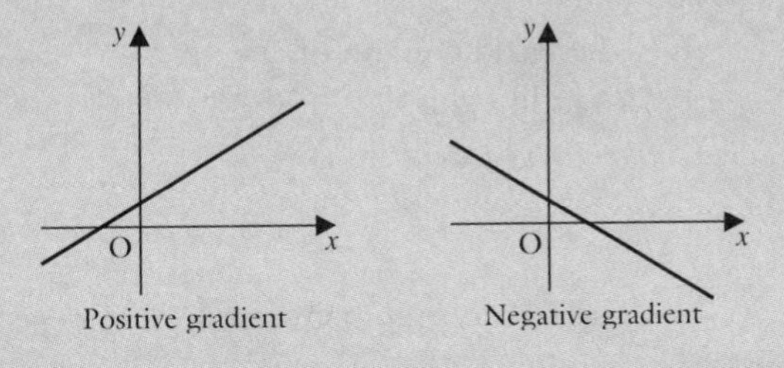

Positive gradient Negative gradient

The equation of a straight line is of the form $y = mx + c$

where m is the gradient of the line

and c is the y-intercept,

e.g. the line whose equation is $y = 2x - 3$

has gradient 2 and y-intercept -3.

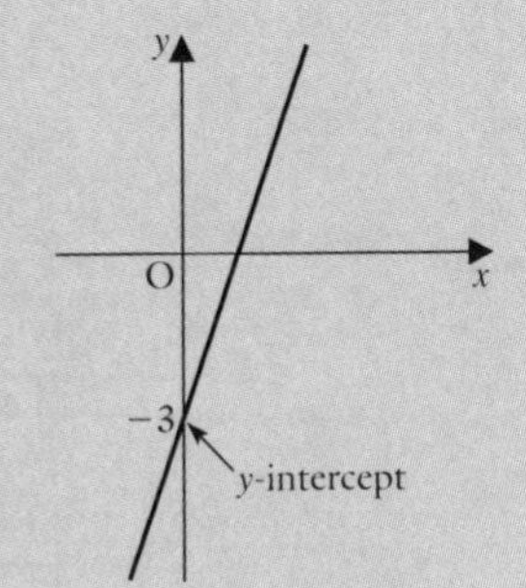

An equation of the form $y = c$ gives a line parallel to the x-axis.

An equation of the form $x = b$ gives a line parallel to the y-axis.

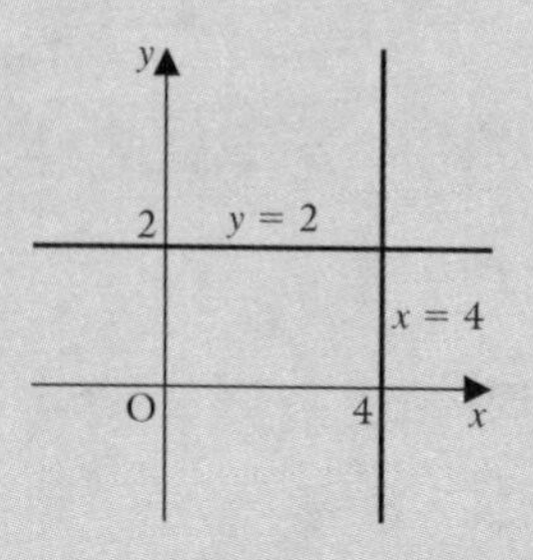

A *parabola* is a curve whose equation is in the form $y = ax^2 + bx + c$.

The curve looks like this:

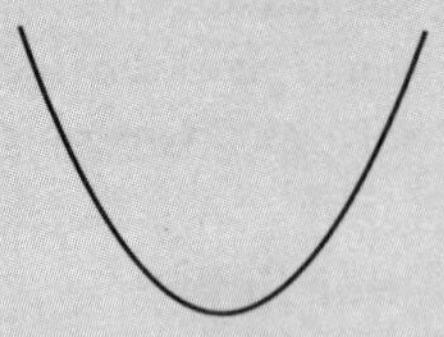

When the x^2 term is positive it is the way up shown above.

When the x^2 term is negative the curve is upside down.

This, for example, is the graph of $y = x^2 - 2x$:

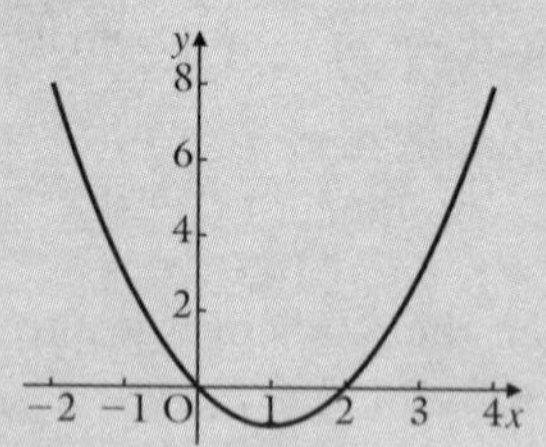

whereas the graph of $y = 2x - x^2$ looks like this:

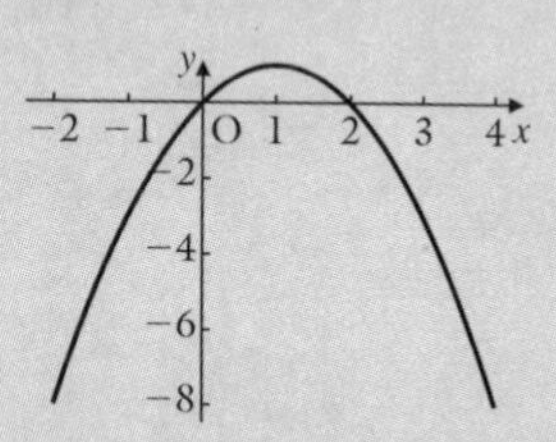

DISTANCE, SPEED AND TIME

The relationship between distance, speed and time is given by

$$\text{Distance} = \text{Speed} \times \text{Time}$$

which can also be expressed as $\text{Speed} = \dfrac{\text{Distance}}{\text{Time}}$

or as $\text{Time} = \dfrac{\text{Distance}}{\text{Speed}}$

These relationships can be remembered from the triangle:
(Cover up the one you want to find.)

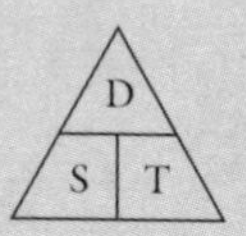

Average speed for a journey $= \dfrac{\text{Total distance covered}}{\text{Total time taken}}$

REVISION EXERCISE 4.1 (Chapters 11 and 12)

1 a Simplify the ratio **i** 12 m : 30 m **ii** £3 : £4.50 : £5

b Divide £66 into two shares in the ratio 5 : 6.

2 a If $5 : 3 = x : 6$ find x.

b The ratio of the length of a rectangular rug to its width is 9 : 5. The length is 2.7 m. Find the width.

3 a Find the map ratio of a map on which 5 cm represents 1 km.

b The map ratio of a map is 1 : 200 000. The distance between two villages is 12 km. What is this on the map?

4 a Simplify the ratio 2 kg : 1.6 kg

b A piece of wood, 3.15 m long, is cut into two pieces whose lengths are in the ratio 8 : 7. How much longer is the one piece than the other piece?

5 a Alison's pet spaniel had a litter of 6 puppies, 4 of which are females. Find the ratio of the number of female puppies to the number of male puppies.

b The ratio of the base of a triangle to its height is 3 : 2. Its base is 5 cm. Find its height.

6 a Calculate **i** $(+5) \times (2)$ **iii** $7 \times (-4)$ **ii** $(-7) \times (-5)$ **iv** $2(-5)$

b Simplify **i** $11x - 3(x + 4)$ **iii** $5(x + 5) - 4(x + 3)$ **ii** $2(x + 5) - (x - 6)$ **iv** $4(x - 3) + 2(x - 6)$

c If $P = 2x + 3y$ find P when
i $x = 3$ and $y = 4$ **ii** $x = 6$ and $y = -3$

7 a Solve the equations **i** $5 + 4(x + 3) = 25$ **ii** $0.84x = 4$

b Solve the following inequalities, illustrating each solution on a number line.
i $x - 6 < -4$ **ii** $5 - x > -3$ **iii** $x - 2 > 7$

8 a Write in index notation **i** $5a \times a$ **ii** $3b \times b \times b$

b Simplify **i** $3 + (5x - 4)$ **ii** $7x + 5x - 3(4x + 3)$

9 a Solve **i** $0.4x = 5.6$ **ii** $10x - 3(x + 7) = 0$

b Solve the equation $x^2 = 0.66$, giving your answer correct to 3 significant figures.

10 Use trial and improvement to find a positive solution of the equation $x^2 + 7x = 12$. Start by trying $x = 1$ and give the solution correct to 1 decimal place.

REVISION EXERCISE 4.2 (Chapters 13 to 15)

1 **a** Find the y-coordinates of points on the line $y = -2x$ which have x-coordinates of **i** 3 **ii** -4 **iii** $\frac{1}{2}$ **iv** $-\frac{3}{4}$

b Find the x-coordinates of points on the line $y = 3x$ which have y-coordinates of **i** 2 **ii** -5 **iii** $2\frac{1}{2}$ **iv** 3.6

2 **a** For the pair of lines $y = 4x$ and $y = \frac{1}{4}x$, state which line is the steeper. Sketch both lines on the same diagram.

b Write down the gradient, m, and the y-intercept, c, for the straight line with equation **i** $y = 7x - 5$ **ii** $y = 4 - 5x$

3 Draw x- and y-axes on graph paper. Scale the x-axis from -8 to 8 and the y-axis from -10 to 10, using 1 cm as 1 unit on both axes. Draw the graphs of $y = \frac{1}{2}x + 2$ and $y = -x + 8$.
Hence find the value of x and the value of y that satisfies both equations simultaneously.

4 **a** The equations of two straight lines are $y = 3x$ and $y = \frac{1}{2}x$. Which line is steeper? Sketch both lines on the same diagram.

b Determine which of the following lines makes an acute angle with the positive x-axis and which lines make an obtuse angle with the positive x-axis.

i $y = -\frac{1}{2}x$ **ii** $y = 0.4x$ **iii** $y = 1.5x$ **iv** $y = -6x$

5 A manufacturer produces a set of jugs, identical in shape but different in size. The capacities of some of the jugs are given.

Height, h cm	7.2	9	10.8	12.6	14.4	16.2	18
Capacity, C cm^3	64	125	216	343	512	729	1000

Draw a graph to show how capacity changes with height. Use 1 cm as 1 unit on the h-axis and as 50 units on the C-axis. Take 6 as the lowest value for h and 0 as the lowest value for C.
Use your graph to estimate

a the capacity of a jug 17 cm high

b the height of a jug that holds 650 cm^3.

6 The equation of a curve is $y = 4x^2$. Which of these sketches could be the curve?

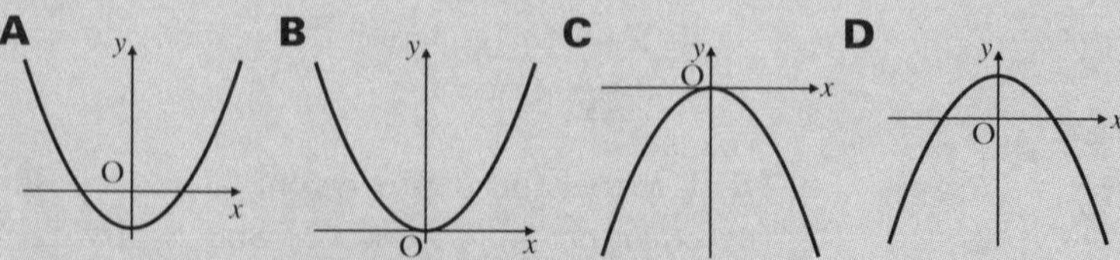

Give reasons why you rejected three of the sketches.

7 Draw a sketch of the curve with equation

a $y = \frac{1}{2}x^2$ **b** $y = -\frac{1}{2}x^2$ **c** $y = \frac{1}{2}x^2 + 2$

8 The graph shows Kim's journey from home to Carlisle.

a What distance did Kim travel?

b How long did she take?

c How far did she travel in 1 hour?

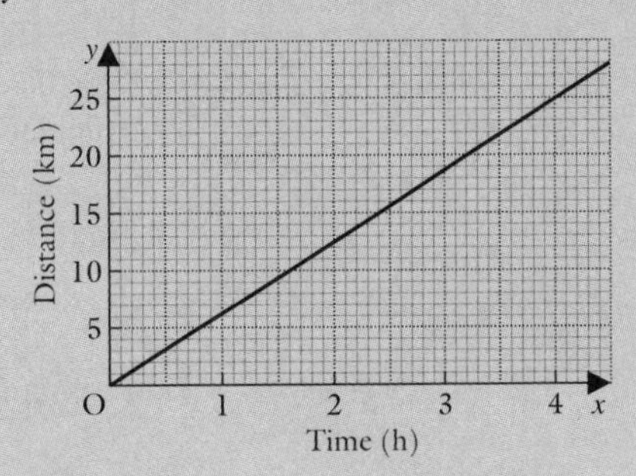

9 The graph shows the journey of a car from Amberley to Brickworth and on to Coldham.

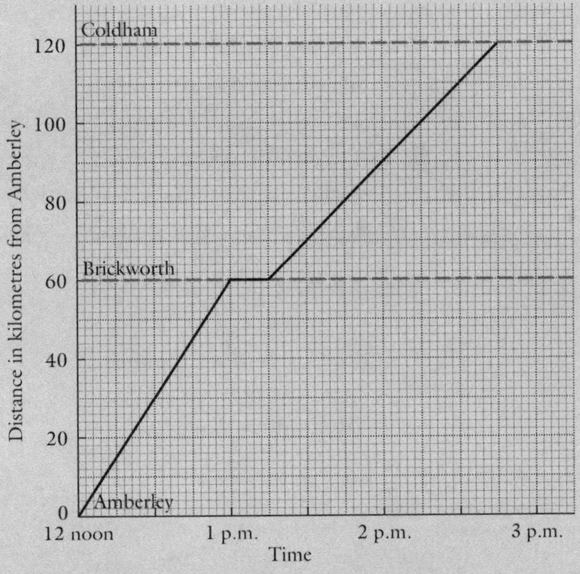

a Where was the car at **i** 12.30 **ii** 2.15?

b What was the average speed of the car between
i Amberley and Brickworth **ii** Brickworth and Coldham?

c For how long does the car stop at Brickworth?

d How long did the journey take including the stop?

e What was the average speed of the car for the whole journey? Give your answer correct to the nearest whole number.

REVISION EXERCISE 4.3 (Chapters 11 to 15)

1 **a** Simplify the ratio **i** £3.50 : 75 p **ii** 24 : 36 : 42

b If $x : 3 = 12 : 18$ find x.

2 **a** Divide £45 among 3 people so that their shares are in the ratio 4 : 5 : 6.

b If the map ratio of a map is 1 : 100 000 and the distance between two places on a map is 8 cm, find the actual distance between the two places.

3 Multiply out the brackets and simplify

a $5(x-3)$

b $4x+2(3x-1)$

c $9-2(x-7)$

d $7x-3(2x+1)$

e $-4(a-2)$

f $3(x-2)-4(x+3)$

4 **a** Solve the equation $3.4x = 8.3$ giving your answer correct to 3 significant figures.

b Solve the inequality $6 - x > 10$ and illustrate your answer on a number line.

c Use a calculator to solve the equation $x^2 = 21.4$, giving your answer correct to 3 significant figures.

5 **a** Determine whether each of the following straight lines makes an acute angle or an obtuse angle with the positive x-axis.

i $y=-5x$ **ii** $y=0.4x$ **iii** $y=-\frac{1}{2}x-4$ **iv** $y=3+4x$

b **i** Find the gradient of this line.

ii Where does the line cross the y-axis?

iii Find the equation of the line.

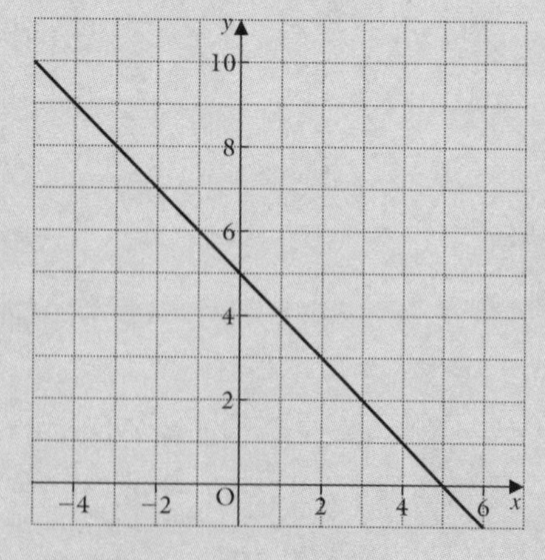

6 Using the same scale on each axis, plot the points $(-3, 4)$, $(3, -4)$, $(6, -8)$ and $(9, -12)$.
What is the equation of the straight line which passes through these points?

7 The equation of a curve is $y = -2x^2$. Which of these sketches could be the curve? Explain why you reject three of the curves.

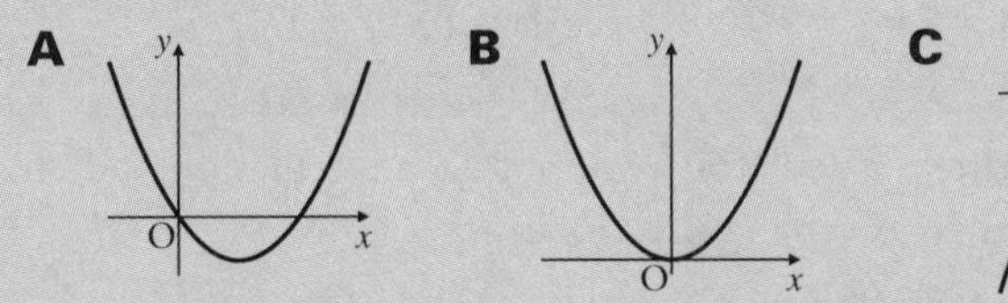

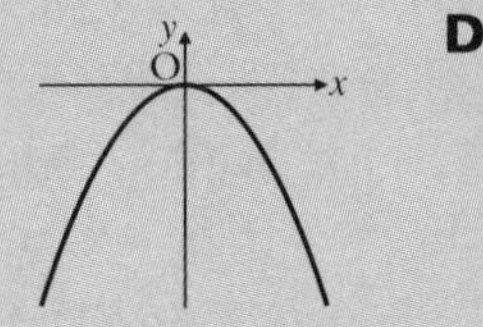

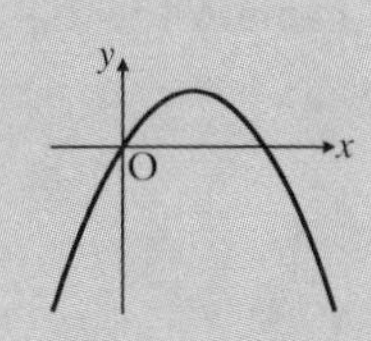

8 Draw a sketch of the curve **a** $y = 4x^2$ **b** $y = -5x^2$

9 **a** An express train travels at 180 km/h. How far will it travel in $2\frac{1}{2}$ hours?

b How long will it take a driver driving at a steady 50 mph to travel 175 miles?

c Find the average speed in km/h for a journey of 150 m in 45 seconds.

10

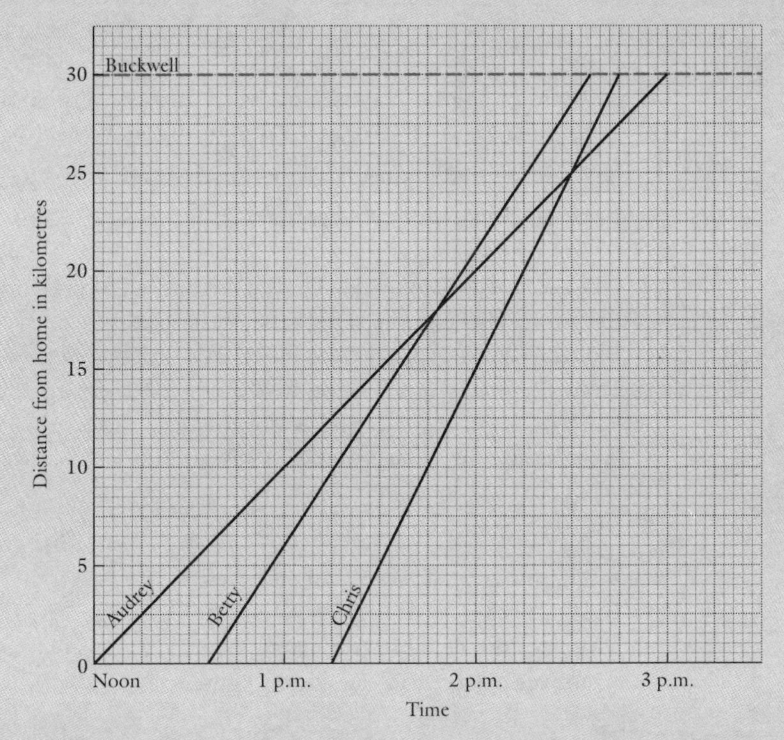

The graph above represents the bicycle journeys of three school friends, Audrey, Betty and Chris, from the village in which they live to Buckwell, the nearest main town, which is 30 km away. Use the graph to find

a their order of arrival at Buckwell

b the average speed for the journey of **i** Audrey **ii** Betty **iii** Chris

c where and when Chris passes Audrey

d how far each is from town at 2 p.m.

e how far Betty is ahead of Chris at 2.15 p.m.

REVISION EXERCISE 4.4 (Chapters 1 to 15)

1 a Write down each number correct to the number of significant figures given in the bracket.

i 806.53 (3) **iii** 0.1279 (2)
ii 0.0243 (1) **iv** 0.2057 (3)

b Without using a calculator work out each calculation and check your answer by reversing the working.

i $26\,631 + 78\,987$ **iii** 378×23
ii $945 \div 35$ **iv** $7264 - 3297$

2 a Give $60\,\text{mm}^2$ as a fraction of $3\,\text{cm}^2$.

b The product of two numbers is 12. One number is $2\frac{1}{4}$. Find the other number.

c Calculate

i $\frac{5}{8} \div \frac{1}{4}$ **ii** $6\frac{2}{5} \div 9\frac{3}{5}$ **iii** $5\frac{1}{4} + 2\frac{4}{5} \div 1\frac{13}{15}$

3 a I buy $2x$ kg of potatoes and y kg of carrots. Write down a formula for W if W kg is the weight of vegetables I have bought.

b If $P = a - 2b$, find P when $a = 5\frac{1}{2}$ and $b = 2\frac{1}{4}$.

c If $Q = abc$, find Q when $a = 2$, $b = -3$, $c = -6$.

4 Draw x- and y-axes. Scale the x-axis from -10 to 4 and the y-axis from 0 to 10. Use the same scale on both axes.
Plot $\triangle$ABC: A(-5, 5), B(-1, 3), C(-4, 2).
Draw the image $\triangle$A′B′C′ of $\triangle$ABC when it is enlarged with the point (-3, 3) as the centre of enlargement and a scale factor of 3.
Write down the coordinates of A′, B′ and C′.

5 The sketch shows a triangular field.

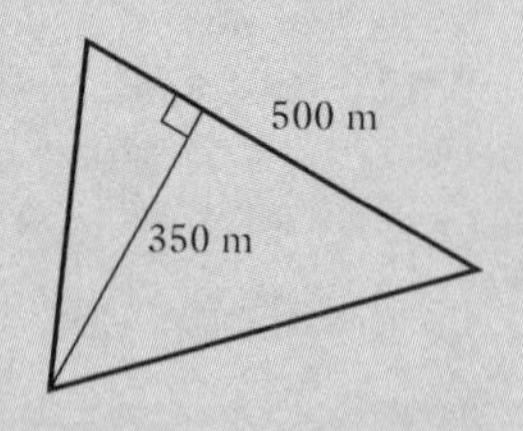

a Find its area **i** in m^2 **ii** in hectares.

b If 1 hectare = 2.471 acres find the area of the field in acres, giving your answer correct to 3 significant figures.

6

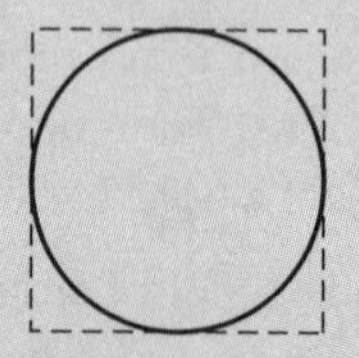

a How long is the perimeter of a square lawn of side 20 m?

b The corners of the lawn are removed to give the largest circular lawn possible.
By how much has the perimeter of the lawn been reduced?

7 a Simplify the ratio 1.2 m : 40 cm

b If $3 : 2 = 4.5 : x$ find x.

8 a I think of a number, add 9 and double the result. This gives 42. What is the number?

b Solve the inequalities **i** $x + 1 > 3$ **ii** $x - 4 < 3$
Illustrate your answers using a number line

c Solve the equation $8.2x = 14$, giving your answer correct to 3 significant figures.

9 Using squared paper and 1 square to one unit on both axes, plot the points $(-3, 6)$, $(-2, 3)$, $(1, -6)$ and $(2, -9)$. These four points lie on a straight line. Find

a the gradient of the line

b where the line cuts the y-axis

c the equation of the line.

10 Sally drives at 36 mph. Draw a graph to show a 3-hour drive. Take 1 cm to represent 10 miles and 4 cm to represent 1 hour. Find how far she drives in

a 2 hours **b** $2\frac{1}{4}$ hours **c** 30 minutes

REVISION EXERCISE 4.5 (Chapters 1 to 15)

1 Write down the size of each marked angle.

a

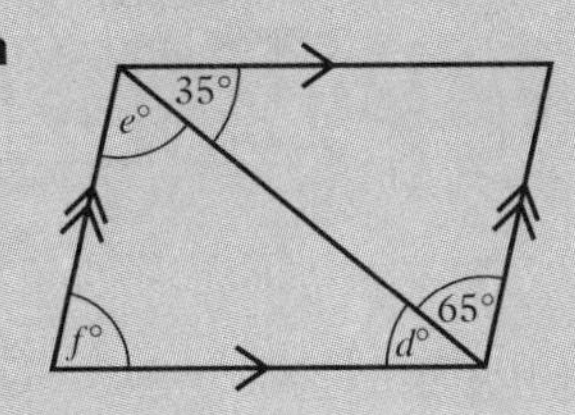

b

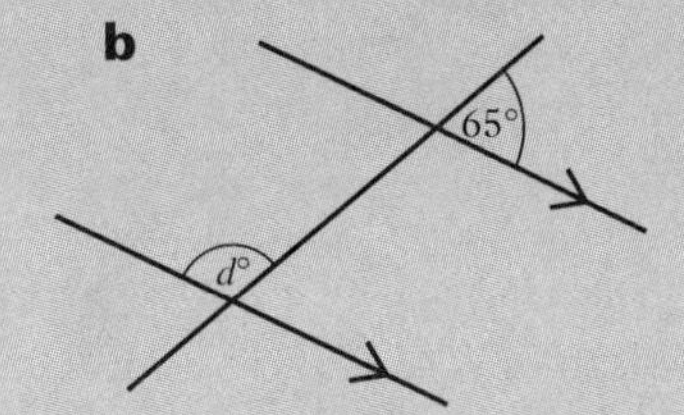

2 a Find **i** 5.5% of 16 cm **ii** $2\frac{3}{4}$% of 930 mm

b A company employs 200 people. Next year it expects to increase the number of employees by 33%. How many employees does it expect to have next year?

c i Decrease 540 g by 55% **ii** Increase 72 cm^2 by $12\frac{1}{2}$%

3 One letter is chosen at random from the letters in the word WEDNESDAY. What is the probability that it is

a the letter D **b** not a vowel **c** not the letter E?

4 **a** The area of this rectangle is $A\ \mathrm{cm}^2$.
Find a formula for A.

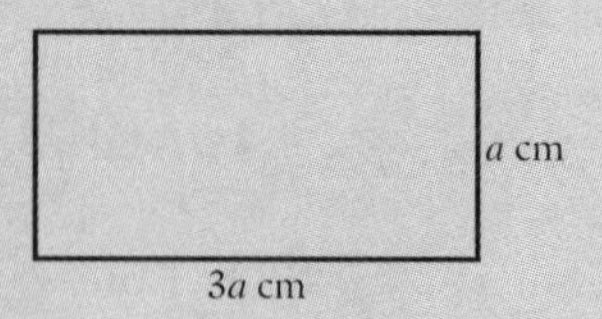

b If $X = 2a + bc$, find X when $a = 5$, $b = 3$, $c = 8$.

c Find a formula for the nth term in terms of n.

n	1	2	3	4	5
nth term	3	6	9	12	15

5 **a** Is it possible for each interior angle of a regular polygon to be **i** 115° **ii** 165°?
Where it is possible, give the number of sides.

b Find the size of the angle marked $p°$.

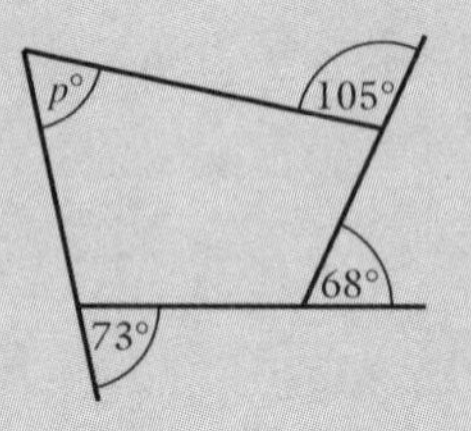

6 **a** The area of a square is $70\ \mathrm{cm}^2$. Find the length of a side.
Give your answer correct to 3 significant figures.

b The area of a triangle is $0.41\ \mathrm{m}^2$. The length of the base is 1.64 m. Find its height.

c The sketch shows the end wall of a building.
Find its area.

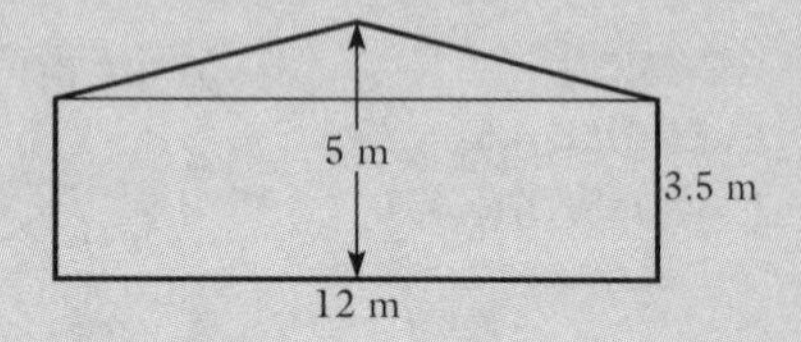

7 A length of wire 120 cm long is cut into two pieces, one of which is three times as long as the other.

a Find the length of each piece of wire.

Each piece is now bent to form a circle.

b For each circle find **i** its diameter **ii** its area.
(Give your answers correct to 3 significant figures.)

c Find, correct to the nearest whole number

i the diameter of the large circle divided by the diameter of the small circle

ii the area of the large circle divided by the area of the small circle.

What simple relation is there between your answers to part **c**?

8 Some pupils in Class 9Q were discussing various things about themselves. They decided to find out if there were relationships between their marks in the recent tests in maths and in science, the number of days they had been absent from school in the last 12 months and the distances from school that they lived. They plotted three scatter graphs.

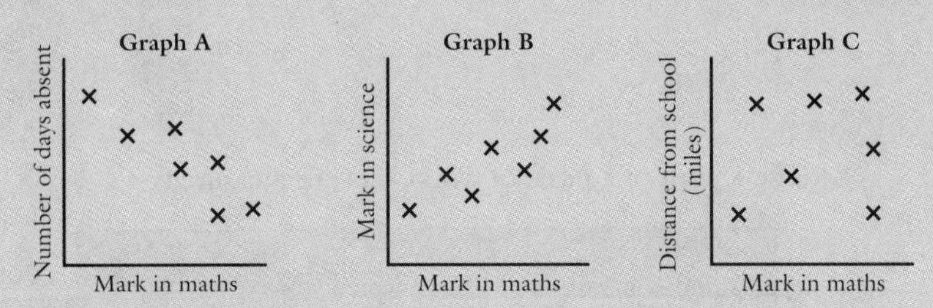

a What does graph **A** show about the relationship between the number of days a pupils was absent and that pupil's mark in maths?

b What does graph **B** show about the relationship between a pupil's mark in maths and that pupil's mark in science?

c What does graph **C** show about the relationship between the distance from school that a pupil lives and that pupil's mark in maths?

d John joins the group. He was top in science. Would you expect him to be good at maths as well? Explain your answer.

9 **a** Simplify **i** $3p \times p$ **ii** $2x \times x \times x$

b Simplify
i $7(x-3)$ **ii** $10-4(x+4)$ **iii** $9x+4-2(3x-7)$

c If $A = \frac{PRT}{100}$ find the value of A when $P = 300$, $R = 3$ and $T = 6$.

10 The sketch shows the graph of $y = x^2$.

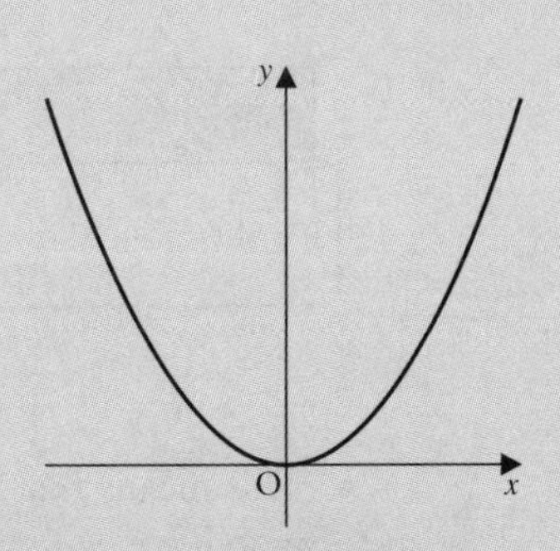

Copy the diagram and add sketches of $y = x^2 + 4$ (mark it A) and $y = x^2 - 4$ (mark it B).

CONTINUOUS DATA

The length of a piece of wood is being measured.

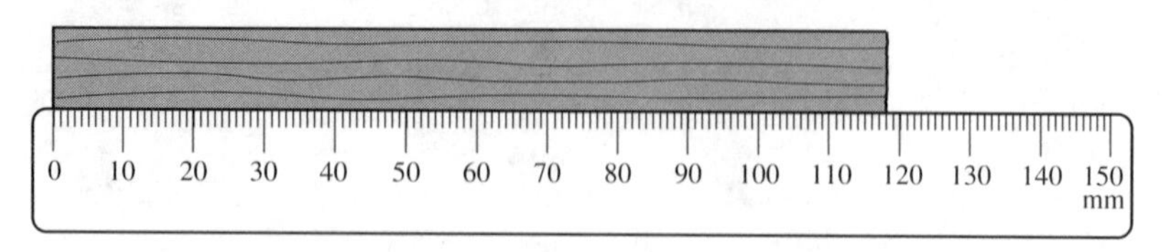

The length is close to 120 mm, so we can give the length as 120 mm to the nearest 10 millimetres.

If we magnify the scale where the end of the wood is, we can see that the length is 118 mm to the nearest millimetre.

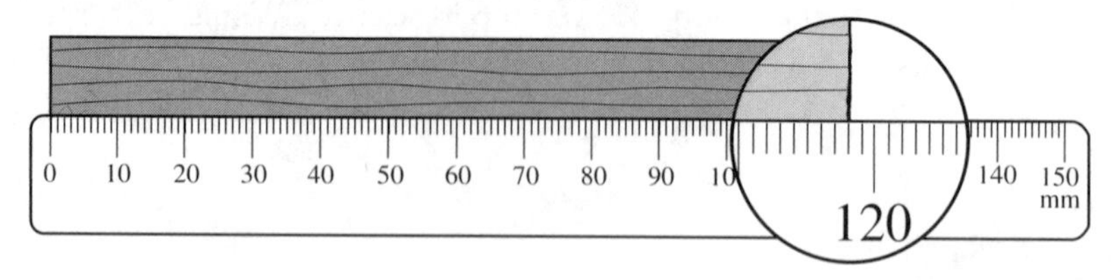

If we use stronger magnification, we can see that it becomes impossible to measure this length any more accurately because the edge is not smooth enough.

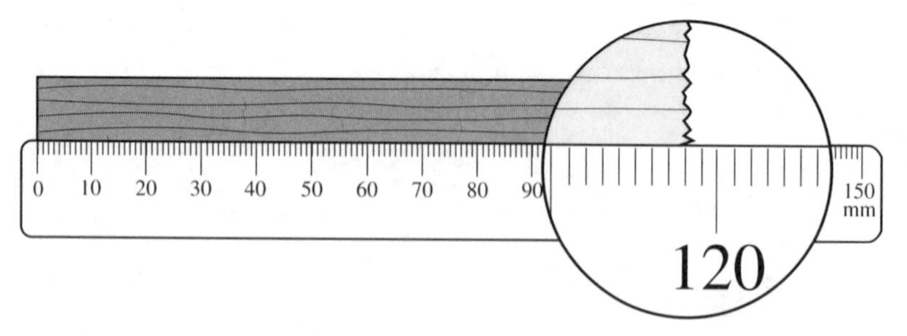

- This means that we cannot give an exact value for the length of this wood; we can say that the length lies between 117.5 mm and 118.5 mm. Any other piece of wood will have a length that can be measured to the nearest centimetre, or millimetre, or tenth of a millimetre, depending how smooth the ends are and how accurate the measuring scale is. But it is *not* possible to give a length of anything exactly.

- On the other hand if you count the number of pupils in your class, you can give an exact value. For example, 28 pupils *is* exact. If we show this number on a number line, it can be marked at only one point. If we mark another number of pupils on the number line, it will be at a separate and distinct point (we cannot have 1.5 pupils, or any other part of a pupil !)

EXERCISE 16A

1 Write down some possible values for

a the number of people standing at a bus stop

b the shoe size of a 13-year-old boy

c a person's weight

d the time it takes to run 100 metres.

2 Discuss with your group whether the values in question **1** are exact or can only be given correct to a number of significant figures.

3 Jane's height is 152 cm correct to the nearest centimetre.
Roy's height is 152 cm correct to the nearest centimetre.
Discuss this statement: ' Jane and Roy are exactly the same height. '

4 You probably have been involved in a conversation like this:
Bus driver: ' How old are you ? '
Sam: ' I'm 13. '
Does Sam mean that he was 13 on his last birthday, or does he mean that he is 13 years old correct to the nearest year ? (We will assume that Sam is telling the truth !)
Discuss the difference between these two possibilities.

DISCRETE AND CONTINUOUS DATA

The examples in the last exercise show that there are two different types of values:

- those that are exact and distinct, for example, the possible number of people standing at a bus stop, possible shoe sizes.
  Quantities like these are *discrete*.
- those that can only be given in a range on a continuous scale, for example, heights, weights, times.
  Quantities like these are *continuous*.

EXERCISE 16B

State whether each quantity is discrete or continuous.

1 The number of pupils in a school.

2 The time it takes you to get to school.

3 The number of peas in a pod.

4 The length of a classroom.

5 Your friend's weight.

6 The volume of liquid in a bottle.

7 The number of words on a page of this book.

8 The time it takes for a train to travel from Manchester to Birmingham.

9 The number of passengers on a train travelling from London to Cheltenham.

10 The temperature at midday on the Met Office roof.

11 The hourly rate of pay for a person working in a supermarket.

12 The age of a pupil in your school.

13 The number of people who can vote in a Parliamentary constituency.

14 The cost of a pair of shoes.

FREQUENCY TABLES FOR CONTINUOUS DATA

This is a list of the heights of 55 children. Each height is rounded down to the nearest complete centimetre, so 141.2 cm and 141.8 cm are both rounded down to 141 cm.
The list has been extracted from a database which has sorted the heights into numerical order.

131 134 136 137 139 141 142 144 145 147 149
132 134 136 137 139 141 142 144 145 148 150
132 134 136 138 140 142 143 144 146 148 150
133 135 136 138 140 142 143 144 147 149 152
133 135 137 139 140 142 144 145 147 149 153

This information can be shown in the following frequency table.

Height (to the nearest complete cm)	131	132	133	134	135	136	137	138	139	140	141	142	143	144	145	146	147	148	149	150	151	152	153
Frequency	1	2	2	3	2	4	3	2	3	3	2	5	2	5	3	1	3	2	3	2	0	1	1

There are 2 children whose heights are recorded as 132 cm.
This means that each child's height is in the range 132 cm up to (but not including) 133 cm.

However the two children are unlikely to be exactly the same height.
This can be shown in the frequency table by giving the heights, x cm, as

$131 \leqslant x < 132$, $132 \leqslant x < 133$, and so on.

(The symbol $\leqslant$ means 'less than or equal to'.)

Because of the space that this notation takes, it is sometimes simplified to 131–, 132–, and so on, where 131–, 132–, means a number from 131 up to, but not including 132, etc.

Height (cm)	131–	132–	133–	134–	135–	136–	137–	138–	139–	140–	141–	142–	143–	144–	145–	146–	147–	148–	149–	150–	151–	152–	153–
Frequency	1	2	2	3	2	4	3	2	3	3	2	5	2	5	3	1	3	2	3	2	0	1	1

Now we can see that *continuous values are already in groups.*

It is easier to understand this information if it is grouped into wider ranges, so we will start the first group at 130 cm, the second group at 135 cm, the third group at 140 cm, and so on. This will give us five groups which we can write as

$$130 \leqslant x < 135, \quad 135 \leqslant x < 140, \quad 140 \leqslant x < 145,$$
$$145 \leqslant x < 150, \quad 150 \leqslant x < 155$$

Any height that is less than 135 cm belongs to the first group, but a height of 135 cm belongs to the second group.

Looking down the list of heights we can see that there are 8 children whose heights are in the first group, 14 children whose heights are in the second group, and so on.

We can write this information in a frequency table.

Height (cm)	Frequency
$130 \leqslant x < 135$	8
$135 \leqslant x < 140$	14
$140 \leqslant x < 145$	17
$145 \leqslant x < 150$	12
$150 \leqslant x < 155$	4
	Total: 55

EXERCISE 16C

1 Use the frequency table immediately above to answer the following questions.

a How many children had a height less than 135 cm?

b How many children had a height of at least 150 cm?

c Which group contains the largest number of heights?

d Two children were away when the survey was carried out. Their heights are 152 cm and 140 cm rounded down to the nearest complete centimetre.
In which group should we place

i 152 cm **ii** 140 cm?

2 This is a list of the weights of 100 adults. The weights are in kilograms rounded *up* to the next complete kilogram, e.g. 63.2 kg is rounded up to 64 kg. The list is in numerical order.

47 51 54 60 63 64 66 68 69 70 72 78 80 85 100
48 51 54 61 63 64 66 68 70 70 73 78 80 88 104
49 52 55 62 63 65 66 68 70 70 73 79 80 90 110
49 52 58 62 63 65 66 68 70 71 74 79 80 92 112
49 53 58 63 63 65 67 69 70 71 75 79 82 94 115
50 53 59 63 64 66 67 69 70 72 78 80 83 95 118
51 53 60 63 64 66 68 69 70 72

a What is the smallest weight?

b How many people have a weight that is 50 kg or less?

c Copy and complete this frequency table.

Weight, w kg	Frequency
$40 < w \leqslant 60$	
$60 < w \leqslant 80$	
$80 < w \leqslant 100$	
$100 < w \leqslant 120$	
	Total:

d How many people have a weight greater than 100 kg?

e How many people have a weight of 80 kg or less?

f Which group contains the largest number of weights?

3 For four weeks Emma kept a record of the time she had to wait for the bus to school each morning. The results are shown in this frequency table.

Time, t minutes	Frequency
$0 < t \leqslant 5$	7
$5 < t \leqslant 10$	9
$10 < t \leqslant 15$	3
$15 < t \leqslant 20$	1

a One morning Emma waited 8 minutes and 30 seconds. In which group should this time be placed?

b On how many mornings did Emma have to wait more than 15 minutes?

c How often did Emma wait no more than 5 minutes?

d On how many mornings did Emma record the length of her wait?

e Did Emma ever have to wait for 20 minutes? Explain your answer.

4 The pupils in Class 9T were given a list of the weights, in grams correct to the nearest gram, of apples gathered from one tree. Eddie made this frequency table to show the weights.

Weight, w grams	Frequency
$85.5 \leqslant w < 87.5$	13
$87.5 \leqslant w < 89.5$	20
$89.5 \leqslant w < 91.5$	45
$91.5 \leqslant w < 93.5$	31
$93.5 \leqslant w < 95.5$	15
$95.5 \leqslant w < 97.5$	9

a One weight in the list is 92 g. In which group should it be placed?

b How many apples were gathered from the tree?

c Can you tell how many apples weighed 90 g to the nearest gram? Explain your answer.

d Nigel made a different tally chart to group the weights.

Weight, w grams	Tally
$85 \leqslant w < 87$	
$87 \leqslant w < 89$	
$89 \leqslant w < 91$	
$91 \leqslant w < 93$	
$93 \leqslant w < 97$	

In which group would Nigel place an apple that weighed 90 g to the nearest gram?

e One apple weighs 89 g correct to the nearest gram. In what range does the weight of this apple lie?

f What problems would Nigel have in placing this weight of 89 g (to the nearest gram) in one of his groups? Would Eddie have the same problems?

5 The pupils in Class 9P were set 3 questions for homework and were asked to write down the number of minutes they spent on this homework.
This frequency table summarises the results.

Time, t minutes	Frequency
$0 < t \leqslant 5.5$	2
$5.5 < t \leqslant 10.5$	15
$10.5 < t \leqslant 15.5$	9
$15.5 < t \leqslant 20.5$	3
$20.5 < t \leqslant 25.5$	1

Use the information in the table to answer these questions. If you cannot give an answer, explain why.

a In which group does a time of 10 minutes, correct to the nearest minute, belong?

b How many pupils spent less than 10 minutes on their homework?

c How many pupils spent no time on their homework?

d How many pupils spent more than 15 minutes on their homework?

e What was the longest time spent by a pupil doing this homework?

BAR CHARTS FOR CONTINUOUS DATA

We can use the frequency table on page 345 to draw a bar chart.

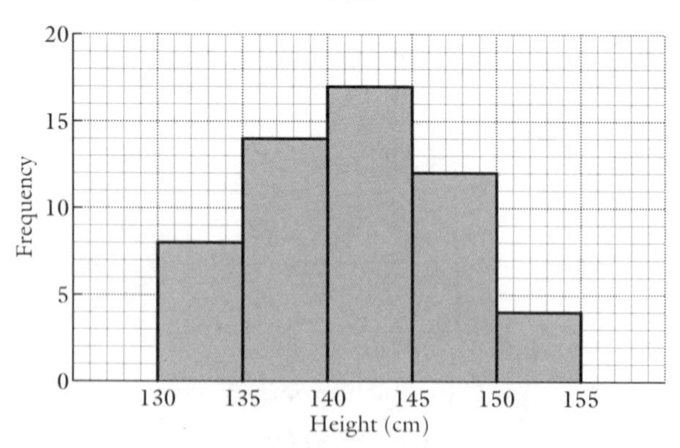

Notice that the horizontal axis gives the heights on a continuous scale, like part of a tape measure, so there are no gaps between the bars.

> A bar chart illustrating continuous data must have no gaps between the bars.

EXERCISE 16D

1 This bar chart summarises the times taken by all the pupils in Year 9 to complete a technology task.

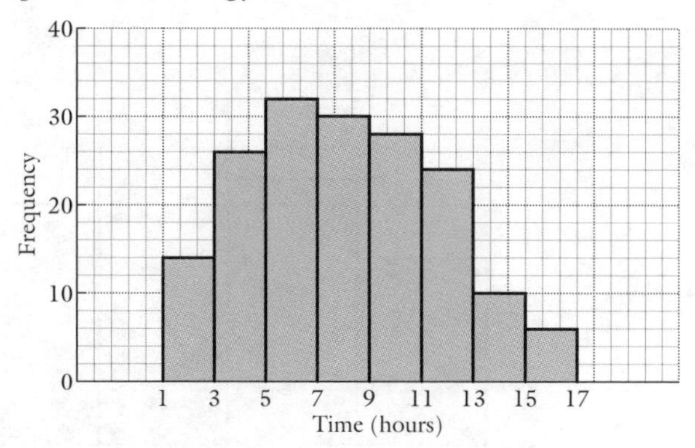

a How many pupils took more than 9 hours?

b How many pupils completed the task?

c There are 200 pupils in Year 9. How many of them did not complete the task?

d Jane was asked to estimate the number of pupils who spent less than 2 hours on this task. Which of these two answers do you think is the better estimate and why? **i** 14 **ii** 7

e Is it true to say that most pupils took between 5 and 7 hours?

f Is it true to say that more pupils took 6 hours than any other time?

2 Here is a frequency table showing the times, in minutes, taken by the pupils in a class on their journeys from home to school on a particular morning.

Time, t minutes	Frequency
$0 \leqslant t < 10$	2
$10 \leqslant t < 20$	9
$20 \leqslant t < 30$	5
$30 \leqslant t < 40$	4
$40 \leqslant t < 50$	2
$50 \leqslant t < 60$	1

Copy and complete this bar chart, using the table.

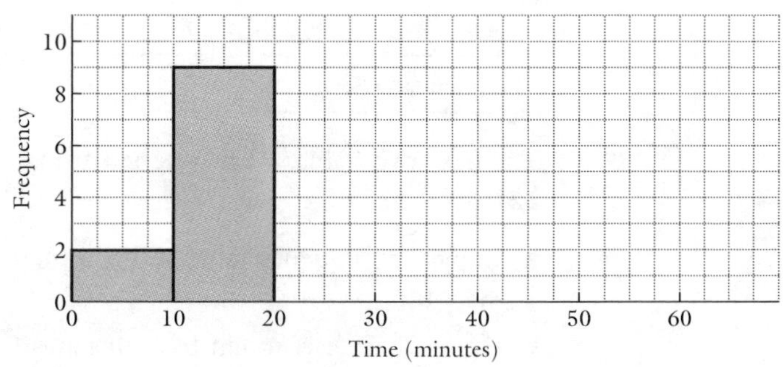

3 The heights of pupils belonging to a trampolining club were recorded; the bar chart summarises the information gathered.

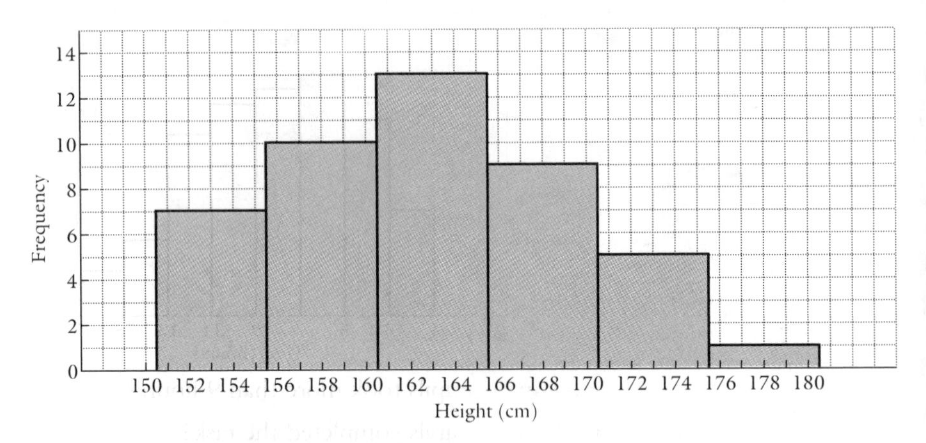

a How many heights were recorded?

b How many of these heights were more than 160 cm?

c In which group should a height recorded as 158 cm, to the nearest centimetre, be placed?

d How would you reply if asked to give the height of the shortest pupil in the club?

e Estimate the number of pupils who are taller than 168 cm, and explain how you get your estimate.

f What can you say about the number of pupils whose heights are 155 cm to 160 cm?

g Can you tell how many pupils are 162 cm tall?

4 At the health-centre, some babies were weighed one afternoon. Their weights, in kilograms, were recorded by the nurse as tally marks in this frequency table.

Weight, w kg	$4 \leqslant w < 8$	$8 \leqslant w < 12$	$12 \leqslant w < 16$
Tally	卌 //	卌 卌 /	卌 /
Frequency			

The next two babies were weighed at just under 12 kg and just over 12 kg.

a Copy the frequency table and add these weights to it. Complete the table.

b Draw a bar chart to illustrate this information.

5 Draw a bar chart to illustrate the data given in question **2**, **Exercise 16C**.

6 This is a list of the weights in kilograms, rounded up to the nearest kg, of 30 fourteen-year-old boys.

50	56	60	62	65	65	67	67	68	69
52	57	60	64	65	65	67	68	68	70
55	57	61	64	65	66	67	68	69	75

You are asked to draw a bar chart to illustrate this data.

a Decide on the groups that you will use and make a frequency table.

b Draw the bar chart.

c Which of your groups contains the largest number of weights?

7 These are two of the charts drawn to illustrate the data in question **6**.

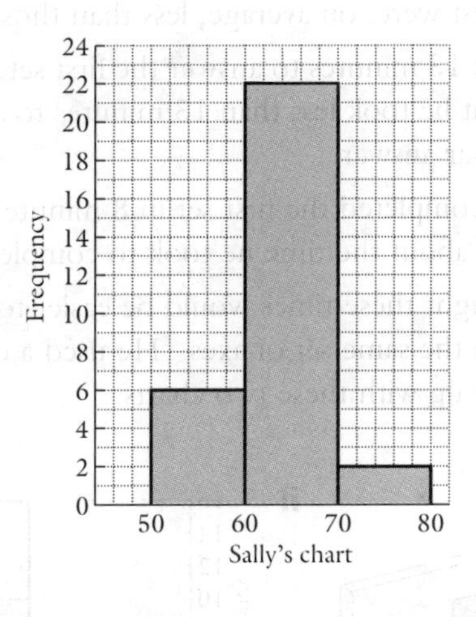

Sally's chart

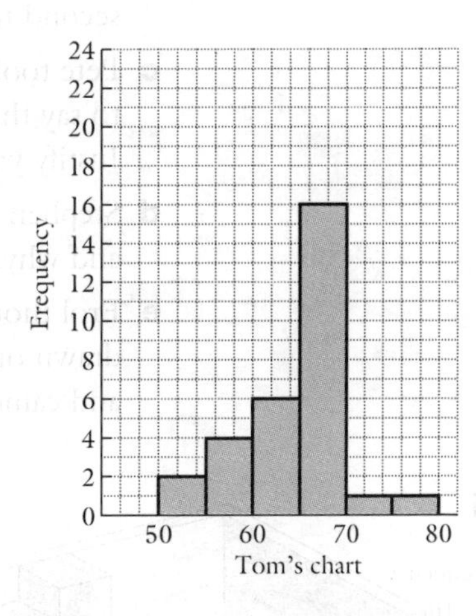

Tom's chart

a What groups did Sally use?

b What groups did Tom use?

c What are the advantages and disadvantages of Sally's choice of groups?

d What are the advantages and disadvantages of Tom's choice of groups?

e What are the advantages and disadvantages of your choice in question **6**?

8 The pupils in Class 9G were given two sets of five multiple choice questions to answer. They did the first set without any previous experience of this type of question. After the first set, they discussed the problems encountered and then they answered another set.

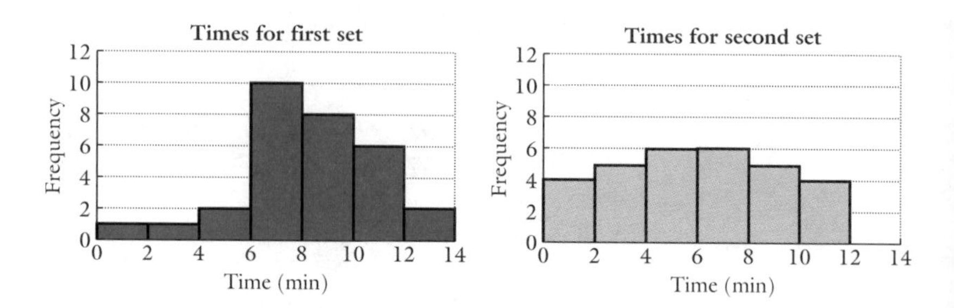

These bar charts illustrate the times taken by the pupils in Class 9G to answer each set of multiple choice questions.

a Give two ways in which these distributions are different.

b Jenny looked at these two bar charts and said, 'Practice helped us to do the second set more quickly.' Is she right?
Can you think of another reason why the times taken for the second test were, on average, less than those for the first test?

c Pete took 13 minutes to answer the first set of questions. Is it true to say that he took less than 13 minutes to answer the second set? Justify your answer.

d Stephen completed the first set in 8 minutes. What can you say, and why, about the time he took to complete the second set?

e Erol thought these times would be easier to compare if they were drawn on the same set of axes. He used a chart drawing program and came up with these two charts.

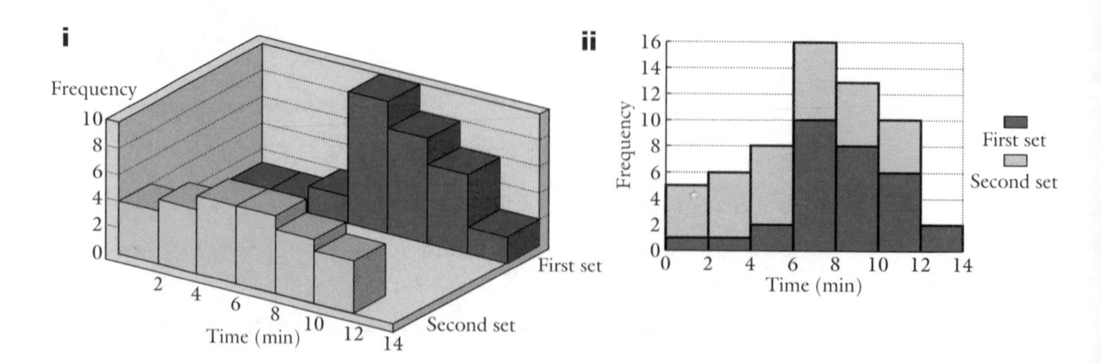

List some advantages and some disadvantages of each of these illustrations.

RANGE AND MODAL GROUP

When values have been placed in groups we lose some of the information.

This bar chart, from page 348, illustrates the distribution of the heights of 55 children.

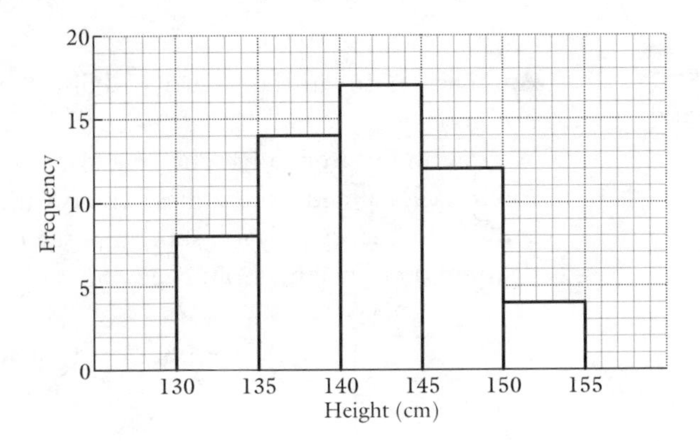

Using just this chart, we cannot tell how many heights of 138 cm there are, nor can we see what the smallest height is, nor the largest height. This means that we cannot give the range of heights.

However we can *estimate* the range by assuming that the smallest height is at the lowest end of the first group, and that the largest height is at the top end of the last group,

i.e. the smallest possible height is 130 cm

and the largest possible height is 155 cm,

so the range is estimated as 155 cm − 130 cm = 25 cm.

For a grouped frequency distribution
the range is estimated as
(the higher end of the last group) – (lower end of the first group)

Also without looking at the original list, we cannot know which height occurs most often, so *we cannot find the mode*. However we can see that the group of heights from 140 cm to 145 cm contains more heights than any other group. We call this the *modal group*.

For a grouped frequency distribution
the modal group
is the group with the largest number of items in it.

EXERCISE 16E

Give the modal group and estimate the range for the following grouped distribution from **Exercise 16D**.

1 Question **1**

2 Question **2**

3 Question **3**

4 a Question **8**, first set

b Question **8**, second set

FREQUENCY POLYGONS

Another way to illustrate a grouped distribution is to draw a frequency polygon.
We can do this from a bar chart by marking a point in the middle of the top of each bar and joining these points with straight lines. This diagram shows a frequency polygon superimposed on the bar chart giving the distribution of heights from page 353.

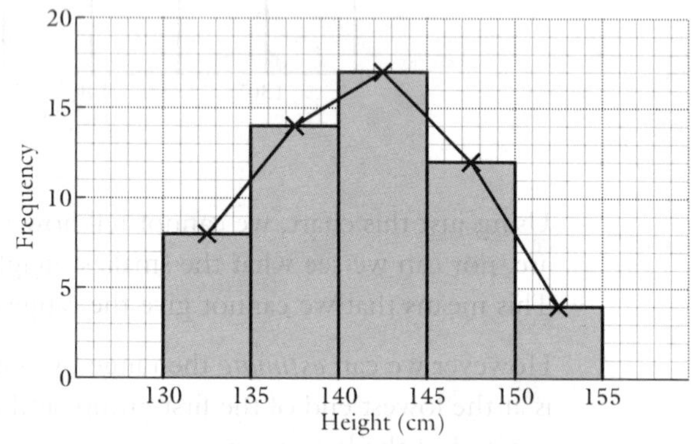

We can draw a frequency polygon directly from a frequency table without having to draw a bar chart first.

We do this by first identifying the middle value of each group (these are called the *mid-class values*).

For the distribution above, the mid-class value of the first group is halfway between 130 cm and 135 cm, i.e. $(130 + 135) \div 2$ cm $= 132.5$ cm.

The mid-class values of the other groups can be found in the same way.

It helps to add a column to the frequency table to show these mid-class values.

Here is the frequency table for these heights with the extra column added.

Height, x cm	Frequency	Mid-class value
$130 \leqslant x < 135$	8	132.5
$135 \leqslant x < 140$	14	137.5
$140 \leqslant x < 145$	17	142.5
$145 \leqslant x < 150$	12	147.5
$150 \leqslant x < 155$	4	152.5
	Total: 55	

Then, for each group, we plot a point on the graph above the mid-class value corresponding to the frequency, and then join all the points with straight lines.

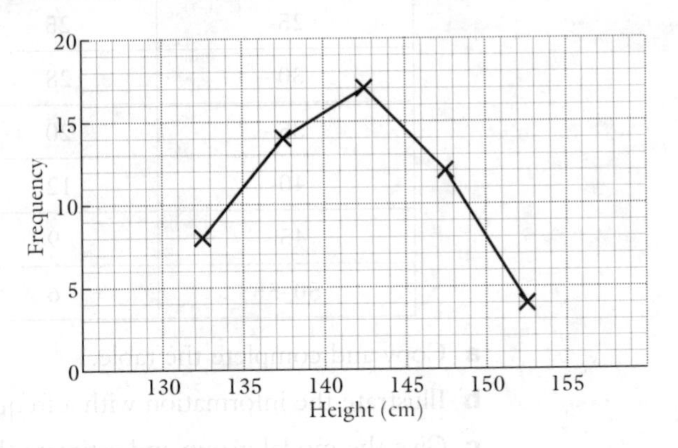

EXERCISE 16F

1 Here is the frequency table from **Exercise 16D**, showing the distribution of the times, in minutes, taken by the pupils in a class on their journeys from home to school on a particular morning.

Time, t minutes	Frequency	Mid-class value
$0 \leqslant t < 10$	2	5
$10 \leqslant t < 20$	9	15
$20 \leqslant t < 30$	5	
$30 \leqslant t < 40$	4	
$40 \leqslant t < 50$	2	
$50 \leqslant t < 60$	1	

a Copy and complete the table.

b Copy and complete the frequency polygon using your table.

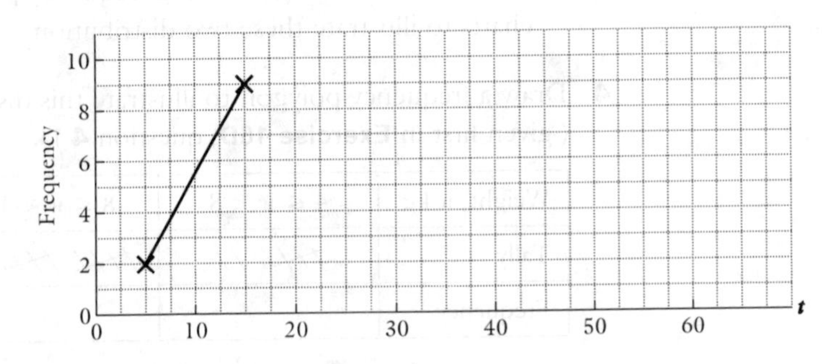

2 This frequency table gives the grouped weights of a sample of 100 eggs.

Weight (grams)	Frequency	Mid-class value
25–	25	27.5
30–	28	
35–	20	
40–	12	
45–	9	
50–55	6	

a Copy and complete the table.

b Illustrate the information with a frequency polygon.

c Give the modal group and estimate the range of these weights.

3 This frequency table gives the grouped weights of a different sample of 100 eggs.

Weight (grams)	Frequency
25–	22
30–	21
35–	23
40–	18
45–	8
50–	6
55–60	2

a Illustrate this information with a frequency polygon drawn on the same set of axes as the frequency polygon for question **2**.
(Use a different colour and make sure that you label your diagram to show which polygon illustrates which distribution.)

b Make one comparison of the distribution of weights in the two samples.

c What is the advantage of using frequency polygons rather than bar charts to illustrate these two distributions?

4 Draw a frequency polygon to illustrate this distribution of weights (given first in **Exercise 16D**, question **4**).

Weight, w kg	$4 \leqslant w < 8$	$8 \leqslant w < 12$	$12 \leqslant w < 16$
Tally	𝍸 //	𝍸 𝍸 /	𝍸 /
Frequency			

5 Mrs Jones timed the pupils changing for games and this frequency polygon shows the results.

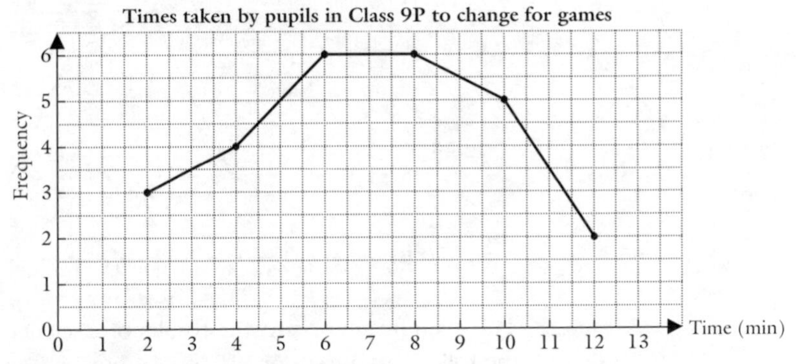

a What are the mid-class values?

b Where does the first group start and where does it end?

c Where does the last group start and where does it end?

d Copy this diagram and superimpose a bar chart on your copy showing the same information.

e Make a frequency table showing this information. (Assume that the times have been rounded up to the nearest complete minute.)

f What is the range of times shown here?

g What is the modal group?

h How many pupils were timed?

6 After a lecture on the time being wasted by several members of the class when changing for games, Mrs Jones repeated the experiment.

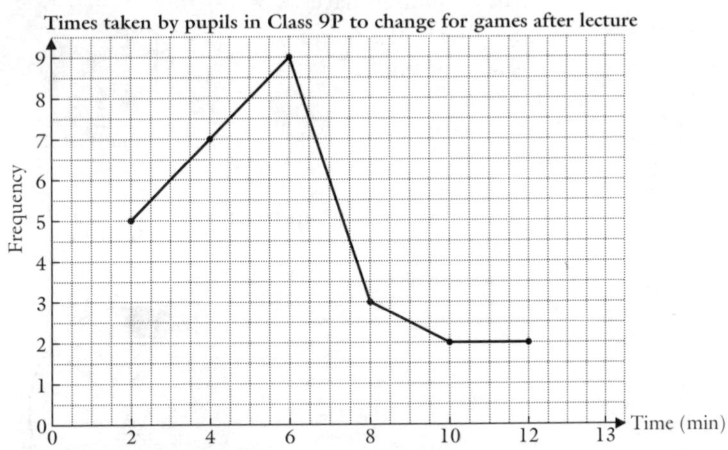

a Illustrate this distribution with a bar chart.

b What is the range and modal group of this distribution?

c How many pupils were timed?

d Say, with reasons, whether you think that the lecture had any effects on the times taken to change for games by the pupils in Class 9P.

7

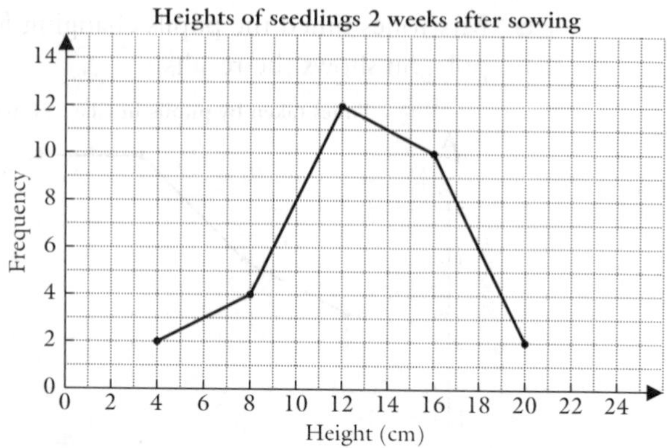

The diagram represents the results of a science experiment. Answer the following questions. If you cannot give an answer say why.

a How many seedlings were measured?

b How many seeds were planted?

c Estimate the range of heights.

d What was the most common height reached by the seedlings?

e Estimate the height which half of these seedlings exceeded.

PIE CHARTS

This bar chart shows the distribution of the heights of 55 children. It is not easy to see what proportion of these children have heights in the range 130–135 cm.

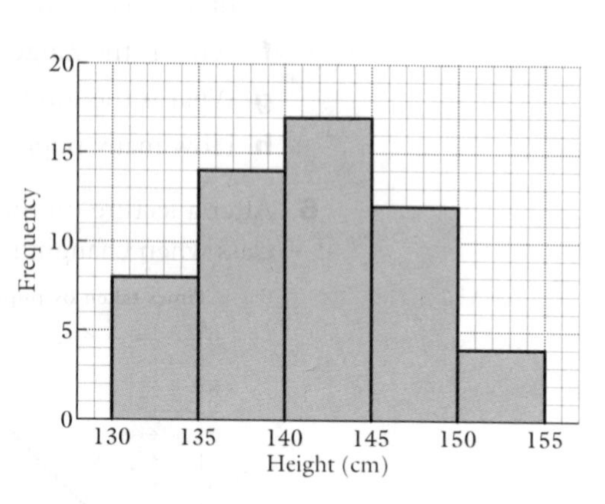

If we want a diagram to show the proportions of heights in each group, we use a pie chart:

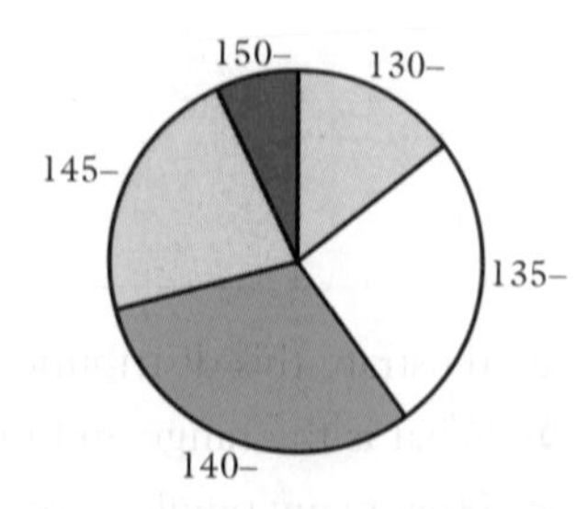

Now we can see immediately that about $\frac{1}{8}$ of the children are between 130 cm and 135 cm tall.

DRAWING PIE CHARTS

The easiest way to draw a pie chart is to get a computer to do it for you.

This table shows the numbers of people with eyes of certain colours.

Eye colour	Brown	Hazel	Blue	Grey
Frequency	22	6	12	20

Entering the last four columns into a spreadsheet program, and then asking it to draw a pie chart, produced this diagram – it even worked out the percentages for each slice.

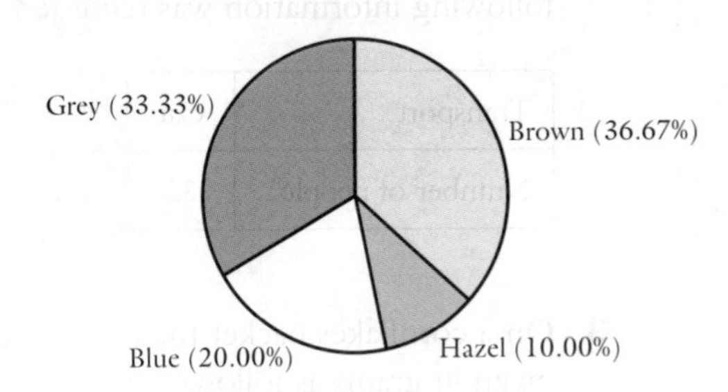

To draw it ourselves, we have to work out the size of each pie slice; this is given by the size of angle at the 'point', that is at the centre. Therefore we have to calculate the sizes of the angles.

The number of people is 60.

As there are 12 blue-eyed people, they form $\frac{12}{60}$ of the whole group and are therefore represented by that fraction of the circle; so the angle at the centre of the slice is $\frac{12}{60}$ of 360°.

Blue: $\frac{12}{60} \times \frac{360^\circ}{1} = 72^\circ$ Grey: $\frac{20}{60} \times \frac{360^\circ}{1} = 120^\circ$

Hazel: $\frac{6}{60} \times \frac{360^\circ}{1} = 36^\circ$ Brown: $\frac{22}{60} \times \frac{360^\circ}{1} = 132^\circ$

Total 360°

Now draw a circle (a radius of about 5 cm is suitable for most charts).
Draw one radius as shown and complete the diagram using a protractor, turning your page into the easiest position for drawing each new angle.
Label each 'slice'.

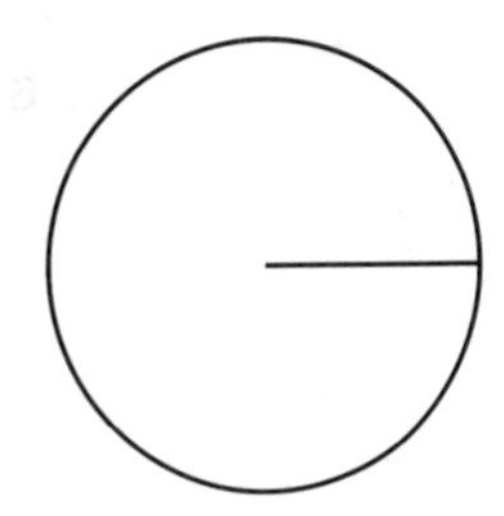

EXERCISE 16G

Draw pie charts to represent the following information, first working out the angles.

1 A box of 60 coloured balloons contains the following numbers of balloons of each colour.

Colour	Red	Yellow	Green	Blue	White
Number of balloons	16	22	10	7	5

2 Ninety people were asked how they travelled to work and the following information was recorded.

Transport	Car	Bus	Train	Motorcycle	Bicycle
Number of people	32	38	12	6	2

3 On a cornflakes packet the composition of 120 g of cornflakes is given in grams as follows.

Protein	Fat	Carbohydrate	Other ingredients
101	1	10	8

4 90 cars passed a survey point. The number of doors on each car was counted and this gave the following figures.

Number of doors	2	3	4	5
Frequency	21	12	51	6

5 A large flower arrangement contained 18 dark red roses, 6 pale pink roses, 10 white roses and 11 deep pink roses.

6 The children in a class were asked what pets they owned and the following information was recorded.

Animal	Dog	Cat	Bird	Small animal	Fish
Frequency	8	10	3	6	3

Sometimes the total number involved does not work as conveniently as in the previous problems. In this case we find the angle correct to the nearest degree.

The eye colour of 54 people is recorded in the table. Draw a pie chart to show the proportions of this group with each different eye colour.

Eye colour	Blue	Grey	Hazel	Brown	
Frequency	10	19	5	20	Total: 54

Angles:

Blue: $\frac{10}{54} \times \frac{360°}{1} = 66.6\ldots° = 67°$ **to the nearest degree**

Use your calculator to find $10 \times 360 \div 54$

Grey: $\frac{19}{54} \times \frac{360°}{1} = 126.6\ldots° = 127°$ **to the nearest degree**

Hazel: $\frac{5}{54} \times \frac{360°}{1} = 33.3\ldots° = 33°$ **to the nearest degree**

Brown: $\frac{20}{54} \times \frac{360°}{1} = 133.3\ldots° = 133°$ **to the nearest degree**

***Check*: $67 + 127 + 33 + 133 = 360$**

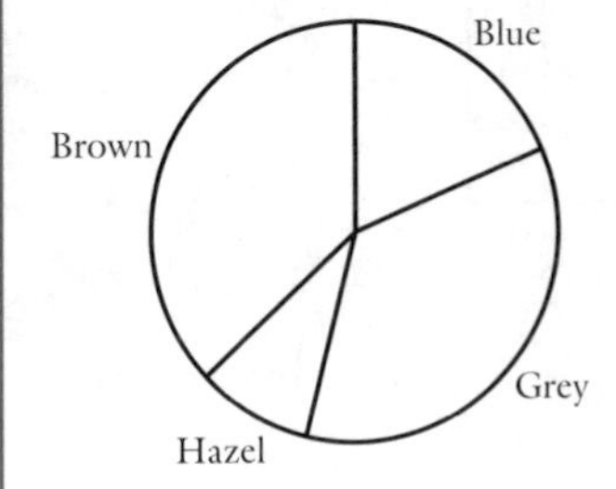

In this case, adding up the angles gives 360°.

Sometimes, because of rounding, the sum of the calculated angles comes to one or two degrees more or less than 360°. If the sum is more than 360, find a rounded-up angle that is nearest to half way between two values, and round it down. If the sum is less than 360°, find a rounded-down angle that is nearest to half way between two values and round it up.

Draw pie charts to represent the following information. Work out the angles first and, where necessary, give the angles to the nearest degree. Try using a chart drawing package, included with most spreadsheet programs, for some of these.

7 300 people were asked whether they lived in a flat, a house, a bedsit, a bungalow or in some other type of accommodation and the following information was recorded:

Type of accommodation	Flat	House	Bedsit	Bungalow	Other
Frequency	90	150	33	15	12

8 In a street in which 80 people live the numbers in various age groups are as follows:

Age group (years)	0–15	16–21	22–34	35–49	50–64	65 and over
Number of people	16	3	19	21	12	9

9 Peter recorded the types of vehicle moving along a road during one hour and drew up this table.

Vehicle	Cars	Vans	Lorries	Motorcycles	Bicycles
Frequency	62	11	15	10	2

10 This table showing the hours of sunshine per day during June was compiled using information from the school's weather station.

Hours per day	0–	3–	5–	7–	8–
Frequency	3	9	11	5	2

11

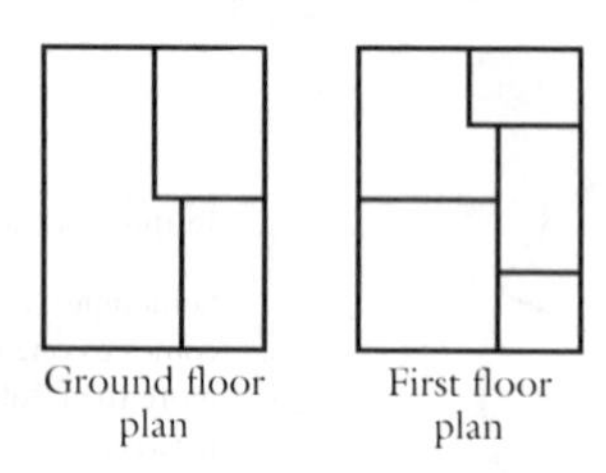

These two pie charts show the proportions covered by carpet of each of the two floors of a house.

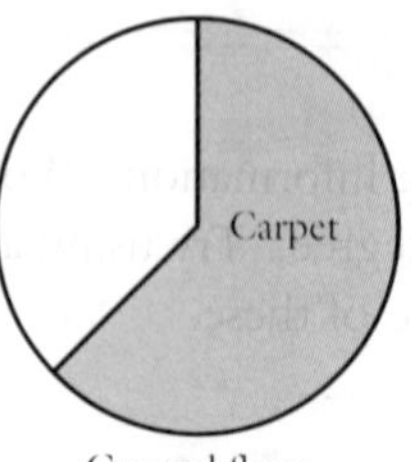

Ground floor

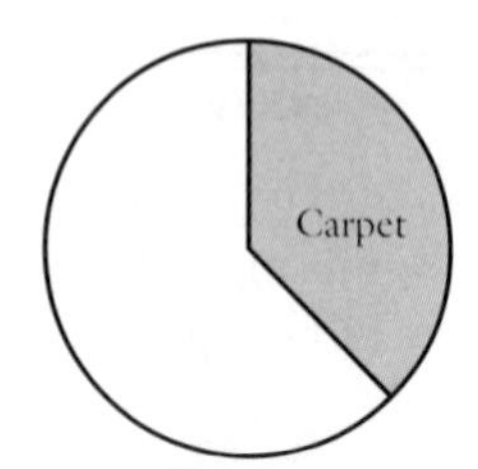

First floor

a Roughly, what percentage of the ground floor is carpeted?

b Roughly, what percentage of the first floor is carpeted?

c *Sketch* a pie chart to show the percentage of the whole floor area of the house covered by carpet.

12 These two pie charts show the proportion of wins and losses of one football team for one season in home matches and in away matches.

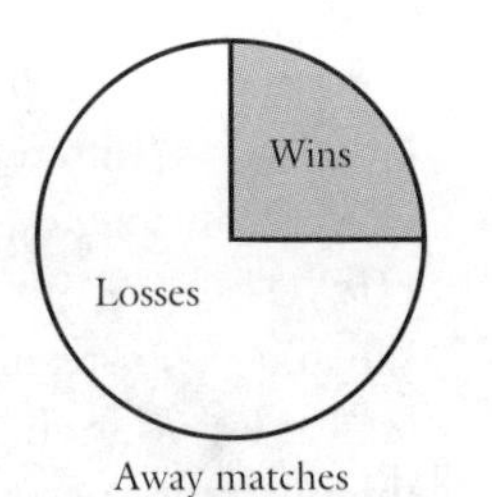

Away matches

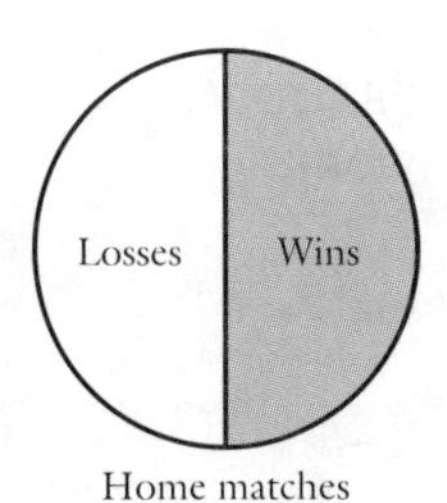

Home matches

This chart shows the wins and losses in all the matches played.
What can you deduce from this?

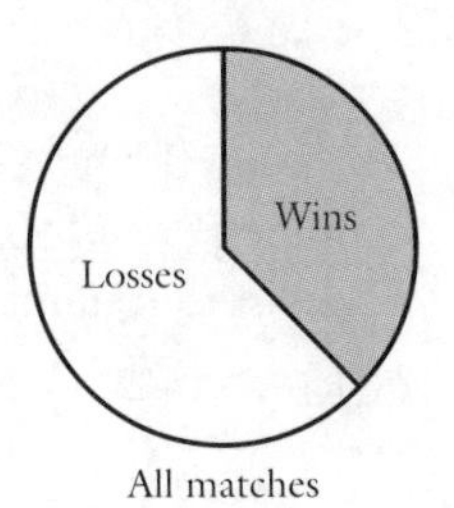

All matches

13 This table, from *Social Trends 22*, shows average attendances at football league (England & Wales) matches for various years.

	Division 1	Division 2	Division 3	Division 4
1961/62	26,106	16,132	9,419	6,060
1966/67	30,829	15,701	8,009	5,407
1971/72	31,352	14,652	8,510	4,981
1976/77	29,540	13,529	7,522	3,863
1980/81	24,660	11,202	6,590	3,082
1986/87	19,800	9,000	4,300	3,100
1987/88	19.300	10,600	5,000	3,200
1988/89	20,600	10,600	5,500	3,200
1989/90	20,800	12,500	5,000	3,400
1990/91	22,681	11,457	5,208	3,253

Source: Football League

a Draw a pie chart showing the proportions attending each division in 1961/62.

b Draw another pie chart showing the proportions attending each division in 1990/91.

c Have the proportions changed between the 1961/62 season and the 1990/91 season?

14 This chart (called a stacked percentage chart) shows the percentage of spending money spent on various categories of purchases by a group of 12-year-olds.

Show this information in a pie chart.

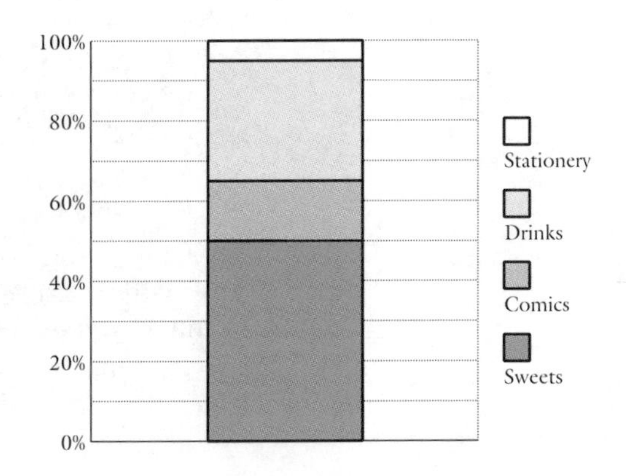

PRACTICAL WORK

1 Choose two different daily newspapers. For each one find the area of the front page used by each of the following categories: HEADLINES, PICTURES, TEXT, EVERYTHING ELSE.
Illustrate your results with either bar charts or pie charts and give a reason for your choice. What comparisons can you make between the two front pages?

2 These are the heights (rounded up to the nearest complete centimetre) of 160 pupils in the first year at Headon Warren School. Each list is in numerical order.

GIRLS

127	143	147	148	152	155	157	158
134	143	147	148	153	155	157	159
134	144	147	148	153	155	157	160
134	144	147	149	154	155	157	160
134	145	147	150	154	155	157	160
137	145	147	150	154	156	157	161
138	145	147	151	154	156	157	161
139	146	147	151	155	156	157	161
140	146	148	152	155	156	158	163
141	146	148	152	155	157	158	165

BOYS

132	141	144	147	150	152	154	156
134	141	145	147	150	152	154	157
137	142	145	148	150	152	155	157
137	142	145	148	150	152	155	157
138	142	145	148	150	152	155	158
138	142	146	149	150	153	155	158
140	142	146	149	150	153	155	159
140	143	146	149	150	154	155	160
140	143	147	149	151	154	155	160
141	144	147	150	151	154	156	161

Compare the distribution of the heights of the girls with that of the boys.
In your report, you should explain what you have done with the data and why you have done it.
Do your results agree with what you expected?

SCALE DRAWING

An architect makes an accurate drawing of a building before it is built. Everything is shown much smaller than it will be in the completed building, but it is all carefully drawn to scale, that is, all the proportions are correct.

Likewise an engineer also makes accurate drawings when he designs small parts for a new machine. However, these drawings usually show small components much larger than they will be when they are manufactured.

In these, as in many other occupations, scale drawings are essential to high quality products and services.

EXERCISE 17A

1 List other occupations where accurate drawings are used. Say whether each occupation tends to make scale drawings that show each object larger or smaller than the finished product.

2 If you had a map of the area within 20 miles of where you live, and the scale was not given, would you be able to decide how far one place was from another?
Would you give the same answer if the map was for a small area of France where you would like to take a holiday? Justify your answer.

3 What information do you think you need to have on any scale drawing?

CONSTRUCTING TRIANGLES AND QUADRILATERALS

In Book 8B we saw that we could construct a triangle provided we were given enough information.

The necessary information is

either one side and two angles

or two sides and the angle between those two sides

or three sides

Some quadrilaterals can also be constructed using similar methods.

The next exercise gives practice in construction before you start on scale drawing.

EXERCISE 17B

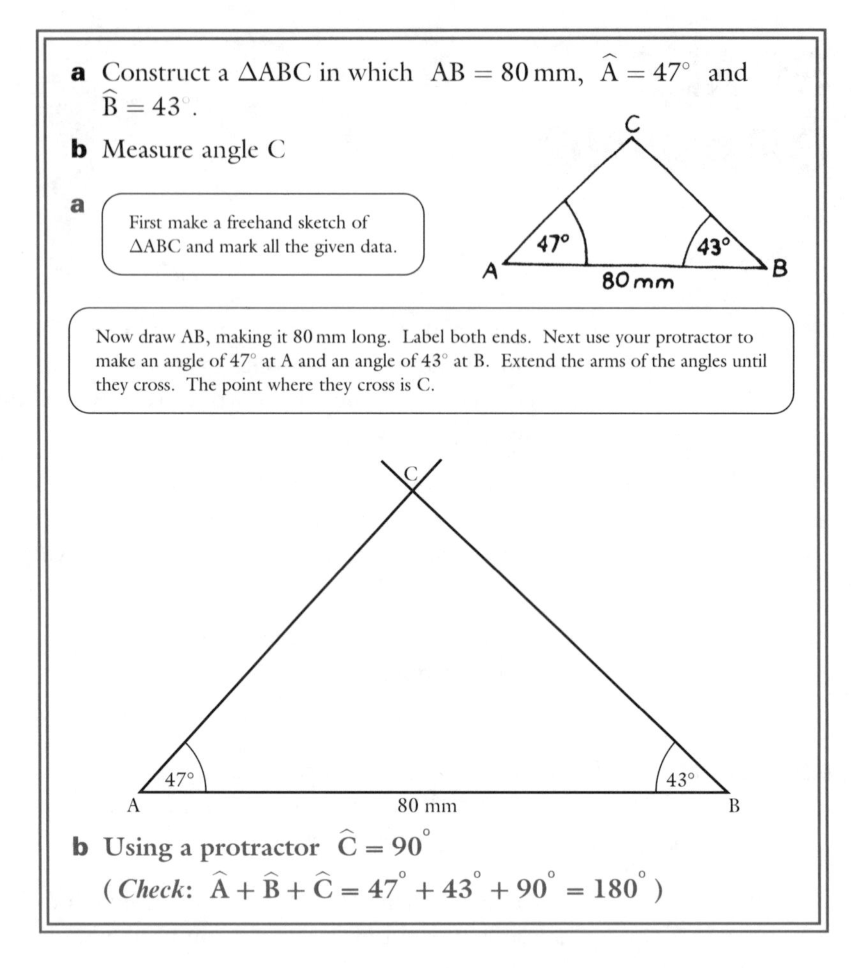

a Construct a ΔABC in which $AB = 80$ mm, $\widehat{A} = 47^\circ$ and $\widehat{B} = 43^\circ$.

b Measure angle C

a First make a freehand sketch of ΔABC and mark all the given data.

Now draw AB, making it 80 mm long. Label both ends. Next use your protractor to make an angle of 47° at A and an angle of 43° at B. Extend the arms of the angles until they cross. The point where they cross is C.

b Using a protractor $\widehat{C} = 90^\circ$

(*Check*: $\widehat{A} + \widehat{B} + \widehat{C} = 47^\circ + 43^\circ + 90^\circ = 180^\circ$)

In questions **1** to **4** use the given information to construct each triangle. Remember to draw a freehand diagram first. It may be necessary to calculate the third angle before you can begin the construction.

1 A metal plate ΔABC in which $AB = 65$ mm, $\widehat{A} = 50^\circ$, $\widehat{B} = 45^\circ$. Measure AC.

2 ΔXYZ in which $\widehat{Y} = 67^\circ$, $XY = 3.7$ cm, $YZ = 6.8$ cm. Measure $\widehat{X}$ and $\widehat{Z}$.

3 A triangular plastic marker DEF in which $DE = 115$ mm, $EF = 92$ mm, $DF = 69$ mm. Measure $\widehat{D}$, $\widehat{E}$ and $\widehat{F}$. (Remember to use compasses for this construction.)

4 Construct a quadrilateral ABCD in which $AB = 47$ mm, $AD = 80$ mm, $BD = 87$ mm, $A\widehat{B}C = 120^\circ$, $A\widehat{D}C = 85^\circ$. Measure BC, DC and $\widehat{C}$. (When you have drawn the rough sketch think of it as made up of two triangles.)

RULER AND COMPASSES CONSTRUCTIONS

Scale drawings need to be accurate; it is difficult to divide a line or an angle accurately in half using only a ruler or a protractor. We now consider other ways of doing this.

BISECTING ANGLES

Bisect means 'cut exactly in half'.

The construction for bisecting an angle makes use of the fact that, in an isosceles triangle the line of symmetry cuts $\widehat{A}$ in half.

To bisect $\widehat{A}$, open your compasses to a radius of about 6 cm.

With the point on A, draw an arc to cut both arms of $\widehat{A}$ at B and C. (If we joined BC, $\triangle$ABC would be isosceles.)

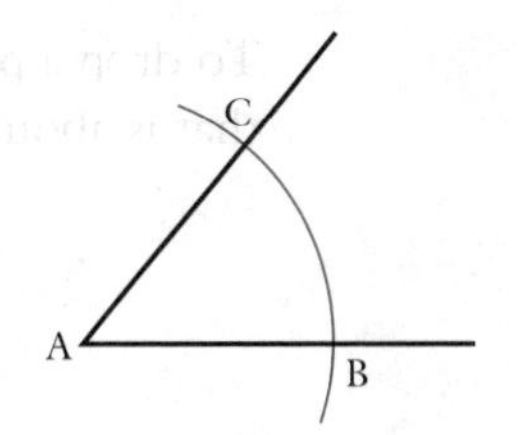

With the point on B, draw an arc between the arms of $\widehat{A}$.

Move the point to C (being careful not to change the radius) and draw an arc to cut the other arc at D.

Join AD.

The line AD then bisects $\widehat{A}$.

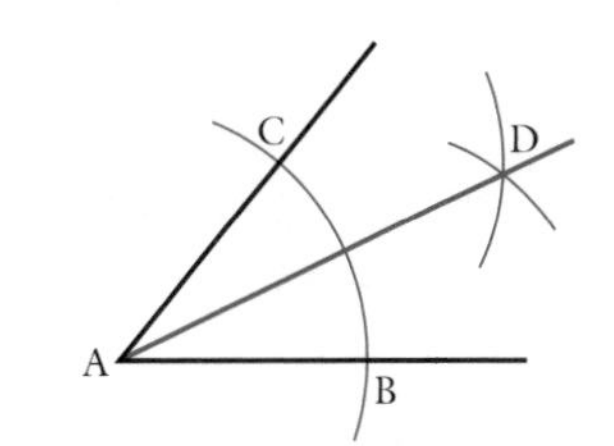

CONSTRUCTION OF THE PERPENDICULAR BISECTOR OF A LINE

The perpendicular bisector of the line XY cuts XY in half at right angles. In order to draw this line we construct a rhombus with the given line (XY) as one diagonal, but we do not join the sides of the rhombus.

To bisect XY, open your compasses to a radius that is about $\frac{3}{4}$ of the length of XY.

With the point on X, draw arcs above and below XY.

Move the point to Y (being careful not to change the radius) and draw arcs to cut the first pair at P and Q.

Join PQ.

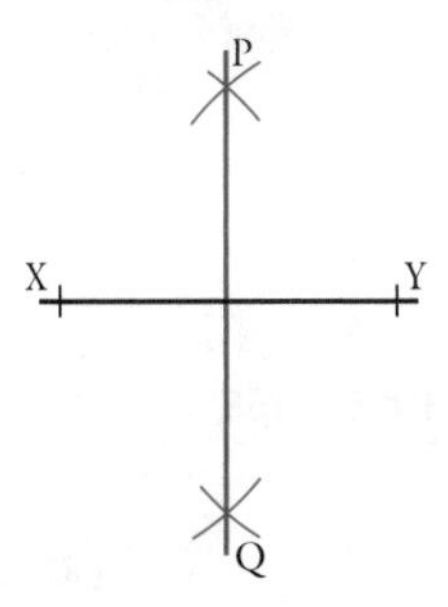

The point where PQ cuts XY is the midpoint of XY, and PQ is perpendicular to XY.

(XPYQ is a rhombus since the same radius is used to draw all the arcs, i.e. XP = YP = YQ = XQ. PQ and XY are the diagonals of the rhombus. The diagonals of a rhombus intersect at right angles so PQ is the perpendicular bisector of XY.)

Note that this construction can also be used to construct an angle of 90°.

DROPPING A PERPENDICULAR FROM A POINT TO A LINE

If you are told to drop a perpendicular from a point C to a line AB, this means that you have to draw a line through C which is at right angles to the line AB.

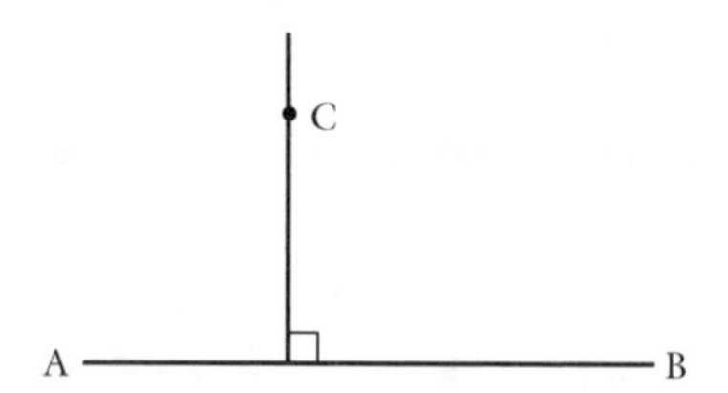

To drop a perpendicular from C to AB, open your compasses to a radius that is about $1\frac{1}{2}$ times the distance of C from AB.

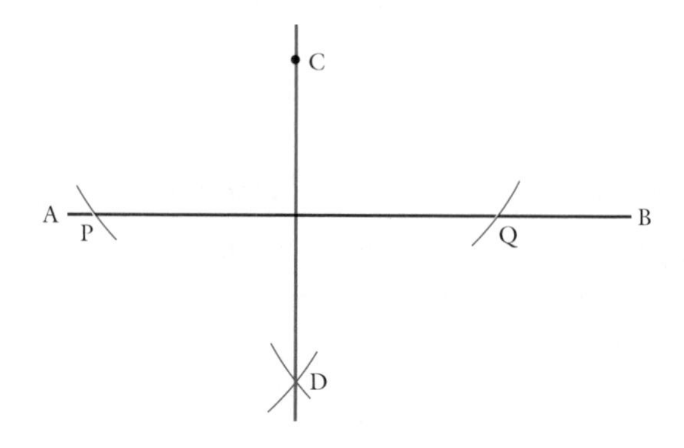

With the point on C, draw arcs to cut the line AB at P and Q.

Move the point to P and draw an arc on the other side of AB. Move the point to Q and draw an arc to cut the last arc at D.

Join CD.

CD is then perpendicular to AB.

Remember to keep the radius unchanged throughout this construction.
You now have a rhombus, PCQD, of which CD and PQ are the diagonals.

EXERCISE 17C

Remember to make a rough sketch before you start each construction. Use suitable instruments including a *sharp* pencil.

1 **a** Construct an equilateral triangle of side 8 cm. What is the size of each angle in this triangle?

b Use what you have learned in part **a** to construct an angle of 60°. Now bisect this angle. What size should each new angle be? Measure both of them.

c Use what you have learned in part **b** to construct an angle of 30°.

2 **a** Draw a straight line and mark a point A near the middle.

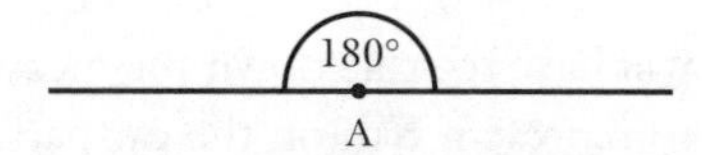

You have an angle of 180° at A. Now bisect angle A. What is the size of each new angle? Measure both of them.

b Use what you have learned in part **a** to construct an angle of 90°.

c Construct an angle of 45°.

3 Construct the following figures using only a ruler and a pair of compasses. They are not drawn to scale.

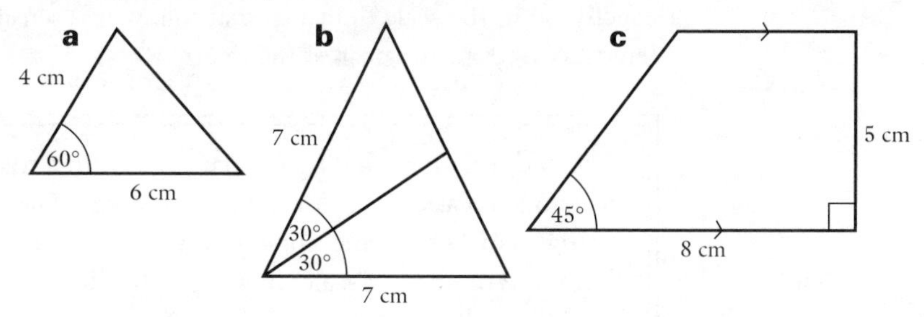

4 Construct a triangle ABC, in which AB = 6 cm, BC = 8 cm and CA = 10 cm. Using a ruler and compasses only, drop a perpendicular from B to AC.

5 Construct a triangle PQR in which PQ = 6 cm, PR = 6 cm and RQ = 10 cm. Using a ruler and compasses only, drop a perpendicular from R to QP. If necessary extend QP.

6 Construct the isosceles triangle LMN in which LM = 6 cm and LN = MN = 8 cm. Construct the perpendicular bisector of the side LM. Explain why this line is a line of symmetry of △LMN.

7 Draw a circle of radius 6 cm and mark the centre, C. Draw a chord, AB, about 9 cm long. Construct the line of symmetry of this diagram.

8 Construct a triangle ABC, in which AB = 8 cm, BC = 10 cm and AC = 9 cm. Construct the perpendicular bisector of AB. Construct the perpendicular bisector of BC. Mark G where these two perpendicular bisectors intersect (i.e. cross). With the point of your compasses on G and with a radius equal to the length of GA, draw a circle.
This circle should pass through B and C, and it is called the *circumcircle* of △ABC.

ACCURATE DRAWING WITH SCALED-DOWN MEASUREMENTS

If you are asked to draw a car-park which is a rectangle measuring 50 m by 25 m, you obviously cannot draw it full size. To fit it on to your page you will have to scale down the measurements. In this case you could use 1 cm to represent 5 m on the car-park. This is called the *scale*; it is usually written as 1 cm ≡ 5 m, and must *always* be stated on any scale drawing.

EXERCISE 17D

Start by making a freehand drawing of the object you are asked to draw to scale. Mark all the full-size measurements on your sketch. Next draw another sketch and put the scaled measurements on this one. Then do the accurate scale drawing. Usually you have to use your scale drawing to measure the length of a line. Such a length cannot be measured exactly, so in the scale drawings that follow it is sensible to measure each length correct to the nearest millimetre.

The end wall of a building is a rectangle with a triangular top. The rectangle measures 12 m wide by 6 m high. The base of the triangle is 12 m and the sloping sides are 8 m long. Using a scale of 1 cm to 2 m, make a scale drawing of this wall. Use your drawing to find, to the nearest tenth of a metre, the distance from the ground to the ridge of the roof.

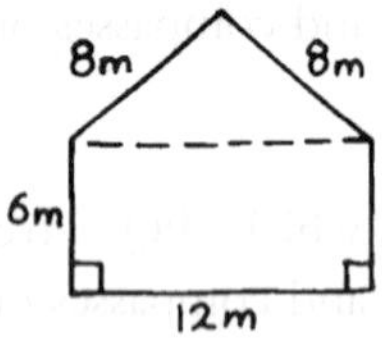

8m 8m 6m 12m

A scale of 1 cm to 2 m means we use 1 cm on the drawing for each 2 m on the building. Hence 12 m becomes $\frac{12}{2}$ cm on the drawing, and so on.

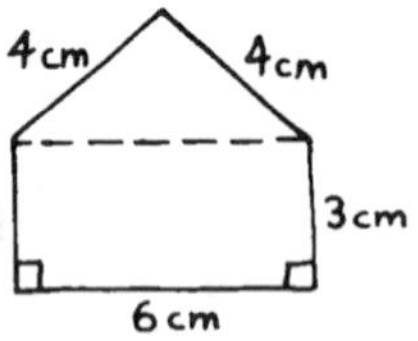

4cm 4cm 3cm 6cm

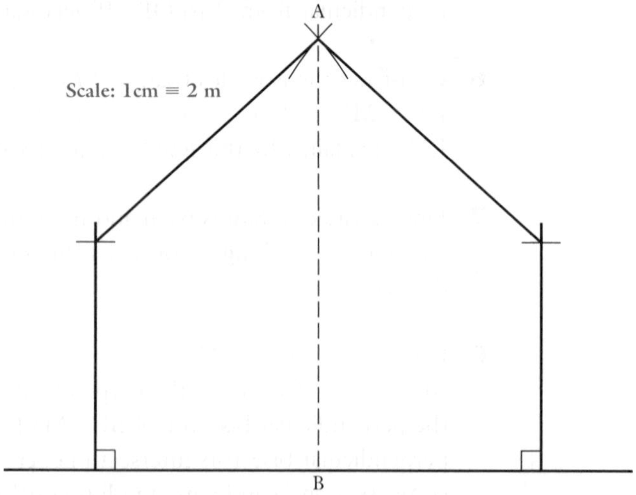

A

Scale: 1cm ≡ 2 m

B

From the drawing, AB measures 5.7 cm.

So the height of the wall is 5.7 x 2 m = 11.4 m

In questions **1** to **5** use the scale given in brackets to make a scale drawing of the given object. Angles can be drawn using a protractor.

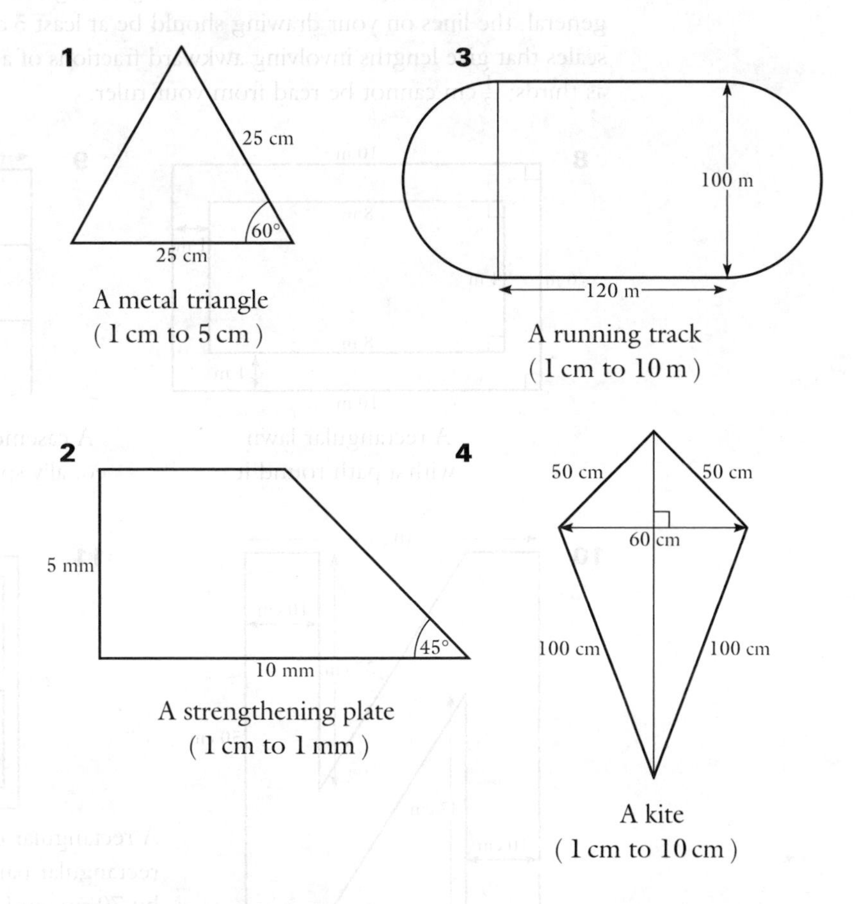

A metal triangle
(1 cm to 5 cm)

A running track
(1 cm to 10 m)

A strengthening plate
(1 cm to 1 mm)

A kite
(1 cm to 10 cm)

5 A field is rectangular in shape. It measures 300 m by 400 m. A land drain goes in a straight line from one corner of the field to the opposite corner. Using a scale of 1 cm to 50 m, make a scale drawing of the field and use it to find the length of the land drain.

6 The end wall of a ridge tent is a triangle. The base is 2 m and the sloping edges are each 2.5 m. Using a scale of 1 cm to 0.5 m, make a scale drawing of the triangular end of the tent and use it to find the height of the tent.

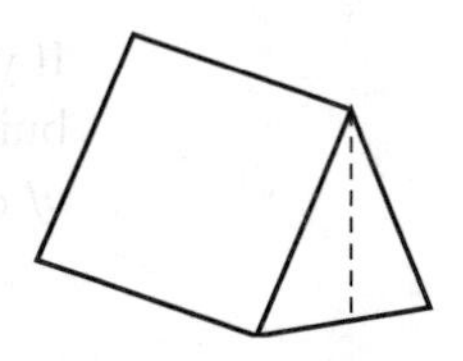

7 The surface of a swimming pool is a rectangle measuring 25 m by 10 m. Choose your own scale and make a scale drawing of the pool. Now compare and discuss your drawing with those of other pupils.

In questions **8** to **11** choose your own scale.

Choose a scale that gives lines that are long enough to draw easily; in general, the lines on your drawing should be at least 5 cm long. Avoid scales that give lengths involving awkward fractions of a centimetre, such as thirds; $\frac{1}{3}$ cm cannot be read from your ruler.

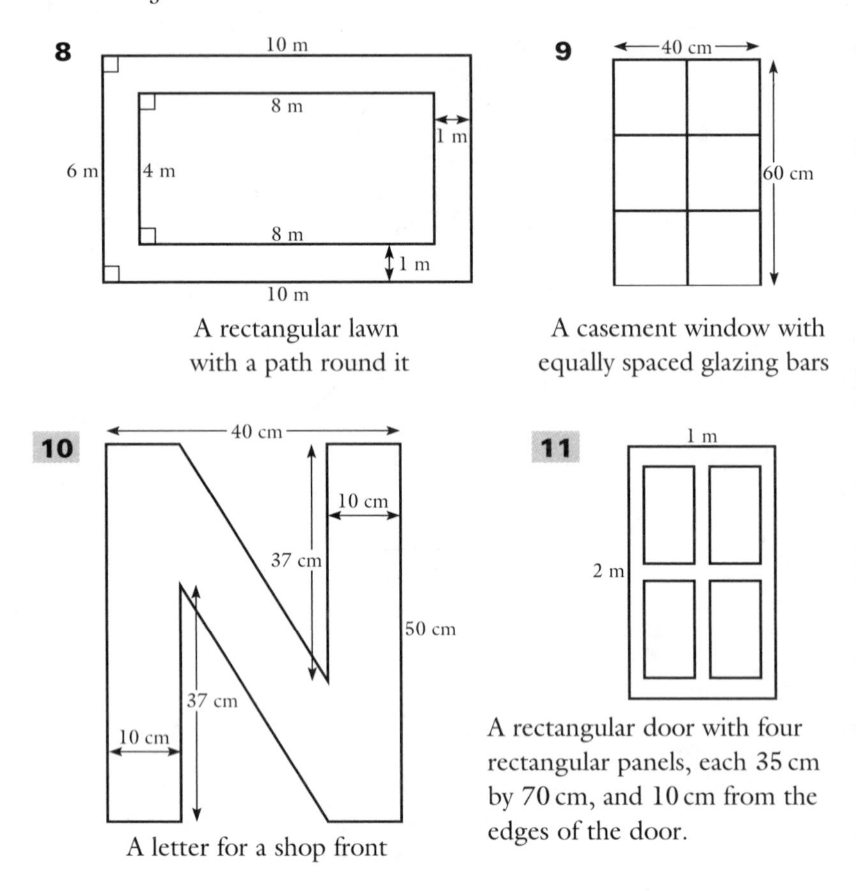

8 A rectangular lawn with a path round it

9 A casement window with equally spaced glazing bars

10 A letter for a shop front

11 A rectangular door with four rectangular panels, each 35 cm by 70 cm, and 10 cm from the edges of the door.

ANGLES OF ELEVATION

If you are standing on level ground and can see a tall building, you will have to look up to see the top of that building.

If you start by looking straight ahead and then look up to the top of the building, the angle through which you raise your eyes is called the *angle of elevation* of the top of the building.

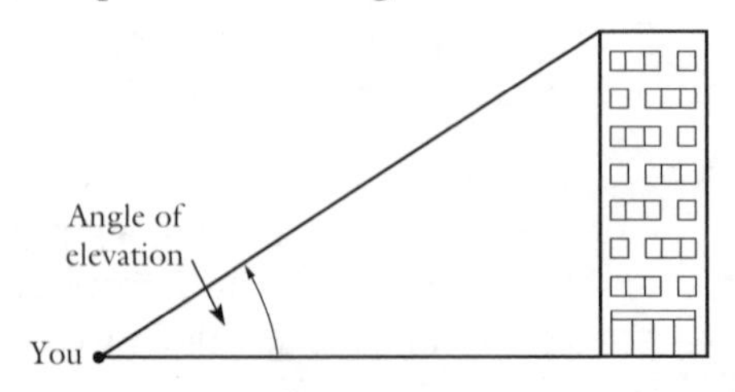

There are instruments for measuring angles of elevation. A simple one can be made from a large card protractor and a piece of string with a weight on the end.

The angle of elevation $\widehat{B}$ is given by $\widehat{B} = 90° - \widehat{A}$. (This method is not very accurate.)

If your distance from the foot of the building and the angle of elevation of the top are both known, you can make a scale drawing of ΔPQR. (Note that *only* ΔPQR needs to be drawn.) This drawing can then be used to work out the height of the building.

EXERCISE 17E

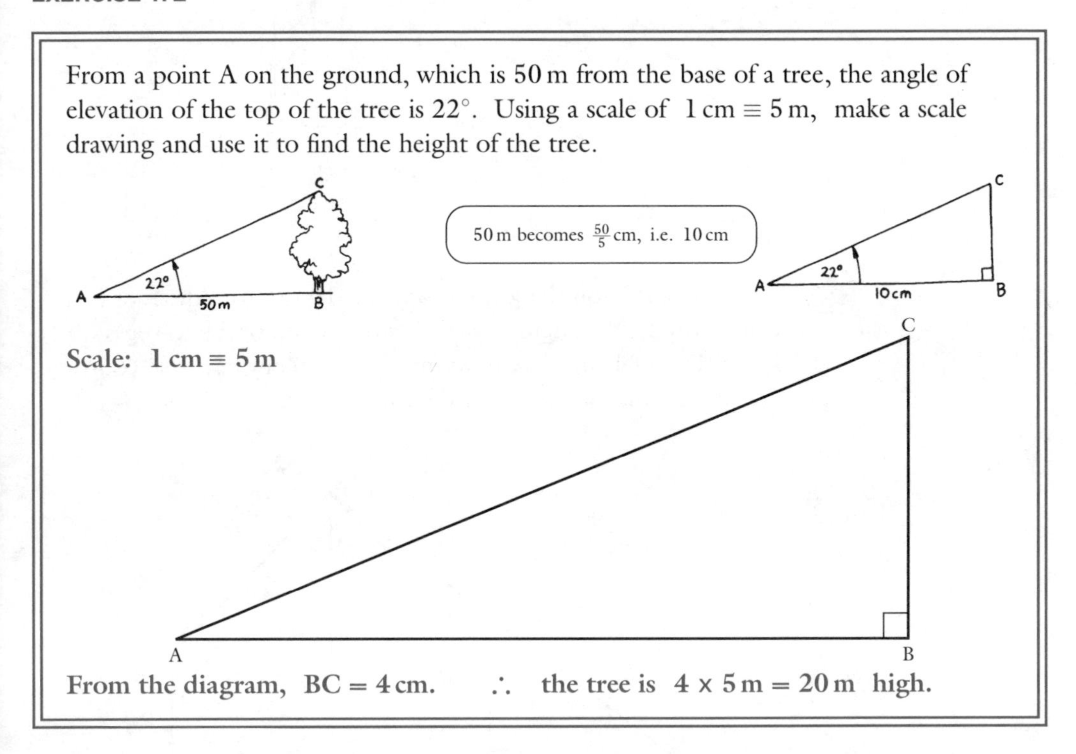

From a point A on the ground, which is 50 m from the base of a tree, the angle of elevation of the top of the tree is 22°. Using a scale of 1 cm ≡ 5 m, make a scale drawing and use it to find the height of the tree.

Scale: 1 cm ≡ 5 m

From the diagram, BC = 4 cm. ∴ the tree is 4 × 5 m = 20 m high.

In questions **1** to **4**, A is a point on the ground, $\widehat{A}$ is the angle of elevation of C, the top of the wall BC of a building. Using a scale of 1 cm ≡ 5 m, make a scale drawing and use it to find the height of the wall BC.

1

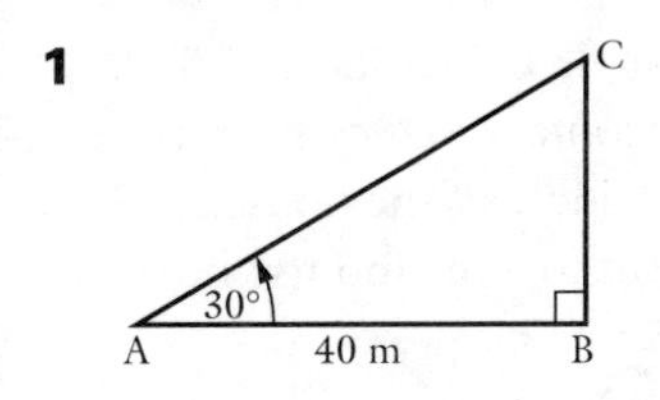

2

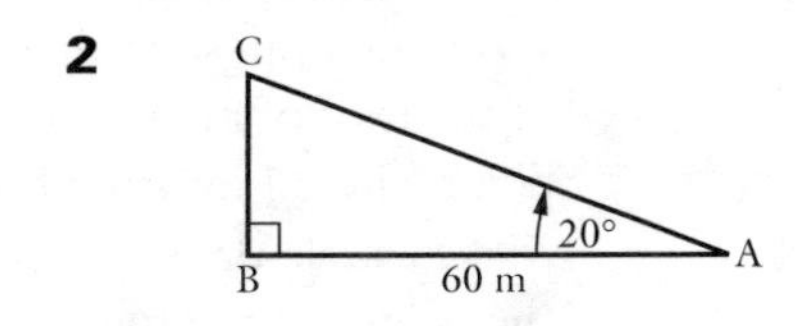

3

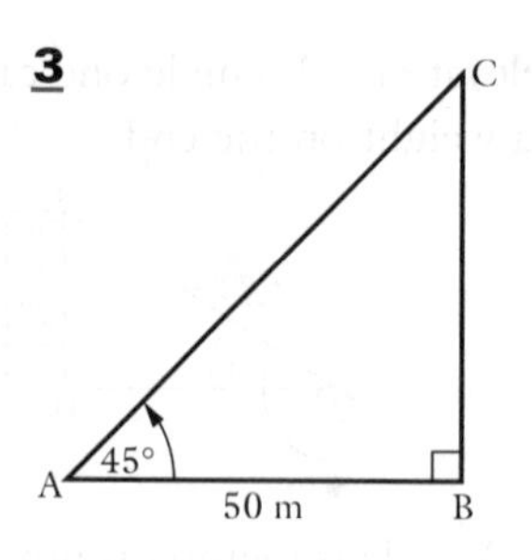

4

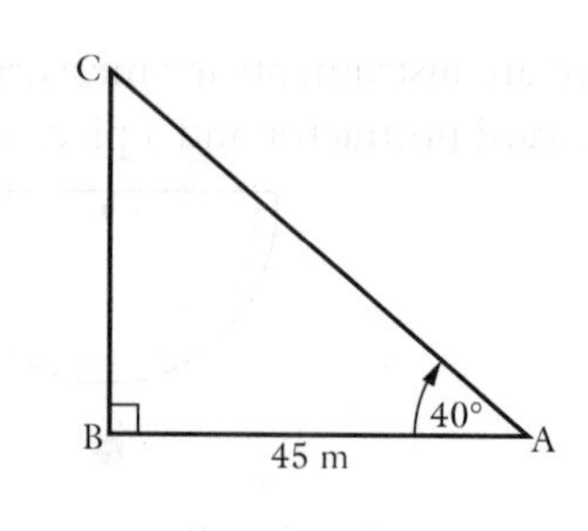

In questions **5** to **9** make a scale drawing of the triangle only; do not add unnecessary details such as buildings.

5

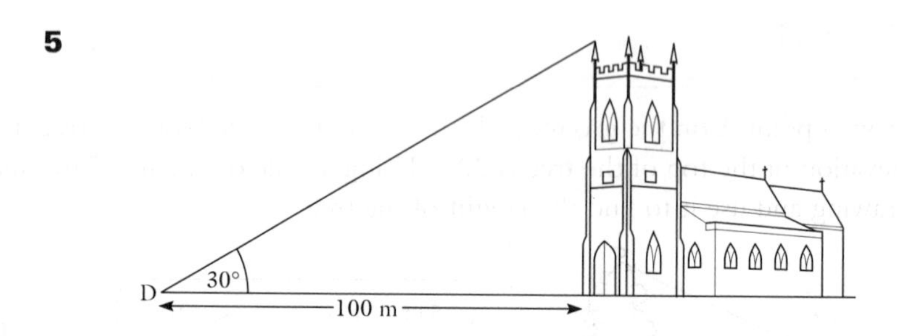

From a point D on the ground which is 100 m from the foot of a church tower, the angle of elevation of the top of the tower is 30°. Use a scale of 1 cm to 10 m to make a scale drawing. Use your drawing to find the height of the tower.

6

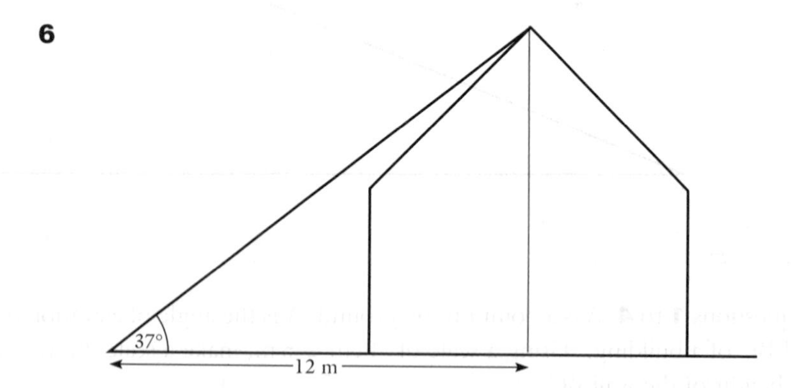

From the opposite side of the road, the angle of elevation of the top of the roof of my house is 37°. The horizontal distance from the point where I measured the angle to the middle of the house is 12 m. Make a scale drawing, using a scale of 1 cm to 1 m, and use it to find the height of the top of the roof.

7

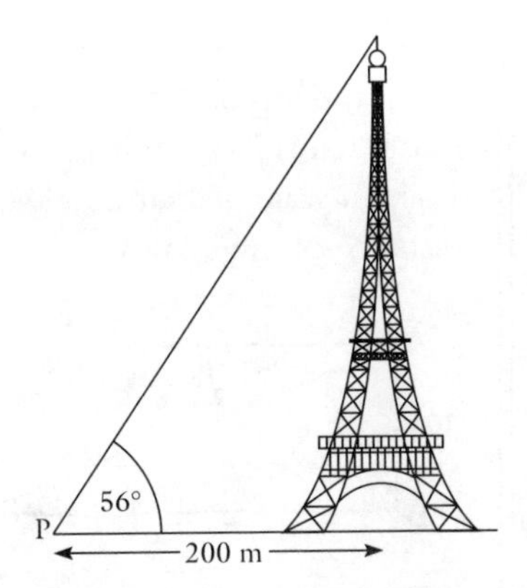

From a point P on the ground which is 200 m from the middle of the base of the Eiffel Tower, the angle of elevation of the top is 56°. Use a scale of 1 cm to 20 m to make a scale diagram and find the height of the Eiffel Tower.

8 From a point on the ground which is 300 m from the base of the National Westminster Tower, the angle of elevation of the top of the tower is 31°. Using a scale of 1 cm to 50 m , make a scale drawing and find the height of the National Westminster Tower. (This is a high office building in the City of London.)

9 The top of a radio mast is 76 m from the ground. From a point P on the ground, the angle of elevation of the top of the mast is 40°. Use a scale of 1 cm to 10 m to make a scale drawing to find how far P is from the bottom of the mast.
(You will need to do some calculation before you can do the scale drawing.)

ANGLES OF DEPRESSION

An *angle of depression* is the angle between the line looking straight ahead and the line looking *down* at an object below you.

If, for example, you are standing on a cliff looking out to sea, the diagram shows the angle of depression of a yacht.

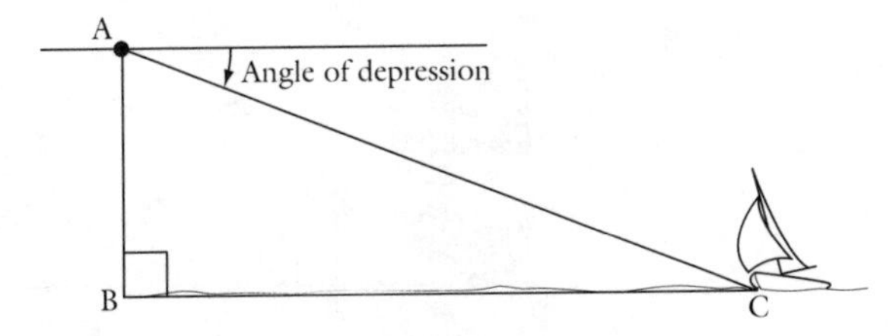

If the angle of depression and the height of the cliff are both known, you can make a scale drawing of ΔABC. Then you can work out the distance of the boat from the foot of the cliff.

EXERCISE 17F

From the top of a cliff 20 m high, the angle of depression of a boat out at sea is 24°.
Using a scale of 1 cm to 5 m, make a scale drawing to find the distance of the boat from the foot of the cliff.

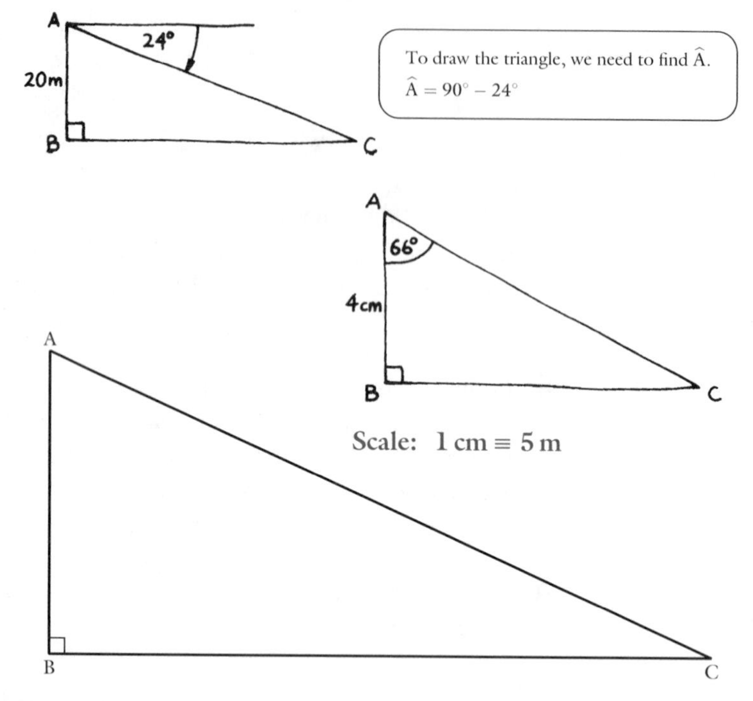

From the drawing, BC = 9.0 cm.

∴ the distance of the boat from the foot of the cliff is

9 x 5 m = 45 m

Draw simple diagrams like those in the worked example; do not draw buildings, trees, etc.

In questions **1** to **4** use a scale of 1 cm ≡ 10 m.

1

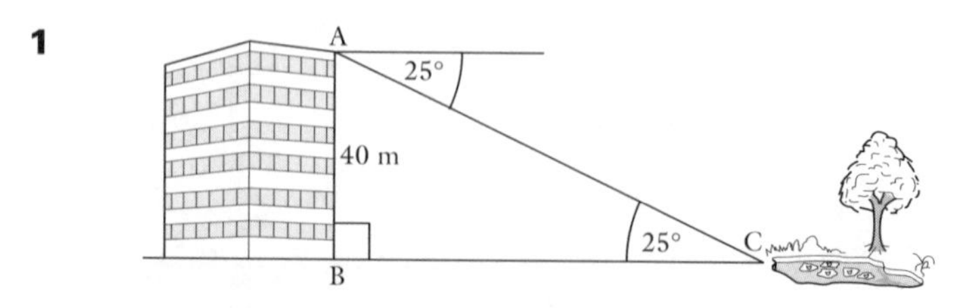

From the top A, of a building the angle of depression of the front edge of an ornamental pond C, is 25°. Find BC, the distance of the pond from the base of the building.

2

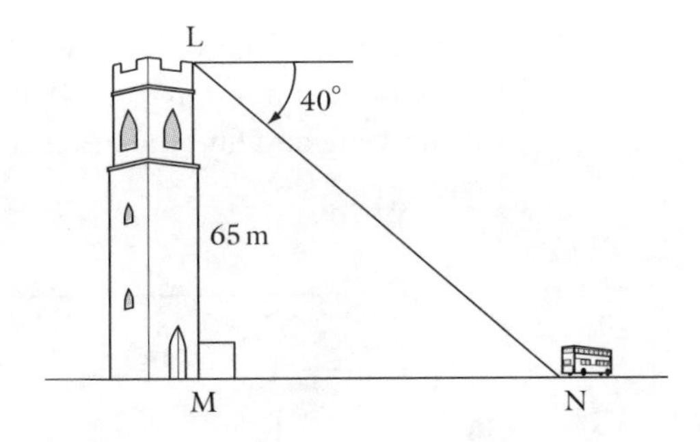

From the top L of a tower the angle of depression of a bus N on the road below, is 40°. Find MN, the distance of the bus from the foot of the tower.

3

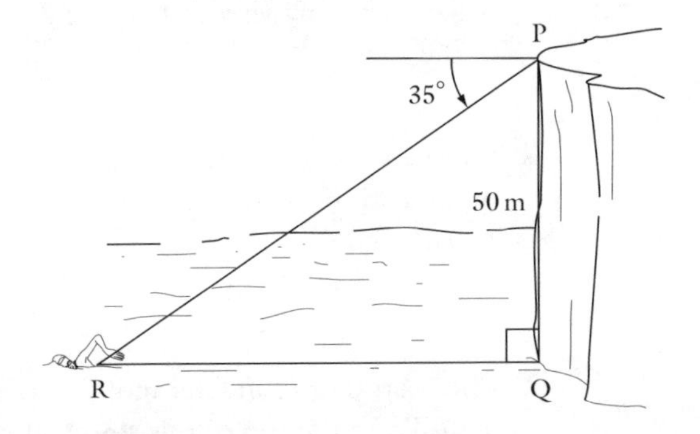

From the top P of a cliff the angle of depression of a swimmer R out at sea, is 35°. Find RQ, the distance of the swimmer from the foot of the vertical cliff.

4

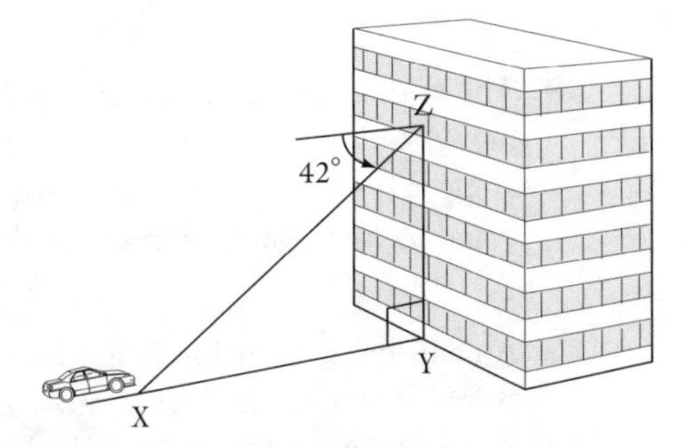

From Z, the position of my window in a multi-storey office block, the angle of depression of my car X in the car park is 42°. Given that Z is 90 m above ground level, find XY, the distance of my car from the point on the ground immediately beneath my window.

5 From the top of the Eiffel Tower, which is 300 m high, the angle of depression of a house is 20°. Use a scale of 1 cm to 50 m to make a scale drawing and find the distance of the house from the base of the tower.

6

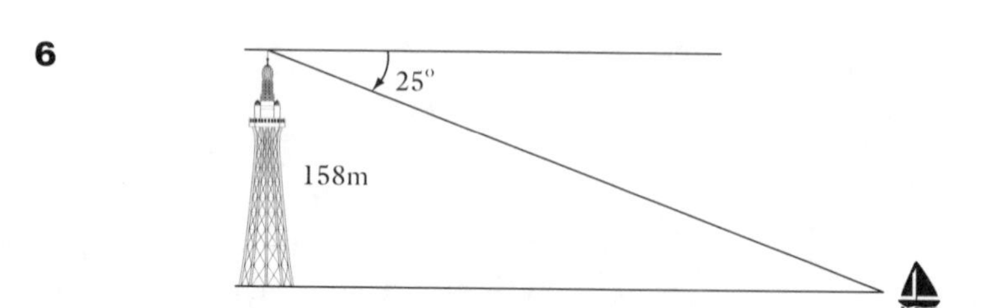

From the top of Blackpool Tower, which is 158 m high, the angle of depression of a yacht at sea is 25°. Use a scale of 1 cm to 20 m to make a scale drawing to find the distance of the yacht from the base of the tower.

7 From an aircraft flying at a height of 300 m, the angle of depression of the end of the runway is noted as 18°. Using a scale of 1 cm to 100 m, make a scale diagram to find the horizontal distance of the aircraft from the runway.

8 The Sears Tower in Chicago is an office building and it is 443 m high. From the top of this tower, the angle of depression of a ship on the lake is 40°. How far away from the base of the building is the ship? Use a scale of 1 cm to 50 m to make your scale drawing.

For the remaining questions in this exercise, make a scale drawing choosing your own scale.

9 The pilot of an aircraft, flying at 5000 m, reads the angle of depression of a point on the coast as 30°. At the moment that the angle is read from the cockpit instrument, how much further has the plane to fly before passing over the coast line?

10 An automatic lightship is stationed 500 m from a point A on the coast. There are high cliffs at A and, from the top of these cliffs, the angle of depression of the lightship is 15°. How high are the cliffs?

11 An airport controller measures the angle of elevation of an approaching aircraft as 20°. If the aircraft is then 1.6 km from the control building, at what height is it flying?

THREE-FIGURE BEARINGS

A bearing is a compass direction.

If you are standing at a point A and looking at a tree B in the distance, as shown in the diagram below, then using compass directions you could say that

from A, the bearing of B is SE

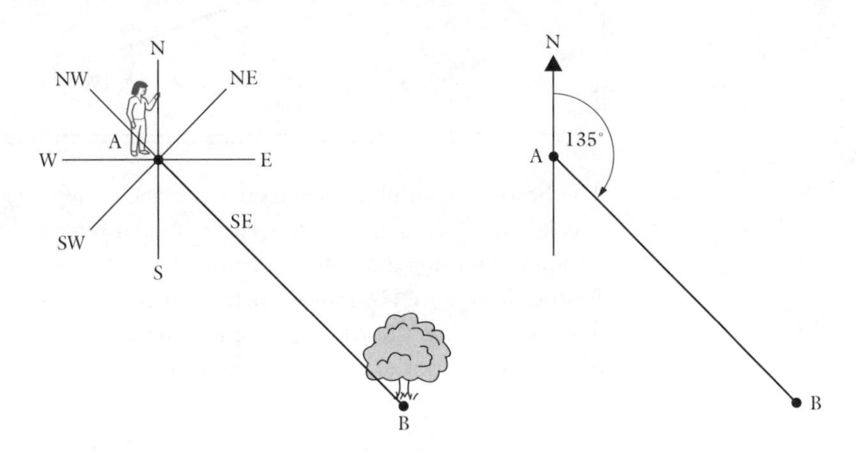

Using a *three-figure bearing* we first look north and then turn clockwise until we are looking at B. The angle turned through is the three-figure bearing.

In this case

from A, the bearing of B is 135°

A three-figure bearing is a clockwise angle measured from north.

If the angle is less than 100°, it is made into a three-figure angle by putting zero in front, so 20° becomes 020°.

EXERCISE 17G

Draw a freehand sketch to illustrate that the bearing of a lighthouse B from a ship, A, is 060°. Mark the angle in your sketch.

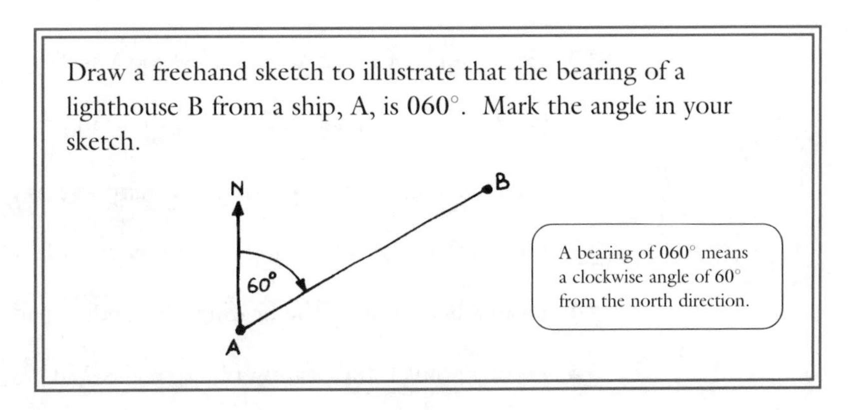

From a ship C the bearing of a ship D is 290°. Make a freehand sketch and mark the angle.

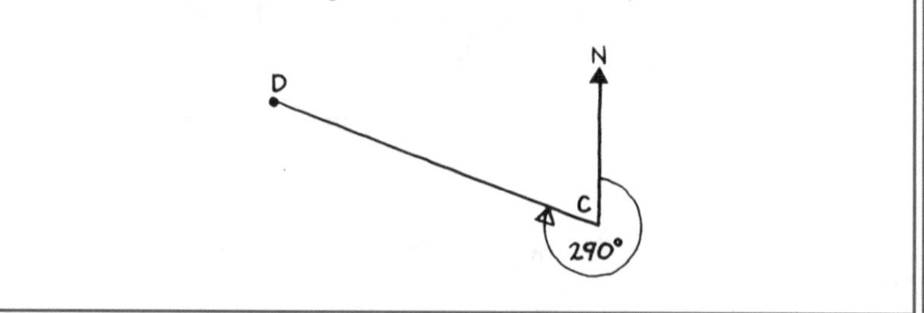

The bearing of an object from an aeroplane, a ship or a control tower is usually found by taking readings from a radar screen. Other bearings can be found by using a hand-held compass.
In questions **1** to **15** draw a freehand sketch to illustrate each bearing. Start by drawing a north-pointing line from where the bearing is being measured. Mark the angle in your sketch.

1 From a ship P the bearing of a yacht Q is 045°.

2 From a control tower F the bearing of an aeroplane A is 090°.

3 From a point A the bearing of a radio mast M is 120°.

4 From a town T the bearing of another town S is 180°.

5 From a point H the bearing of a church C is 210°.

6 The bearing of a ship A from the pier P is 225°.

7 The bearing of a radio mast S from a point O is 140°.

8 The bearing of a yacht Y from a tanker T is 075°.

9 The bearing of a town Q from a town R is 250°.

10 The bearing of a tree X from a hill top Y is 025°.

11 From a ship R the bearing of a port P is 300°.

12 From an aircraft A the bearing of an airport L is 320°.

13 From a town D the bearing of another town E is 260°.

14 From a helicopter G the bearing of a landing pad P is 080°.

15 From a point L the bearing of a tree T is 270°.

In questions **16** to **19** make a freehand copy of the diagram. Do not draw the object. For part **b** add a north-pointing line at the position from where the bearing is to be found.

16

What is the bearing of

a the lighthouse from the ship

b the ship from the lighthouse ?

17

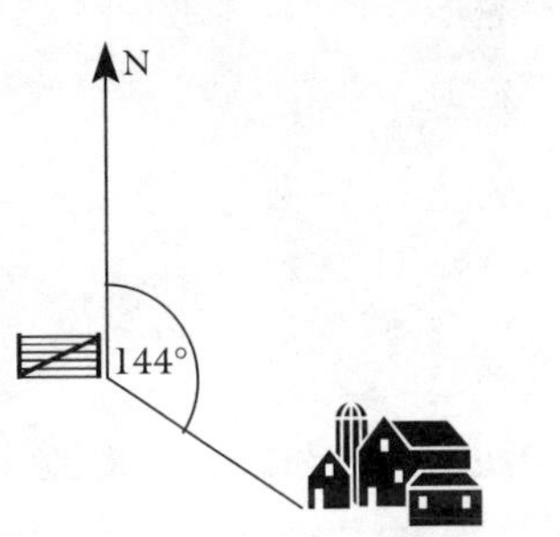

What is the bearing of

a the farm from the gate

b the gate from the farm?

18

What is the bearing of

a the church from the castle

b the castle from the church ?

19

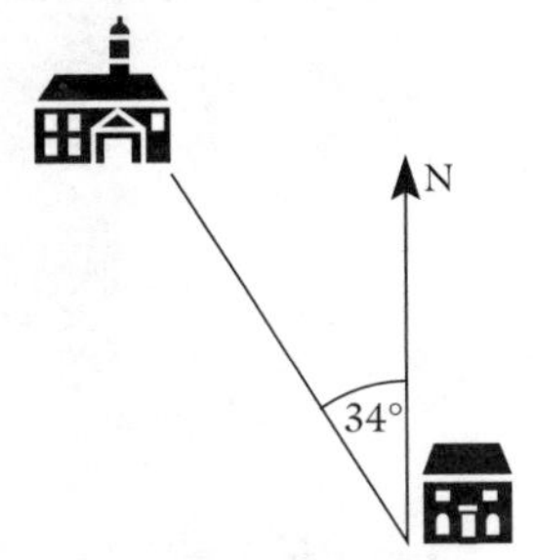

What is the bearing of

a the Town Hall from the Post Office

b the Post Office from the Town Hall ?

20

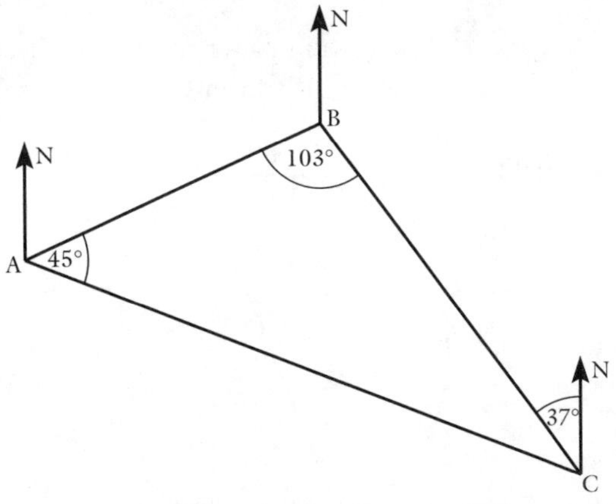

The sketch shows the positions of three villages A, B and C. Use the information given on the diagram to find the bearing of

a B from C
b C from B
c A from B
d B from A
e C from A
f A from C.

21

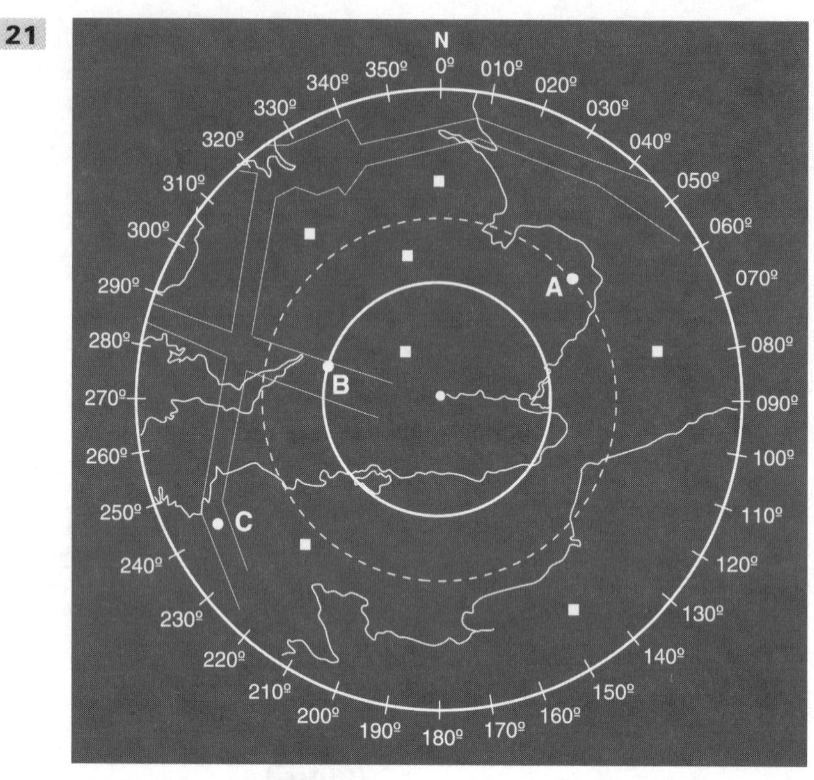

The diagram shows the display on the radar screen in an airport control tower. The centre of the screen shows the position of the control tower. Planes are shown at A, B and C.

a What is the bearing of A from the control tower?

b What is the bearing of B from the control tower?

c Find the bearing of the control tower from C.

d Use tracing paper to mark the positions of B and C. Find the bearing of B from C.

22

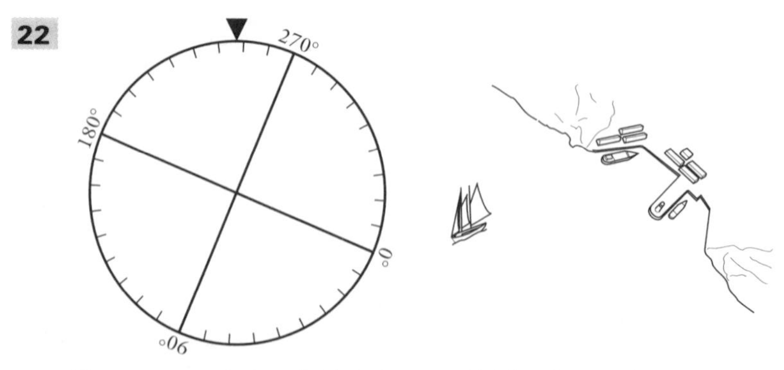

The compass shows the bearing on which a boat is heading out of port. Draw a diagram to show the path of the boat, marking clearly an angle to show its direction in relation to north.

USING BEARINGS TO FIND DISTANCES

If we measure the bearing of a distant object from two different positions and make a scale diagram, we can use this diagram to find the distance of that object from one or other of the positions.

EXERCISE 17H

From one end A of a road the bearing of a building L is 015°. The other end B of the road is 300 m due east of A. From B the bearing of the building is 320°. Using a scale of 1 cm to 50 m, make a scale diagram to find the distance of the building from A.

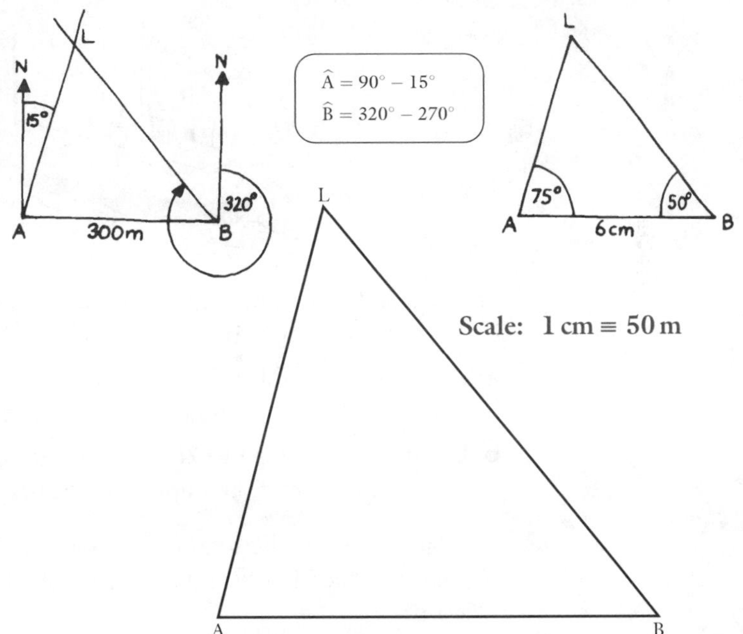

From the diagram, LA = 5.6 cm.

∴ the distance of the building from A is 5.6 x 50 m = 280 m

1

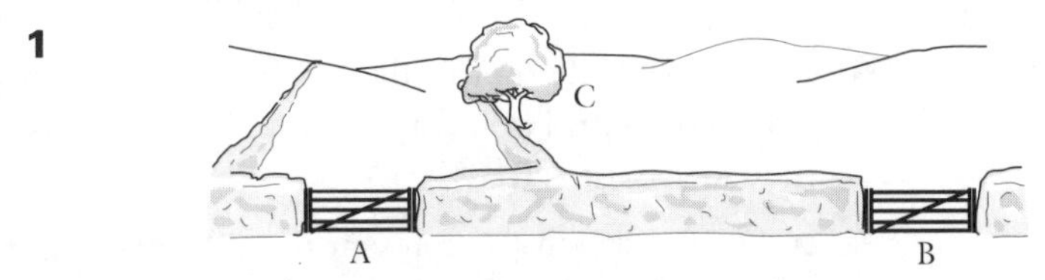

From a gate A the bearing of a tree C is 060°. From a second gate B, which is 100 m due east of A, the bearing of the tree is 330°.

a Draw a sketch to show the positions of A, B and C. Show the north direction and calculate the angles of ΔABC. Show them in your sketch.

b Use a scale of 1 cm to 10 m to make a scale diagram and find the distance of the tree from gate A.

2

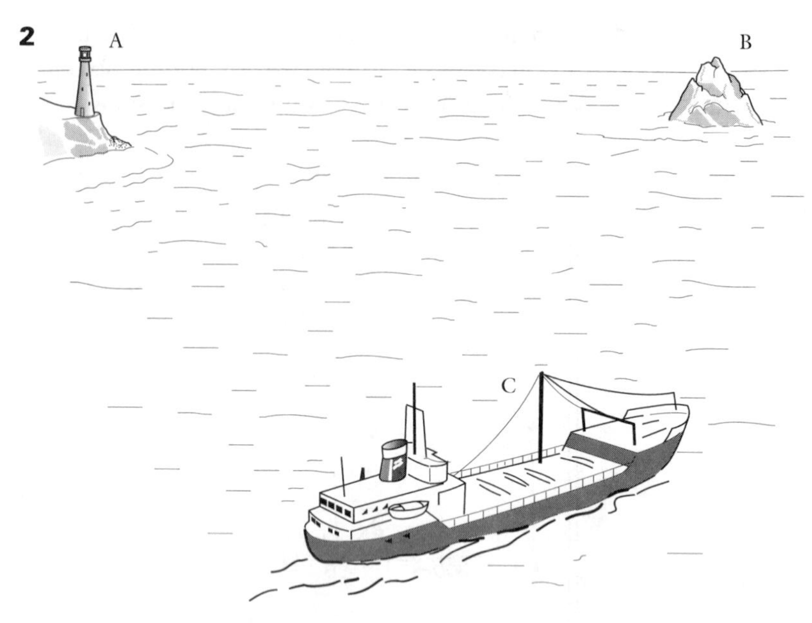

From a ship C the bearing of a lighthouse A is 320°. A rock B, which is 200 m due east of A, is on a bearing of 030° from the ship.

a Draw a sketch to show the positions of A, B and C. Calculate the angles in ΔABC and show them in your sketch.

b Using a scale of 1 cm to 20 m, make a scale diagram and use it to find the distance of the ship from the rock B.

3 From a point A, the bearing of a tower T is 030°. From a second point B, which is 400 m due north of A, the bearing of the tower is 140°.

a Draw a sketch to show the positions of A, B and T. Calculate the angles in ΔABT and show them in your sketch.

b Using a scale of 1 cm to 50 m, make a scale drawing and use it to find the distance of the tower from A.

4 From a control point A, the bearing of a radar mast M is 060°. From a second control point B, which is 40 m due east of A, the bearing of the radar mast is 010°.

a Draw a sketch to represent this information. Calculate the angles in ΔABM and show them in your sketch.

b Use a scale of 1 cm to 5 m and make a scale drawing to find the distance of the radar mast from the control point A.

5 From a ship P the bearing of a submarine S is 020°. From a second ship Q, which is 1000 m due north of P, the bearing of the submarine is 070°. Using a scale of 1 cm to 50 m, make a scale drawing to find the distance of the submarine from P.

6

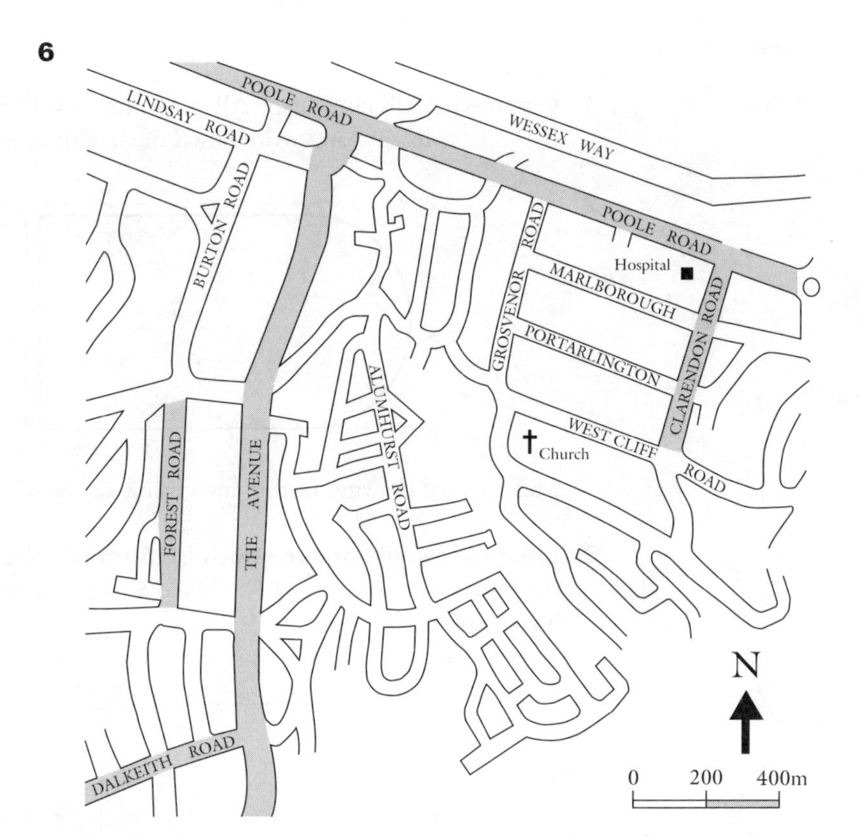

The map shows part of the seaside resort of Bournemouth. Use this map to answer the following questions. Do not draw on this map; if you need to draw, use tracing paper to copy the section of the map that you want to use.

a How long, approximately, is

i Forest Road

ii The Avenue from Dalkeith Road to Poole Road?

b What is the approximate bearing of

i the north end of Clarendon Road from its south end?

ii the south end of Clarendon Road from its north end?

iii the church (✝) on West Cliff Road from the Hospital (■) on Poole Road?

MIXED EXERCISE

EXERCISE 17I

1 Construct ΔABC in which $AB = 64$ mm, $BC = 55$ mm and $\widehat{B} = 53°$. Measure and write down the length of AC.

2 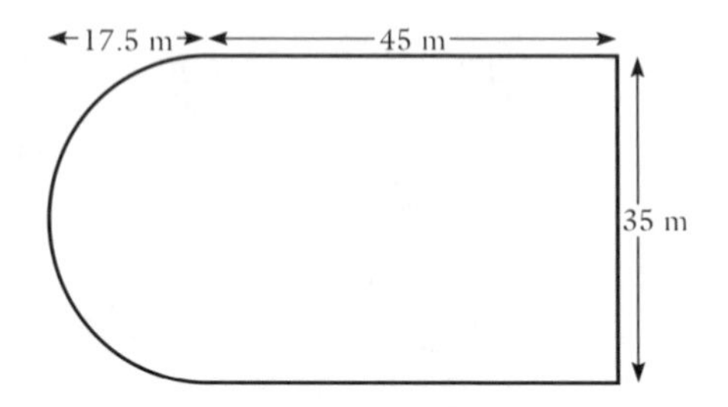

Make a scale drawing of this lawn using a scale of 1 cm to 5 m.

3 From the top of a tower, which is 150 m tall, the angle of depression of a house is 17°. Make a freehand sketch to show this information.

4 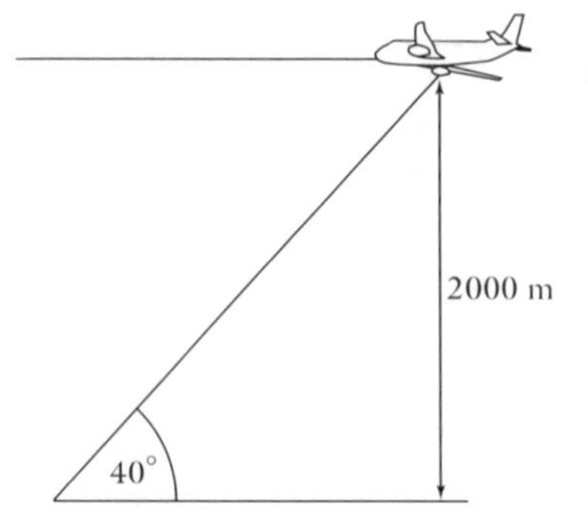

An aircraft is flying at a height of 2000 m, and from a point on the ground an observer measures the angle of elevation of the aircraft as 40°. Make a scale drawing, choosing your own scale, to find the distance from the observer to the point on the ground immediately beneath the aircraft.

5 A cottage C is 850 m due east of a farm F. From the farm the bearing of a barn B is 063° and from the cottage the bearing of the barn is 330°.

a Draw a sketch to show this information. Find the angles in ΔBCF and show them in your sketch.

b Using a scale of 1 cm to 100 m make a scale diagram and use it to find the distance of the barn

i from the farm

ii from the cottage.

PRACTICAL WORK

1 The whole class working together can collect the information for this exercise.
Measure your classroom and make a freehand sketch of the floor plan. Mark the position and width of doors and windows.
Choosing a suitable scale, make an accurate scale drawing of the floor plan of your classroom.
If you would like a bigger challenge show the position of all the furniture in the room.

2 The sketch shows the measurements of Ken Barker's bathroom. There is only one outside wall and the bottom of the window is 120 cm above the level of the floor.
Draw an accurate diagram of the floor, using a scale of 1 cm to 10 cm.

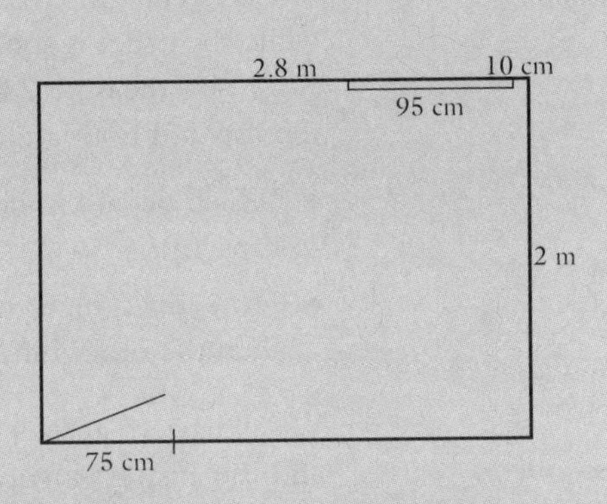

Ken wants to have a new bathroom suite. The units he would like to install, together with their measurements, are:

bath 170 cm × 75 cm
handbasin 60 cm × 42 cm, the longer edge against a wall
shower tray 80 cm square
toilet 70 cm × 50 cm, the shorter measurement against a wall
bidet 55 cm × 35 cm, the shorter measurement against a wall.

Using the same scale make accurate drawings of the plans of these units, cut them out and see if you can place them on your plan in acceptable positions.
If they will not all fit into the room, which unit(s) would you be prepared to do without? Give reasons for your answer.

Is it possible to arrange your chosen units so that all the plumbing is against

a the outside wall

b not more than two walls at right angles, one of which is the outside wall? Illustrate your answer with a diagram.

VOLUMES

Sally is thinking of buying a new pedal-bin for the kitchen. At the Department Store, bins of many different shapes and sizes are on display. Her final choice is between two bins, each priced at £9.99; one is circular in cross-section while the other is square. Both bins measure 240 mm across the top and both are 38 cm high.

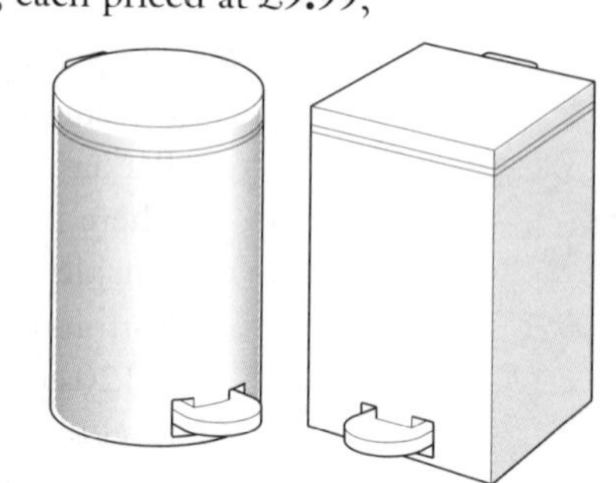

- Which pedal-bin has the larger capacity?
- How much more will it hold than the other bin?

We all have to answer these and similar questions at one time or another, and the answers involve knowing how to calculate volumes.

EXERCISE 18A Discuss these questions with members of your group.

1 What information does a builder need before he can order the blocks to build a wall?

2 A manufacturer of reinforced steels joists (RSJs) can supply joists to order with different cross-sections. The cost, for each RSJ of a given length, depends on the amount of material used. Given below are sketches, drawn to scale, of several different RSJs. All are the same length.

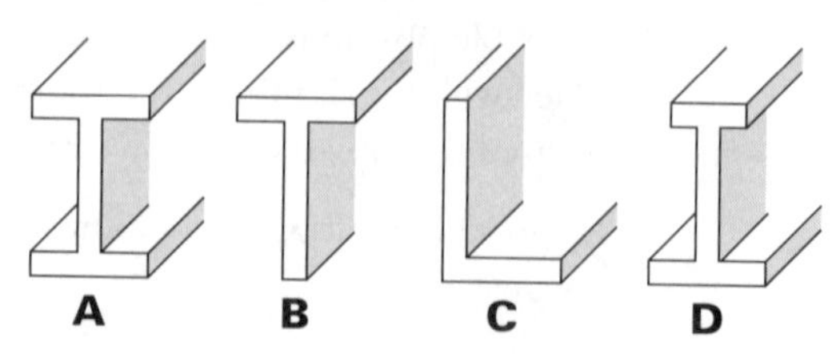

a Which RSJ do you think would be **i** the cheapest **ii** the dearest?

b What information do you need to find the exact cost of each one?

(Assume that if you use twice the amount of material you will double the cost.)

3 Alex wants to put a new tiled roof on his garage. He measures the area of the roof and sets off for the builders' merchant. After choosing a rectangular tile he calculates its area, then divides his answer into the area of the roof. He thinks this gives him the number of tiles he should buy.

a Explain why this calculation will not give him the number of tiles he needs.

b What measurements should he make and how should he use them to get a more accurate value of the number of tiles he needs?

c Why should he order more tiles than he found in part **b**?

d He wants to transport the tiles home using his pick-up truck. How can he calculate the number of journeys he needs to make if the tiles must not be loaded above the height of the sides of the truck which are 50 cm high?

e Can you think of a reason why he should stop loading the tiles before they are 50 cm high?

UNITS OF VOLUME

Volume is measured in standard-sized cubes.
In metric units these are the cubic centimetre (cm^3), the cubic metre (m^3) and the cubic millimetre (mm^3).
In Imperial units these are the cubic inch (cu in), the cubic foot (cu ft) and the cubic yard (cu yd).

Capacity is the volume inside a container.
The metric units of capacity are the litre, the centilitre (cl) and the millilitre (ml).
Imperial units of capacity are the gallon and the pint.

EXERCISE 18B

Copy and complete the following sentences, inserting an appropriate number or unit.

1 The volume of milk most people add to a cup of tea is about 25 __.

2 A kitchen bucket holds about __ litres.

3 The petrol tank of my car holds 10 __ of petrol.

4 A spoon used to give medicine holds 5 __.

VOLUME OF A CUBOID

Remember that we find the volume of a cuboid (that is, a rectangular block) by multiplying length by width by height,

i.e. volume = length × width × height

or $V = l \times w \times h$

Remember also that the measurements must all be in the same unit before they are multiplied together.

EXERCISE 18C

Find the volume of a wooden cuboid of length 10 cm, width 66 mm and height 7 cm.

Width = 66 mm = 6.6 cm

$V = l \times w \times h$

$= 10 \times 6.6 \times 7 = 462$

Volume = 462 cm^3

We must change 66 mm to centimetres so that all measurements are in the same unit.

1 Find the volume of a cuboid of length 9 cm, width 6 cm and height 4 cm.

2 Find the volume of a cuboid of length 12 in, width 8 in and height 4.5 in.

3 Find the volume of a rectangular block of metal 300 mm long, 20 mm wide and 30 mm high.

4 Find the volume of a cuboid of length 6.2 cm, width 3.4 cm and height 5 cm.

Find the volume of the following cuboids, changing the units first if necessary. Do *not* draw a diagram.

	Length	Width	Height	Volume units
5	3.2 cm	5 mm	10 mm	mm^3
6	4 cm	$3\frac{1}{4}$ cm	$4\frac{1}{2}$ cm	cm^3

	Length	Width	Height	Volume units
7	9.2 m	300 cm	1.8 m	m^3
8	6.2 m	32 mm	20 cm	cm^3

Compound solids are made by putting two or more cuboids together.

Find the volume of this solid.

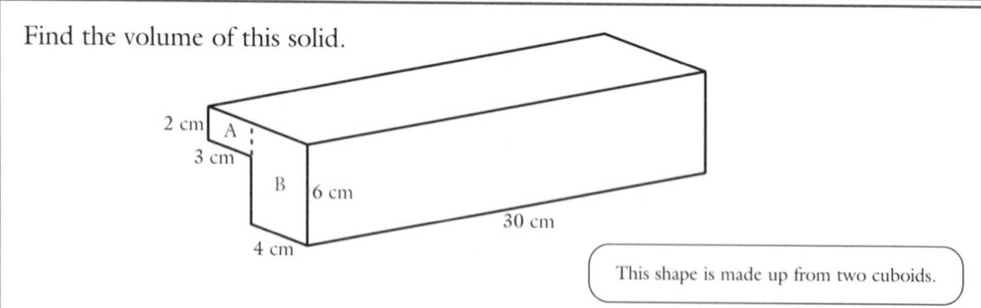

This shape is made up from two cuboids.

Cuboid A measures 2 cm × 3 cm × 30 cm
and cuboid B measures 4 cm × 6 cm × 30 cm.

$\therefore$ Volume of cuboid A = $2 \times 3 \times 30$ cm^3 = 180 cm^3

Volume of cuboid B = $4 \times 6 \times 30$ cm^3 = 720 cm^3

$\therefore$ Volume of the solid = 180 cm^3 + 720 cm^3 = 900 cm^3

In questions **9** to **11** find the volume of each solid assuming that it has been made from two or more cuboids.

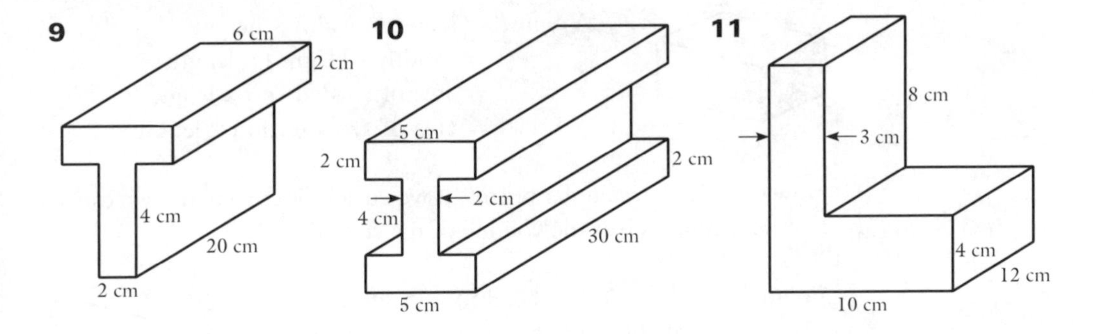

In questions **12** and **13** find the capacity, in litres, of each container.

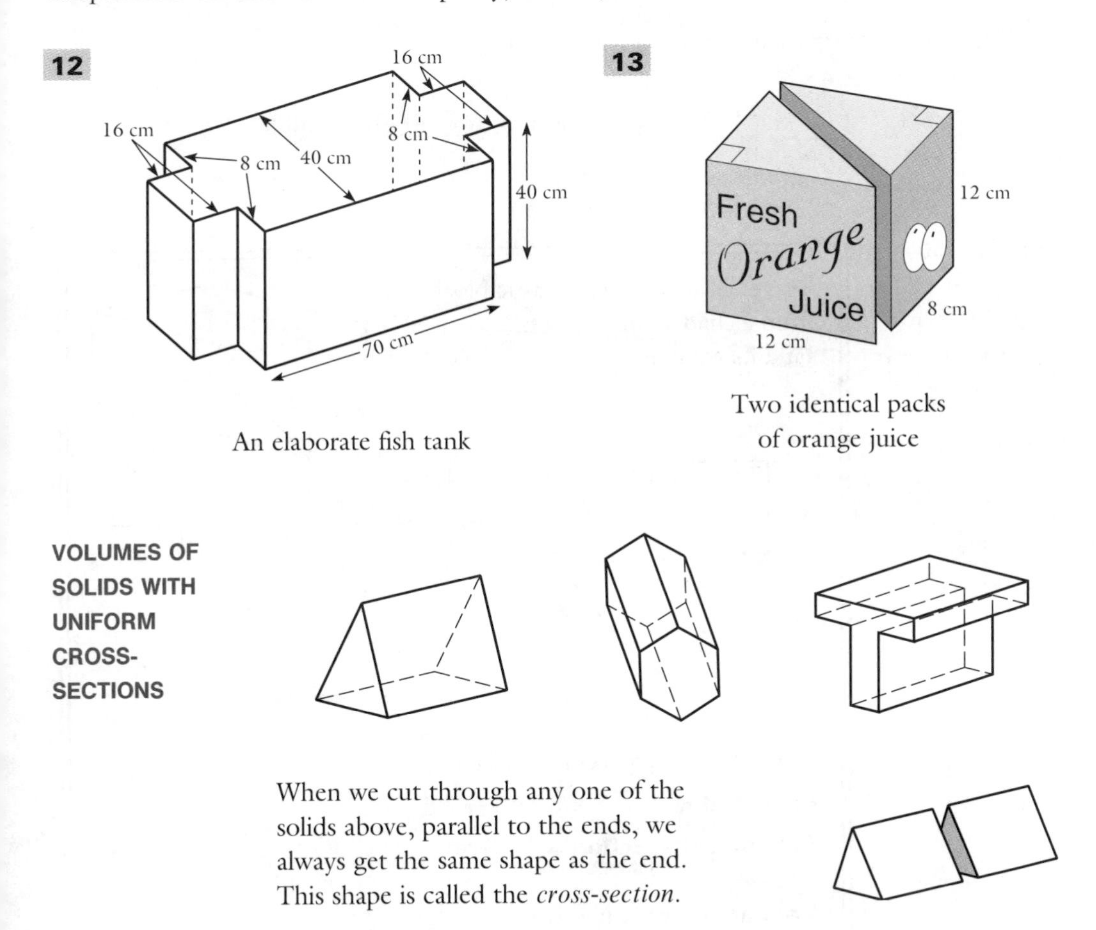

An elaborate fish tank

Two identical packs of orange juice

VOLUMES OF SOLIDS WITH UNIFORM CROSS-SECTIONS

When we cut through any one of the solids above, parallel to the ends, we always get the same shape as the end. This shape is called the *cross-section*.

As the cross-section is the same shape and size wherever the solid is cut, the cross-section is said to be *uniform* or *constant*. These solids are also called *prisms* and we can find the volumes of some of them.

First consider a cuboid (which can also be thought of as a rectangular prism).

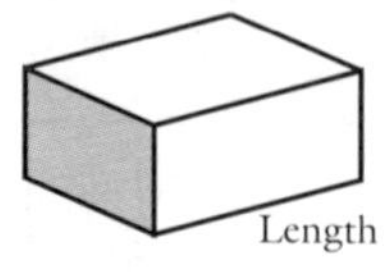

Volume = length × width × height
= (width × height) × length
= area of shaded end × length
= area of cross-section × length

Now consider a triangular prism. If we enclose it in a cuboid we can see that its volume is half the volume of the cuboid.

Volume = ($\frac{1}{2}$ × width × height) × length
= area of shaded triangle × length
= area of cross-section × length

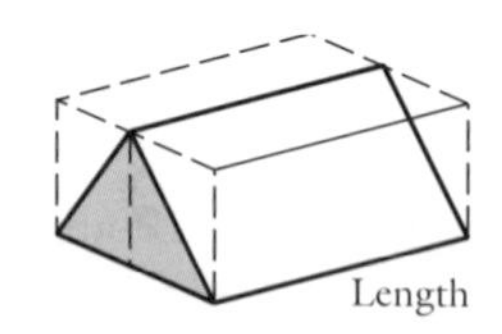

This is true of any prism so that

Volume of a prism = area of cross-section × length

EXERCISE 18D

This solid represents a plastic block from a child's building set.
Find its volume.

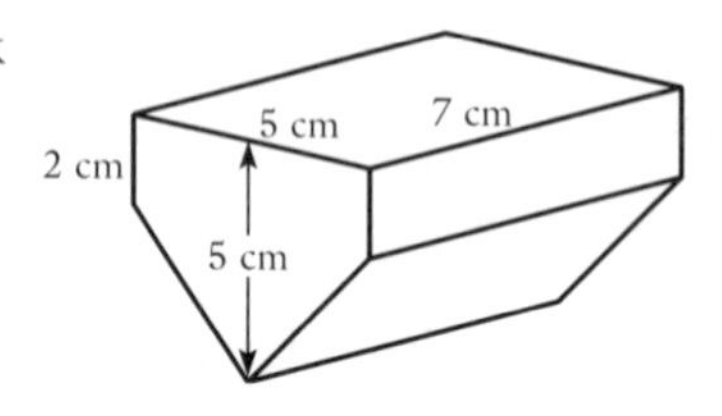

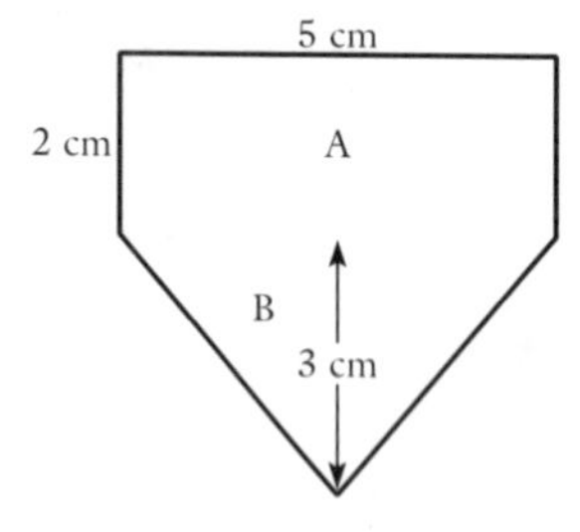

We draw the cross-section only, not the solid.

Area of A = $2 \times 5\ \text{cm}^2 = 10\ \text{cm}^2$
Area of B = $\frac{1}{2} \times 5 \times 3\ \text{cm}^2 = 7.5\ \text{cm}^2$
Area of cross-section = $17.5\ \text{cm}^2$

Volume = area × length
= $17.5 \times 7\ \text{cm}^3$
= $122.5\ldots\ \text{cm}^3 = 123\ \text{cm}^3$ (correct to 3 s.f.)

1

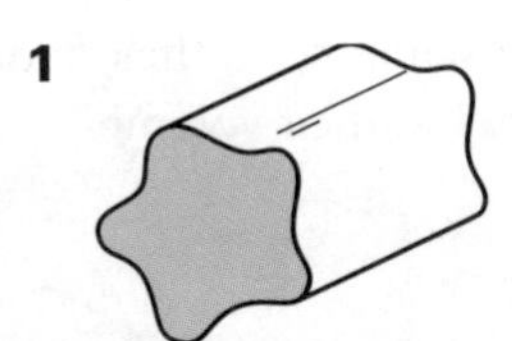

The area of the cross-section of the given solid is 42 cm^2 and the length is 32 cm. Find its volume.

2 Find the volume of the solid.

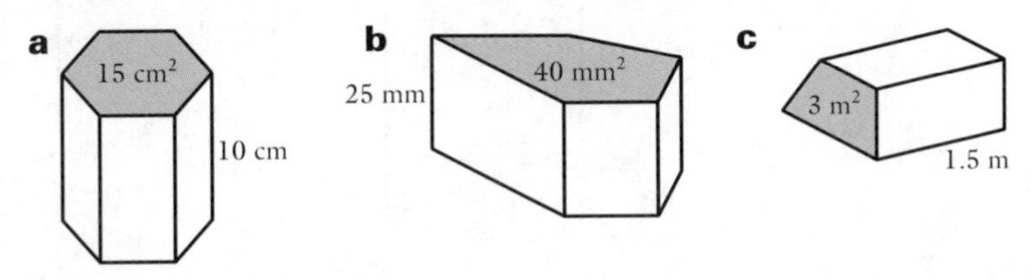

For each prism find **a** the area of the cross-section **b** the volume.
Draw a diagram of the cross-section but do *not* draw a picture of the solid.

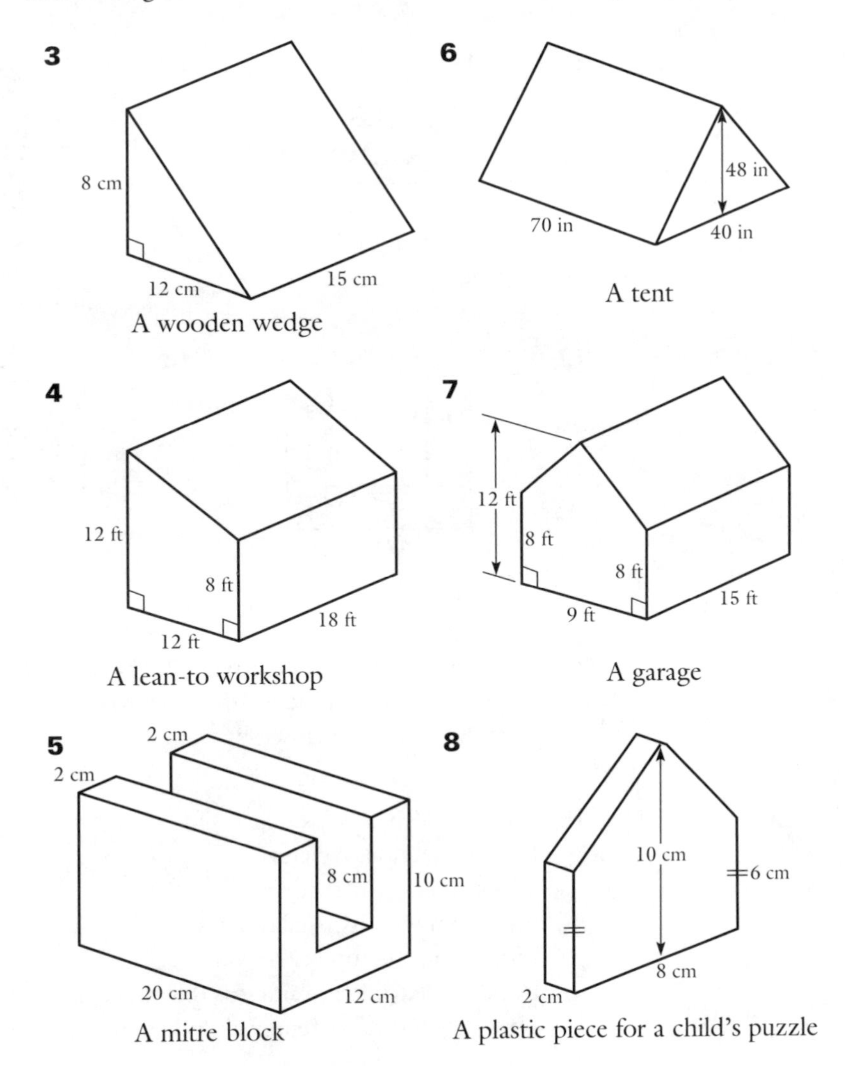

The following two solids are standing on their ends so the vertical measurement is the length. Find their volumes.

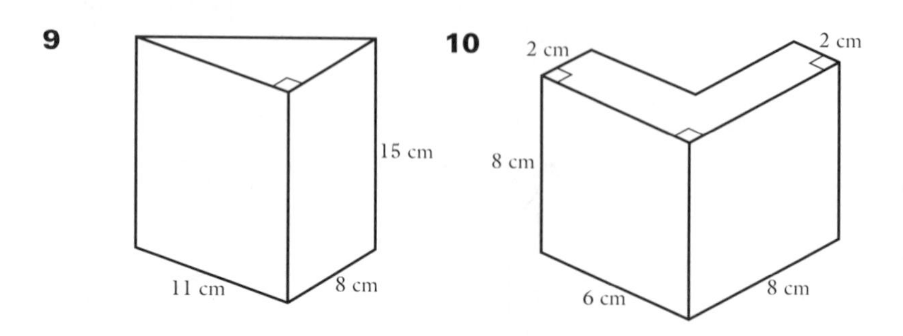

In questions **11** to **14**, the cross-sections of the prisms and their lengths are given. Find their volumes.

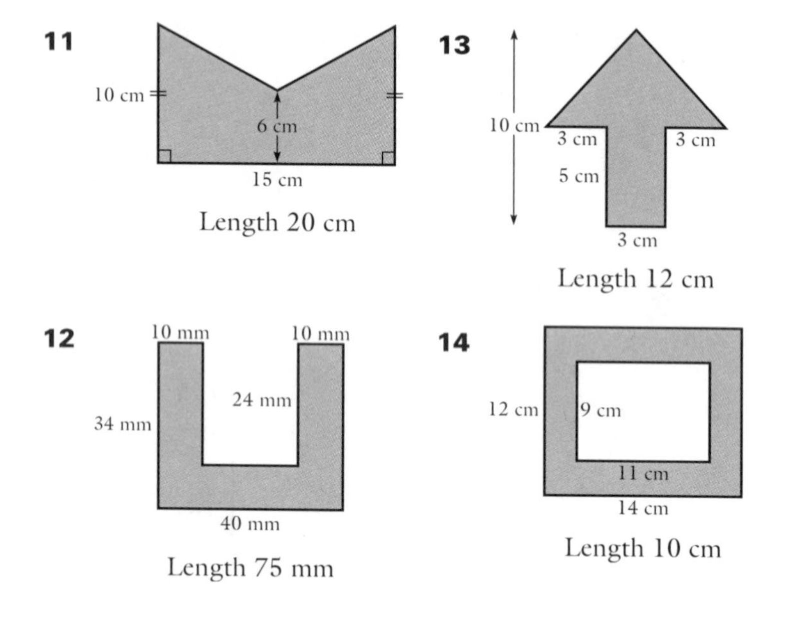

15 A tent is in the shape of a triangular prism. Its length is 2.4 m, its height is 1.8 m and the width of the triangular end is 2.4 m. Find the volume enclosed by the tent.

16 A trench 15 m long is dug. Its cross-section, which is uniform, is in the shape of a trapezium with its parallel sides horizontal. Its top is 2 m wide, its base is 1.6 m wide and it is 0.8 m deep. How much earth is removed in digging the trench?

0.2 m ← 1.6 m → 0.2 m

0.8 m

1.6 m

17

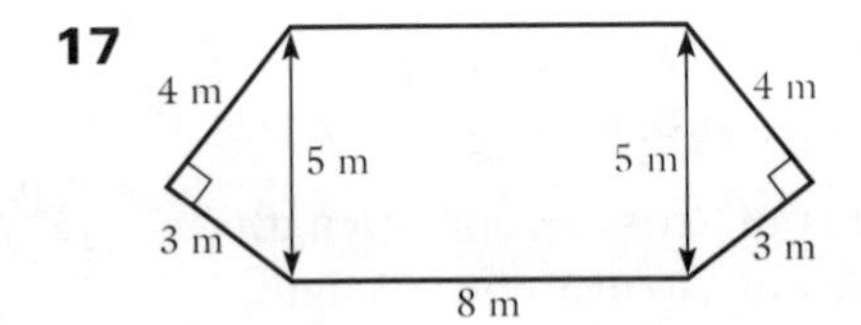

A solid of uniform cross-section is 12 m long. Its cross-section is shown in the diagram. Find its volume.

18

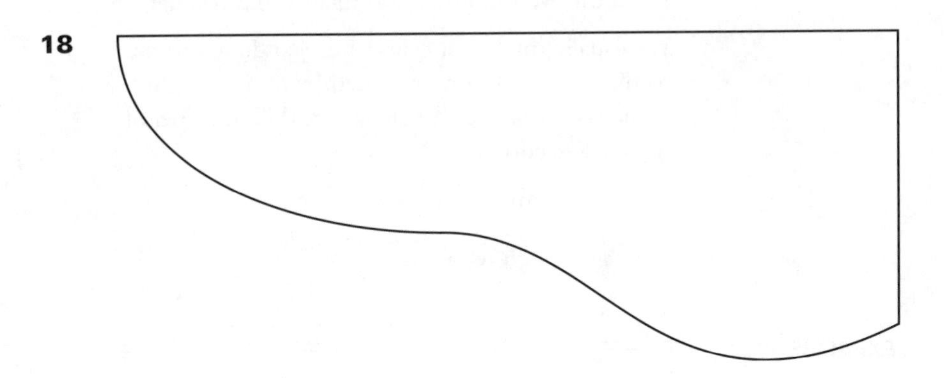

The diagram shows the cross-section of a gutter which carries away the rain water that falls on the roof of a house. The total length of gutter along the front of the house is 12 m.

a Trace this cross-section and place your tracing over a 1 cm grid. By counting squares, estimate the area of cross-section in square centimetres.

b Hence find the maximum volume of water that the gutter can hold. Give your answer in cm^3 correct to 2 significant figures.

c What is the capacity, in litres, of the gutter?

19

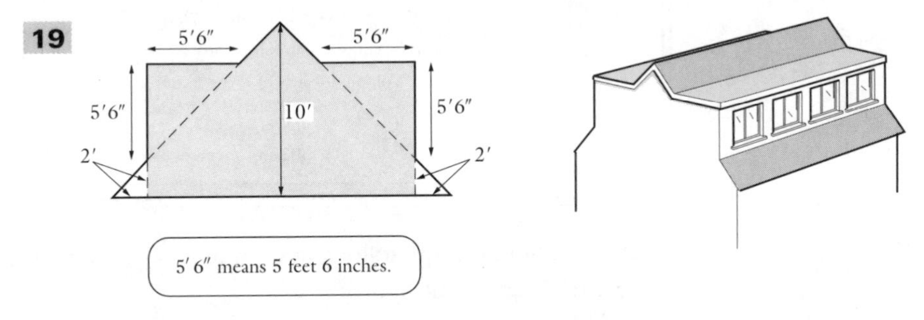

The diagram shows the cross-section through the roof space inside a chalet bungalow. There are dormer windows along the whole of both sides.

a Use the measurements given on the diagram to find the area of cross-section of the usable space (shown shaded).

b If the bungalow is 40 ft long find the total volume of the roof space that can be used.

VOLUME OF A CYLINDER

A cylinder can be thought of as a circular prism so its volume can be found using

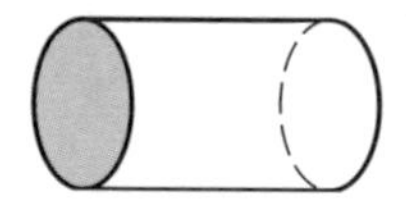

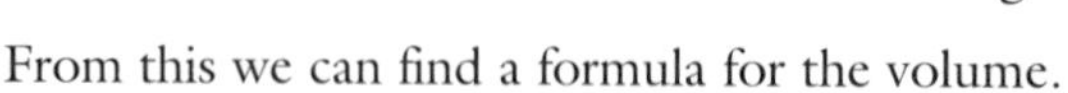

$$\text{volume} = \text{area of cross-section} \times \text{length}$$
$$= \text{area of circular end} \times \text{length}$$

From this we can find a formula for the volume.

We usually think of a cylinder as standing upright so that its length is represented by h (for height). If the radius of the end circle is r, then the area of the cross-section is πr^2

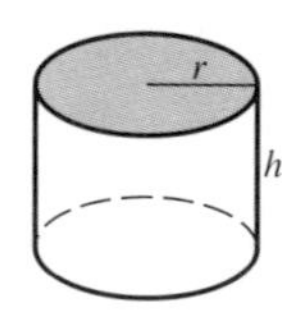

$\therefore \quad \text{volume} = \pi r^2 \times h$

$$V = \pi r^2 h$$

EXERCISE 18E

Find the volume inside a cylindrical mug of internal diameter 8 cm and depth 6 cm. Use the π button on your calculator.

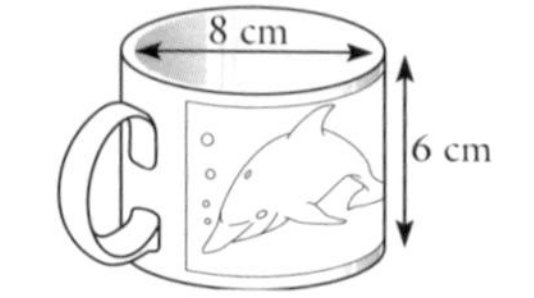

As the diameter is 8 cm, the radius is 4 cm.

The volume is given by the formula

$\boldsymbol{V = \pi r^2 h}$

So volume $= \pi \times 4 \times 4 \times 6\ \text{cm}^3 = 301.59\ldots\ \text{cm}^3$

The volume of the mug is 302 cm³ (correct to 3 s.f.)

An alternative method would be:

The area of cross-section is given by the formula $A = \pi r^2$

$A = \pi \times 4 \times 4 = 50.265\ldots$

$\therefore$ Area of cross-section $= 50.265\ldots\ \text{cm}^2$

Volume $=$ area of cross-section $\times$ length
$= (50.265\ldots \times 6)\ \text{cm}^3$
$= 301.59\ldots\ \text{cm}^3$
$= 302\ \text{cm}^3$ (correct to 3 s.f.)

Find the volumes of the following cylinders. Give all your answers correct to 3 significant figures.

1 Radius 2 cm, height 10 cm

2 Radius 3 cm, height 4 cm

3 Radius 3 in, height $2\frac{1}{2}$ in

4 Diameter 2 cm, height 1 cm

<u>5</u> Radius 1 cm, height 4.8 cm

<u>6</u> Radius 4 in, height 3 in

<u>7</u> Radius 12 cm, height 1.8 cm

<u>8</u> Radius 7 cm, height 9 cm

9 Radius 3.2 cm, height 10 cm

10 Diameter 10 cm, height 42 cm

11 Radius 4.8 mm, height 13 mm

12 Radius 8 cm, height 44 mm

13 Diameter 2.4 cm, height 6.2 cm

14 Radius 6 cm, height 3.6 cm

15 Diameter 16.2 cm, height 4 cm

16 Diameter 16 mm, height 5.2 cm

Find the volumes of the following compound shapes. Give your answers correct to 3 significant figures.
Draw diagrams of the cross-sections but do not draw pictures of the solids.

17

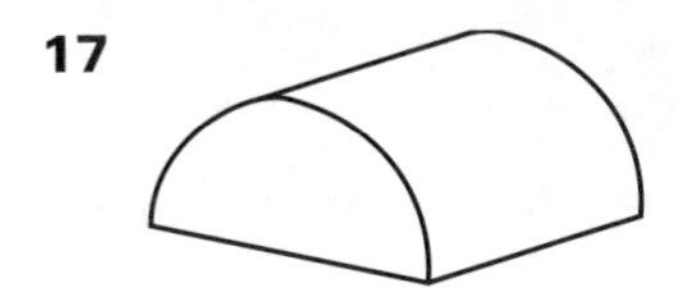

A half-cylinder of length 16 cm and radius 4 cm.

18

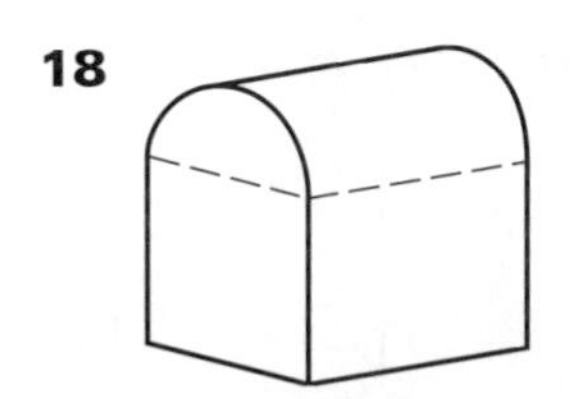

A solid of length 6.2 cm, whose cross-section consists of a square of side 2 cm surmounted by a semicircle.

19

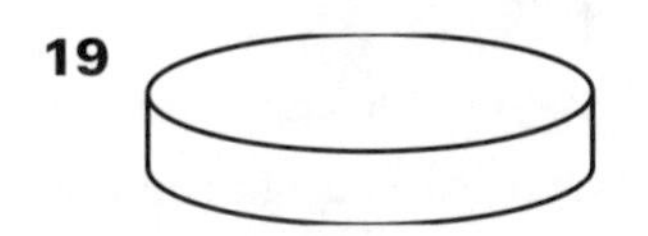

A disc of radius 9 cm and thickness 0.8 cm.

20

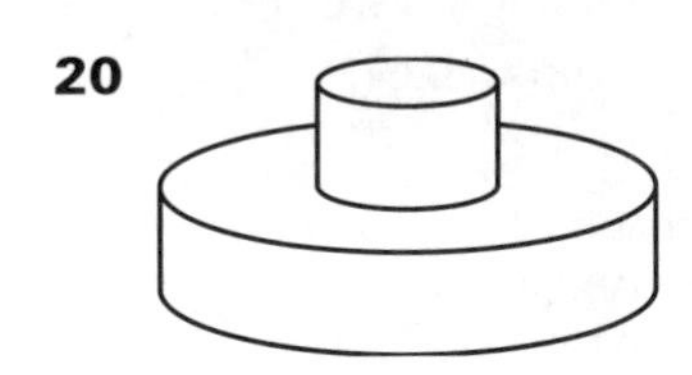

A solid made of two cylinders each of height 5 cm.
The radius of the smaller one is 2 cm and of the larger one is 6 cm.

21

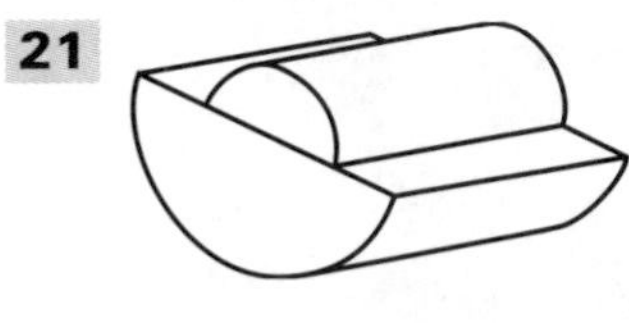

A solid made of two half-cylinders each of length 11 cm. The radius of the larger one is 10 cm and the radius of the smaller one is 5 cm.

22

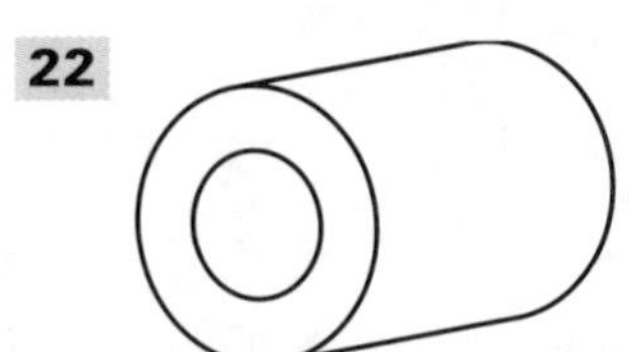

A tube of length 20 cm. The inner radius is 3 cm and the outer radius is 5 cm.

23 The diagram shows a cylindrical hole, diameter 42 mm, in a concrete block which is buried in the ground to support a clothes line.

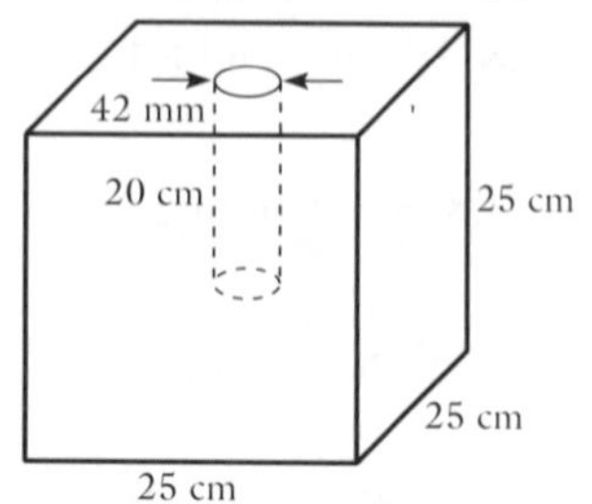

a What volume of water would fill the hole?

b What volume of concrete is used to make the block?

c One cubic centimetre of this concrete weighs 8 grams.
How much does the block weigh?

24 The walls of a cylindrical wooden egg cup are 3 mm thick and the base is 6 mm thick.

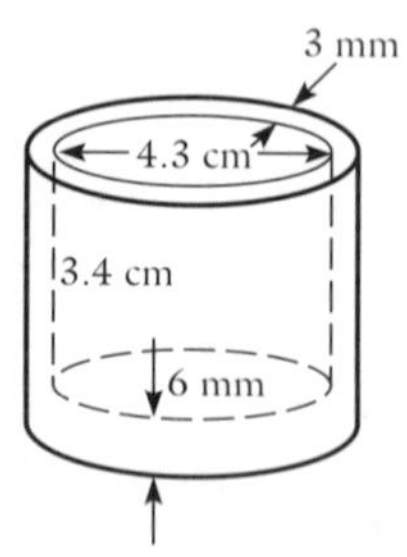

a Calculate the volume of wood in the egg cup.

b How many millilitres of water will the egg cup hold?

c Each cubic centimetre of the wood weighs 0.9 grams.
How much does the egg cup weigh?

25 At the beginning of the chapter Sally was thinking about buying a pedal-bin for the kitchen. Which one has the larger capacity?

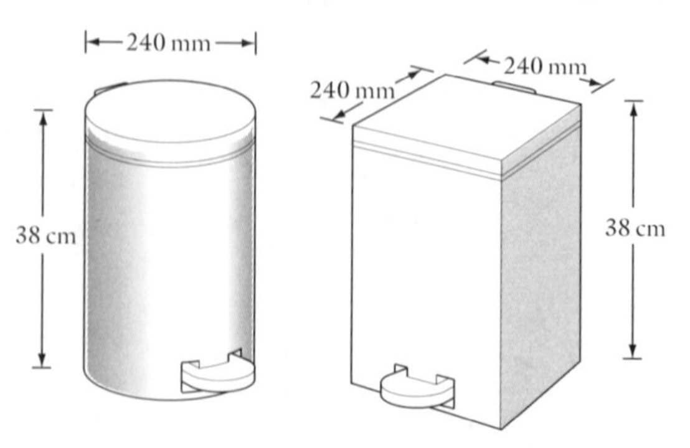

Find the difference between the capacities of the two bins.

26 Having decided to buy the cylindrical bin, Sally needs to buy some plastic bin liners. She has a choice of three packs: in pack A the capacity of the liners is 5 litres, in pack B the capacity is 10 litres, and in pack C the capacity is 25 litres.
Which pack should she buy and why?

MIXED EXERCISE

EXERCISE 18F

1 Find the volume of a concrete block measuring 16 cm by 24 cm by 1.4 m.

In questions **2** and **3**, the cross-sections of the prisms and their lengths are given.
Find **a** the area of the cross-section **b** the volume.

2

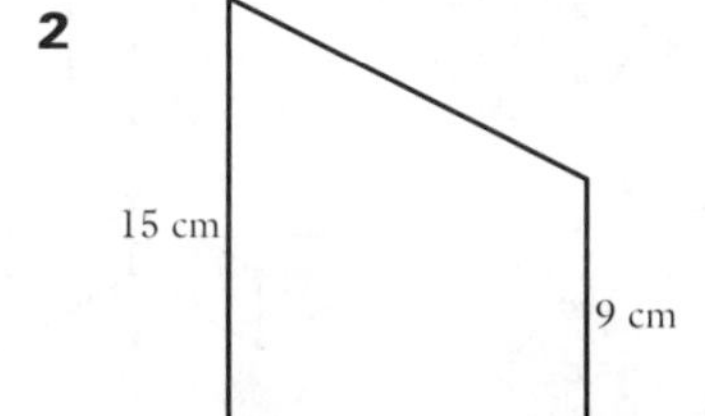

Length 20 cm

3

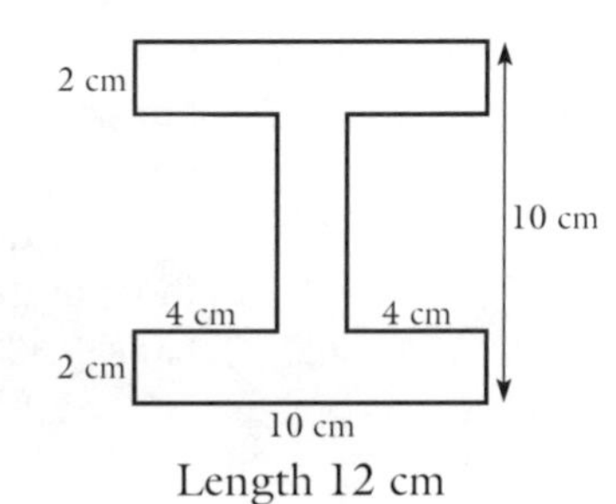

Length 12 cm

4 Find the volume of a cylinder with

a radius 3 cm and height 6.5 cm

b diameter 8 in and height 4 in.

(Give your answers correct to 3 significant figures.)

5 The diagram shows a solid model of a house which has been made from wood.

a Use the measurements given on the diagram to find

i the area of the uniform cross-section

ii the volume of wood used to made the model.

b If the mass of 1 cm^3 of the wood is 8.5 g, find the mass of the model.

INVESTIGATION

a Betty has a bag of identical triangular wooden blocks.

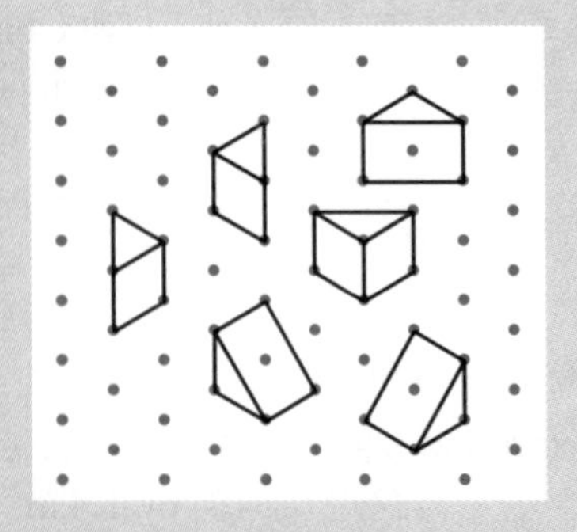

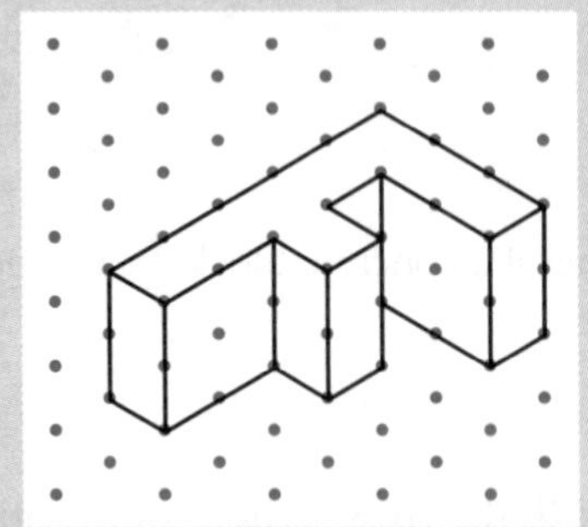

She uses some of them to make the letter F.
How many blocks does she need?

b Betty also has a bag of triangular blocks identical to each other but with a different shape and size from those in the first bag.

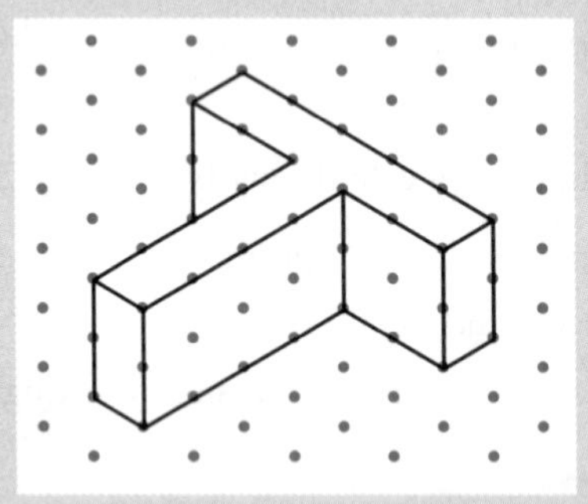

How many of these does she need to make the letter T?

c How does the volume of one of the larger blocks compare with the volume of one of the smaller blocks?

d Which letter uses the more wood, the F or the T?

e How many cubical blocks of side 1 unit would Betty need to make **i** the F **ii** the T?

f Which other letters in the alphabet can be drawn on isometric paper using cubes? Draw at least two of them. Draw additional letters using blocks like those shown in part **a**.

PYTHAGORAS' THEOREM

Thousands of years ago the Egyptians used knotted ropes to mark out land and buildings. They used a rope with 13 knots to make sure that there were right angles at the corners. One knot was made at each end and the other 11 were equally spaced along its length.

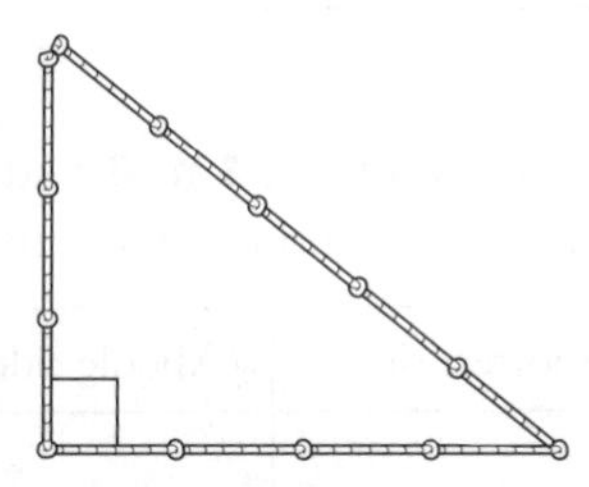

The rope was arranged in a triangle, as shown, so that there were 3 equal lengths along one side, 4 equal lengths along a second side and 5 equal lengths along the third side. The ends of the rope met and each section was pulled taut. The largest angle in this triangle is a right angle.

With such a simple system the corners of buildings like the great pyramids could be made square.

While the 3,4,5 triangle is the simplest triangle that contains a right angle, many other triangles were discovered that will do the same job.

The formal relationship between the lengths of the three sides is attributed to Pythagoras, a Greek philosopher and mathematician who lived about 2500 years ago.

RIGHT-ANGLED TRIANGLES

Any triangle whose largest angle is 90° is called a *right-angled triangle*.

The side opposite the right-angle is called the *hypotenuse*.

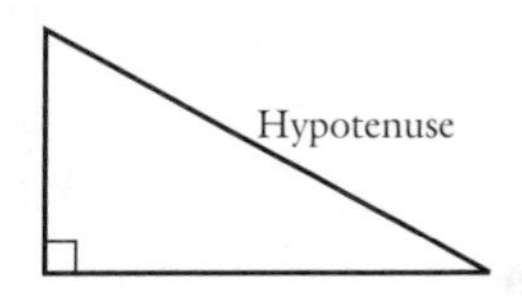

EXERCISE 19A

In this exercise we investigate the relationship between the lengths of the three sides. First we will collect some evidence. Bear in mind that however accurate your drawing may be it is not perfect.

Construct the triangles in questions **1** to **4** and in each case measure the third side, the hypotenuse.

1

6 cm

8 cm

3

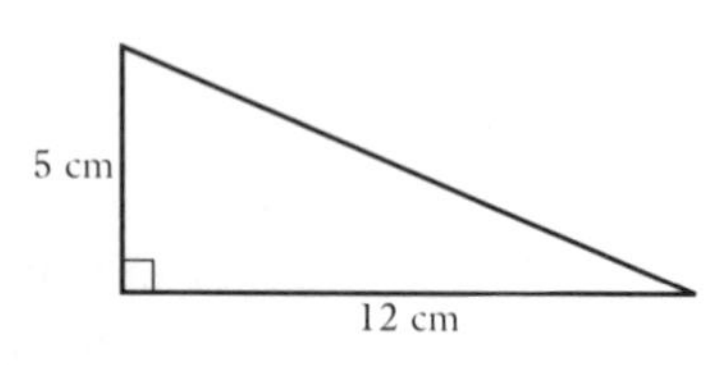

2

6 cm

10 cm

4

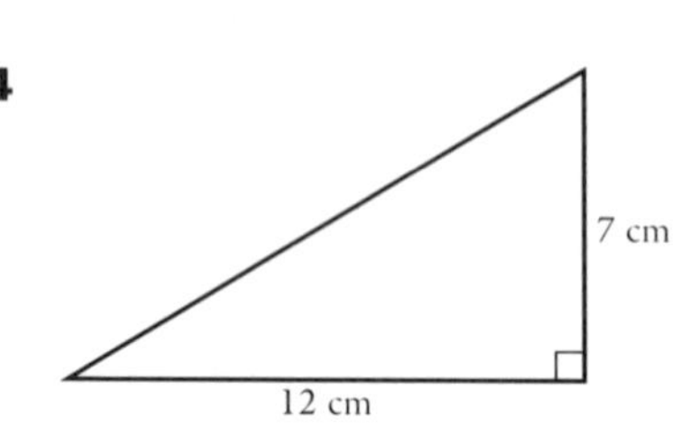

5 In each question from **1** to **4** find the squares of the lengths of the three sides. Copy and complete the following table.

	(Shortest side)^2	(Middle side)^2	(Side opposite right angle)^2
1			
2			
3			
4			

What is the relationship between the numbers in the first two columns and the number in the third column?

PYTHAGORAS' THEOREM

If your drawings are reasonably accurate you will find that by adding the squares of the two shorter sides you get the square of the hypotenuse.

E.g.

$$AB^2 = 16$$
$$BC^2 = 9$$
$$AC^2 = 25$$
$$25 = 16 + 9$$

so $AC^2 = AB^2 + BC^2$

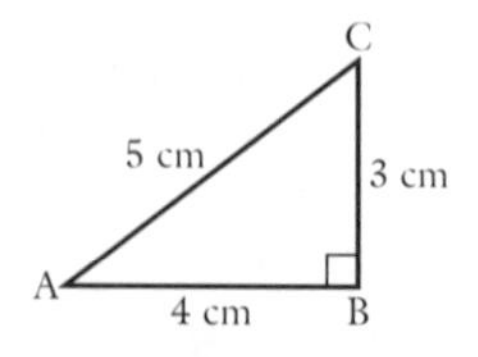

This result is called Pythagoras' theorem, which states that

> in a right-angled triangle the square of the hypotenuse is equal to the sum of the squares of the other two sides.

EXERCISE 19B Give your answers correct to 3 significant figures.

The diagram shows a rope arranged to form a triangle PQR. If $\hat{R} = 90^\circ$, $PR = 7\,\text{m}$ and $QR = 6\,\text{m}$, find the length of PQ.

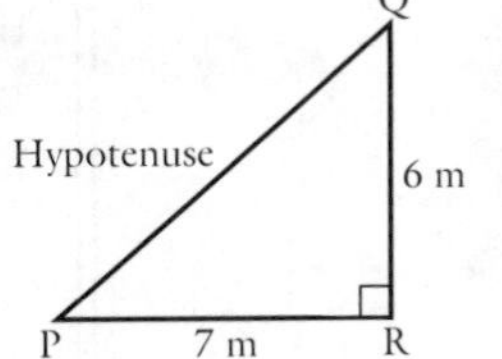

$$PQ^2 = PR^2 + QR^2 \quad (\textbf{Pythagoras' theorem})$$
$$= 7^2 + 6^2$$
$$= 49 + 36 = 85$$
$$PQ = \sqrt{85} = 9.219\ldots$$

Length of PQ = 9.22 m correct to 3 s.f.

In the following right-angled triangles find the required lengths.

1 Find AC.

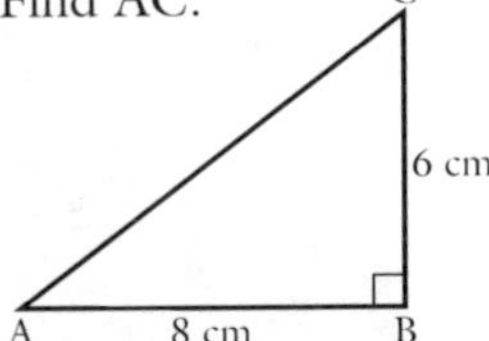

2 Find PR.

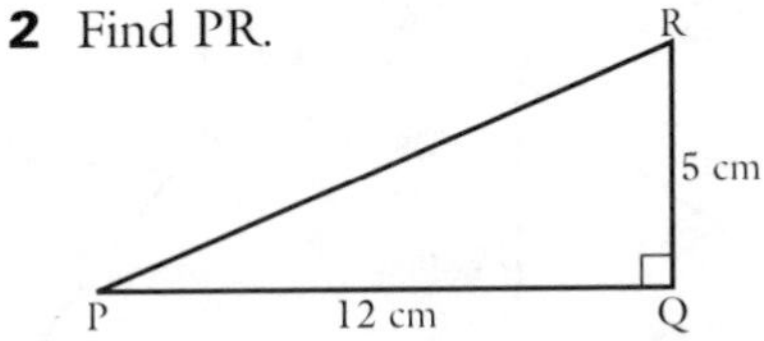

3 Find QR.

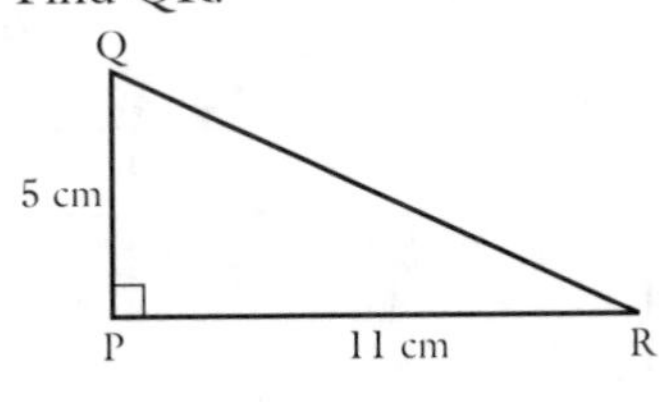

4

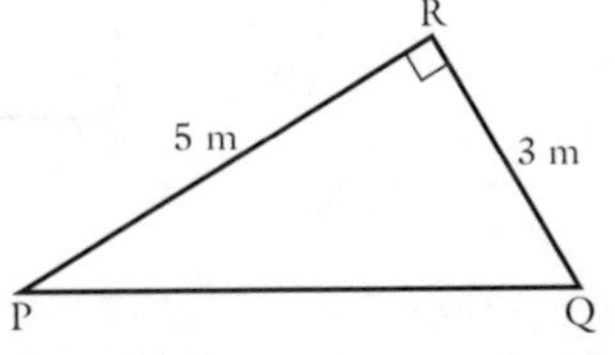

The diagram shows a simple roof support. What distance does PQ span?

5 Find MN.

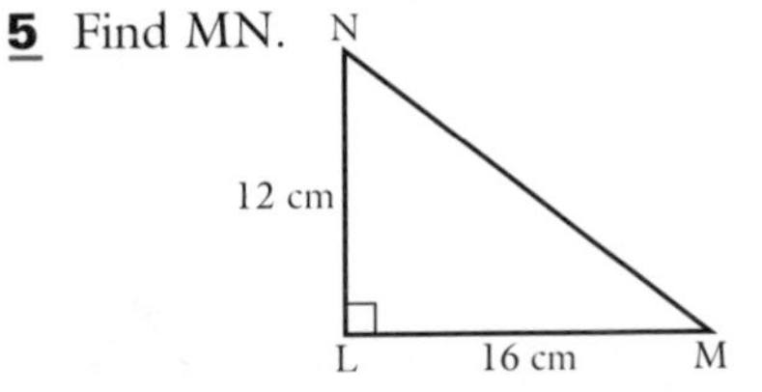

6 Find AC.

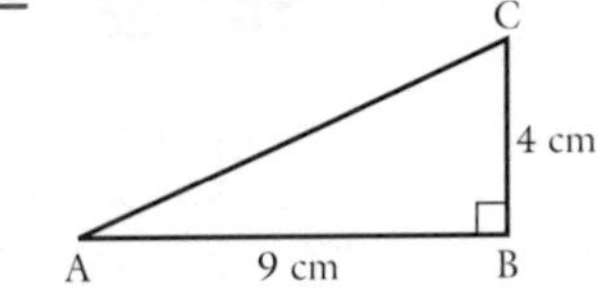

7 Find EF.

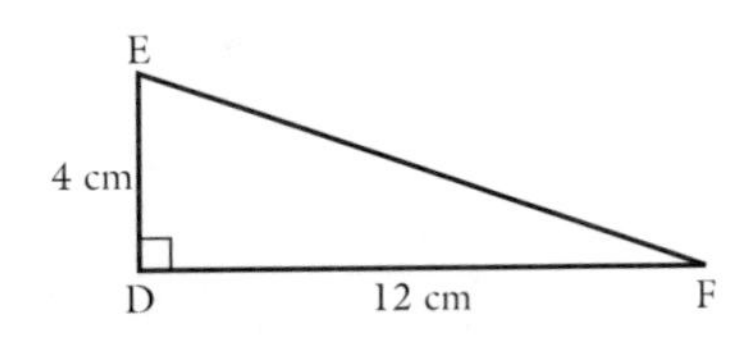

8

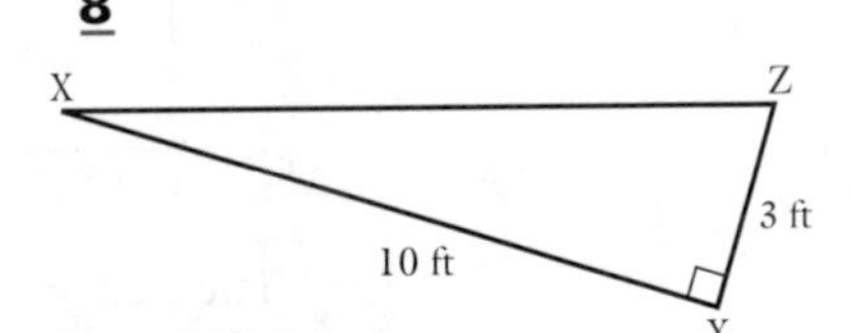

The diagram shows the cross-section of a drainage ditch. How wide is the ditch at the surface?

A manufacturer wants to make a quantity of plastic triangles like the one shown in the diagram. Use the given information to find the length of XY.

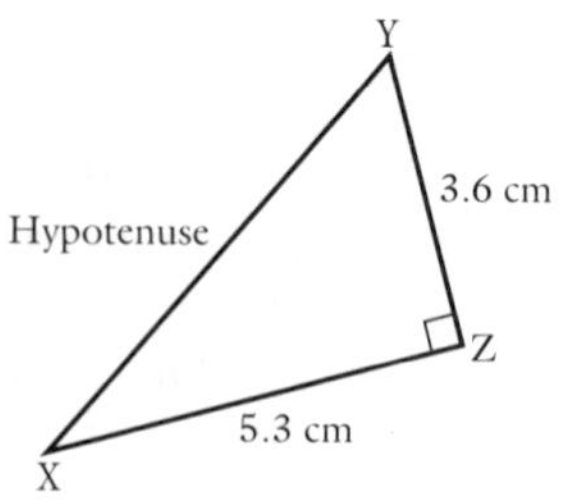

$$\begin{aligned} XY^2 &= XZ^2 + ZY^2 \quad \text{(Pythagoras' theorem)} \\ &= 5.3^2 + 3.6^2 \\ &= 28.09 + 12.96 \\ &= 41.05 \end{aligned}$$

Check: $XY^2 \approx 5^2 + 4^2 = 25 + 16 = 41$

$XY = \sqrt{41.05} = 6.407\ldots$

Length of XY = 6.41 cm correct to 3 s.f.

9 Find AC.

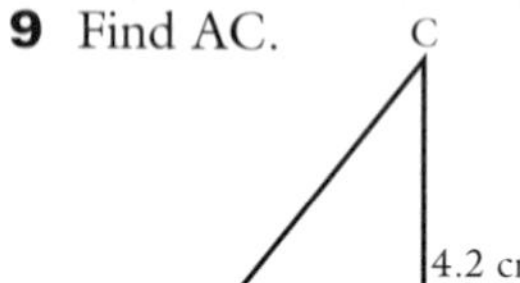
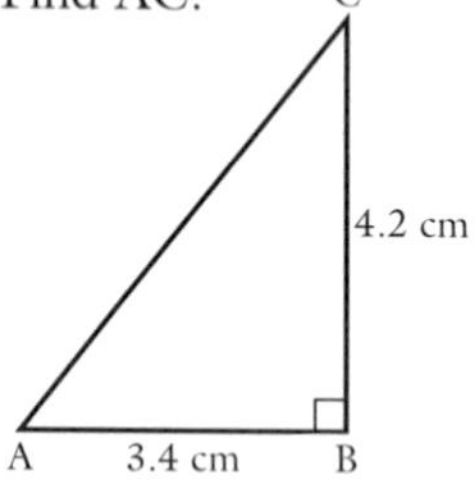

12 Find XY.

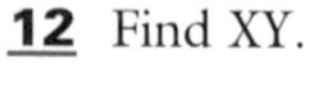
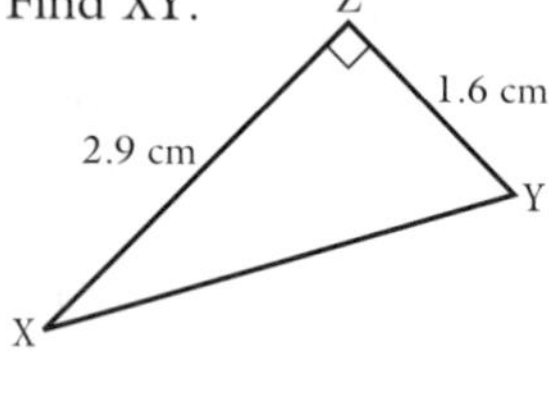

10 Find AC.

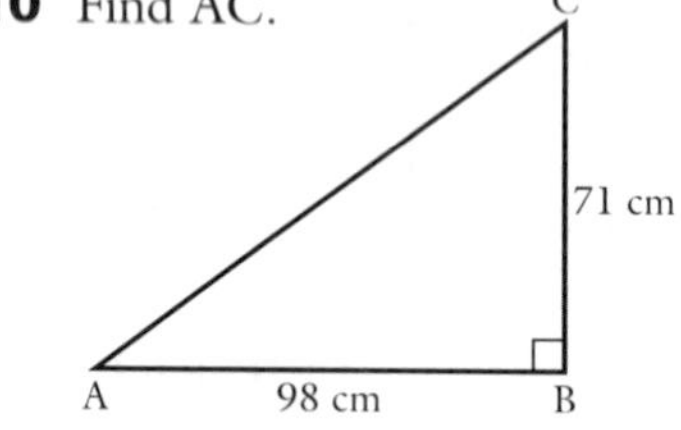

13 Find PR.

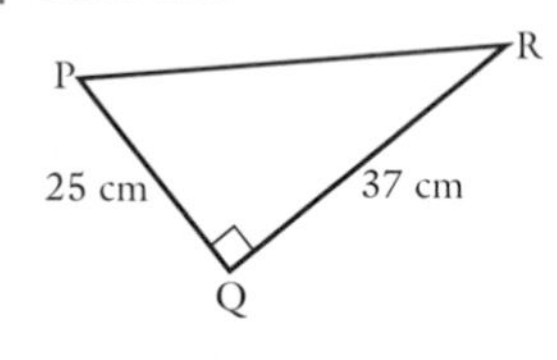

11

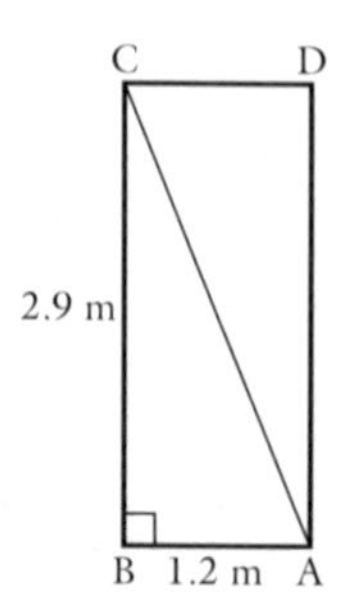

The sketch shows a door ABCD.
Find the length of the diagonal AC.

14

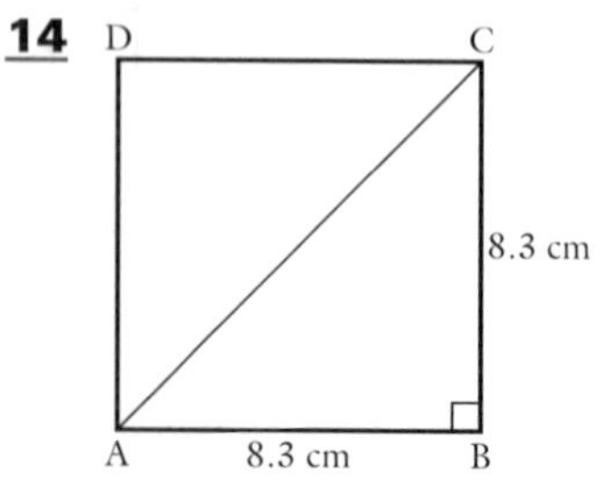

A small square table mat has an edge of 8.3 cm. How far is it from one corner to the opposite corner?

A man starts from A and walks 4 km due north to B, then 6 km due west to C. Find how far C is from A.

Start by drawing a diagram.

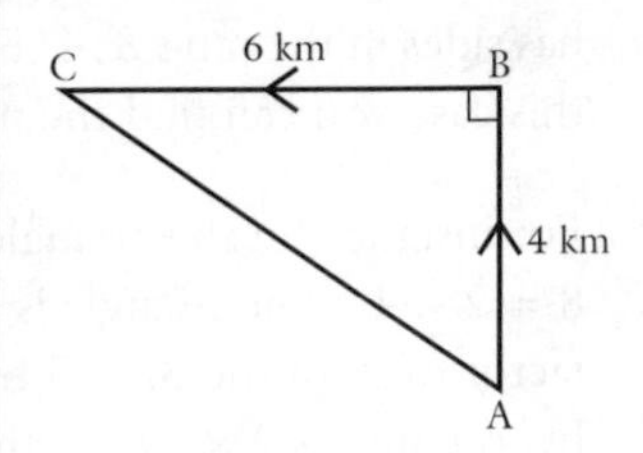

$$AC^2 = BC^2 + AB^2 \quad \text{(Pythagoras' theorem)}$$

$$= 6^2 + 4^2$$

$$= 36 + 16$$

$$= 52$$

$$AC = \sqrt{52} = 7.211\ldots$$

C is 7.21 km from A correct to 3 s.f.

15 A hockey pitch measures 55 m by 90 m. Find the length of a diagonal of the pitch.

16

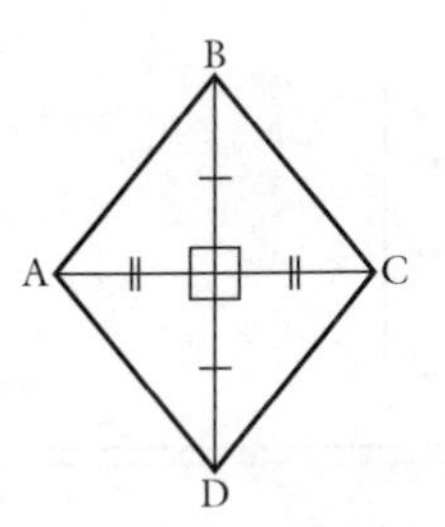

ABCD is a rhombus. The diagonals bisect each other. AC = 10 cm and BD = 12 cm.
Find the length of a side of the rhombus.

17 A carpenter is making a teak front door that is to be 6 ft 4 inches high and 32 inches wide. He checks that it is square (i.e. that all the corners are 90°) by measuring both diagonals. How long should each one be when the door is finished?

18

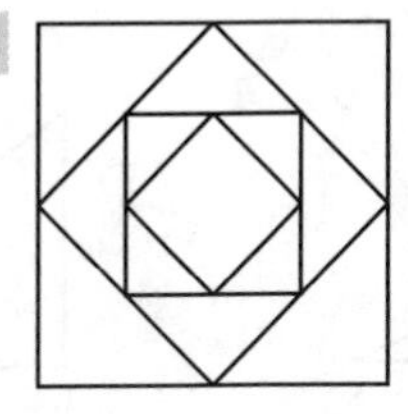

The diagram shows a nest of 4 squares set one within another. The side of the outer square is 20 cm. The midpoints of the sides are joined to give a second square and the process repeated to give the third and fourth squares. Find the length of a side of the smallest square.

THE 3,4,5, TRIANGLE

You will have noticed that, in most cases when two sides of a right-angled triangle are given and the third side is calculated using Pythagoras' theorem, the answer is not an exact number. There are a few special cases where all three sides are exact numbers.

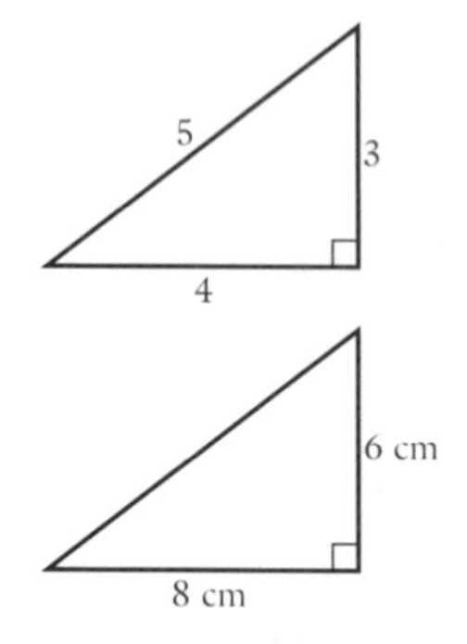

The simplest one is the 3,4,5 triangle.
Any triangle that is an enlargement of this one has sides in the ratio $3:4:5$ so whenever you spot this case you can find the missing side very easily.

For instance, in this triangle, $6 = 2 \times 3$ and $8 = 2 \times 4$. The triangle is an enlargement, by a factor of 2, of the 3, 4, 5 triangle, so the hypotenuse is 2×5 cm, that is, 10 cm.

The Eqyptians' knotted rope is based on this triangle.

Another right-angled triangle with exact sides which is useful to know about is the 5,12,13 triangle.

EXERCISE 19C

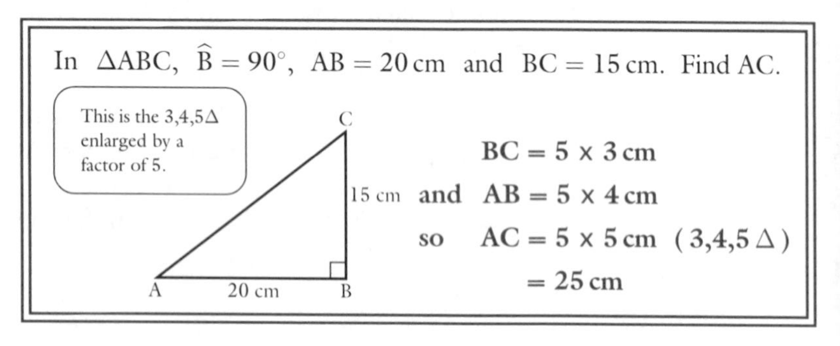

In ΔABC, $\widehat{B} = 90°$, $AB = 20$ cm and $BC = 15$ cm. Find AC.

BC = 5 x 3 cm

and AB = 5 x 4 cm

so AC = 5 x 5 cm (3,4,5 Δ)

= 25 cm

In each of the following questions decide whether the triangle is an enlargement of the 3,4,5 triangle or of the 5,12,13 triangle or of neither.

Find the hypotenuse, using the method you think is easiest.

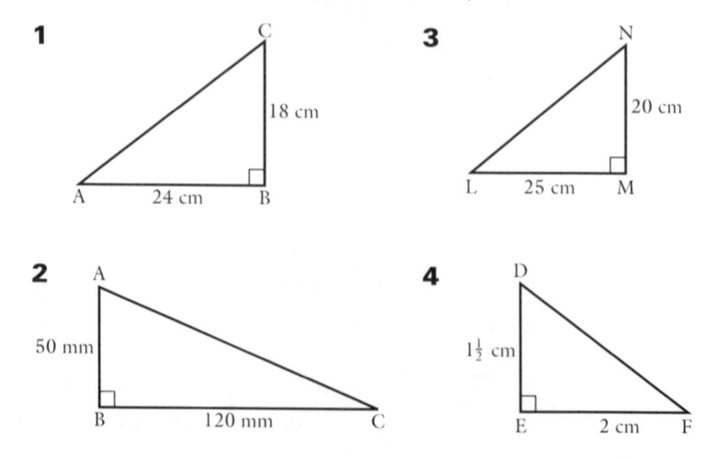

5

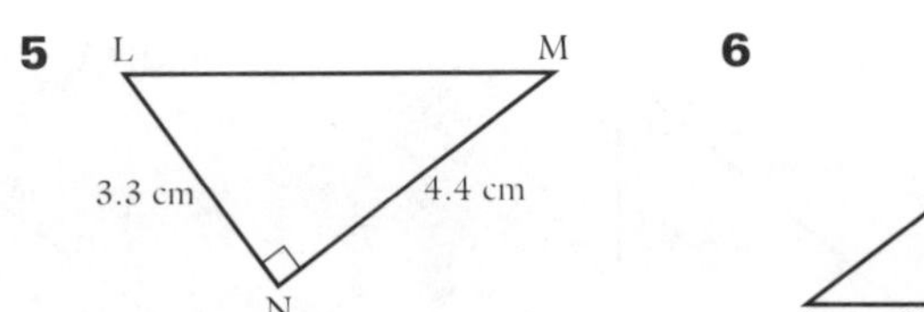

6

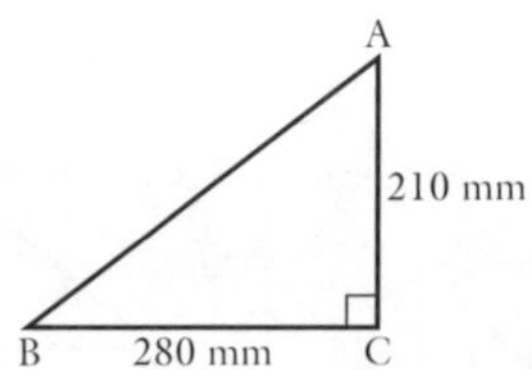

FINDING ONE OF THE SHORTER SIDES

If we are given the hypotenuse and one other side we can find the third side.

EXERCISE 19D

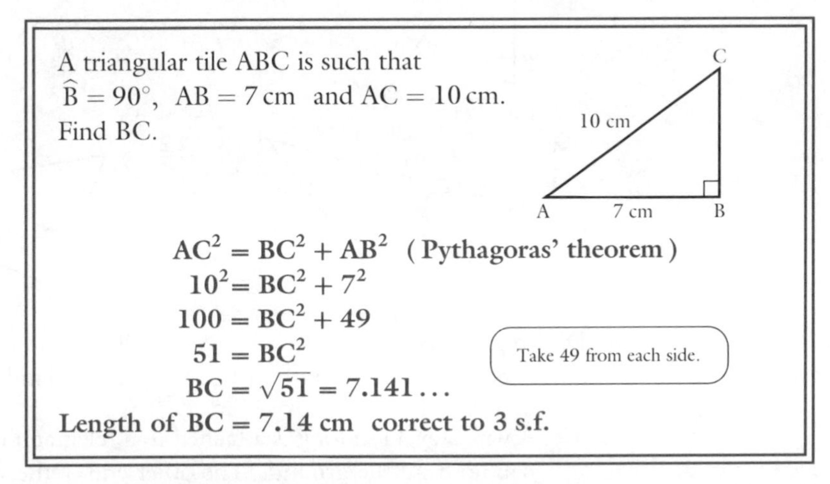

A triangular tile ABC is such that $\widehat{B} = 90^\circ$, AB = 7 cm and AC = 10 cm. Find BC.

$$\mathbf{AC^2 = BC^2 + AB^2} \quad \textbf{(Pythagoras' theorem)}$$
$$\mathbf{10^2 = BC^2 + 7^2}$$
$$\mathbf{100 = BC^2 + 49}$$
$$\mathbf{51 = BC^2}$$
$$\mathbf{BC = \sqrt{51} = 7.141\ldots}$$

Take 49 from each side.

Length of BC = 7.14 cm correct to 3 s.f.

Give all answers that are not exact to 3 significant figures.

1 Find BC.

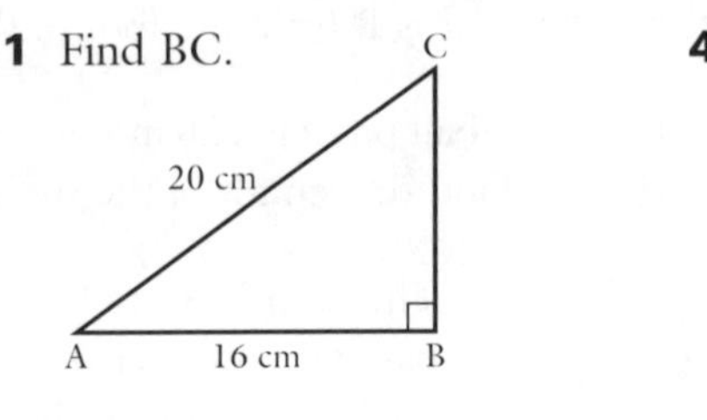

2 Find LM.

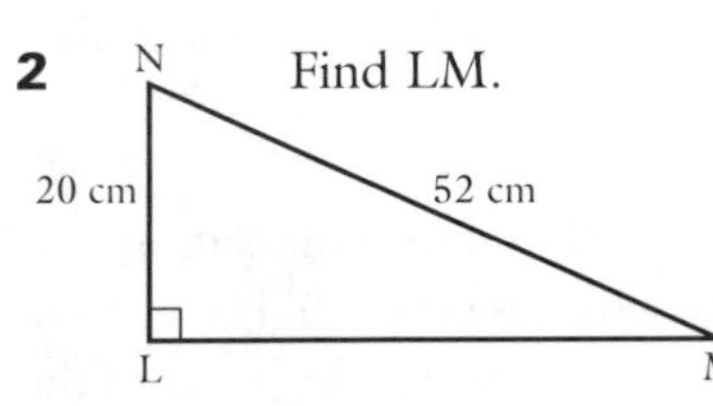

3 Find BC.

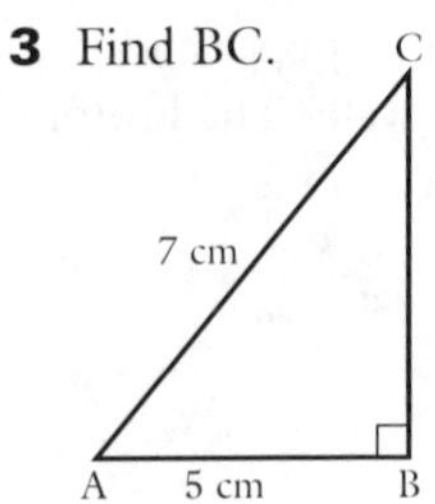

4 Find PQ.

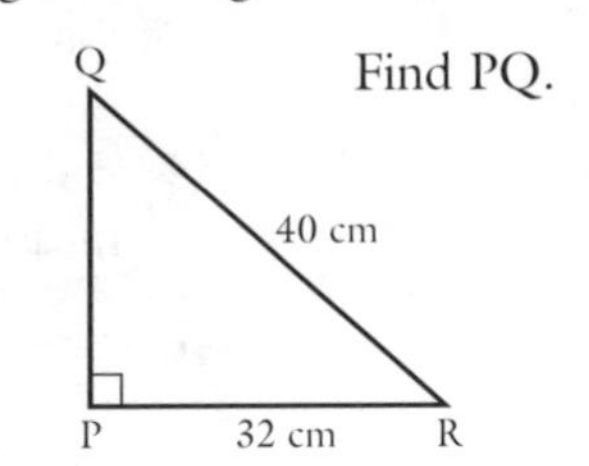

5 Find YZ.

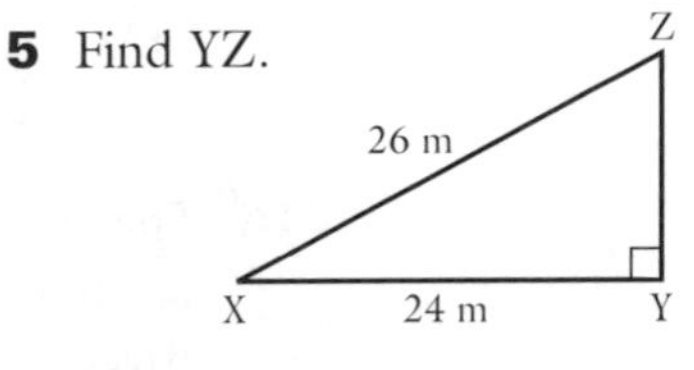

6 Find BC.

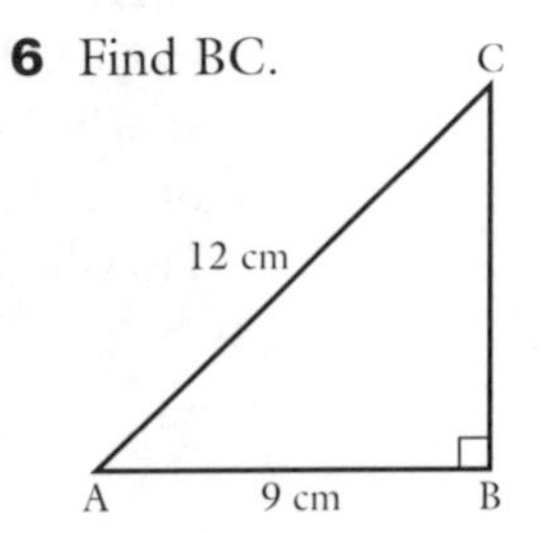

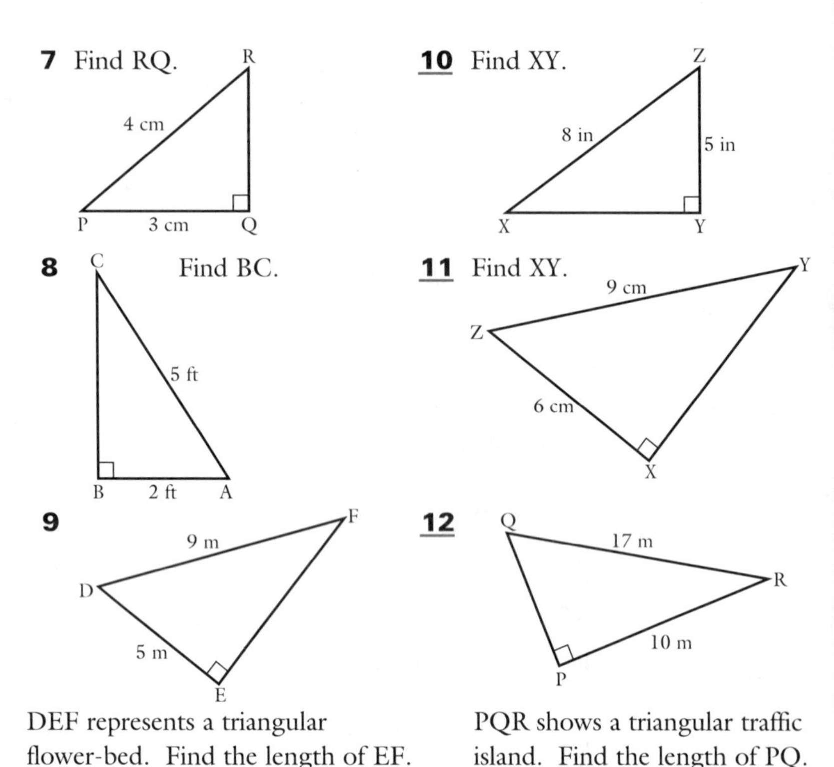

7 Find RQ.

8 Find BC.

9 DEF represents a triangular flower-bed. Find the length of EF.

10 Find XY.

11 Find XY.

12 PQR shows a triangular traffic island. Find the length of PQ.

13 A wire stay 11 m long is attached to a telegraph pole at a point A, 8 m up from the ground. The other end of the stay is fixed to a point B, on the ground. Draw a suitable diagram showing this information. How far is B from the foot of the telegraph pole?

14 A diagonal of a football pitch is 130 m long and the long side measures 100 m. Find the length of the short side of the pitch.

15

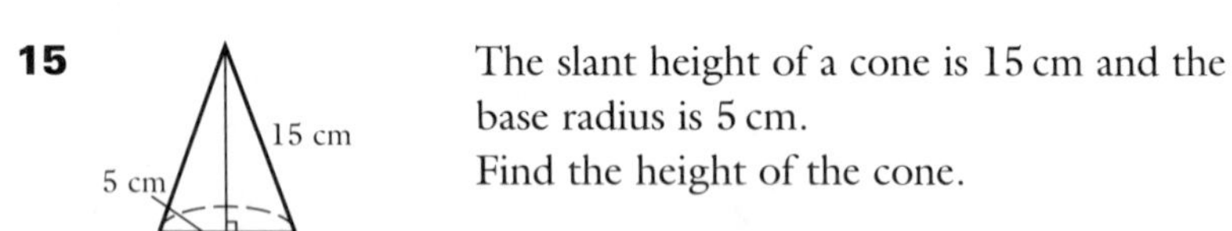

The slant height of a cone is 15 cm and the base radius is 5 cm.
Find the height of the cone.

16 The sketch shows an inn sign measuring 1.2 m by 0.8 m which is supported by a frame attached to the wall. The sloping edge of the frame is 1.8 m long and at its upper end is attached to the top of the wall. The bottom of the sign is 3 m above ground level.
How high is the wall?

17 A rubbish skip is in the shape of a prism.

When viewed from the side, the cross-section of the skip is an isosceles trapezium ABCD, where $AB = 3.4\text{ m}$, $DC = 2\text{ m}$ and $AD = BC = 1.4\text{ m}$

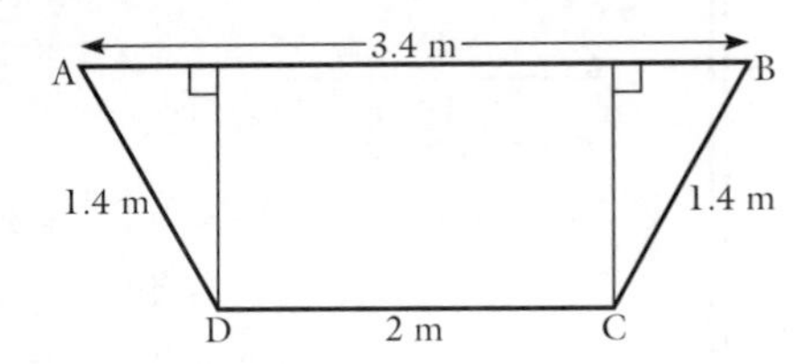

a Find the depth of the skip.

b Find the area of cross-section of the skip.

c The skip is 1.65 m wide.

Calculate the capacity of the skip in **i** cubic metres **ii** litres.

18 **a** Draw a triangle ABC in which $AB = 8\text{ cm}$, $BC = 6\text{ cm}$ and $AC = 10\text{ cm}$. (Remember that in this triangle $A\hat{B}C$ is 90°.) For this triangle we know that $AC^2 = AB^2 + BC^2$

b Now draw a triangle ABC in which $AB = 8\text{ cm}$, $BC = 6\text{ cm}$ and $A\hat{B}C$ has any value less than 90°. Measure AC.
Find $AB^2 + BC^2$ and AC^2.
Is $AB^2 + BC^2$ greater than AC^2 or less than AC^2?

c Next draw a triangle ABC in which $AB = 8\text{ cm}$, $BC = 6\text{ cm}$ and $A\hat{B}C$ has any value greater than 90°. Measure AC.
Find $AB^2 + BC^2$ and AC^2.
Is $AB^2 + BC^2$ greater than AC^2 or less than AC^2?

d Draw any other right-angled triangle ABC in which AC is the hypotenuse. Find $AB^2 + BC^2$ and AC^2. In any $\triangle ABC$ what conclusion can you draw about the angle B if

i $AB^2 + BC^2 > AC^2$

ii $AB^2 + BC^2 < AC^2$?

FINDING LENGTHS IN AN ISOSCELES TRIANGLE

An isosceles triangle can be split into two right-angled triangles and this can sometimes help when finding missing lengths.

EXERCISE 19E

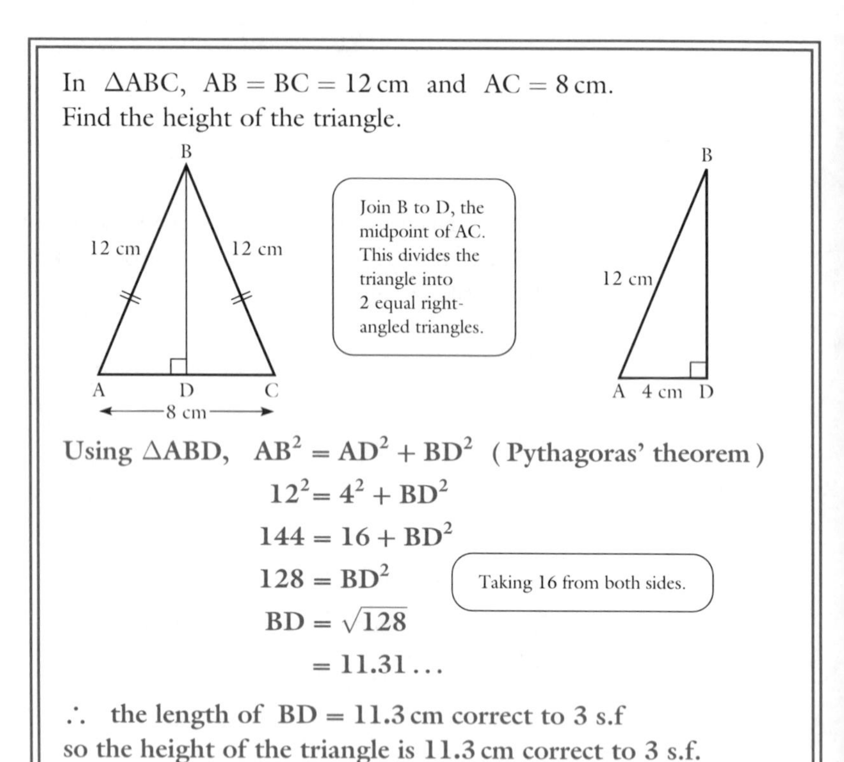

In ΔABC, $AB = BC = 12$ cm and $AC = 8$ cm.
Find the height of the triangle.

Using ΔABD, $AB^2 = AD^2 + BD^2$ **(Pythagoras' theorem)**

$$12^2 = 4^2 + BD^2$$
$$144 = 16 + BD^2$$
$$128 = BD^2$$

Taking 16 from both sides.

$$BD = \sqrt{128}$$
$$= 11.31\ldots$$

$\therefore$ the length of BD = 11.3 cm correct to 3 s.f
so the height of the triangle is 11.3 cm correct to 3 s.f.

Give your answers correct to 3 significant figures.

1 The sketch shows the front of a ridge tent in which $AB = AC = 150$ cm. $BC = 120$ cm. Find the height of the ridge above the ground.

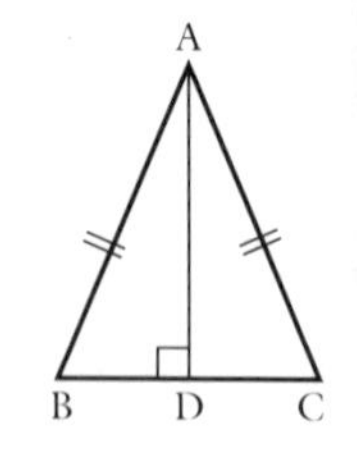

2 A vertical flagpole ED is supported by two stays attached to the pole at B, 1 m from the top and fixed to two points in the ground, A and C, on opposite sides of the pole.
If $AB = BC = 7.9$ m, $AC = 5$ m and D is the midpoint of AC find the height of the flagpole.

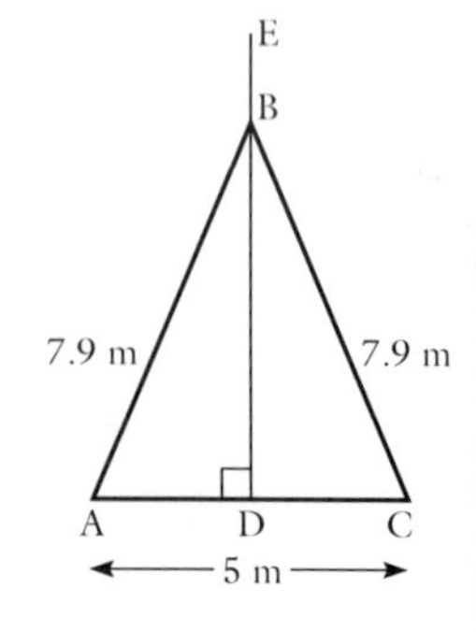

3

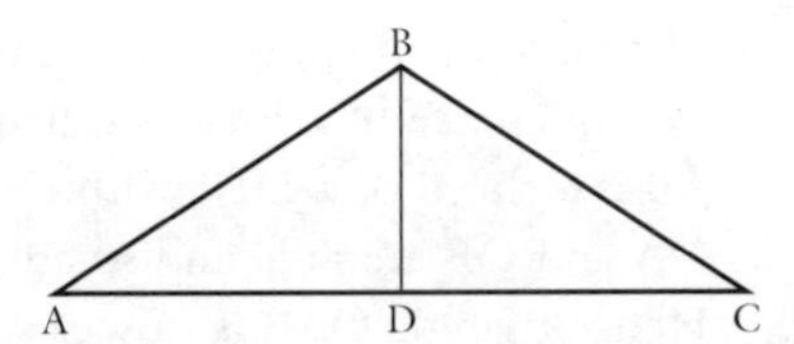

The sketch shows a roof truss for a garage. If AC = 3.5 m and BD = 1.3 m, find the lengths of the sloping timbers AB and BC.

4 In ΔABC, AB = BC = 5.2 cm and AC = 6 cm. Find the height of the triangle measured from B.

5 In ΔPQR, PQ = QR = 9 cm and the height of the triangle measured from Q is 7 cm. Find the length of PR.

6 The main feature of a carnival float is made from an equilateral triangle of side 12 ft. The triangle is fixed on a trailer so that one side rests on the base of the trailer which is 4 ft above road level.
Will the carnival float pass under a bridge that will take vehicles up to 14 ft high? Give reasons for your answer.

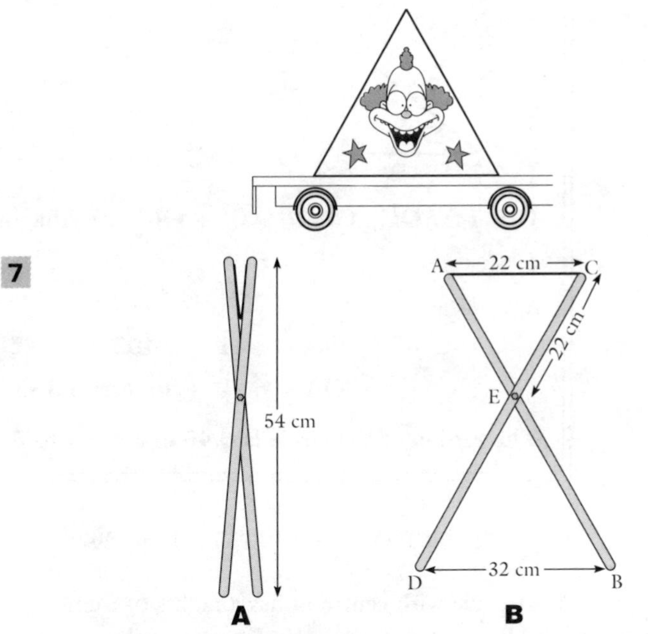

7 Diagram **A** shows a folding stool in its closed postion. When closed it reaches a height of 54 cm.
In diagram **B** the stool is shown opened out. The two supports AB and CD pivot at E such that AE = EC = 22 cm, AC = 22 cm and the distance between the feet of the stool is 32 cm. Find

a the height of the seat AC above the pivot

b the equal lengths EB and ED

c the height of the seat above the ground.

FINDING THE DISTANCE OF A CHORD FROM THE CENTRE OF A CIRCLE

A straight line joining two points on the circumference of a circle is called a *chord*. AB is a chord of a circle with centre O. OA and OB are radii and so are equal. Hence triangle OAB is isosceles and we can divide it through the middle into two right-angled triangles.

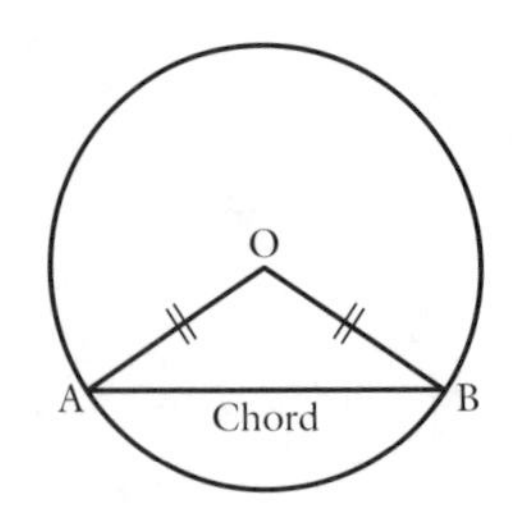

EXERCISE 19F

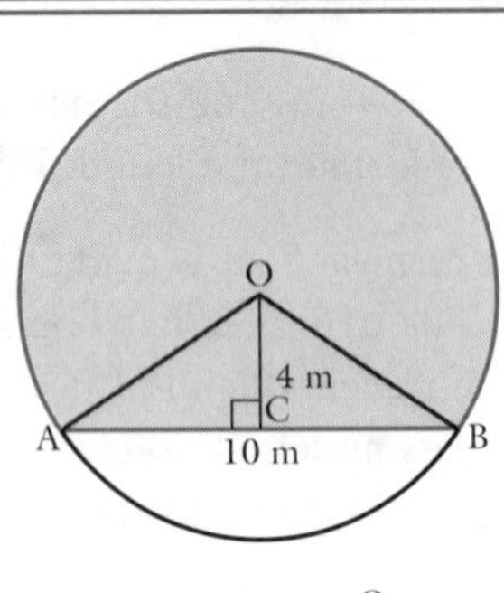

The diagram shows a cross-section through a tunnel.
AB, which represents the floor of the tunnel, is 10 m long and is a chord of a circle, centre O.
If the floor is 4 m from O, find the radius of the circle.

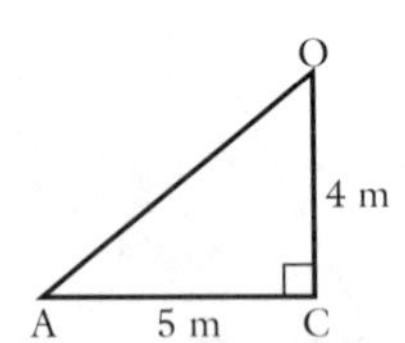

The distance from the centre is the perpendicular distance so OC = 4 m.
From symmetry AC = 5 m.

Using ΔAOC, $OA^2 = AC^2 + OC^2$ (Pythagoras' theorem)

$$= 5^2 + 4^2$$

$$= 25 + 16 = 41$$

$$OA = \sqrt{41} = 6.403\ldots$$

$$OA = 6.40 \quad \text{(correct to 3 s.f.)}$$

The radius of the circle is 6.40 m correct to 3 s.f.

Give your answers correct to 3 significant figures.

1 A circle with centre O has a radius of 5 cm. AB = 8.4 cm. Find the distance of the chord from the centre of the circle.

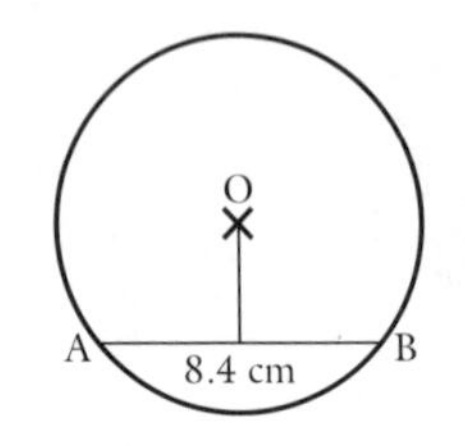

2 O is the centre of the circle and AB is a chord of length 7.2 cm.
The distance of the chord from O is 3 cm.
Find the radius of the circle.

3 The sketch shows a hole in a door ready to take a lock. AB is a chord of length 15 mm in a circle, centre O, of radius 14 mm.
Find the distance of the chord from O.

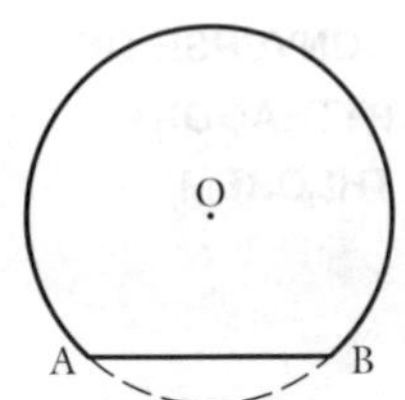

4 The diagram shows the cross-section through a tunnel. AB, which represents the floor of the tunnel, is of length 4 m and the radius of the circle is 3 m. O is the centre of the circle.
Find

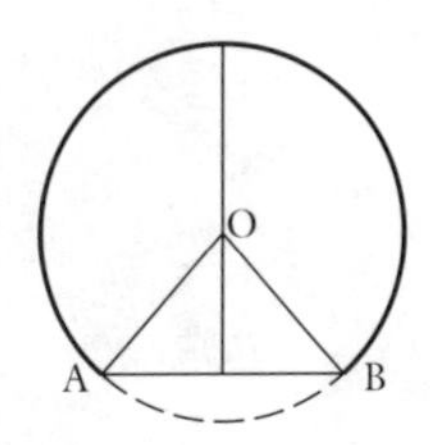

a the distance of O above the floor of the tunnel

b the height of the tunnel.

5 The diagram shows the stage in an arena. The stage is part of a circle, centre P and radius 7.6 m. The front of the stage, which is a chord of the circle, is 9.4 m wide.
Find

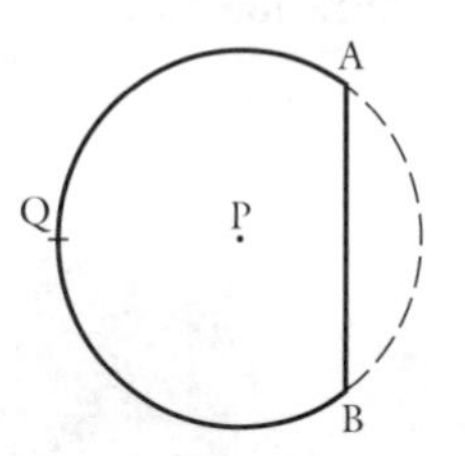

a the distance from P to the front of the stage

b the maximum depth of the stage, i.e. the distance from the front of the stage to Q.

6

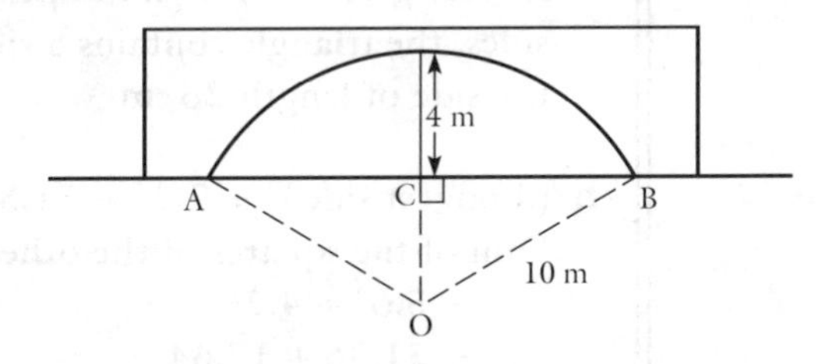

The diagram shows the cross-section of a tunnel which has a maximum height of 4 m above the horizontal base AB. The roof of the tunnel is part of a circle, centre O and radius 10 m.
C is the midpoint of AB. Find

a the length of OC

b the length of AC

c the width of the tunnel at its base.

CONVERSE OF PYTHAGORAS' THEOREM

The last question in **Exercise 19D** showed that if AC is the longest side in ΔABC

and $\widehat{B} < 90°$, then $AC^2 < AB^2 + BC^2$

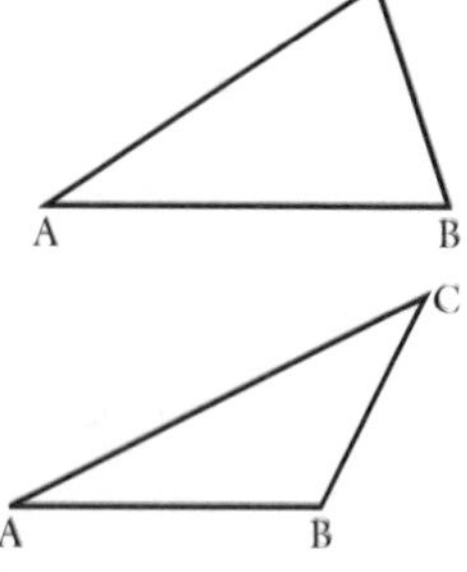

but if $\widehat{B} > 90°$, $AC^2 > AB^2 + BC^2$

We can see that $AC^2 = AB^2 + BC^2$ only when $\widehat{B} = 90°$.

These results give us the converse of Pythagoras' theorem.

In a triangle, if the square of one side is equal to the sum of the squares of the other two sides, the triangle contains a right angle, and this right angle is opposite the longest side.

EXERCISE 19G

The lengths, in centimetres, of the sides of two triangles are

a 10, 24 and 26 **b** 4.2, 5.6 and 7.2.

Determine whether or not each triangle contains a right angle.

a If the triangle contains a right angle it is opposite the longest side.

$(\text{Longest side})^2 = 26^2 = 676$

Sum of the squares of the other two sides

$= 10^2 + 24^2$

$= 100 + 576 = 676$

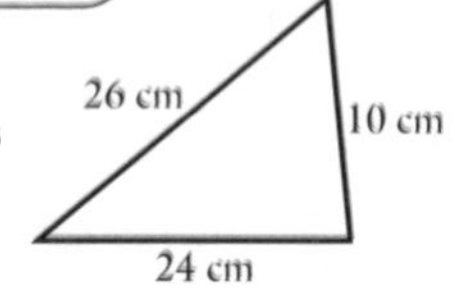

As $(\text{longest side})^2$ = sum of the squares of the other two sides, the triangle contains a right angle and this is opposite the side of length 26 cm.

b $(\text{Longest side})^2 = 7.2^2 = 51.84$

Sum of the squares of the other two sides

$= 5.6^2 + 4.2^2$

$= 31.36 + 17.64$

$= 49$

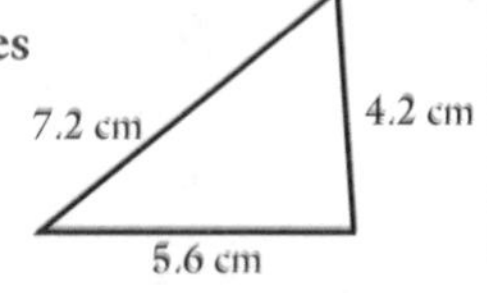

$(\text{Longest side})^2$ is not equal to the sum of the squares of the other two sides so this triangle does not contain a right angle.

We can also deduce that the angle opposite the longest side is greater than 90° because the square of that side is greater than the sum of the squares of the other two sides.

In each question from **1** to **6** the lengths, in centimetres, of the three sides of a triangle are given. Find whether or not the triangle contains a right angle.

Give reasons for your answers.

1 6, 7, 9

2 21, 72, 75

3 4.7, 5.9, 7.5

4 3.9, 5.2, 6.5

5 9, 39, 40

6 15, 36, 39

7 A gardener pegs out the ground to sow a rectangular lawn which is to measure 45 m by 35 m. When he checks a diagonal he finds it to be 57.0 m correct to the nearest tenth of a metre. What would you expect the length of the other diagonal to be compared with the one already measured – that is, is it longer or shorter or the same?

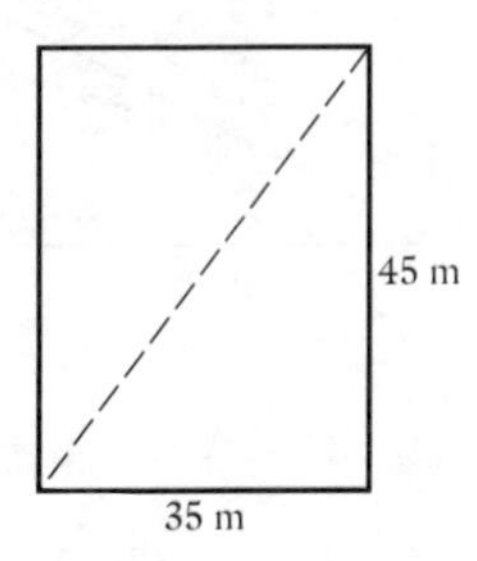

8 Jim buys a flatpack wardrobe which, when assembled, measures 2000 mm high by 900 mm wide by 580 mm deep. Before fitting the doors he checks the lengths of the diagonals of the front to see that the wardrobe is standing vertically and that the doors will fit squarely. The first diagonal measures 2193 mm. Should the doors fit squarely when he hangs them? Justify your answer.

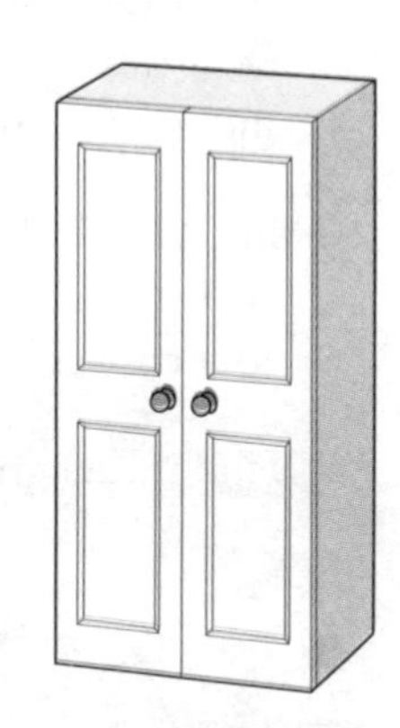

9 Lucy is making a frame for a wedding photograph. The frame is to measure 30 cm by 20 cm. When she checks it for squareness she finds that the length of one diagonal is 36.3 cm.
Is the frame square (i.e. are the corners all 90°)?

10

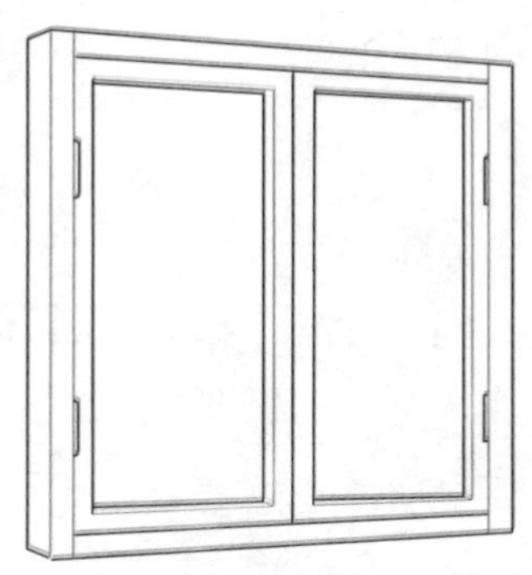

A carpenter is making a rectangular window frame that is to measure 5 ft by 4 ft.
He checks the length of one diagonal and finds it to be 6 ft 4.8 in, correct to the nearest tenth of an inch.
Is the window square?
Justify your answer.

MIXED EXERCISE

EXERCISE 19H

In questions **1** to **3** find the length of the missing side. If any answers are not exact give them correct to 3 significant figures.
If you notice a 3,4,5 triangle or a 5,12,13 triangle, you can use it to get the answer quickly.

1 Find AC.

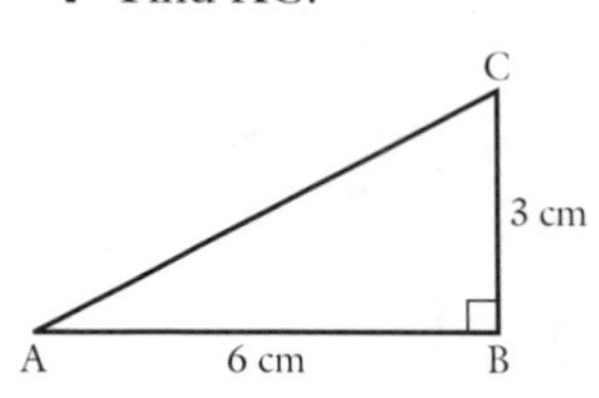

2 Find LM.

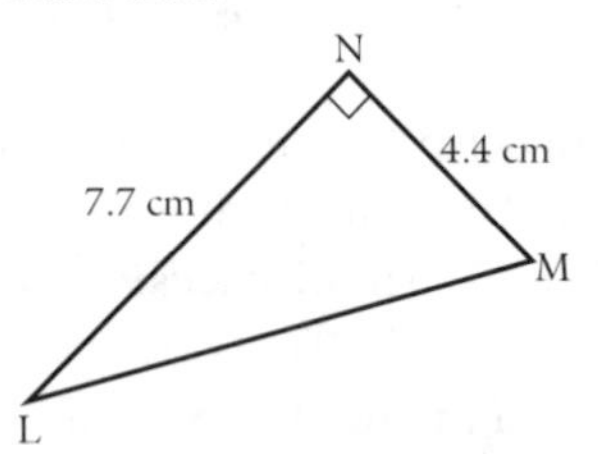

3 Find YZ.

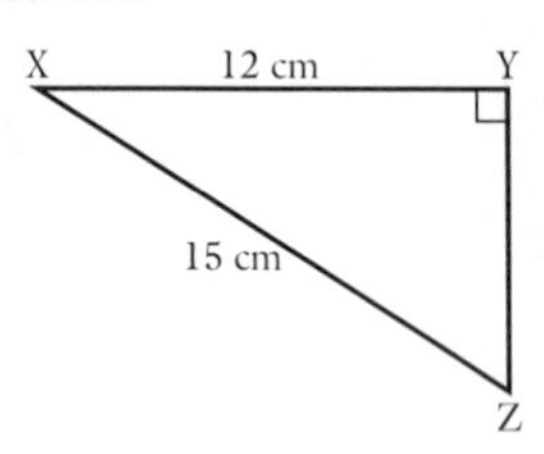

4 In $\triangle ABC$, $\widehat{B} = 90°$, $AB = 1.25$ m, $CA = 8.25$ m. Find BC.

5 In $\triangle ABC$, $AB = 1.8$cm, $BC = 8$ cm and $AC = 8.4$ cm.
Does this triangle contain a right angle? If your answer is 'yes', state which angle it is and justify your answer.

6 In $\triangle DEF$, $DE = 42$mm, $EF = 56$ mm and $DF = 70$ mm.
Is DEF a right-angled triangle? If your answer is 'yes' state which angle is 90° and justify your answer.

7 Find the length of **a** a diagonal of a square of side 10 cm
b an edge of a square whose diagonals are of length 10 cm.

8

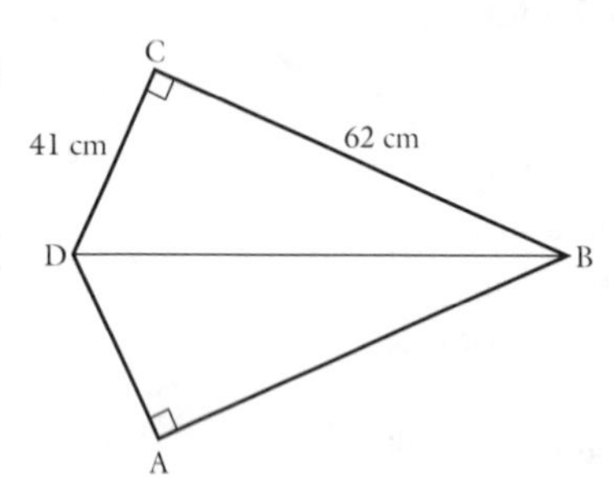

In the kite ABCD, $\widehat{A} = \widehat{C} = 90°$.
$DC = 41$ cm and $BC = 62$ cm.
Find the length of the diagonal BD.

9 The diagram shows the side view of a coal bunker.
Find the length of the slant edge.

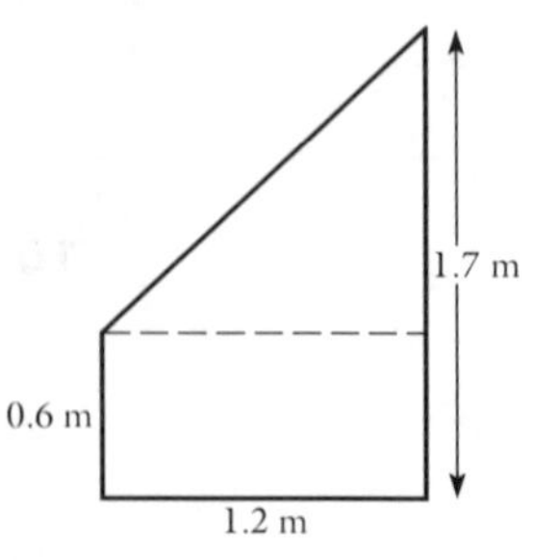

10

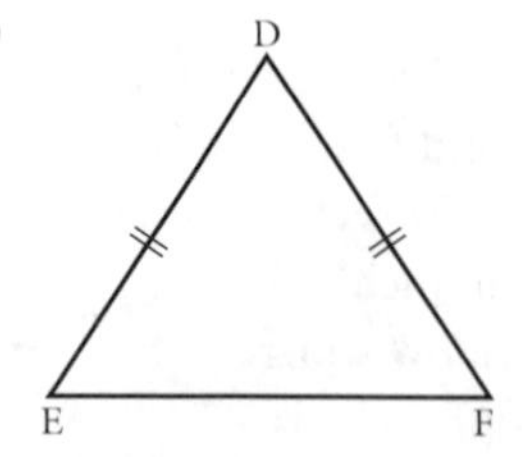

In $\triangle DEF$, $DE = DF = 3.4$ in and $EF = 3.8$ in.
Find the height of the triangle.

11 O is the centre of the circle and AB is a chord of length 18.2 cm.
The perpendicular distance of the chord from O is 6.3 cm.
Find the radius of the circle.

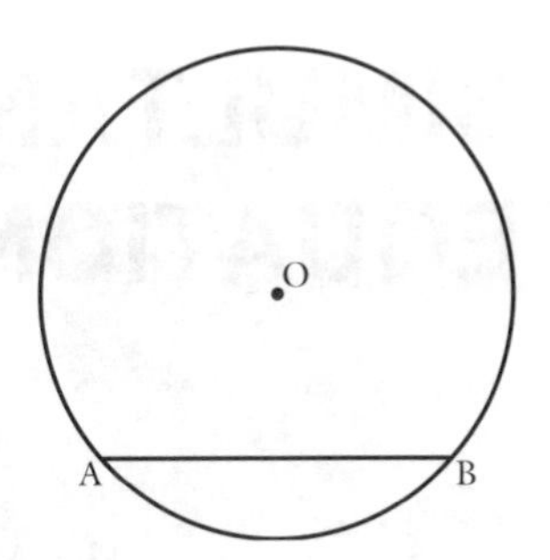

12 A groundsman is marking out a new tennis court on grass.
The length of the court is 78 ft and the width is 36 ft.
He lays out a rectangle with these measurements, but wants to check that his angles are true right angles.
He checks the lengths of the two diagonals which should be the same length. To the nearest tenth of a foot, how long should they be?

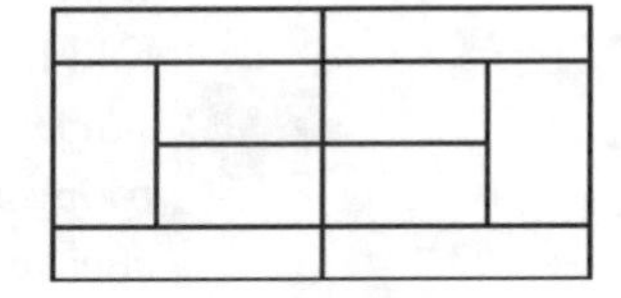

PRACTICAL WORK

Draw any right-angled triangle and draw the square on each of the three sides.
Mark the four areas A, B, C and X as shown in the diagram.
Cut out one of each shape and make another three triangles identical to X.
Arrange the shapes in two different ways as shown below.
Sketch the two arrangements and mark in as many lengths as possible with a, b or c.

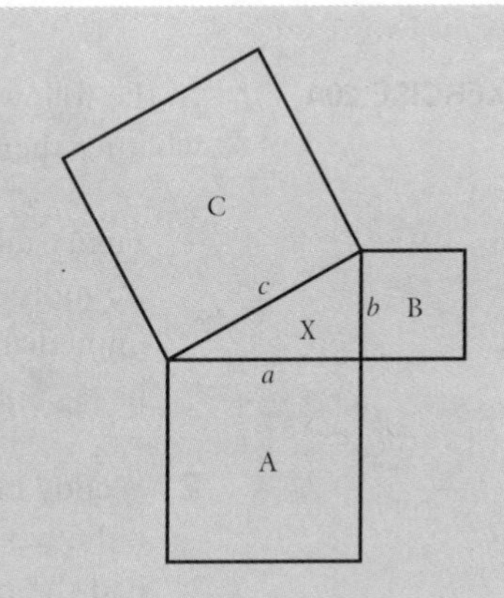

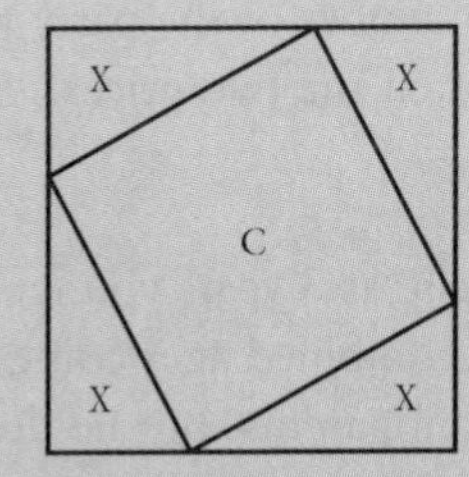

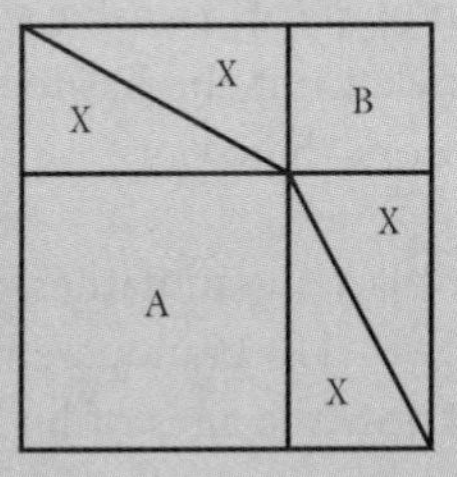

a What can you say about the areas of these two diagrams? Justify your answer.

b If the four triangles marked X are removed from each diagram, what can you say about the areas that remain? What relation does this give for

i areas A, B and C **ii** lengths a, b and c?

SIMULTANEOUS EQUATIONS

20

The Westbourne Hotel was chosen by Rackham Electronics for a weekend break for the staff. When Emma rang the hotel the receptionist told her that they had 134 rooms and could accommodate up to 253 in single or double rooms. She said that she wasn't certain how many single rooms this included, but promised to ring back as soon as she had checked. Emma told her not to bother as she could easily work that out from the information she had already been given.
Emma could find the number of single and double rooms

- either by trial and error
- or by forming equations and solving them.

EXERCISE 20A

In the following problems, discuss what quantities are unknown and whether there is enough information to find them.

1 Henry takes delivery of 40 copies of a book knowing that there are 20 more with soft covers than with hard covers. He has an immediate unexpected order for 12 copies of the hardback. Does he have enough ?

2 Wendy rang the box office to book tickets for a concert. There were only two ticket prices. She booked for a party of 18, some of whom had the more expensive seats. The total cost came to £405. Wendy now needs to ask each member of the party for the price of their ticket but she has forgotten the two prices. Should she be able to work these out ?

3 Stuart's grandfather, Wally, is 3 years younger than his grandmother, Eve. His grandparents' combined ages come to 181. Stuart wants to know the ages of his grandparents, but he doesn't think he has enough information. Has he ?

FORMING EQUATIONS

Each of the problems above contains two unknown quantities.
Before problems similar to these can be solved, we must be able to form equations from given information. This means we have to identify the unknown quantities and then relate them to the information given.

EXERCISE 20B

In Franconia it cost Henry 75 cents to send 1 postcard and 1 letter home. His wife, Isobel, sends 5 postcards and 1 letter which, in total, costs her 195 cents. Form two equations in words and symbols.

The unknown quantities are the cost of sending 1 postcard and the cost of sending 1 letter.

Cost of sending 1 postcard + cost of sending 1 letter = 75 cents

Cost of sending 5 postcards + cost of sending 1 letter = 195 cents

In questions **1** to **7** first identify the unknown quantities, then use the given information to write equations in words and symbols.

1 Olive Thorne frames pictures. For frames up to $40\text{ cm} \times 30\text{ cm}$ she charges one rate and for larger frames up to $80\text{ cm} \times 60\text{ cm}$ she charges a higher rate. One frame of each size together cost £65 whereas two large frames and four small frames cost £170.

2 At the garden centre each tray of bedding plants is marked at one of two prices. The cost of 3 trays at the lower price and 3 trays at the higher price is £8.25 and the cost of 3 trays at the cheaper rate and 5 trays at the dearer rate is £11.25.

3 Two numbers are such that their sum is 27 and their difference is 13.

4 Two numbers are such that their sum is 32 and the larger number is three times the smaller number.

5 The cost of one protractor and one set square is 120 p whereas the cost of one protractor and two set squares is 185 p.

6 It costs £30 for Mr Holder to take his son on a day-trip to Alton Towers. If he were to take his daughter as well it would cost £42.

7 When Owen buys one tabloid newspaper and one broadsheet newspaper he pays 60 p. He pays the newsagent on a Friday for all the papers he had received from Monday to Friday. One week, when he had collected the two papers every day except Thursday, he paid £2.65. His regular broadsheet newspaper had not been printed on Thursday so he had to make do with just the tabloid.

EQUATIONS WITH TWO UNKNOWN QUANTITIES

In previous chapters the equations we have solved have had one unknown quantity only, but in the equations formed in the exercise above there are two.
Using letters for unknown numbers, the equations formed from problems like those in **Exercise 20B** are of the type $2x + y = 8$.

Looking at the equation $2x + y = 8$, we can see that there are many possible values which will fit,
for instance $x = 2$ and $y = 4$, or $x = 1$ and $y = 6$.
We could also have $x = -1$ and $y = 10$ or even
$x = 1.681$ and $y = 4.638$.
Indeed, there is an infinite set of pairs of solutions.

If however we are *also* told that $x + y = 5$, then we shall find that not every pair of numbers which satisfies the first equation also satisfies the second. While $x = 2$, $y = 4$ satisfies the first equation, it does not satisfy $x + y = 5$. On the other hand $x = 3$, $y = 2$ satisfies both equations.

These two equations together form a pair of *simultaneous equations*. 'Simultaneous' means that the two equations are both satisfied by the same values of x and y; that is, when x has the same value in both equations then y has the same value in both.

There are several different methods for solving simultaneous equations.

ELIMINATION METHOD

Whenever we meet a new type of equation, we try to reorganise it so that it is similar to equations we have already met.

Previous equations have had only one unknown quantity, so we try to *eliminate* one of the two unknowns.

Consider the pair of equations

$$2x + y = 8 \qquad [1]$$

$$x + y = 5 \qquad [2]$$

In this case, if we try subtracting the second equation from the first we find that the y term disappears but the x term does not,

i.e. [1] – [2] gives $\qquad x = 3$

Then, substituting 3 for x in equation [2],
we see that $3 + y = 5$ so $y = 2$.

We can check that $x = 3$ and $y = 2$ also satisfy equation [1].

Notice that it is essential to number the equations and to say that you are subtracting them.

Sometimes it is easier to subtract the first equation from the second rather than the second equation from the first. (In this case we would write equation [1] again, underneath equation [2].)
Sometimes we can eliminate x rather than y.

EXERCISE 20C

Solve the equations $x + y = 5$, $3x + y = 7$

$$x + y = 5 \quad [1]$$
$$3x + y = 7 \quad [2]$$
$$x + y = 5 \quad [1]$$

[2] – [1] gives $2x = 2$

$$x = 1$$

TO FIND Y CHOOSE THE SIMPLER EQUATION, I.E. THE FIRST.

Substituting $x = 1$, in [1] gives $1 + y = 5$

$$y = 4$$

Check the values found for x and y in the equation *not* used for finding y.

Check in [2] Left-hand side (LHS) $= 3 + 4 = 7 =$ RHS

Therefore the solution is $x = 1,\ y = 4$

Solve the following pairs of equations.

1 $x + y = 5$
$4x + y = 14$

2 $x + 2y = 12$
$x + y = 7$

3 $2a + b = 11$
$4a + b = 17$

4 $2x + 3y = 23$
$x + 3y = 22$

5 $9c + 2d = 54$
$c + 2d = 6$

6 $5x + 2y = 14$
$7x + 2y = 22$

7 $4p + 3q = -5$
$7p + 3q = -11$

8 $12x + 5y = 65$
$9x + 5y = 50$

9 $9x + 5y = 45$
$4x + 5y = 45$

Not all pairs of simultaneous equations can be solved by subtracting one from the other.

Consider $4x + y = 6 \quad [1]$

$2x - y = 0 \quad [2]$

If we subtract we get $2x + 2y = 6$ which is no improvement.

On the other hand, if we add we get $6x = 6$ which eliminates y.

If the signs in front of the letter to be eliminated are the same we should *subtract*; if the signs are different we should *add*.

EXERCISE 20D

Solve the equations $\begin{aligned} x - 2y &= 1 \\ 3x + 2y &= 19 \end{aligned}$

$x - 2y = 1$ [1]

$3x + 2y = 19$ [2]

[1] + [2] gives $4x = 20$ i.e. $x = 5$

It is easier to use the equation with the + sign to find y.

Substitute 5 for x in [2] $15 + 2y = 19$

Take 15 from both sides $2y = 4$ i.e. $y = 2$

Check in [1] LHS = $5 - 4 = 1$ = RHS

Therefore the solution is $x = 5$, $y = 2$

Solve the following pairs of equations.

1 $\begin{aligned} x - y &= 2 \\ 3x + y &= 10 \end{aligned}$

2 $\begin{aligned} 3a - b &= 10 \\ a + b &= 2 \end{aligned}$

3 $\begin{aligned} 6x + 2y &= 19 \\ x - 2y &= 2 \end{aligned}$

4 $\begin{aligned} 4x + y &= 37 \\ 2x - y &= 17 \end{aligned}$

5 $\begin{aligned} 2x - y &= 6 \\ 3x + y &= 14 \end{aligned}$

6 $\begin{aligned} 5p + 3q &= 5 \\ 4p - 3q &= 4 \end{aligned}$

7 $\begin{aligned} 3x - 4y &= -24 \\ 5x + 4y &= 24 \end{aligned}$

8 $\begin{aligned} 3x + 2y &= 12 \\ x + 2y &= 8 \end{aligned}$

9 $\begin{aligned} x - 2y &= 6 \\ 4x + 2y &= 14 \end{aligned}$

10 $\begin{aligned} x + 3y &= 12 \\ x + y &= 8 \end{aligned}$

11 $\begin{aligned} 2x + 3y &= 13 \\ 2x + 5y &= 21 \end{aligned}$

12 $\begin{aligned} 5x - 2y &= 24 \\ x + 2y &= 0 \end{aligned}$

Solve the equations $\begin{aligned} 4x - y &= 10 \\ x - y &= 1 \end{aligned}$

$4x - y = 10$ [1]

$x - y = 1$ [2]

The signs in front of the y terms are the same so we subtract. $-y - (-y) = -y + y = 0$

[1] − [2] gives $3x = 9$ i.e. $x = 3$

Substitute 3 for x in [2] $3 - y = 1$

Add y to each side.

$3 = 1 + y$

$2 = y$ i.e. $y = 2$

Check in [1] LHS = $12 - 2 = 10$ = RHS

Therefore the solution is $x = 3$, $y = 2$

Solve the following pairs of equations.

13 $x + 3y = 0$
$x - y = -4$

14 $2x - y = 4$
$x - y = 1$

15 $2p - 3q = -7$
$4p - 3q = 1$

16 $x - y = 3$
$3x - y = 9$

17 $3p - 5q = -3$
$4p - 5q = 1$

18 $3p + 5q = 17$
$4p + 5q = 16$

19 $6a - b = 20$
$6a + 5b = 8$

20 $6x - y = 7$
$2x - y = 1$

21 $5x - 2y = -19$
$x - 2y = -7$

22 $2x - 3y = 14$
$2x - y = 10$

23 $3p - 5q = 35$
$4p - 5q = 0$

24 $3x + y = 10$
$x + y = -2$

I think of two numbers. If I add three times the smaller number to the bigger number I get 14. If I subtract the bigger number from twice the smaller number I get 1. Find the two numbers.

We can solve this problem by forming a pair of simultaneous equations. First we have to decide what the unknown quantities are, and then use letters to represent the unknown numbers.

Let the smaller number be x and the bigger number be y.

$$3x + y = 14 \quad [1]$$
$$2x - y = 1 \quad [2]$$

[1] + [2] gives $5x = 15$

$x = 3$

Substitute 3 for x in [1] $9 + y = 14$

$y = 5$

Therefore, the two numbers are 3 and 5

Check by reading the original statements to see if the numbers fit.

Solve the following problems by forming a pair of simultaneous equations in x and y. Let the smaller number be x and the larger number y.

25 The sum of two numbers is 20 and their difference is 4. Find the numbers.

26 If I add twice the smaller of two numbers to the larger number I get 14. If I subtract the larger number from five times the smaller number I get 7. Find the two numbers.

27 The sum of two numbers is 18. The larger number is twice the smaller number. What are they?

28 Find two numbers such that twice the first added to the second gives 25 whereas three times the first is 10 more than the second.

A shop sells bread rolls. Six brown rolls and six white rolls cost 132 p while six brown rolls and three white rolls cost 102 p. Find the cost of each type of roll.

We do not know the cost of a brown roll or the cost of a white roll.

Let one brown roll cost x p and one white roll cost y p.

$$6x + 6y = 132 \quad [1]$$
$$6x + 3y = 102 \quad [2]$$

[1] – [2] gives $3y = 30$

Divide both sides by 3 $y = 10$

Substitute 10 for y in [2] $6x + 30 = 102$

Take 30 from each side $6x = 72$ i.e. $x = 12$

So one brown roll costs 12 p and one white roll costs 10 p.

29 A cup costs x pence and a saucer costs y pence. Work in pence.

a A cup and saucer cost £3.15. Write down an equation relating x and y.

b A cup and two saucers cost £4.50. Write down another equation relating x and y. (If a saucer costs y pence how much do two saucers cost?)

c By subtracting the first equation from the second you can find the value of y. Hence find the cost of a cup and of a saucer.

30 In a test Harry scored x marks and Adam scored y marks.

a Together Harry and Adam scored 42 marks. Write down an equation relating x and y.

b Sam has twice as many marks as Adam, and the sum of Harry's and Sam's marks is 52. Write down another equation relating x and y.

c Solve these two simultaneous equations by subtracting one from the other. What are the marks of each of the three boys?

31 In a right-angled triangle the two angles apart from the right angle measure $x°$ and $y°$. The difference between x and y is 18 and x is bigger than y.

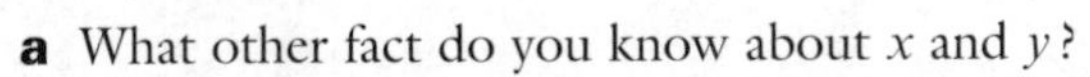

a What other fact do you know about x and y?

b Write down two equations relating x and y.

c Find x and y.

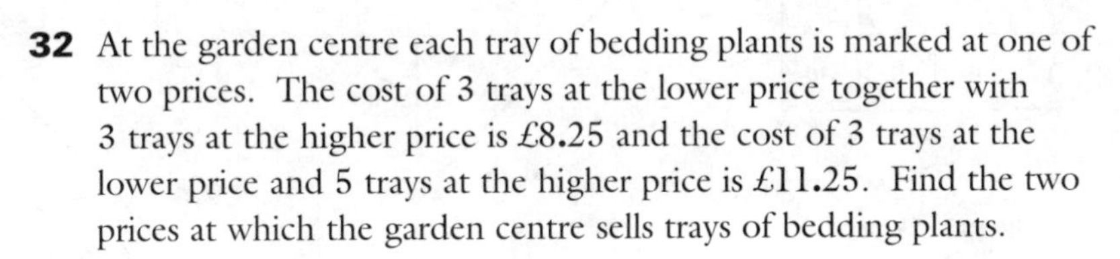

32 At the garden centre each tray of bedding plants is marked at one of two prices. The cost of 3 trays at the lower price together with 3 trays at the higher price is £8.25 and the cost of 3 trays at the lower price and 5 trays at the higher price is £11.25. Find the two prices at which the garden centre sells trays of bedding plants.

(Use letters instead of words to represent the unknown numbers and remember to state what each letter represents.)

33 In a triangle ABC, AC is x cm, BC is $2x$ cm and AB is y cm.

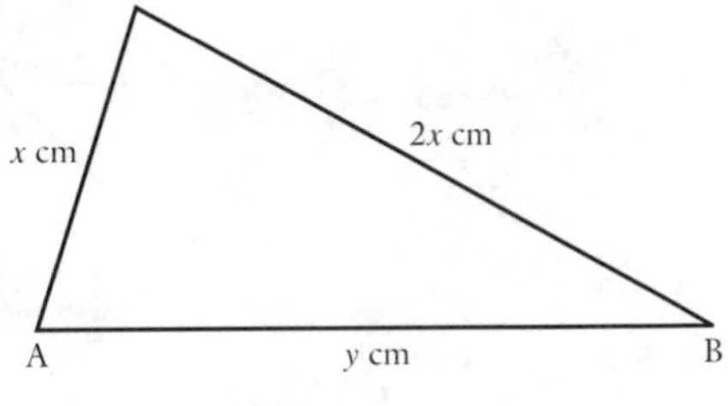

a If AB is 2 cm longer than AC write down an equation relating x and y.

b The perimeter of the triangle is 14 cm. Write down another equation relating x and y.

c Find x and y.

34 The equation of a straight line is $y = mx + c$. When $x = 1$, $y = 6$ and when $x = 3$, $y = 10$. Form two equations for m and c and hence find the equation of the line.

35

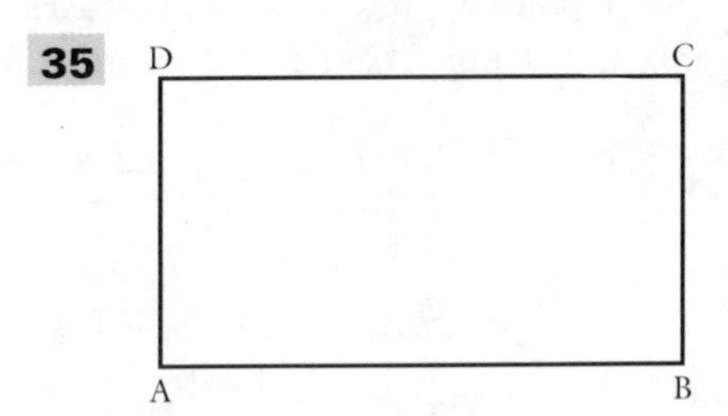

The perimeter of the rectangle is 31 cm. The difference between the lengths of AB and BC is $3\frac{1}{2}$ cm.

Find the lengths of AB and BC.

GRAPHICAL SOLUTIONS OF SIMULTANEOUS EQUATIONS

We saw in a previous chapter that when we are given an equation we can draw a graph. Any of the equations in this chapter will give us a straight line. Two equations give us two straight lines which usually cross one another.

Consider the two equations $\quad x + y = 4$

$$y = 1 + x$$

Suppose we know that the x-coordinate of the point of intersection is in the range $0 \leqslant x \leqslant 5$. We can then draw these lines for that range of values of x.

$x + y = 4$

x	0	4	5
y	4	0	-1

$y = 1 + x$

x	0	2	5
y	1	3	6

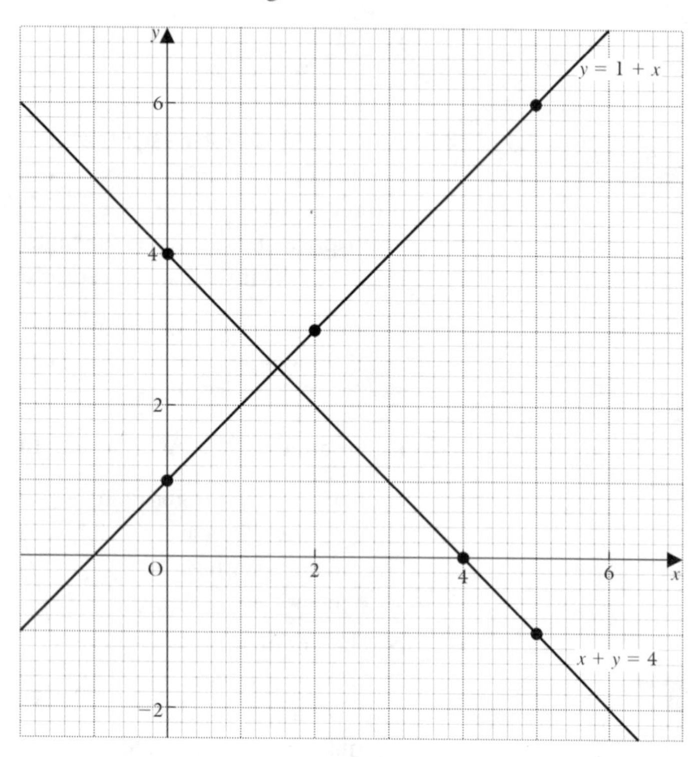

At the point where the two lines cross, the values of x and y are the same for both equations, so they are the solutions of the pair of equations.

From the graph we see that the solution is $x = 1.5$, $y = 2.5$

With this scale, it is only possible to give answers correct to 1 decimal place.

EXERCISE 20E

In questions **1** to **3** solve the equations graphically. In each case draw axes for x and y and use values in the ranges indicated, taking 2 cm to 1 unit. Give answers correct to 1 decimal place.

1 $x + y = 6$, $y = 3 + x$ $\quad 0 \leqslant x \leqslant 6,\ 0 \leqslant y \leqslant 6$

2 $x + y = 5$, $y = 2x + 1$ $\quad 0 \leqslant x \leqslant 6,\ 0 \leqslant y \leqslant 6$

3 $x + y = 1$, $y = x + 2$ $\quad -3 \leqslant x \leqslant 2,\ -2 \leqslant y \leqslant 4$

4 $5x + y = 1$, $y = x - 1$ $\quad -1 \leqslant x \leqslant 3,\ -3 \leqslant y \leqslant 2$

5 Rearrange each equation in the form $y = \dots$,
then use a graphics calculator to solve

$2x + y = 3$ $\quad 0 \leqslant x \leqslant 3, \ -3 \leqslant y \leqslant 3$
$x + y = 2\frac{1}{2}$

6 Allan and Nita are brother and sister. The sum of their ages is 30 and the difference between their ages is 6.

a If Nita is x years old and her younger brother is y years old, form two equations in x and y.

b Draw a pair of axes on 5 mm squared paper, scaling both axes from 0 to 35 in intervals of 5 units. Use 2 cm to represent 5 units on both axes.

c Draw graphs of the two equations and hence solve them.

d **i** How old is Nita? **ii** How old is Allan?

e How accurate do you think your answers are?
Give reasons for your answer.

7 A teaset includes one milk jug and six cups. The jug holds 130 ml more than a cup, but two cups hold 140 ml more than the jug.

a If a cup holds x ml and the jug holds y ml, write down two simultaneous equations in x and y.

b Use a graphics calculator to plot graphs of these two equations for the ranges $-200 \leqslant x \leqslant 500, \ 0 \leqslant y \leqslant 1000$.

c Hence find the capacity of **i** the jug **ii** a cup.

8 At the beginning of the chapter a problem was posed concerning the number of single and double rooms at the Westbourne Hotel.

a Use the information to form two simultaneous equations.

b Draw suitable graphs to solve these equations and hence find the number of single rooms and the number of double rooms at the Westbourne Hotel.

c Solve the equations algebraically. Which method do you find easier – graphical or algebraic? Discuss the advantages and disadvantages of each method.

MIXED EXERCISE

EXERCISE 20F

1 In a furniture store one chair plus the dining table costs £310 while a set of six chairs plus the dining table costs £660.
Use this information to form a pair of simultaneous equations, explaining what the letters that you use represent.

In questions **2** to **10** solve the simultaneous equations.

2 $x + y = 7$ $4x + y = 13$	**3** $x + y = 8$ $3x + y = 14$	**4** $4x - y = 18$ $x - y = 3$

5 $5x - 2y = 14$
$3x + 2y = 18$

6 $5x - 3y = 3$
$4x + 3y = 24$

7 $3x - 2y = 13$
$5x + 2y = 43$

8 $3x - y = 19$
$x - y = 3$

9 $x - y = 1$
$12x + y = 25$

10 $3x + 5y = 25$
$2x - 5y = 0$

11 The total mass of three large boxes and five small boxes is 12.7 kg, whereas the total mass of three large boxes and eight small boxes is 16.9 kg. Let the mass of the smaller box be x kg and the mass of the larger box y kg. Form two simultaneous equations and solve them. Hence find the mass of each type of box.

12 **a** Solve the equations $y = 5 - x$, $y = 2 + x$ graphically for $0 \leqslant x \leqslant 5$, $0 \leqslant y \leqslant 7$.
b Check your answers by solving the equations algebraically.

13 Solve graphically, the equations $y = 3x - 2$, $y = 4 - 2x$ for $-1 \leqslant x \leqslant 3$, $-3 \leqslant y \leqslant 6$. Give your answers correct to 1 decimal place.

INVESTIGATION

a Draw the graphs of $y = -x + 9$, $y = -x + 4$ for $0 \leqslant x \leqslant 9$, $0 \leqslant y \leqslant 9$.

b Why is it not possible to use these two graphs to solve the given pair of simultaneous equations? How are the two lines related?

c Repeat parts **a** and **b** for the equations $y = 2x + 3$, $y = 2x - 1$ for $0 \leqslant x \leqslant 4$, $-1 \leqslant y \leqslant 11$.

d Repeat parts **a** and **b** for the equations
$y = -2x + 3$, $y = -2x + \frac{7}{2}$ for $0 \leqslant x \leqslant 3$, $-3 \leqslant y \leqslant 4$.

e Find the gradient of each line given in part **c** and the gradient of each line given in part **d**. What do you notice about the gradients of the lines in each pair? How would you describe the lines in each pair?

f Draw the graphs of $y = -x + 6$, $y = x - 4$ for $0 \leqslant x \leqslant 8$, $-5 \leqslant y \leqslant 7$. Hence solve the equations. In what way are the graphs of these two equations related?

g Draw the graphs of $y = -\frac{1}{2}x + 2$, $y = 2x - 6$ for $0 \leqslant x \leqslant 6$, $-7 \leqslant y \leqslant 3$. In what special way are these two lines related?

h What conclusions can you make that will determine whether the straight lines drawn to represent two linear equations are parallel, perpendicular or neither of these?

i Try solving the following pair of equations algebraically.
Comment on why the method breaks down.

$$y = 4 + 2x$$
$$y = 6 + 2x$$

SUMMARY 5

STATISTICS

Discrete values are exact and distinct, e.g. the number of people in a queue.

Continuous values can only be given in a range on a continuous scale, e.g. the length of a piece of wood.

A bar chart illustrating grouped continuous data must not have gaps between the bars.

A frequency polygon is drawn by drawing straight lines between the mid-points of the tops of the bars of a bar chart.

For a grouped frequency distribution,
the *range* is estimated as

the higher end of the last group − the lower end of the first group

the *modal group* is the group with the largest number of items in it.

CONSTRUCTIONS

The diagrams show 'ruler and compasses only' constructions.

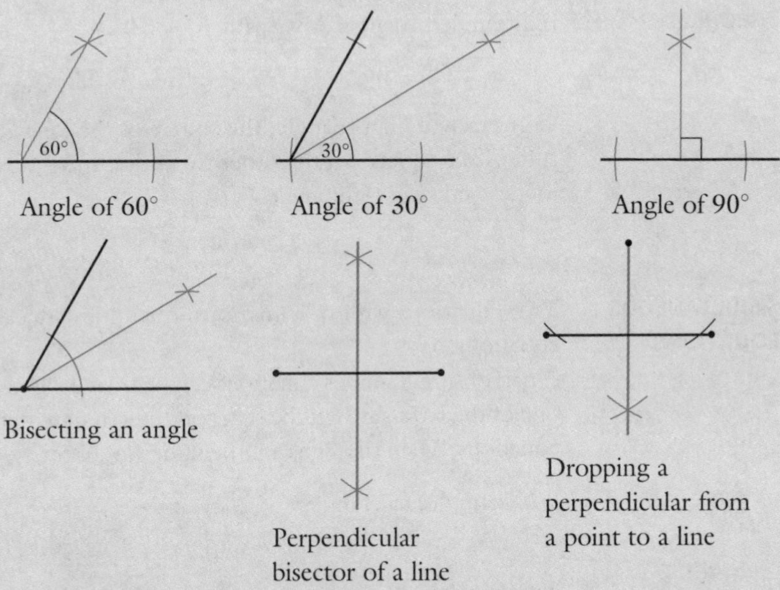

ANGLES OF ELEVATION AND DEPRESSION

If you start by looking straight ahead, the angle that you turn your eyes through to look *up* at an object is called the angle of elevation, the angle you turn your eyes through to look *down* at an object is called the angle of depression.

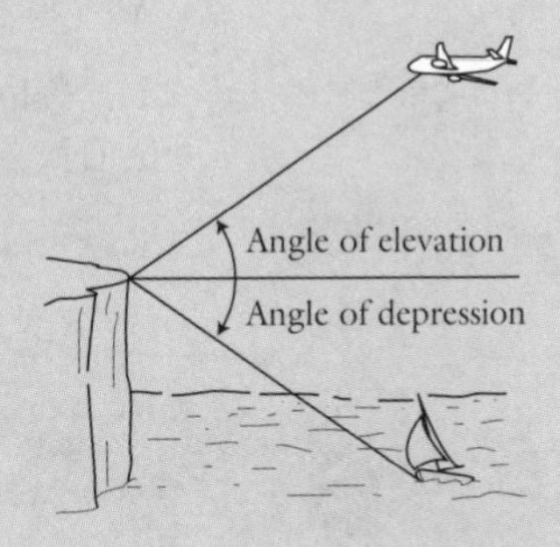

THREE-FIGURE BEARINGS

A three-figure bearing of a point A from a point B gives the direction of A from B as a clockwise angle measured from the north.

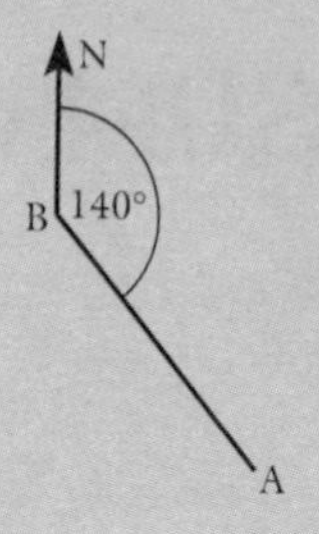

For example, in this diagram, the bearing of A from B is 140°.

VOLUMES

A solid with a constant cross-section is called a *prism*.

The *volume of a prism* is given by

area of cross-section × length

The *volume of a cylinder* is given by $V = \pi r^2 h$

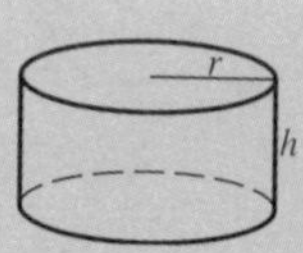

PYTHAGORAS' THEOREM

Pythagoras' theorem states that in any right-angled triangle ABC with $\widehat{C} = 90°$,

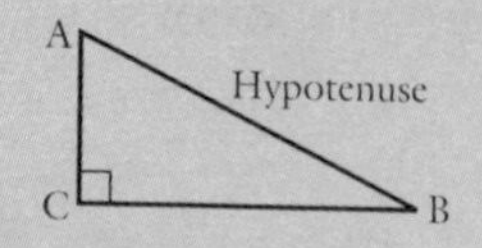

$AB^2 = AC^2 + BC^2$

Conversely if, in a triangle, the square of the longest side is equal to the sum of the squares of the other two sides, then the angle opposite the longest side is a right angle.

SIMULTANEOUS EQUATIONS

Two equations with two unknown quantities are called simultaneous equations.
A pair of simultaneous equations can be solved algebraically by eliminating one of the letters; when the signs of this letter are different, we add the equations, when the signs are the same we subtract the equations.

For example, to eliminate y from $2x + y = 5$ [1]

and $3x - y = 7$ [2]

we add [1] and [2] to give $5x = 12$ [3]

The value of x can be found from [3]. This value is then substituted for x in [1] or [2] to find y.

To eliminate y from $4x + y = 9$ [1]

and $3x + y = 7$ [2]

we work out [1] – [2] to give $x = 2$

Now we can substitute 2 for x either in [1] or in [2] to find y.

Two simultaneous equations can be solved graphically by drawing two straight lines and finding the coordinates of their point of intersection.

For example, to solve $2x + y = 7$ [1]

and $x - y = 9$ [2]

we first rearrange the equations so they are each in the form $y = \ldots$

i.e. $y = 7 - 2x$ [3]

and $y = x - 9$ [4]

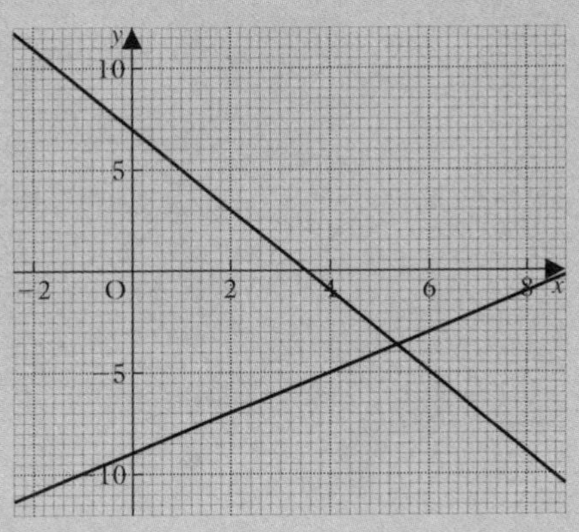

We then plot these lines.
As accurately as we can read from the graph, the point of intersection is $(5.3, -3.6)$.
So the solution is $x = 5.3$ and $y = -3.6$

REVISION EXERCISE 5.1 (Chapters 16 to 18)

1 A survey of Year 9 pupils gave the following information about the way they came to school.

Way of coming to school	Bus	Car	Walk	Bicycle
Number of pupils	43	21	14	12

a How many pupils in Year 9 took part in the survey?

b Draw a pie chart to represent this information after you have calculated the angles corresponding to each slice.

2 a Correct to the nearest 10, 240 people took part in a demonstration.
What is the largest number of people that may have taken part?

b The profits for Comco plc were reported as £45 000 000 last year. This figure is correct to the nearest million.
What is the smallest profit that the company could have made?

3 Using ruler and compasses only, construct $\triangle$ABC in which AB = 72 mm, AC = 88 mm and $\widehat{A} = 90°$.
Measure and write down the size of

a the largest angle **b** the smallest angle.

4 At a veterinary clinic all the dogs seen in one day were weighed. Their weights, in kg, were recorded in this observation chart.

Weight, w kg	$0 < w \leqslant 10$	$10 < w \leqslant 20$	$20 < w \leqslant 30$	$30 < w \leqslant 40$
Tally	~~////~~	~~////~~ ~~////~~ ////	~~////~~ ~~////~~ ~~////~~ ///	///
Frequency				

a The vet saw two dogs after-hours. One weighed just over 20 kg and the other just under 10 kg. Copy the table, add tally marks for these two weights and then complete the table.

b How many of the dogs weighed that day were

i more than 20 kg **ii** 30 kg or less?

c How many dogs were there altogether?

d Draw a bar chart to illustrate this information.

5 From the church tower the Post Office is 300 m away on a bearing of 137°, and the City Hall is 180 m away on a bearing of 245°.

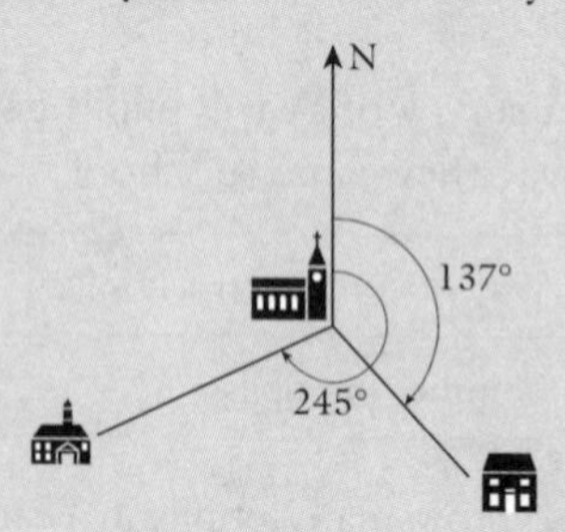

a Using a scale of $1 \text{ cm} \equiv 30 \text{ m}$, make a scale drawing and use it to find the distance of the City Hall from the Post Office.

b What is the bearing of

i the Church Tower from the Post Office

ii the City Hall from the Post Office

iii the Post Office from the City Hall?

6 Construct a triangle ABC in which $AB = 12$ cm, $AC = 11$ cm and $BC = 7.5$ cm. Using ruler and compasses only, drop the perpendicular from C to AB. Measure and record its length.

7 Find the capacity, in litres, of a cylinder with

a radius 2.5 cm and height 5 cm

b diameter 7.4 cm and height 6.8 cm.

(Give each answer correct to 3 significant figures.)

8 The diagram shows the cross-section of a metal girder which is 2 m long. Find

a the area of cross-section in cm^2

b the volume of the metal used to cast the girder measured in

i cm^3 **ii** m^3.

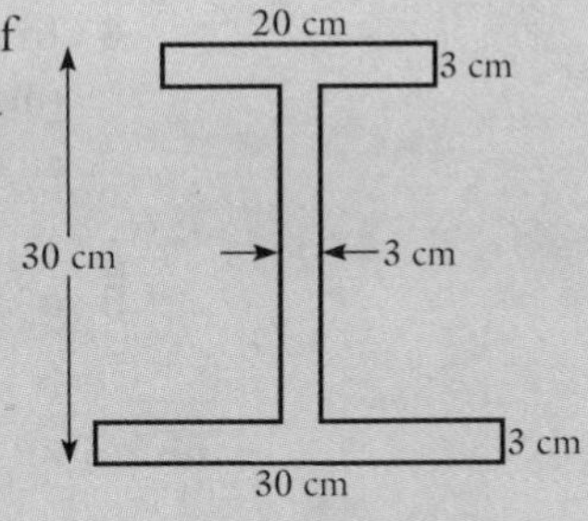

9 The sketch shows a wooden table lamp before the electrical fittings are attached. It has been made from two pieces of wood. The base is a circular disc of radius 3 inches and 1 inch thick, while the column is a cylinder of radius 1 inch and height 15 inches.
Find the total volume of wood in one lamp.

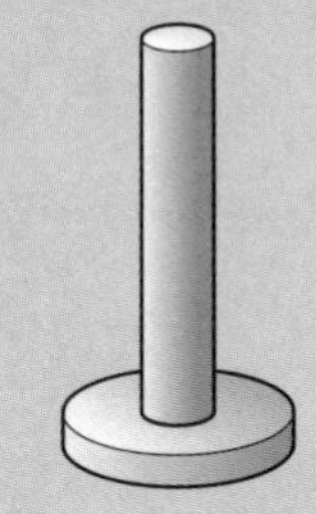

10 The diagram shows a wooden chest. The internal measurements of the base are 120 cm by 48 cm and the chest is 48 cm deep.
The lid is half of a cylinder.
Find, in cubic centimetres, the capacity of the chest

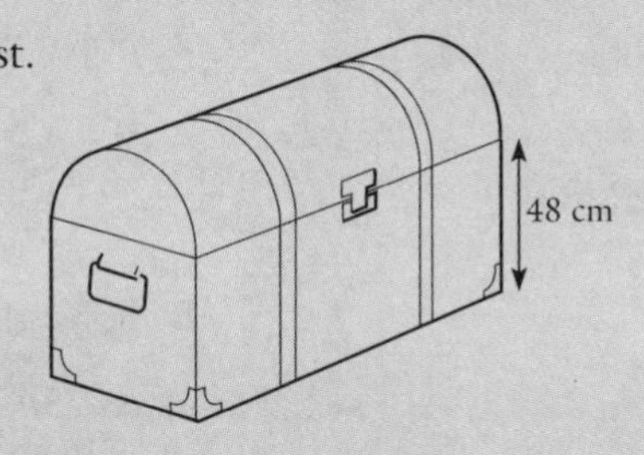

a excluding the lid **b** including the lid.

REVISION EXERCISE 5.2 (Chapters 19 and 20)

1 In triangle ABC, $A\hat{B}C = 90°$, AB = 6 cm and BC = 4 cm. Find AC.

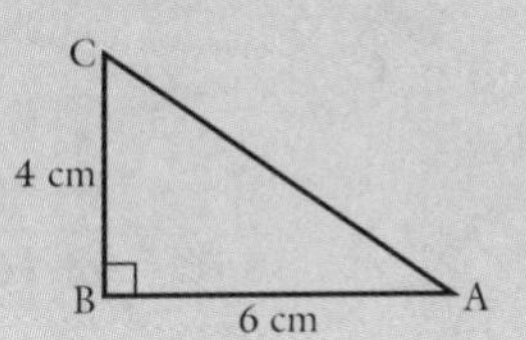

2 In triangle PQR, $P\hat{Q}R = 90°$, PQ = 7 cm and PR = 10 cm. Find QR.

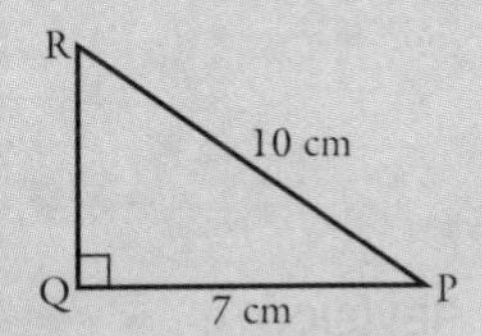

3 The diagram shows the cross-section through a lean-to conservatory which is attached to the back wall of a house.
Calculate the length of the slant edge of the roof.

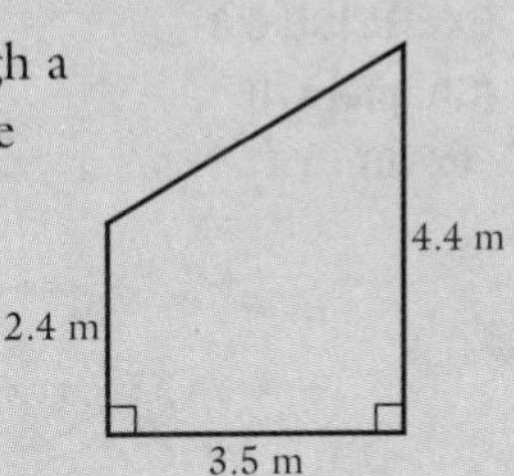

4 In $\triangle ABC$, $AB = 2.2$ cm, $BC = 8$ cm and $AC = 8.2$ cm. Does the triangle contain a right angle? If your answer is 'yes' state which angle it is and justify your answer.

5 **a** Find the length of a diagonal of a square whose side is 14 cm.

b **i** What is the relationship between the lengths of the sides of this square and the length of its diagonal?

ii Form an equation in x and solve it to find the length of a side of the square.

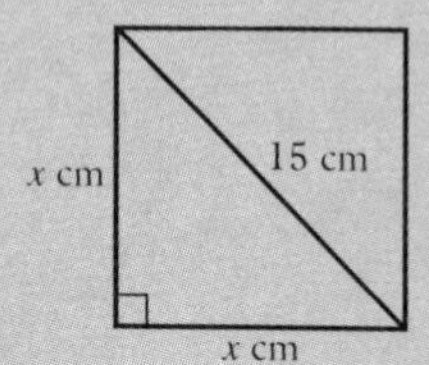

6 Solve the simultaneous equations

a $x + y = 14$
$x - y = 4$

b $2x + y = 16$
$x + y = 10$

7 Solve the simultaneous equations

a $x + y = 5$
$3x + y = 9$

b $x - y = 2$
$3x + y = 14$

8 Solve the simultaneous equations

a $5a - b = 27$
$5a + 3b = 19$

b $3a + 2b = 21$
$a + 2b = 11$

9 The sum of two numbers, x and y, is 22 and their difference is 4. If the larger number is x, form a pair of simultaneous equations in x and y and solve them. What are the two numbers?

10 Solve graphically the equations $x + y = 6$
$y = 3x - 1$

Draw axes for $0 \leqslant x \leqslant 6$ and $0 \leqslant y \leqslant 6$, taking 2 cm as 1 unit. Give your answers correct to 1 decimal place.

REVISION EXERCISE 5.3 (Chapters 16 to 20)

1 State whether the possible values of each quantity are discrete or continuous.

a The number of passengers on a bus.

b The time a bus takes to travel from one bus stop to the next one.

c The amount of milk in a carton.

d The cost of a cup of coffee.

e Your best friend's height.

2

Weight, w kg	Frequency
$40 \leqslant w < 50$	5
$50 \leqslant w < 60$	13
$60 \leqslant w < 70$	18
$70 \leqslant w < 80$	7
$80 \leqslant w < 90$	7
$90 \leqslant w < 100$	4

This frequency table shows the weights of a group of teenage boys.

a How many boys are there in the group?

b How many boys have a weight that is
 i less than 50 kg **ii** at least 70 kg?

c Which is the modal group?

d Draw a bar chart to represent this information.

e On a separate diagram illustrate this data with a frequency polygon.

3 From a point on the ground 220 m from the base of a multi-storey block of flats the angle of elevation of the top is 33°. Make a scale drawing and use it to find the height of the block.

4 This diagram is not drawn accurately.

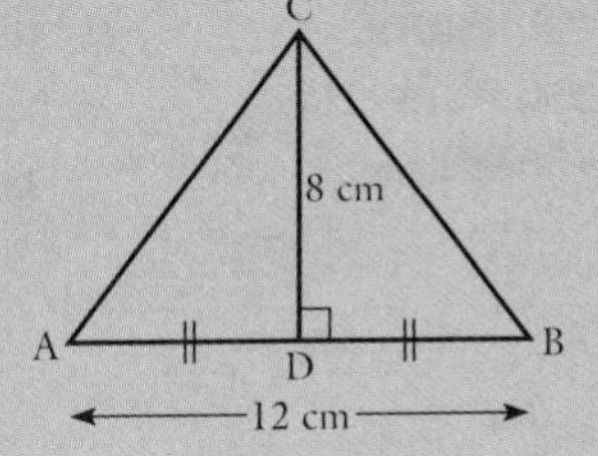

a Use ruler and compasses only to make an accurate full size copy of this diagram.

b Use your diagram to measure CB and $\widehat{A}$.

5 **a** Find the volume of a rectangular block measuring 12 cm by 8 cm by 5 cm.

b Find the volume of a cylindrical can whose diameter is 3.5 cm and whose height is equal to the diameter of its base. Give your answer correct to 3 significant figures.

6 The diagram shows the cross-section of a metal pipe support that is 28 cm long. Find

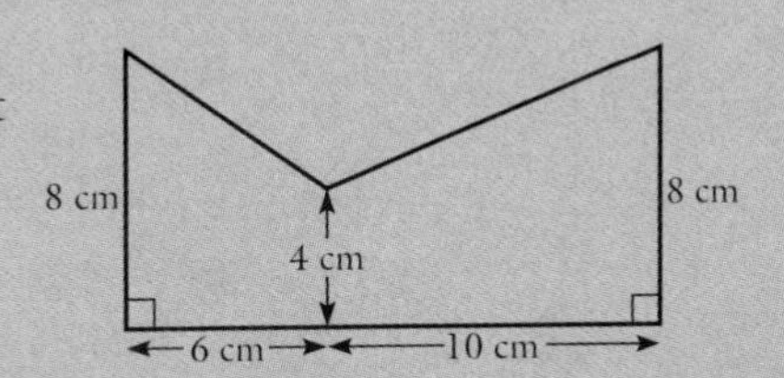

a the area of cross-section

b the volume of the block.

7 The door on a rectangular cupboard measures 172 cm by 63 cm. What is the length of a diagonal of this door? Give your answer correct to 1 decimal place.

8 **a** AB is a chord of length 9.8 cm in a circle, centre O. The distance of the chord from the centre of the circle is 3.7 cm. Find, correct to 3 significant figures, the radius of the circle.

b A second chord, CD, is 4.3 cm from O. Find the length of CD.

9 Solve the simultaneous equations $7p + 3q = 33$
$4p - 3q = 0$

10 The sizes of the three angles in a triangle are $105°$, $x°$ and $y°$ where x is larger than y. The difference between x and y is 12.

a What other fact do you know about x and y?

b Write down two equations relating x and y.

c Find x and y.

REVISION EXERCISE 5.4 (Chapters 1 to 20)

1 **a** Without using a calculator find, correct to 2 significant figures
i $40 \div 6$ **ii** $50 \div 9$ **iii** $0.08 \div 3$ **iv** $0.5 \div 7$

b Write down an estimate for each of the following calculations.
i $420 \div 19.7$ **iii** 1.88×2.79
ii $9.774 + 2.034$ **iv** $52.55 - 19.44$

2 **a** Find, without using a calculator
i $\frac{2}{3}$ of £39 **ii** $3\frac{1}{8} \div 3\frac{3}{4}$ **iii** $5\frac{1}{2} \div 3 + \frac{2}{9}$ **iv** $\frac{4}{5} \div \frac{1}{6} + \frac{1}{3} \times 1\frac{1}{2}$

b Which of these statements are true?
A $\frac{5}{9} \div 5 = \frac{1}{9}$ **B** $5 \div 9 = \frac{5}{9}$ **C** $\frac{4}{9} \div \frac{1}{2} = \frac{2}{9}$ **D** $\frac{4}{9} = 9 \div 4$

3 **a** Paul buys n pencils and pays a total of C pence for them. If one pencil costs x pence find a formula for x.

b Write down the first four terms of the sequence generated by starting with 14 and subtracting 4 each time. Find an expression for the nth term in terms of n.

c If $P = 12a - 3b$ find P when
i $a = 2, b = 6$ **ii** $a = 1.6, b = 0.9$

4 Copy the diagram.

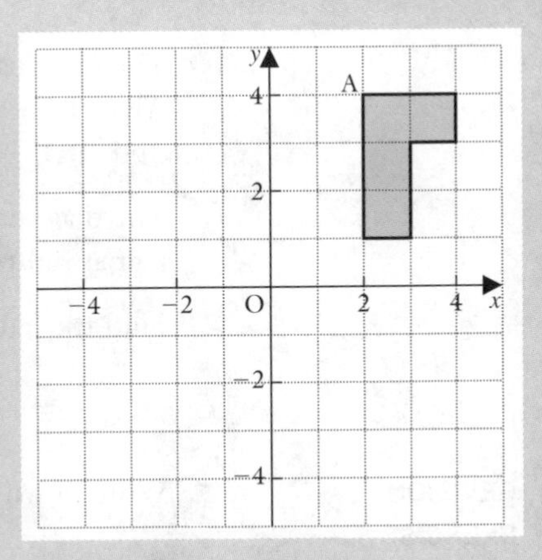

a Reflect the object in the x-axis.

b Rotate the image from part **a** 90° clockwise about the origin.

c Write down the coordinates of the point on the final image corresponding to the point A.

5 **a** Find the area of a quadrant of a circle of radius 12 cm.

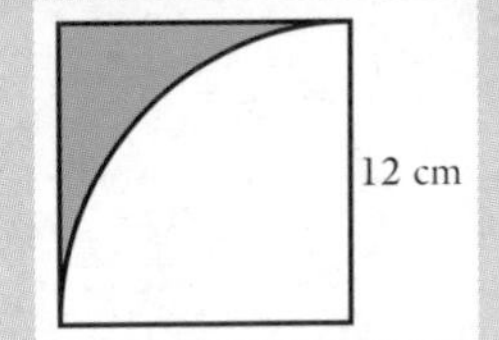

b Hence find the area of the shaded part of the diagram.

6 **a** If $4 : 7 = 16 : x$, find x.

b A carpet is made from wool and nylon in the ratio 4 : 1 by weight. How much wool is there in a carpet that weighs 55 kg?

7 **a** Write down the gradient m, and y-intercept, c, for the straight line with equation

i $y = -4x + 6$ **ii** $y = 3 - x$

b On the same diagram sketch the straight lines with equations

i $y = 2x - 5$ **ii** $y = 6 - 2x$

8 Les sets out on his bike on a journey of 12 km. He has cycled 10 km at 15 km/h when his bicycle suffers a puncture. As a result, he pushes his bike the rest of the distance at 5 km/h.

a How long does he cycle before the breakdown?

b How far does he have to push the bike and for how long?

c Find the total time for his journey.

d Find his average speed for the whole trip.

9 **a** Without using a protractor, construct ΔABC in which $AB = 115$ mm, $\widehat{A} = 30°$ and $\widehat{B} = 60°$. Measure and write down the length of

i AC **ii** BC.

b From a point on the top of a building 55 m high, the angle of depression of a small boat on the river below is 53°. Make a scale drawing using 1 cm ≡ 5 m. Use your drawing to find the distance of the boat from the base of the building.

10 The diagonals of a kite ABCD meet at E.
AB = BC = 9.5 cm, AC = 8.2 cm
and BD = 19.7 cm.

The diagonal BD cuts AC exactly in half at right-angles.

Find the length of **a** BE **b** CD.

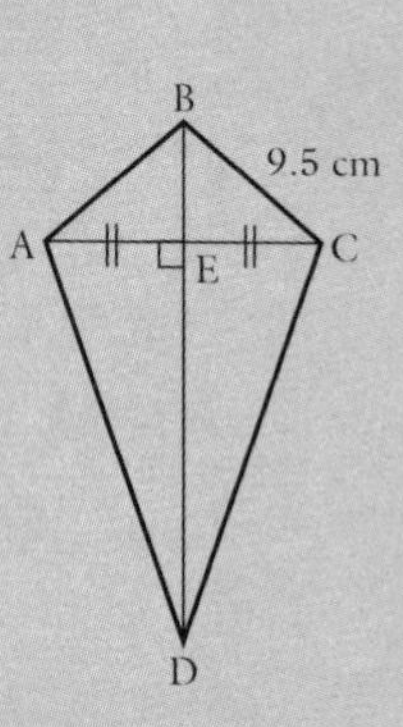

REVISION EXERCISE 5.5 (Chapters 1 to 20)

1 Write down the size of each marked angle.

a

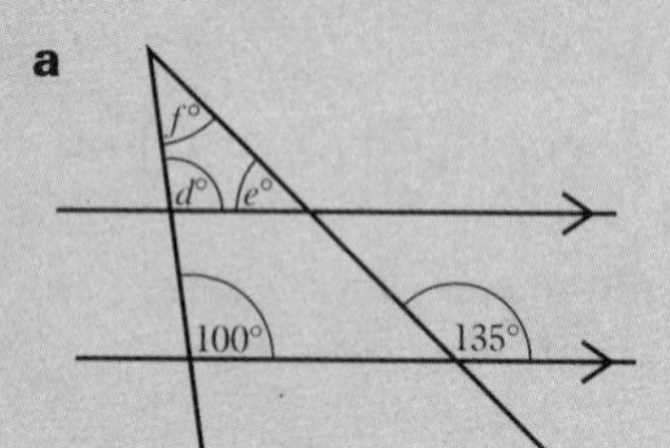

b

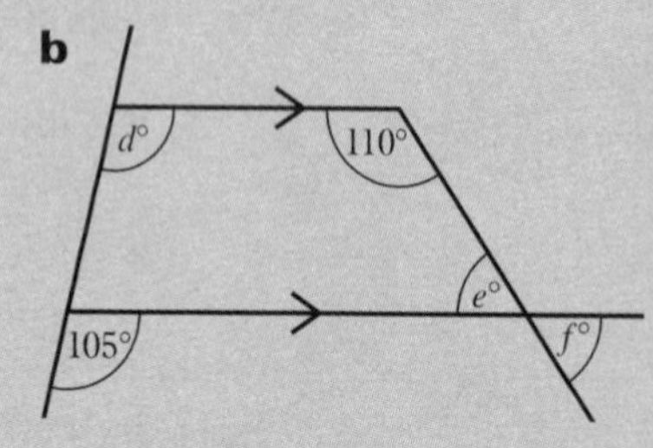

2 Draw up a possibility space showing all the possible combinations of scores if two dice are rolled together. The scores on each dice are added. Use this possibility space to find the probability of getting

a 5 or less **c** at least 8

b 10 or more **d** a score that is exactly divisible by 3.

3 a Is it possible for each exterior angle of a regular polygon to be 36°?

b Is it possible for each interior angle of a regular polygon to be 156°?
In each case, where possible, give the number of sides.

4 The table gives the long jump and high jump results for the eight competitors who entered both events in an athletics meeting.

Long jump (m)	4.20	5.88	5.32	5.83	4.55	5.35	4.80	5.65
High jump (m)	1.50	1.92	1.64	1.80	1.67	1.78	1.74	1.75

a What relationship would you expect to find between the length of a long jump and the height of a high jump achieved by one competitor?

b Plot the data on a scatter diagram. Use 10 cm ≡ 1 m on both axes. Scale the long-jump axis from 4 m to 6 m and the high jump axis from 1.5 m to 2 m.

c Does the scatter diagram support your answer to part **a**?

5 Find the area of each shape.

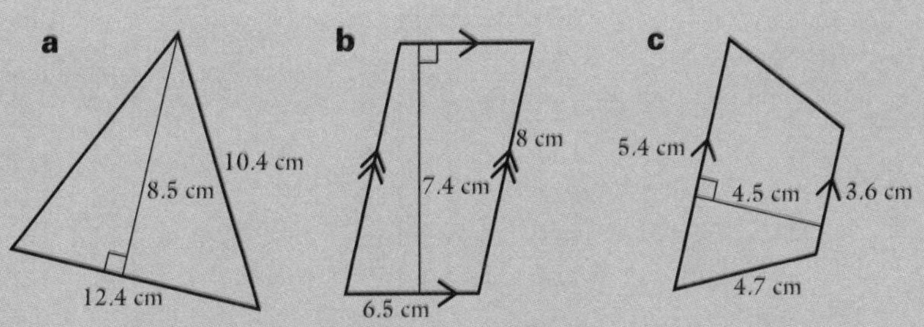

6 **a** Multiply out the brackets and simplify

i $3(4x - 2)$ **iii** $10 - 4(x - 4)$

ii $3x + 4(2x + 3)$ **iv** $3x - x(2 - x)$

b Solve the equations

i $3 + 2(x + 2) = 13$ **ii** $0.3x = 12$

7

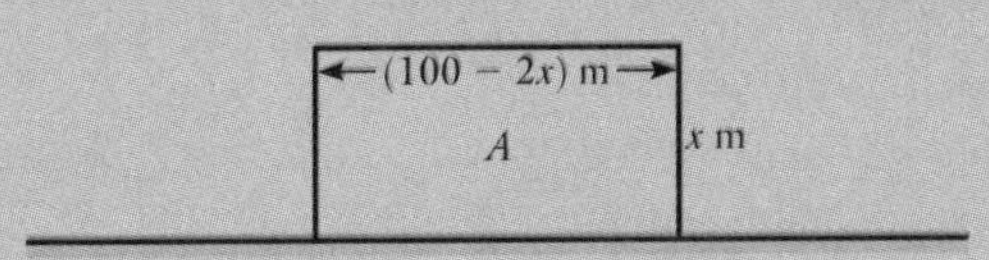

A gardener encloses a rectangular piece of ground as an allotment by using 100 m of fencing and a straight wall as one side.

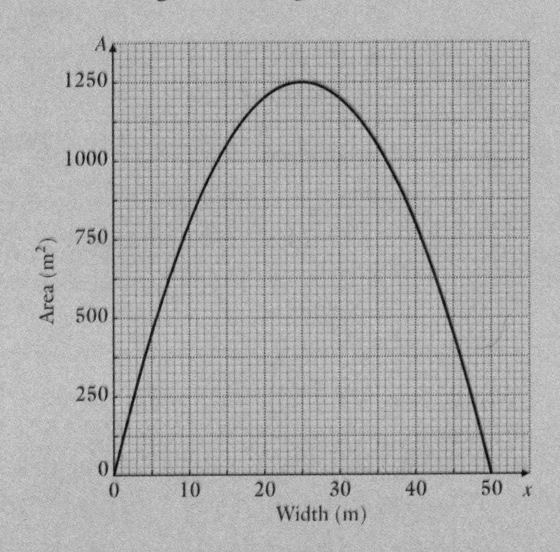

The graph shows the relationship between the area enclosed, $A\,\text{cm}^2$, and its width, x m. Use the graph to find

a the width of the rectangle when its area is $1000\,\text{m}^2$

b the maximum area that can be enclosed and the corresponding value of x

c the area enclosed when the width is 20 m.

8 Given below is a list of the heights, in centimetres rounded up to the nearest centimetre, of 60 girls. The list is in numerical order.

132	135	137	139	140	140	144	146	147	149
132	136	137	139	140	141	145	146	147	150
133	136	138	139	140	142	145	147	148	152
134	136	138	139	140	142	146	147	148	152
134	136	138	139	140	143	146	147	148	153
134	137	139	140	140	144	146	147	149	154

a What is the height of
i the tallest person **ii** the shortest person?

b Copy and complete this frequency table.

Height, h cm	Frequency
$130 < w \leqslant 135$	
$135 < w \leqslant 140$	
$140 < w \leqslant 145$	
$145 < w \leqslant 150$	
$150 < w \leqslant 155$	

c How many girls have a height that is
i greater than 140 cm **ii** 145 cm or less?

d Which group is the modal group?

e Draw
i a bar chart
ii a frequency polygon, to illustrate this information.

9 **a** A cupboard is 1.5 m wide, 30 cm deep and 120 cm high.
Find its volume in **i** cm^3 **ii** m^3.

b A child's paddling pool is an open cylinder of diameter 2.6 m which is 30 cm deep. It is filled with water to a depth of 18 cm.
i How many litres of water are there in the pool?
ii How many more litres are needed to fill the pool?

10 Solve the simultaneous equations

a $7x + 3y = 2$
$5x + 3y = 4$

b $2x + 5y = 17$
$4x - 5y = 19$

11 Anne, Bob, Cathy and David have a French oral examination. Anne insists on going in last, but Bob, Cathy and David do not mind when they go in.
List all the possible orders in which they can go in.
In how many of these is Bob first?

INDEX